RUSSIAN-ENGLISH

BIOLOGICAL & MEDICAL DICTIONARY

BIOLOGY. Morphology: Anatomy, Embryology, Histology. Biophysics. Physiology. Taxonomy. Hydrobiology. Microbiology. Radiobiology.

BOTANY. Bacteria, Algae, Spore and Seed Plants, Phytopathology.

ZOOLOGY. Invertebrates, Vertebrates. Entomology, Helminthology, Ichthyology, Ornithology, etc.

MEDICINE: Aviation, Internal, Legal, Military, Veterinary. Dermatology, Gynecology, Hematology, Inf. diseases, Neurology, Obstetrics, Ophthalmology, Otolaryngology, Pathology, Pediatrics, PSYCHIATRY, Radiotherapy, Surgery, Urology, Venerology, etc.

Agriculture: domestic animals, cultured plants.

Dr. EUGENE A. CARPOVICH

SECOND IMPROVED EDITION

1960

TECHNICAL DICTIONARIES CO.

BOX 144, NEW YORK 31, NY

Library of Congress Catalog Card Number: 58-7915

Printed by LAWRENCE-MONARCH Printing Corp. 12 W. 17 St. • N.Y. 11, N.Y.

Bound by I. & E. BINDERY 420 E. 9 St. • N.Y. 9, N.Y.

PREFACE TO THE SECOND EDITION

The favorable reception of the First Edition prompted the preparation of the present Second Improved Edition. A number of emendations and spelling corrections have been introduced within the technical limitations of the photo-offset method. Some pages have been reworked and reshot; many terms on other pages have been marked with an * sign which refers to the CORRIGENDA list, pp. 398-400. Essential help rendered by Dr. J. Munro MacLennan, the author of the ***Russian-English Bird Dictionary*** (Department of North Affairs and National Resources, Ottawa, Canada), in checking terms and introducing improvements is acknowledged. Thanks are due to other persons and organizations who kindly sent their comments and corrections. Terms covering Pharmaceutics and Agriculture are being prepared for the Third Edition of the Dictionary.

PREFACE TO THE FIRST EDITION

This pioneer photo-offset edition contains about 35.000 Russian entries and presents fundamental terms in BIOLOGY and MEDICINE. Its broad coverage is detailed on the title page. The Dictionary has been prepared for English-speaking scientists, researchers, medicine doctors, biologists, editors, librarians, translators, students, and other workers who deal with Russian-language publications in the biomedical field.

Russian entries are arranged in a single alphabetical list so that no matter what term is desired the reader needs to open the dictionary only once. Here, however, the conventional word order of Russian biological terms, somewhat inconsistent, should be kept in mind. Ichthyologic, entomologic and botanic compound terms begin with the noun which is followed by an adjective, like долгоносик клеверный. All other biological and medical terms begin with the adjective which is followed by a noun, like почечная артерия.

An effort has been made to include all important Russian terms, scientific, practical, colloquial, and also "wrong" terms, the criterion being simply that the term is used in Russian publications. On the contrary, in the English translations we have tried to use only correct and reliable terms.

Three types of cross-reference are used: *see* refers to a synonym or a near-synonym; *see also* refers to a closely related or derived term; *cf.* refers to a different part of speech, or a term of different meaning, or an antonym. As a rule, each Russian term is translated only once; when Russian synonyms occur they are referred to the term translated by means of = sign or *see*.

As is customary, only the imperfective aspects of Russian verbs are translated. Perfective aspects, that often prove so difficult for non-Russians, are also given, and their connections with the imperfective forms are indicated by the abbreviation *p. a. of.*

That some errors and inaccuracies may have crept into this pioneer work is beyond doubt; the author will appreciate any correction or criticism. Author's most sincere thanks go to Dr. Nicholas N. Sergeeff, other Russian American MDs, and to other specialists whose valuable advices and suggestions were used in the Dictionary. Special thanks are also due to Mrs. Vera Klinushkov for her meticulous and painstaking lexicographic and technical work.

ABBREVIATIONS USED

adj adjective
agr agriculture
anat anatomy
anthr anthropology
attr attributive
av med aviation medicine
bact bacteriology
bio biology
bot botany
Brit British term
cf confer
chem chemistry
collq colloquial
derm dermatology
embr embryology
endocr endocrinology
entom entomology
genet genetics
gyn gynecology
helm helminthology
hem hematology
hist histology
ichth ichthyology
imm immunology
infect infectious diseases
int internal medicine
lab laboratory techniques
legl legal medicine
mcbio microbiology
mcscop microscopy
med medicine
metab metabolism
mil military
morph morphology
neur neurology
obs obsolete
obstet obstetrics
odont odontology
oncol oncology
ophth ophthalmology
orn ornithology
orthop orthopedics
otolar otolaryngology
p. a. of perfective aspect of
path pathology
ped pedology
pharm pharmacology
physl physiology
phys-ther physiotherapy
phytp phytopathology
pl plural
psych psychiatrics, psychic phenomena
rad radiotherapy, radiobiology, etc
san sanitation
surg surgery
tox toxicology
urol urology
ven venerology
vet veterinary medicine
x-ray roentgenology
zool zoology

SOURCES USED

Авиационная медицина, Г. Армстронг. Москва 1954.

Анатомия человека, Н. В. Колесников. Москва 1954.

Англо-русский гидробиологический словарь, Н. Н. Смирнов. Москва 1955.

Англо-русский медико-биологический словарь, С. Л. Санкин. Москва 1933.

Англо-русский сельскохозяйственный словарь, Б. Н. Усовский и др. Москва 1956.

Англо-русский химико-технологический словарь, К. М. Герцфельд. Москва 1953.

Ботаника, В. Н. Исаин. Москва 1951.

Ботаника, тт. 1 и 2, Л. И. Курсанов и др. Москва 1951.

Ветеринарный энциклопедический словарь, К. И. Скрябин, А. Я. Шапиро. Москва 1951.

Зоология беспозвоночных, С. В. Аверинцев. Москва 1952.

Зоология беспозвоночных, В. Ф. Натали. Москва 1951.

Краткий словарь клинических терминов, Б. П. Александровский. Киев 1955.

Курс зоологии, тт. 1 и 2, А. Г. Банников. Москва 1956.

Латинско-русский словарь, А. М. Малинин. Москва 1952.

Медицинский справочник, А. Н. Шабанов ред. Москва 1957.

Немецко-русский медицинский словарь, С. Д. Чашник и В. Г. Шустер. Москва 1953.

Определитель вирусов человека и животных, М. В. Жданов. Москва 1953.

Определитель низших растений, Л. И. Курсанов и др. Москва 1953.

Определитель промысловых рыб СССР, П. Г. Борисов и Н. С. Овсянников. Москва 1954.

Очерки по радиобиологии, АН СССР. Москва 1956.

Практический курс систематики растений, Т. Н. Гордеева и др. Москва 1953.

Психиатрия, В. А. Гиляровский. Москва 1954.

Психиатрия, И. Ф. Случевский. Ленинград 1957.

Психология, А. А. Смирнов и др. ред. Москва 1956.

Русско-англо-китайский медицинский словарь. Пекин 1954.

Словарь медицинской терминологии, латинско-украинско-русский, Ерофеев и др. Киев 1948.

Словарь-справочник энтомолога, В. Н. Щеголев ред. Москва 1955.

Audubon Guides: All the Birds of Eastern and Central North America; Waler Bird Guide by R. H. Pough. Garden City, NY, 1953.

Blackiston's Illustrated Pocket Medical Dictionary, N. L. Hoerr, A. Osol ed. New York 1952.

Blackiston's New Gould Medical Dictionary, N. L. Hoerr, A. Osol ed. New York 1956.

Dictionary of Microbiology by M. B. Jacobs et al. Princeton, N.J., 1957.

Distribution and Abundance of Animals by H. G. Andrewartha and L. C. Birch. Chicago 1954.

Dorland's Illustrated Medical Dictionary, L. B. Arey et al. ed. Philadelphia and London 1957.

Fieldbook of Natural History by E. L. Palmer. New York 1949.

Fresh-Water Invertebrates of the US by R. W. Pennak. New York 1953.
General Zoology by T. I. Storer. New York 1951.
German-English, English-German Dictionary for Physicians by Fritz Lejeune. New York 1952.
German-English Medical Dictionary by L. De Vries. New York 1952.
Glossary of Botanic Terms by B. D. Jackson. New York 1950.
Gray's Manual of Botany by M. L. Fernald. New York 1950.
Illustrated Encyclopedia of American Birds by L. A. Hausman. New York 1944.
Invertebrates, three volumes, by L. H. Hyman. New York 1940—51.
Kinships of Animals and Man by A. H. Morgan. New York 1955.
Mammal Guide by Ralph S. Palmer. New York 1954.
Manual for the Study of Insects by J. H. Comstock et al. Ithaca, N.Y., 1938.
Principles and Practice of Aviation Medicine by H. G. Armstrong. 1952.
Psychiatric Dictionary by L. E. Hinsie and J. Shatzky. New York 1954.
Russian-English Atomic Dictionary by E. A. Carpovich. New York 1957.
Shorter Medical Dictionary by T. L. Stedman. Chicago 1953.
Snakes of the World by R. L. Ditmars. New York 1954.
Source-Book of Biological Names and Terms by E. C. Jaeger. Springfield, Ill., 1955.
Stedman's Medical Dictionary, N. B. Taylor, A. E. Taylor ed. Baltimore 1957.
Systematics and the Origin of Species by Ernst Mayr. New York 1949.
Text-Book of Zoology by T. J. Parker and W. A. Haswell. London 1949.

RUSSIAN ALPHABET

а б в г д е ж з и й к

л м н о п р с т у ф х

ц ч ш щ ъ ы ь э ю я

A

"ааронова борода" = зверобой чашечный.
абазия path: abasia.
абарача = авокадо.
абатический abatic, abasic.
абдоминальное дыхание abdominal respiration.
абдоминогистерэктомия surg: abdominohysterectomy.
абдоминогистеротомия surg: abdominohysterotomy, abdominouterotomy.
абдукция abduction.
аберрация aberration.
~ хромосомы bio: chromosome aberration.
абиогенез abiogenesis.
абиогенетический abiogenetic, abiogenous.
абиосестон abioseston.
абиотический abiotic.
абиссальный abyssal.
аблактировка bot: side grafting, inarching g., approach g.
аборальный anat: aboral.
~ полюс zool: aboral end.
аборт gyn: abortion.
абортивное лечение abortive treatment
~ средство gyn: abortient, abortifacient, ecbolic agent.
"абортист(ка)" collq: abortionist.
абразия abrasion.
абрептор zool: postabdomen.
абрикос bot: apricot (Prunus armeniaca).
~ сандоминго mammee (Mammea americana, L.); see also лукума.
~ чёрный black apricot, purple a. (Prunus dasycarpa).
~ японский Japanese apricot (Prunus mune, Sieb. et Zuss.)
абсанс psych: absence.
абсолютная сердечная тупость int: superficial cardiac dullness.
абсолютная тупость int: flatness (percussion).
абстинент abstinent.
абстиненция psych: abstinence delirium.
абстракция abstraction.
абсцесс path: abscess, see нарыв.
абузус abuse.
абулия psych: abulia.
абутилон = грудника.
аваби zool: awabi (Haliotis gigantea).
аварийный инструментарий av med: crash tools.
авдотка = купава.
авертин pharm: avertin, tribromoethanol or tribromoethyl alcohol.
авиационная гигиена aviation hygiene.
~ медицина aviation medicine.
~ медсестра av med: flight nurse.
~ психология aviation psychology.
авиационные очки aviation goggles.
авиационный врач flight surgeon.
авиргулятный nonvirgulate.
авирулентный avirulent.
авитаминоз avitaminosis.
авокадо bot: avocado (Persea gratissima, Gaertn.)
авран bot: hedge hyssop, goldenpert (Gratiola).
~ аптечный Gratiola officinalis.
аврикула = первоцвет.
аврикулярный auricular.
австралийские страусы orn: Australian ostriches (Casuariiformes).
австралийсикй желобчатый червец = ицерия.
~ рогозуб ichth: Neoceratodus forsteri.
австралопитек australopithecine.
авто- auto-, self-, see ауто-, само-.
автовакцина autovaccine.
автовакцинация autovaccination, self-inoculation.
автогамия bio: autogamy.
автогамный bio: autogamous.

автогемотерапия autohemotherapy, autogenous blood treatment.
автоиммунизация autoimmunization.
автоинтоксикация autointoxication.
~ вследствие задержки (стула, мочи и т.п.) path: retention toxicosis. [self-infection
автоинфекция autoinfection,
автокаталитический autocatalytic.
автоклав autoclave.
автоклавированный экстракт auto-
автолиз autolysis. claved extract.
автолизат autolysate.
автолизин autolysin.
автолитический autolytic.
автомассаж self-massage.
автомат automaton.
автоматизм automatism.
автоматизированное действие psych: automatic action.
автоматическая подчиняемость psych: catalepsy.
автоматический automatic.
автомобиль скорой помощи ambulance.
автомобильная болезнь carsickness.
автономный autonomic, autonomous.
автопластика surg: autoplasty.
автопластический surg: autoplastic.
автополиплоид bot: autopolyploid.
автопсихический autopsychic.
автопсихоз autopsychosis.
автосинноя psych: autosynnoia.
автосома genet: autosome.
автосомный genet: autosomal.
автоспора bot: autospore.
автотомия autotomy, fission.
автотропизм bot: autotropism.
автотропный autotropic.
автотрофная бактерия autotrophic bacterium.
автотрофное растение bot: autophyte.
~ хемосинтетическое питание chemoautotrophy.
автотрофный autotrophic.
автофагия path: autophagy.
автохтонный autochthonous.
автоцидный пояс = самоубивающий пояс.
агава bot: agave, American aloe (Agave).
~ колючая silk grass (A. spinosa, Auct.)
~ сизаль = сайсл.
агами = трубач агами. [aemia.
агаммаглобулинемия agammaglobulin-
агамы zool: Agamidae (of Squamata).
агар agar; bot: Gelideum cartilagineum.
~ -агар pharm: agar-agar.
агар с кровью bact: blood agar.
агаровая пластинка bact: agar plate.
агаровый студень bact: agar jelly.
агарообразный agarlike.
агарообразующий agar-producing.
агарум bot: sea collanders (Agarum cribosum) brown alga.
агломерация agglomeration.
агглютинационная способность agglutinative capacity.
агглютинация agglutination.
агглютинин agglutinin.
агглютинировать agglutinate.
агглютинируемый agglutinable.
агглютинирующая способность agglutinative capacity.
агглютинирующее вещество agglutinating substance.
агглютиноген agglutinogen.
агглютиноид agglutinoid.
агглютиноскоп agglutinoscope.
агглютиноскопия agglutinoscopy.
агглютинофор agglutinophore.
аггравация aggravation.
аггрегат = агрегат.
агезия path: ageus(t)ia.
агеляйус orn: swamp blackbird, red-winged b. (Agelaius phoeniceus).
агенезия path: agenesia, agenesis.
агенетический path: agenetic.
агениталия path: agenitalism.
агент agent.
агератум bot: floss flower (Ageratum).
аглобулия path: aglobulia.
агнозия psych: agnosia.
агональное состояние path: agonal
агония agony. |state, moribund state.
агорафобия psych: agoraphobia.
агранулоцит agranulocyte.
агранулоцитный agranulocytic.
агранулоцитоз hem: agranulocytosis.
аграфия neur: agraphia.
агрегат aggregate, clump.
~ бактерий при ложной агглютинации lab: pseudoclump.
агрегатный aggregate, agminated.
агрегация aggregation, agmination.
~ одинаковых сегментов eumerism.
агрессивное поведение aggressive behavior.
агрессивность aggressiveness.
агримония bot: agrimony (Agrimonia odorata, Mill., A. eupatoria, L.)
агромания psych: agromania.
агростология bot: agrostology.
агрум bot: agrum (Citrus, L.)

агути zool: agouti, agouty (Dasyprocta aguti).
адалин pharm: adalin, carbomal.
адамантинома path: adamant(in)oma.
адамово яблоко anat: Adam's apple, pomum Adami.
адансония bot: adansonia (Adansonia, L.)
адаптация adaptation.
адаптированный adapted.
адаптометр ophth: adaptometer.
адвентициальная клетка adventitial cell.
адвентиция anat: adventitia.
адгезивный adhesive.
адгезиотомия surg: adhesiotomy.
аддисон-бирмеровская анемия pernicious anemia.
аддисонова болезнь Addison's disease.
аддисоновская болезнь = аддисонова б.
аддукция adduction.
аделоморфная клетка hist: chief cell, adelomorphous cell.
адениловая кислота pharm: adenylic acid.
аденин adenine.
аденит path: adenitis.
аденозин adenosine.
аденозинтрифосфат adenosine triphosphate.
аденоид adenoid.
аденоидная ткань anat: adenoid tissue.
аденоидное лицо path: adenoid face.
~ перерождение path: adenization.
~ разращение path: adenoid vegetation.
аденоидный adenoid, glandlike, lymphoid.
аденоиды = разрастание лимфаденоидной ткани носоглотки.
аденокарцинома oncol: adenocarcinoma.
аденома path: adenoma.
аденосаркома oncol: adenosarcoma.
аденотомия surg: adenotomy.
аденская язва Aden ulcer.
аджирык = свинорой.
адзуки = фасоль адзуки.
адиантум = венерин волос.
адиастола path: adiastole.
адинамичный adynamic, inert, apathetic.
адинамия adynamia.
адипоз path: adiposis, adiposity.
адлюмия bot: climbing fumitory, mountain fringe (Adlumia, Raf.); fumitory (A. fungosa, Greene).
адолескария zool: adolescaria.
адонис весенний bot: adonis (Adonis vernalis, L.)
адреналин adrenalin, epinephrine.
адреналэктомированный surg: adrenalectomized.
адреналэктомировать surg: adrenalectomize.
адренокортикальный adrenocortical.
адренокортикотропин adrenocorticotrop(h)in.
адронокортикотропный гормон adrenocorticotrophic hormone, ACTH.
адренолитический препарат pharm: adrenergic blocking agent.
адренэргический adrenergic.
адский камень = ляпис.
адсорбируемость adsorbability.
адсорбция adsorption.
ажитация agitation.
ажитированная депрессия psych: agitated depression.
ажитированное слабоумие psych: dementia agitata.
азалия bot: azalea (Azalea indica, L.)
азасерин azaserine.
азиатская корюшка ichth: rainbow herring (Osmerus dentex).
азиатский жук entom: Asiatic beetle (Anomala orientalis).
азооспермия path: azoospermia.
азопротеиновый гаптен azoprotein hapten.
азот nitrogen, N.
азотемия path: azotemia.
азотистое равновесие metab: nitrogen equilibrium.
азотистый chem: nitrogenous, nitrous.
~ баланс bot: nitrogen balance.
~ обмен nitrogenous metabolism.
~ эфир со спиртом pharm: sweet spirit of niter.
азотнокислое серебро pharm: silver nitrate.
азотнокислый висмут (основной) pharm: bismuth subnitrate.
азотный chem: nitric.
азотобактер bot: azotobacter.
азотобактерин azotobacterin.
азотопотребитель bot: nitrogen-loving plant.
азотособиратель bot: nitrogen gatherer.
азотосодержащий nitrogen-bearing, nitrogenous.
азотоусвояющие бактерии nitrogen-gathering bacteria.
азотофиксатор nitrogen fixer.
азотофиксирующая способность nitrogen-fixing capacity.
азотурия path: azoturia.
азотфиксация nitrogen fixation.
аидоиомания aidoiomania.
аизоевые (сем.) bot: carpetweed fam. (Aizoaceae).

аир bot: sweetflag, calamus, flagroot (Acorus, L.)
аира bot: hairgrass (Aira, L.); see also луговик.
~ дернистая tufted hairgrass (A. caespitosa, L.)
аирный корень bot: flagroot, calamus [root.
аирол pharm: bismuth iodosubgallate.
аист orn: stork (Ciconia ciconia).
аистник bot: storksbill (Erodium, L'Her.)
~ цикутолистный alfileria, pinclover (E. cicutarium).
аистопода zool: Aistopoda (extinct amphibians).
ай-ай = руконожка.
айва bot: quince, Cydonian apple (Cydonia oblonga, Mill.)
~ японская Japanese quince, flowering quince, (Chaenomeles japonica, Lindl.)
айлант bot: ailanthus, tree of heaven (Ailanthus glandulosa, Desf., A. altissima, Swingle).
акажу = 1.анакард; 2.свиетения.
акант bot: acanthus, bear's breech (Acanthus spinosus, L.)
акантовые (сем.) bot: acanthus family (Acanthaceae).
акантоды ichth: Acanthodii (extinct).
акантоз derm: acanthosis.
акантолиз derm: acantholysis.
акантома derm: acanthoma.
акантотический derm: acanthotic.
акантоцефалы helm: Acanthocephales.
акантоцибиум ichth: wahoo (Acanthocybium).
акапния hem: acapnia.
акарицид ent agr: acaricide, acarid--killing material.
акароидин = травяное дерево.
*акатка orn: stilt (Recurvirostridae).
акация bot: acacia (Acacia sp.)
~ австралийская A. decurrens, Willd.
~ бабла broom wattle (A. calamifolia, Sweet).
~ белая black locust, false acacia (Robinia pseudoacacia, L.)
~ деальбатая Acacia dealbata.
~ жёлтая yellow acacia, pea tree (Caragana arborescens).
~ песчаная Ammodendron.
~ серебристая Acacia dealbata, Link.
~ шёлковая silktree, "mimosa" (Albizzia Julibrissin, Dur.)
аквилегия = водосбор.
акиби = кольчатая нерпа.

акинезия path: akinesia, motor paralysis.
акинета akinete.
акклиматизация acclima(tiza)tion.
акклиматизированный acclimatized.
аккомодативный accomodative.
аккомодационная астенопия ophth: accomodative asthenopia.
~ деятельность accomodative activity.
~ способность accomodation power.
~ усталость accomodative fatigue.
аккомодация accomodation.
акнѐ path: acne.
акнида bot: water hemp (Acnida).
акоазма acoasma.
аконит bot pharm: aconite, monkshood.
~ аптечный = борец синий.
аконитин pharm: aconitine.
акрания path: acrania.
акридин acridine.
акрихин pharm: quinacrine.
акрихиновый психоз quinacrine-induced psychosis.
акроклинум bot: acroclinium (Acroclinium roseum, Hook.)
акромегалия acromegaly, Marie's syndrome.
акромиальный anat: acromial.
~ отросток acromion.
акромикрия acromicria.
акропетальный лист bot: acropetal leaf.
акросома zool: acrosome.
акротизм path: acrotism.
акроцианоз path: acrocyanosis.
аксиллярная линия anat: axillary [line.
аксолотль zool: axolotl (Siredon pisciformis).
аксон neur: axon.
аксоподия zool: axopod.
аксостиль zool: axostyle.
акт act.
активатор activator.
активируемый адреналином [adrenergic.
активная сила active force.
активное начало agent.
~ сознание av med: useful consciousness.
активность activity.
активный туберкулез path: active tuberculosis.
актинаструм bot: Actinastrum (algae).
актинидия bot: actinidia (Actinidia kolomikta, Maxim.)
актинистии (отр.) ichth: Actinistia.
актиничный actinic.
актиния zool: actinia(n), anemone, beadlet (Actinia).
актино- actino-.

актинометр actinometer.
актинометрия actinometry.
актиномикоз vet: actinomycosis, lumpy jaw, clyers, wooden tongue.
актиномикозный vet: actinomycotic.
актиномикотический узел bact: actinomycotic node.
актиномиксидии (отр.) zool: Actino- [myxidia.
актиномицет bot: Actinomyces.
актиномицин actinomycin.
актиноморфный bot: actinomorphous.
актиноневрит actinoneuritis.
актиноскопия x-ray: actinoscopy.
актинотерапия actinotherapy, radio- therapy.
актомиозин actomyosin.
акула ichth: shark, dogfish, tope (Cynias, Galeorhinus, Galeus, etc.)
~ белая white shark (Carcharodon carharias).
~ -людоед ground shark (Carcharhinus); maneater (Carcharodon).
акуловые = пластиножаберные.
акулообразная рыба elasmobranch (fish).
акулоподобный shark-like.
акулы (отр.) ichth: sharks (Selachoi- dea)
акупрессура surg: acupressure.
акупунктура surg: acupuncture.
акупункция acupuncture.
акушёр obstetrician.
акушёрка female obstetrician, midwife.
акушёрская сумка obstetrical bag.
акушёрские щипцы obstetric forceps.
акушёрство obstetrics.
акушёрствовать practice obstetrics.
алалия path: alalia.
аланин alanine, lactamine, lactamic acid.
аланинртуть pharm: mercury amidopropi- |onate.
алария bot: Alaria (brown algae).
~ съедобная henware (A. escu- |lenta).
аластрим infect: parasmallpox.
алгидность algidity.
алгидный algid.
алгия algia, pain.
алевриты aleurites (Aleurites, Euphorbiaceae).
алейкия aleukia (blood disease).
алейрод(ид)а = белокрылка.
алейронат aleuronat.
александрийский лист = сенна.
алексия psych: alexia, word blindness.
алектис threadfish (Alectis ciliaris).
алеурод(ид)а = белокрылка.
алецитальный alecithal.
алиментарная дистрофия nutritional dystrophy.

алиментарно-дистрофический психоз alimentary dystrophy psychosis.
алиментарный alimentary, nutritional.
алинит alinit (Bacillus ellenbachensis culture).
алиссум bot: alyssum (Alyssum, L.)
~ душистый = а. приморский.
~ извилистый gold dust (A. tortuosum, W. et K.)
~ приморский sweet alyssum (A. maritinum, Lam.)
алкалемия hem: alkalemia.
алкалинурия path: alkalinuria.
алкалоз alkalosis.
алкалоид chem: alkaloid.
алкалоидный alkaloidal.
алкалоидомания psych: alkaloid (morphine, heroin , etc.) addiction.
алкалоиды хинной коры chinchona bases.
алкоголозм alcoholism.
алкоголик alcoholic, alcohol addict, drunkard.
алкоголический бред alcoholic [delirium.
алкоголическое слабоумие psych: alcoholic dementia.
алкоголь alcohol.
алкогольная депрессия psych: alcoholic depression.
алкогольное опьянение alcoholic intoxication.
~ слабоумие alcoholic dementia.
алкогольный делирий = белая горячка.
~ псевдопаралич psych: alcoholic pseudoparalysis.
~ психоз alcoholic psychosis.
алкоголят chem: alcoholate.
аллантоин allantoin.
аллантоис embr: allantois.
аллель allele.
аллерген allergen.
аллергенность allergenicity.
аллергический allergic.
аллергия allergy.
аллётис orange spotted sunfish (Allotis humilis).
аллигатор zool: alligator.
~ американский American alligator (Alligator mississippiensis).
аллигаторова груша bot: alligator pear, see авокадо.
~ трава bot: alligator weed (Alternanthera philoxeroides, Grieseb.)
аллил chem: allyl.
аллогенный allogenic.

аллопат allopath(ist).
аллопатия allopathy.
аллопластический surg: alloplastic.
аллопластия surg: alloplasty.
аллополиплоид genet: allopoliploid.
аллоритмия allorhythmia.
аллосиндез genet: allosyndesis.
аллосома allosome.
аллотерм bio: allotherm.
аллотопия obstet: allotopia, malposition.
аллотропический allotropic.
аллотропия allotropia, allotropy.
аллохтонный allochthonous.
аллоэротика alloerotism.
аллоэротический alloerotic.
алмазный карандаш diamond pencil.
алоин pharm: aloin, barbaloin.
алопесия = облысение.
алоэ bot: aloe (Aloe, L.)
~ американское = агава.
~ настоящее yellow-flowered aloe (Aloe vulgaris, Lam., Aloe vera, L.)
алтей bot: Althaea, L.
~ аптечный marshmallow (Althaea officinalis).
~ лекарственный = а. аптечный.
~ розовый hollyhock (A. rosea).
алтейная трава = алтей аптечный.
алтейный корень = алтея.
алтея pharm: althea, marshmallow root (Althaea officinalis).
алые пятна petechia, purpura.
алыча bot: myrobalan, cherry-plum (Prunus cerasifera, Ehrh.)
альбатрос orn: albatross, wandering a. (Diomedea exulans).
альбатросы (сем.) orn: albatrosses (Diomedeae). Cf. трубконосые.
альбинизм path: albinism(us), congenital achroma, achromatosis.
альбинос path: albino.
альбинотический albinotic.
альбиция bot: Albizzia, Dur.
альбуго phytp: white rust on salsify (Albugo).
альбуля bonefish, ladyfish (Albula vulpes).
альбумин albumin.
альбуминат albuminate.
~ железа pharm: iron a.
альбуминозный albuminous.
альбумино-глобулиновый коэффициент albumen-globulin ratio.
альбуминометр lab: albuminometer.
альбуминурия path: albuminuria.
альбумоза chem: albumose.
альвеола alveolus.
альвеолярная карцинома oncol: alveolar carcinoma.
альвеолярная пиоррея odont: alveolar pyorrhea, periodontosis.
альвеолярный воздух alveolar air.
~ отросток anat: alveolar process.
~ ход anat: alveolar duct.
альгидный algid.
альгин algin.
альгиническая вата alginate wool.
альгиновая кислота alginic acid.
альголог bot: algologist.
альгология bot: algology.
альдегид chem: aldehyde.
альдолаза aldolase.
альдостерон aldosterone.
альдрихетта ichth: yellow-eyed mullet (Aldrichetta forsteri).
альканна = румянка.
алье orn: little auk (Alle a. alle).
альпага = альпака.
альпака zool: alpaca (Lama pacos). See also гуанако.
альпинариум bot: rock garden.
альтерация lesion (of a tissue).
альттуберкулин old tuberculin.
альфа-токоферилгидрохинон pharm: alpha-tocopherylhydroquinone.
~ трава bot: alfa grass (Stipa tenacissima, Macrochloa tenacissima).
альционария zool: alcyonarian.
алютера filefish (Alutera).
амавроз ophth: amaurosis, blindness.
амавротическая идиотия psych: amaurotic familial idiocy.
амазонский попугай orn: Amazon parrot (Chrysotis amazonicus).
аманита bot: amanita toadstool.
амарант bot: amaranth (Amaranthus, L.)
~ жминдовидный spreading a. (A. blitoides, Wats.)
~ колосистый green a., pigweed, wild beet, beetroot (A. retroflexus, L.)
~ хвостатый tassel flower, love-lies-bleeding, (A. caudatus, L.)
~ шарообразный bachelor's button (Gomphrena globosa, L.)
амарель = морель.
амариллис bot: belladonna lily (Amaryllis belladonna, L.)
амариллисовые (сем.) bot: amaryllis family (Amaryllidaceae).
амбивалентность psych: ambivalence, ambivalency.
амбивалентный psych: ambivalent.
амбисексуальность ambisexuality, ambosexuality.
амбисексуальный ambisexual.

амбистомовидная саламандра zool: ambystomid salamander.
амбистомы (сем.) zool: Ambystomidae.
амблёплитес ichth: goggle-eye (Ambloplites rupestris).
амблиопический path: amblyopic.
амблиопия amblyopia.
амбоцептор amboceptor, sensitizer.
~ бактериолиза bacteriolytic a.
~ гемолиза hemolytic a.
амбра zool: ambergris.
амброзия bot: ragweed (Ambrosia); 2. great ragweed, buffalo weed (A. trifida).
~ полыннолистная common ragweed, Roman wormwood, hogweed, bitter weed (A. artemisiifolia).
амбулакральная бороздка zool: ambulacral groove.
амбулатория outpatient clinic, outpatient department, dispensary.
амбулаторное лечение outpatient treatment.
амбулаторный ambulatory, ambulant.
~ больной ambulant patient, outpatient.
~ тиф ambulatory typhoid, walking t.
амбулякральная ножка zool: tube foot.
амёба amoeba, ameba (Amoeba).
~ -протей Amoeba proteus.
амёбицид amebicide.
амёбицидный amebicidal.
амёбная дизентерия amebic dysentery.
~ инвазия amebic invasion, amebism.
амёбный amoebic, amebic.
~ абсцесс amebic abscess.
амёбоид ameboid.
амёбоидный ameboid.
амёбообразный ameboid.
амёбоцит germ cell.
амёбы (отр.) zool: Amoebozoa, Lobosa.
амелобласт odont: ameloblast, ganoblast.
аменомания psych: amenomania.
аменоррея amenorrhea, amenia.
аментивная речевая спутанность psych: amentive speech confusion.
аменция psych: amentia.
американская вшивая трава = мытник американский.
~ камбала ichth: American topknot (Ancylopsetta quadrocellata). [rinae.
~ куропатка orn: bobwhite (Odontopho-
американские грифы (подотр.) orn: American vultures (Cathartae).
~ сирены zool: Sirenidae family.
~ страусы orn: American ostriches, rheas (Rheae).

американские устрицы zool: American oysters, blue points (Ostrea edulis).
американский благородный олень wapiti, elk (cervus canadensis).
~ окунь ichth: yellow perch (Perca flavescens).
~ омар zool: American lobster (Homarus americanus).
аметропический ophth: ametropic.
аметропичный ametropic.
аметропия ophth: ametropia.
амид chem: amide.
амидокапроновая кислота = лейцин.
амидокислота amido acid.
амидомуравьиная кислота amidoformic acid, carbamic acid.
амидосоединение amido compound.
амии (отр.) ichth: Amioidei.
амил chem: amyl.
амилобактерия amylobacterium (Bacillus amylobacter).
амилоид amyloid. [liver, waxy l.
амилоидная печень path: amyloid
амилоидное перерождение path: amyloid degeneration, (secondary)
амилоидоз amyloidosis. |amyloidosis.
амилолиз amylolysis.
амилолитический amylolytic.
амин chem: amin(e).
аминирование chem: aminating.
аминоацидурия path: aminoaciduria.
аминокислота amino acid.
аминопептидаза aminopeptidase.
аминопирин pharm: aminopyrine.
аминопурин chem: aminopurine.
аминосалициловая кислота pharm: aminosalicylic acid.
аминотриазол chem: aminotriazole.
аминофиллин pharm: aminophylline.
амиостазия path: amyostasia.
амиостатический amyostatic.
амиотрофия amyotrophia, muscle
амитал pharm: amytal. atrophy.
~ натрия sodium amytal.
амитоз hist: amitosis.
амитотический amitotic.
амитотическое деление = прямое
амиэлия path: amyelia. |деление.
аммиак chem: ammonia (gas).
аммиачная вода chem: ammonia water.
аммиачный ammoniac(al).
аммоний chem: ammonium (radical).
аммониты (отр.) zool: ammonites (Ammonidea).
аммониурия path: ammoniuria.

аммонов рог anat: Ammon's horn, cornu ammonis.
аммофил = песчанка.
амнезия psych: amnesia.
амнестический psych: amnestic, amnesic.
амнион embr: amnion.
амниотическая жидкость embr: amniotic fluid.
~ складка embr: amniotic fold.
амниоты zool: Amniota.
амок psych: amuck, amok.
аморальный amoral.
аморфинизм path: amorphinism.
аморфное состояние amorphism, amorphia.
аморфность = аморфное состояние.
аморфный amorphic, amorphous.
аморфофаллус bot: Amorphophallus.
ампелопсис bot: ampelopsis.
амплитуда amplitude.
~ аккомодации глаза ophth: range of accomodation.
ампула ampul, amp(o)ule.
ампулка small ampul.
ампутационная пила surg: amputation saw.
ампутационный нож surg: amputating knife.
~ рубец surg: amputation scar.
ампутация surg: amputation.
~ выше лодыжек или запястья major amputation.
~ на протяжении amputation in continuity.
~ не на суставе a. in continuity.
ампутировать surg: amputate.
амузия path: amusia.
амузыкальность amusia.
амузыкальный amusical.
амур белый ichth: Ctenopharyngodon.
~ чёрный Mylopharyngodon.
амурский бархат = бархатное дерево.
амурское пробковое дерево = бархатное дерево.
амфиастральный митоз amphiastral mitosis.
амфибии zool: amphibians, see земноводные.
амфибийный adj zool: amphibious, amphibiotic.
амфибия zool: amphibian.
амфигенный amphigean.
амфигония bio: amphigony.
амфидиск zool: birotulate(gemmule spicule).
амфизоида riffle beetle (Amphizoidae).
амфилина helm: cestodarian Amphilina foliacea.
амфиокс = ланцетник.
амфипода zool: amphipod (crustacean).
амфисбены zool: Amphisbaenidae (lizards).
амфитеатр amphitheater.
амфитокия bio: amphitokia.
амфиума zool: Amphiuma.
амфиумовые (сем.) zool: Amphiumidae.
амфицельный zool: amphicelous.
амфорическое дыхание path: amphoric respiration.
амфорный amphoric.
амфотерный amphoteric.
амфофильный amphophilic.
анабазис bot: anabasis.
анабена bot: Anabena (filamentous algae).
анаболизм anabolism.
анагиры entom: Anagyrus (genus).
анадромный ichth: anadromous.
анакард bot: cashew (Anacardium occidentale, L.)
анакардиум = анакард.
анакардия западная = анакард.
анакардовое дерево cashew tree.
анакардовые (сем.) bot: cashew family (Anacardiceae).
аналгезия analg(es)ia.
анализ analysis, assay, test.
~ мочи urinalysis.
~ мочи на удельный вес urine test for specific gravity.
~ мочи на цилиндры urine test for casts.
анализатор analyzer.
анализировать analyze.
аналитик analyst, analyzer.
аналитическая психология analytic psychology (Jung).
~ химия analytic chemistry.
аналитические весы lab: chemical balance.
аналогичный analogous.
аналогия analogy.
анальгезия analg(es)ia.
анальгетический analgesic.
анальгия analg(es)ia.
анальная железа anat: anal gland.
~ жилка entom: anal vein, vena analis.
~ область anat: anal region, hindquarters.
~ перепонка embr: anal plate.
~ складка anat: anal fold.
~ эротика anal erotic.
анальное отверстие anat: anus, anal aperture.
анальноэротический anal-erotic.
анальный край крыла entom: inner margin of the wing.
~ плавник anal fin, portal fin (zool).

анальный сфинктер (внутренний, наружный) anat: anal sphincter (internal, external).
анамнез anamnesis.
анамнетический anamnestic.
анамнии zool: Anamnia. [cuvier).
анампсес ichth: opule, hilu (Anampses
ананас bot: pineapple (Ananas sativus, Bromelia ananas, Schult.)
ананасные = бромелиевые.
анаплазия embr: anaplasia.
анапластика anaplasty, plastic surgery.
анапластический anaplastic.
анапсида zool: Anapsida (reptiles).
анартрия anarthria, defective articulation in speaking.
анасарка path: anasarca. [tion.
анастомоз anastomosis; surg: inoscula-
~ между веточками артерии anat: homocladic anastomosis. [anastomosis.
~ посредством пуговки surg: button
~ толстых кишёк surg: colocolostomy.
анастомозировать anastomose, communicate.
анастомозирующая псевдоподия zool: anastomosing pseudopod.
анастомозный anastomotic.
анастус entom: Anastus disparis.
анатоксин anatoxin, toxoid.
анатом anatomist.
анатомировать anatomize, dissect.
анатомическая медицина anatomic me-
~ табакерка anatomic snuffbox. | dicine.
~ шейка anatomic neck, collum anatomicum (of the humerus).
анатомический anatomic(al).
~ возраст anatomic age.
~ пинцет dissecting forceps, thumb f.
~ театр anatomic theater.
анатомия anatomy. [tomy.
~ растений anatomy of plants, phyto-
~ сосудистой и лимфатической системы angiology.
анафаза hist: anaphase.
анафилаксия anaphylaxis.
анафилактический anaphylactic.
анафилактоидная пурпура anaphylactoid purpura.
анафилактоидный anaphylactoid(al).
анафорез anaphoresis.
анафродизм path: anaphrodisia.
анафродит anaphrodite.
анаша = гашиш.
анаэроб mcbio: anaerobe, anaerobion.
анаэробиоз anaerobiosis.
анаэробионт anaerobion, anaerobe.
анаэробия anaerobia.
анаэробная пробирка anaerobic tube.
ангелика bot: angelica (Angelica hirsuta, Muhl.)
ангеликовое масло pharm: angelica
ангидремия path: anhydremia. oil.
ангидрометиленлимоннокислый натрий pharm: sodium anhydromethyle-
ангиит path: angiitis. | necitrate.
ангина infect: angina; sore throat.
~ Людовика Ludwig's angina.
ангинный anginal, anginous.
ангиобласт embr: angioblast.
ангиобластома oncol: angioblastoma, angiosarcoma.
ангиография angiographia, angiography.
ангиокардиографический angiocardiographic.
ангиокардиография angiocardiography.
ангиокератома oncol: angiokeratoma.
ангиология anat: angiology.
ангиома path: angioma.
ангионевроз angioneurosis.
ангионевротический angioneurotic.
ангиопаралич angioparalysis.
ангиосаркома oncol: angiosarcoma.
ангиоспазм angiospasm.
ангиоспастический angiospastic.
ангиотриб surg: angiotribe.
английская болезнь ped: English disease, rickets.
~ соль Epsom salt, magnesium sulphate.
ангорская коза zool: Angora goat (Capra angorensis).
андроген androgen.
андрогенез androgenesis.
андрогенный androgenic, androgenous.
андромеда bot: andromeda (Andromeda).
~ дубравниколистная marsh a., wild rosemary (A. polypholia).
андромедотоксин pharm: andromedoto-
андроспора androspore. xin.
андрофор bot: androphore.
андроцей bot: androecium.
аневризма path: aneurysm. [aneurismatic.
аневризматический aneurysmal,
аневризмотомия surg: aneurysmotomy.
анейрин aneurin, vitamin B_1.
анемический шум path: hemic murmur.
анемия path: anemia.
~ от недоедания deficiency a., nutritional a.
анемон bot: anemone, windflower (Ranunculaceae, Anemone, Pulsatilla).
анергический anergic.
анергия anergy.

анестезирование anesthetization.
анестезировать anesthetize.
анестезирующее действие anesthetic effect, anesthetization.
~ средство anesthetic.
анестезия anesthesia.
~ авертином avertin a.
~ хлороформом chloroform a.
анестетический adj: anesthetic.
анеуплоид bio: aneuploid.
анизокория ophth: anisocoria.
анизометропия ophth: anisometropia.
анизоперистальтический int: anisoperistaltic.
анизостремус porkfish (Anisostremus virginicus).
анизотропный anisotropic.
анизофилия bot: anisophylly.
анизоцитоз hem: anisocytosis.
анилиновое отравление aniline poisoning.
анимальный adj: animal.
анис bot: anise (Pimpinella anisum).
~ звездчатый = бадьян.
анисовое масло pharm: anise(ed) oil.
~ семя pharm: anise seed, aniseed.
анисовые капли pharm: anise drops.
анкилоблефарон ophth: ankyloblepharon.
анкилоглоссон path: ankyloglossia, tongue-tie.
анкилоз path: ankylosis.
анкилостома helm: hookworm Ancylostoma duodenale.
анкилостомоз helm: necatoriasis, uncinariasis.
аннато bot: annato tree (Bixa orellana, L.)
аннелида zool: annelid (worm).
аннона bot:custard apple,annona (Annona).
~ чешуйчатая sugar apple (Annona squamosa).
анноновые (сем.) bot: custard-apple family (Annonaceae).
ановуляторный anovulatory.
анодное включение phys-ther: anodal closure.
аноксемия av med: anoxemia.
аноксибиоз entom: anoxibiosis.
аноксия av med: anoxia.
аномалия anomaly.
аномальный anomalous.
~ цветок bot: abnormal flower.
анопластика surg: anoplasty.
анорексия anorexia.
анормальный abnormal.
аносмия path: anosmia.
анофелес = комар малярийный.
анофелицид pharm: anophelicide.
антабус pharm: antabuse, tetraethylthiuram disulfide.
антагонизм antagonism.
антагонист antagonist.
антагони(сти)ческий antagonistic.
антеверсия anat: anteversion.
антенатальный antenatal.
антенна entom: antenna.
~ первой пары entom: antennule.
антеннула entom: antennule.
антеридий bot: antheridium.
антероградная амнезия psych: anterograde amnesia.
~ память psych: anterograde memory.
антерозоид antherozoid.
антефлексия anat: anteflexion.
анти- anti- , see против-.
антиагглютинин antiagglutinin.
антиамбоцептор imm: anti-intermediary body.
антианемическое (средство) antianemic.
антиантитело bio: antiantibody.
антиартритное (средство) antiarthritic.
антиас ichth: barbier (Anthias).
антибактериальное вещество antibacterial (substance).
антибактерийное (средство) antibacterial (means).
антибиоз antibiosis.
антибиотик antibiotic.
антибиотический adj: antibiotic.
антивиральный imm: antiviral.
антивирус imm: antivirus.
антивитамин antivitamin.
антигеморроидальное средство antihemorrhoidal (agent).
антиген imm: antigen.
антигенная смесь antigen mixture.
антигенный antigenic.
антигигиеничный san: unhygienic, insanitary.
антигистамин pharm: antihistamine.
антигистаминный antihistaminic.
антигормон antihormone.
антидизентерийное (средство) antidysenteric (agent).
антидиуретический antidiuretic.
антидот antidote.
антиинфекционное (средство) antiinfective (agent).
антиканцероген oncol: anticarcinogen.
антикариозный odont: anticarious.
антикарциноген oncol: anticarcinogen.

антикатализатор chem: anticatalyst, anticatalyzer.
антикоагулянт hem: anticoagulant.
антикомплемент anticomplement, antialexin.
антикомплементарный anticomplementary
антилизин antilysine.
антилопа zool: antelope (Antilocarpa).
~ американская pronghorn (A.americana)
~ -джейран gazelle (Gazella subgutturosa).
~ пятнистоносая = мендес-антилопа
антималярийный antimalarial.
антимицин imm: antimycin.
антинаркотическое (средство) antinarcotic.
антинаучный unscientific.
антиневралгическое (средство) antineuralgic.
антипепсин antipepsin.
антиперистальтика path: antiperistal-
антипирин pharm: antipyrine. |sis.
антипка = вишня душистая.
антипластический antiplastic.
антипневмококковый antipneumococcic.
антирабический antirabic.
антирахитический antirachitic.
антиревматическое средство antireumatic.
антиретикулярная цитотоксическая сыворотка antireticular cytotoxical serum. [tion.
антисанитарное состояние insanita-
антисанитарный insanitary.
антисептика antisepsis.
антисептическая повязка surg: antiseptic dressing.
антисептическое средство antiseptic.
антисифилитический antisyphilitic, antiluetic.
антисифилитическое средство antisyphilitic, antiluetic.
антисоциальность psych: antisocialism
антисоциальный psych: antisocial.
антистрептолизин mcbio: antistrepto-
антисыворотка antiserum. |lysin.
антитело antibody.
антитоксиген antitoxi(no)gen.
антитоксин imm: antitoxin.
антитоксический antitoxic.
антитрипсин antitrypsin.
антитромбин hem: antithrombin.
антитромбический hem: antithrombic.
антифагоцитарный imm: antiphagocytic.
антифебрин pharm: antifebrin, acetanilid
антифермент antiferment; antienzyme.

антифон otolar: antiphone.
антиформин pharm: antiformin.
антифриз antifreeze. [esterase.
антихолинэстераза chem: anticholin-
антицынготный antiscorbutic.
античеловеческая сыворотка antihuman serum.
антиэнзим antienzyme.
антокарпус(ный) bot: anthocarpous.
антонов огонь = гангрена.
антоцеротовые (пор.) bot: Anthocerotales.
антракноз бобов phyt: pod spot.
~ виноградной лозы phyt: smallpox, black spot (Glocosporium ampelinum).
антракоз anthracosis (a form of pneumonoconiosis).
антракс 1. carbuncle; 2. vet: anthrax, malignant pustule, milzbrand.
антраниловая кислота anthranilic acid.
антрахинон chem: anthraquinone.
антрацин chem: anthracene.
антропоид anthropoid.
антропоидный adj: anthropoid.
антропологический anthropic.
антропология anthropology.
антропометрия anthropometry.
антропоморфический anthropomorphic.
антропофагия psych: anthropophagy.
анурия urol: anuria, anury, anuresis.
~ от закупорки obstructive anuria.
анус anat: anus.
анхинга water turkey (Anhinga, Plotus anhinga).
анховия ichth: silver anchovy, spearing, sardine (Anchovia browni).
анчар bot: antiar, upas tree (Antiaris toxicaria, Lesch.)
анчоус ichth: anchovy (Engraulis).
анчоусовые (сем.) ichth: anchovies (Engraulidae).
"анютины глазки" bot: pansy, heartsease (Viola tricolor, L.).
~ ~ дикие love-in-idleness, wild
аорта anat: aorta. |pansy.
аортальная недостаточность path: aortic insufficiency.
аортальное отверстие в диафрагме anat: aortic hiatus, a. foramen.
~ притупление path: aortic dullness.
~ сплетение anat: aortic plexus.
аортальный клапан anat: aortic
~ порок path: aortic failure. |valve.
~ шум aortic murmur.
аортит int: aortitis.

апантелес entom: braconid Apanteles
glomeratus. [tic mood.
апатичное настроение psych: apathe-
апатичность psych: apathism.
апатия psych: apathy.
апельсин orange (Citrus aurantium, L.)
~ алжирский clementine (C. aethiopium).
~ горький = померанец.
~ "Навель" navel orange.
~ оседж = маклюра. [trifoliata, Raf.)
~ трехлистный hardy orange (Poncirus
апериодический aperiodic.
апериодичность aperiodicity. [dendrite
апикальный дендрит anat: apical
апико-каудальный anat: apico-caudal
(from apex to cauda).
апиколиз apicolysis.
апиоль pharm: parsley camphor.
аплазия path: aplasia.
апланоспора aplanospora. [anemia.
апластическая анемия path: aplastic
аплёдинотус ichth: white perch, fresh-
water drum (Aplodinotus grunniens).
апноe apno(e)a, transient suspension
of respiration. [mous.
апогамический genet: apogamic, apoga-
апогамия apogamy, apomixis, partheno-
апокарпный bot: apocarpous. |genesis.
апомиксис bot: apomixis.
апоморфин pharm: apomorphine. [tendon.
апоневроз anat: aponeurosis, expanded
апоневротический aponeurotic.
апоплексический удар path: apoplexy,
apoplectic stroke.
апоплексическое слабоумие psych:
apoplectic dementia.
~ сложение apoplectic habit.
апоплексия path: apoplexy.
апоплектик apoplectic (person), person
suffering apoplexy.
апоплектиформный path: apoplectiform.
апоплектический = апоплексический.
апорт Alexander apple.
апоспория bio: apospory, aposporosis.
апотеций bot: apothecium.
апофиз anat: apophysis.
апофизарный apophyseal, apophysial.
апофильный bot: apophyllous.
апохлоротический bot: apochlorotic.
апохроматический apochromatic.
апоциновые (сем.) bot: dogbane family
(Apocynaceae).
апоцинум bot: apocynum, dogbane, Indian
hemp (Apocynum, L.)
аппарат apparatus.
~ для вливаний surg: infusor.
аппарат для вливания сальварсана
salvarsan outfit.
~ для вытяжения surg: stretch machine.
~ для определения основного обмена metabolimeter.
~ для пастеризации pasteurizer.
~ для разрезания марли surg:
gauze cutter.
аппаратура apparatae, apparatus. [lic.
аппендальгия path: appendicular co-
аппендектомия surg: appendectomy.
аппендикс anat: appendix.
аппендикулярии zool: appendicularians
(Appendiculariae).
аппендикулярия zool: appendicularian
(Occopleura cophocerca, Falia, etc.)
аппендицит int: appendicitis.
аппендицитный абсцесс int: appendiceal abscess. [nitis.
~ перитонит int: appendiceal perito-
аппендэктомия = аппендектомия.
аппетит appetite.
аппетитный appetizing.
аппликатор applicator.
аппликационный метод лечения rad:
(external) applicator method of treat
ment, see контактная радиотерапия.
аппликация application.
апраксия neur: apraxia.
апрезолин pharm: apresoline.
апресолин = апрезолин.
апсидоспондили zool: Apsidospondyli
(extinct amphibians).
аптека pharmacy, drugstore.
аптекарская такса druggist's rate(s).
аптекарские весы druggist's scales.
аптекарский вес apothecaries' weight.
~ магазин drugstore without prescription service, officinal store.
~ помощник assistant pharmacist; Brit:
compounder.
~ товар druggist ware, medicaments.
аптекарь pharmacist, druggist.
аптечка medicine chest, m. kit.
аптечное дело pharmacy.
аптечные весы = аптекарские
весы. [officinal (officinalis).
аптечный bot: pharmaceutical,
~ шкафчик medicine cabinet.
~ ящик medicine chest.
ар = ара.
ара orn: ara, American parrot Ara
арабка = нектарин. macao.
аравийская камедь pharm: Arabic gum.
аралиевые (сем.) bot: ginseng family
(Araliaceae).

аралия bot: aralia (Aralia papyrifera, Hook.)
арамина bot: aramina, Caesar weed (Urena lobata, L.)
арарас = ара.
араукариевые (сем.) bot: araucaria family (Araucariaceae).
араукария araucaria (Araucaria).
~ высокая Norfolk Island pine (A. excelsa, R.Br.)
арахис bot: peanut (Arachis, L.); common p., Brit: groundnut (A. hypogaea).
арахисное масло peanut oil.
арахнида = паукообразные.
арахнодактилия path: arachnodactyly, spider fingers.
арахнология zool: arachnology.
арбуз watermellon (Citrullus vulgaris).
~ горький = колоквинт.
~ китайский Chinese w. (Benincasa hispida, Cogn.)
~ ~ цукатный = тыква восковая.
~ кормовой citron.
аргемон = мак колючий.
аргентина = серебрянка.
аргинин arginine.
аргирия path: argyria, silver staining.
аргирозомус ichth: tullibee (Argyrosomus tullibee).
аргирол pharm: argyrol.
аргирофильные волокна hist: argyrophil fibers.
аргон argon, Ar.
аргонавт = кораблик.
аргус orn: argus phesant (Argusianus).
~ щавелевый = голубянка.
ареактивность unresponsiveness.
ареал area.
арека bot: areca (Areca).
арековая пальма bot: areca palm (Areca catechu)
ареола areola, areolation.
ареосцелис zool: reptile Araeoscelis (extinct).
аржанец = тимофеевка.
Аржиль Argyll.
арибофлавиноз ophth: ariboflavinosis.
ариста entom: arista.
аристида = проволочная трава.
аристогеничный aristogenic.
аристогения aristogenics.
аристотелев фонарь zool: Aristotle's lantern.
аритмический = аритмичный.
аритмичный arrhythmic.
аритмия int: arrhythmia.
арифметическое мышление av med: arithmetic reasoning.
арифмомания psych: arithmomania.
арка anat: arcus, arch.
аркада anat: arcade.
арканчик zool: branched tentacle; lasso cell, colloblast.
арктическая крачка orn: arctic tern (Sterna paradisaea).
армадил = броненосец.
армерия bot: thrift, sea pink (Armeria).
Армстронг Armstrong.
арнато = аннато.
арника pharm: arnica.
~ горная leopard's bane (Arnica montana).
ароидные = аронниковые.
аролиум entom: arolium.
аромат aroma.
ароматизировать aromatize.
ароматический aromatic.
арония bot: chokeberry (Aronia, Spech)
аронник = арум.
аронниковые (сем.) bot: arum family (Araceae).
аррау zool: turtle Podocnomis.
арренотокичный bio: arrhenotokous.
арренотокия bio: arrhenotoky, arrhenotokia.
аррорут bot: arrowroot.
арсаниловая кислота arsanilic acid.
арсенат chem: arsenate.
арсенит chem: arsenite.
арсеноксид chem: arsenoxide.
арсин chem: arsine.
арсиновая кислота arsinic acid.
арсонокислота arsonic acid.
артеренол arterenol.
артериализация arterialization.
артериальная ветвь anat: arterial ramus.
~ кровь arterial blood.
~ опухоль path: aneurysm.
~ связка anat: ligamentum arteriosum.
артериальное давление arterial pressure.
~ отверстие, правое anat: ostium arteriosum dextrum (heart).
артериальный зажим surg: artery forceps, hemostat(ic forceps).
~ камень path: arteriolith.
~ конус anat: arterial cone, conus arteriosus (heart).
~ круг anat: circle of Willis.
~ проток embr: ductus arteriosus.
~ ствол anat: arterial trunk.
~ шов surg: arteriorrhaphy.
артериит int: arteritis.
артерийка anat: arteriola.
артериовенозный arteriovenous.
артериограмма arteriogram.
артериография arteriography.
артериокапилляр arteriocapillary.

артериокапиллярный (сосуд) anat: arteriocapillary.

артериола anat: arteriola, arteriole.

артериопластика surg: arterioplasty, aneurysmorrhaphy.

артериопластический arterioplastic.

артериосклероз path: arteriosclerosis.

артериосклеротический arteriosclerotic.

артериотомия surg: arteriotomy.

артерия anat: artery.

~ вилочковой железы thymic a.

~ грудино-ключично-сосцевидной мышцы sternocleidomastoid a.

~ грудной клетки thoracic a.

~ желудка и большого сальника gastroepiploic a.

~ желчного пузыря cystic a.

~ клитора a. of clitoris.

~ матки uterine a.

~ мозга (задняя соединяющая, передняя, средняя) (posterior, anterior, middle) cerebral a.

~ молочной железы (внутренняя, наружная) (internal, external) mammary a.

~ мочевого пузыря vesical a.

~ надпочечника suprarenal a.

~ окружающая подвздошную кость iliac circumflex a.

~ пищевода esophageal a.

~ семявыносящего протока deferential a.

~ червеобразного отростка appendicular a.

~ щитовидной железы (верхняя, нижняя)(superior, inferior) thyroid a.

артеро- = артерио-.

артефакт hist: artefact, artifact.

артикуляция articulation.

артишок bot: artichoke (Cynara scolymus).

~ испанский cardoon (C. cardunculus).

артралгия arthralgia, articular neuralgia.

артрит path: arthritis.

артритик arthritic (patient).

артритический adj: arthritic.

артродез surg: arthrodesis.

артрология anat: arthrology.

артропатия arthropathy.

артропластика surg: arthroplasty.

артропластический arthroplastic.

артроспира bot: alga Arthrospira, Spirulina.

артроспора bot: arthrogenous spore.

артротомия surg: arthrotomy.

арум bot: yautia (Arum sagittifolium).

~ кукушечный arum lily, cuckoopint (A. maculatum).

архаический archaic.

архар zool: Central-Asia sheep Ovis ammon.

архегониат bot: archegoniate.

архегоний bot: archegonium.

архедиктион entom: archedyction.

археоптерикс orn: archeopteryx (extinct).

археспорий bot: archesporium.

архибентонный zool: archibenthal.

архимицеты bot: Archimycetes (fungi).

архитектоника architectonics.

архитектонический architectonic.

архозавры zool: Archosauria (extinct reptiles).

архосаргус ichth: southern sheepshead (Archosargus probatocephalus).

арча = можжевельник.

арчёвый лес bot: juniper forest.

асафетида bot: asafetida.

асбест asbestos.

асбестоз path: asbestosis.

асексуальный asexual.

асемия neur: asemia, asemasia, asymbolia.

асептика asepsis.

асептический aseptic.

асинергия path: asynergy.

асистолический path: asystolic.

асистолия path: asystolia, asystole.

аск bot: ascus (of ascomycetes).

аскарида helm: ascarid, nematode worm (Ascaridae).

~ червеобразная helm: ascaris (Ascaris lumbricoides).

аскаридиол ascaridiol.

аскаридоз helm: ascariasis.

аскариды (сем.) helm: Ascaridae.

аскарицид pharm: ascaricide.

аскетизм asceticism.

аскетический ascetic.

аскомицетный bot: ascomycetous.

аскомицеты bot: ascomycetous fungi (Ascomycetes).

асконоидный тип zool: asconoid type.

аскорбат chem: ascorbate.

аскорбиновая кислота ascorbic acid.

аскофиллум bot: algae Ascophyllum.

~ узловатый rockweed, knobbed wrack, knotted w., yellow w. (Ascophyllum nodosum).

аскохитоз phytp: ascochyta, black stem.

~ гороха ascochyta leaf blight.

аспарагин asparagine.

аспарагиназа asparaginase.

аспарагин(овая кислота) asparagin(ic acid).

аспедо ichth: Aspedo levis.

аспергиллёз aspergillosis.

аспергиллин aspergillin.

аспергиллус bot: Aspergillus (fungi).

аспермия path: aspermia, aspermatism.

аспид zool: asp, elapine snake (Elaps, Micrurus).
аспиды (сем.) zool: asps, elapine snakes (Elapidae).
аспиратор aspirator.
аспирационная пневмония int: aspiration pneumonia.
аспирация aspiration.
аспирин pharm: aspirin.
ассамская лихорадка Assam fever, see калаазар.
ассенизация san: sludge removal.
ассимилировать assimilate.
ассимилироваться to be assimilated.
ассимилируемый assimilable; being assimilated.
ассимилирующий assimilating, assimilative, assimilatory.
ассимилят assimilant.
ассимиляционная ткань assimilative tissue.
ассимиляция assimilation.
ассистент аптекаря = аптекарский помощник.
~ клиники clinical assistant.
ассистентура assistantship.
ассоциативное мышление associative thinking.
ассоциационное волокно anat: association fiber.
ассоциационный опыт psych: association test.
ассоциация association.
~ идей psych: a. of ideas.
~ по смежности psych: simultaneous occurrence a.
~ по сходству psych: similar ideas a.
астазия neur: astasia.
~ -абазия neur: astasia-abasia.
астаксантин astaxantin.
астеник anat: asthenic type (Kretschmer).
астенический asthenic.
астеничный asthenic.
астения path: asthenia.
астенометр asthenometer.
астенопик ophth: asthenope.
астенопический asthenopic.
астенопия asthenopia.
астерионелла bot: asterionella (alga).
астигмограф ophth: astigmagraph.
астигматизм astigmatism.
астма int: asthma.
астматик person afflicted with asthma.
астматическая аура aura asthmatica.
астматический asthmatic.
астмогенный asthmogenic.
астра bot: aster (Aster, L.)
астрагал bot: milk vetch (Astragalus, L.)
астрагал толстоплодный bot: ground plum, buffalo bean (A. crassicarpus, A. caryocarpus).
астроглия neur: astroglia, macroglia, Cajal's cells, spider cells.
астроцит hist: astrocyte.
астроцитарная глия neur: astroglia.
астроцитома neur: astrocytoma.
асфиксия av med: asphyxia.
асфиктический asphyxial.
асфоделина жёлтая = златок.
асцидии zool: ascidians (Ascidiae).
асцидия zool: ascidian (Ascidia mentula); sea squirt, sea lemon (Botryllus)
~ звёздочка golden stars tunicate (Botryllus).
асцит path: ascites, abdominal dropsy.
асцитная жидкость path: ascitic fluid.
~ опухоль ascitic tumor.
атавизм atavism, reversion.
атавистический atavistic, reversionary.
атаксиграф ataxigraph.
атаксический = атактический.
атаксия ataxia.
атактическая походка neur: ataxic gait, stamping g.
~ речевая спутанность psych: ataxic speech confusion.
~ речь ataxic speech.
атактический atactic, ataxic.
атактическое замыкание psych: ataxic combination of words/phrases, scrambled speech, word-salad.
атбасарка entom: Dociostaurus kraussi; see also крестовичка.
ателектаз(а) path: atelectasis, lung collapse.
ателектатический atelectatic.
атерина ichth: friar (Atherina); smelt (Atherinopsis).
атеринка = атерина.
атериновые (сем.) ichth: atherine family (Atherinidae).
атерома path: atheroma, sebaceous cyst.
атероматоз atheromatosis.
атероматозный atheromatous.
атеросклероз int: atherosclerosis.
атетоз athetosis, posthemiplegic chorea.
атетозный athetosic, athetoid, athetotic.
атипическая чума птиц Newcastle disease.
атипические формы заболевания formes frustes.
атипический atypical.
атипичный atypical.
атлант anat: atlas.

атлантическая сардина ichth:
Atlantic sardine (Sardina).
атлантический палоло (червь) zool:
Atlantic palolo (Eunice fucata).
атлантозатылочный сустав anat:
atlanto-occipital joint.
атлантоэпистофейный сустав anat:
atlantoepistophic joint.
атлет athlete.
атлетический athletic.
атмосфера atmosphere. [pressure.
атмосферное давление atmospheric
атоксил pharm: atoxyl, sodium
атоксический atoxic. |arsanilate.
атолл atoll.
атонический atonic.
атоничность atonicity.
атония path: atonia, atony.
~ почек nephratony.
атопический atopic.
атофан pharm: atophan, cinchophen.
~ натрий cinchophen-sodium.
атрезия path: atresia, imperforation.
~ заднего прохода path: aproctia,
imperforate anus.
~ матки atretometria.
~ пузыря atretocystia.
~ рта atretostomia.
атрепсия ped: atrepsia.
атретическое тельце atretic
follicle, corpus atreticum.
атриальный zool: atrial. [tricular.
атриовентрикулярный anat: antrioven-
атриум anat: atrium.
атропин pharm: atropine.
атропинирование atropinization.
атропинировать antropinize.
атропиновая мазь pharm: atropin
(sulphate) ointment.
атрофированный atrophied.
атрофировать(ся) atrophy.
атрофический atrophic.
атрофия atrophy.
~ возбудимости = потеря чувствительности.
~ зрительного нерва optic atrophy.
~ конечностей melatrophy.
~ на одной стороне органа
hemiatrophy.
~ от бездействия disuse atrophy.
~ от давления compression atrophy.
аттенуированный attenuated.
аттик anat: attic.
аудиограмма audiogram.
аудиология audiology.
аудиометр audiometer.

ауксин auxin.
ауксоспора auxospore.
ауксотрофный mcbio: auxotrophic.
аура neur: aura.
ауральный aural.
ауреомицин imm: aureomycin.
аурикулярная фибрилляция path:
auricular fibrillation, atrial f.
аурофак aurofac (a preparation containing aureomycin and vitamin B_{12}).
аускультативный звук auscultatory
sound.
аускультационный auscultatory.
аускультация auscultation.
аускультировать auscult(ate).
аутизм psych: autism.
аутический autistic.
ауто- auto-, self-, see авто-, само-.
аутогемотерапия autohemotherapy.
аутогенная кость autogenous bone.
аутогенный autogenic.
аутоиммунизация autoimmunization.
аутоинвазия autoinvasion.
аутоинтоксикация autointoxication.
аутолизат autolysate.
аутопсия autopsy.
аутотрансплант surg: autoplastic
graft, autograft. [-plantation.
аутотрансплантация surg: autotrans
аутофония otolar: autophonia.
аутохтонный autochthonous.
аутэкологический autecological.
аутэкология autecology.
ауха = китайский окунь.
Ауэски Aueski.
афазия path: aphasia.
афакический ophth: aphakic,
афакия ophth: aphakia. |aphakial.
афанизоменон bot: Aphanizomenon
(filamentous algae). [Aphelinus mali.
афелинус entom: chalcid parasite,
афелины (сем.) entom: chalcid para-
афемия path: aphemia.|sites Aphelinidae
афиброногенемия hem: afibrinogenemia.
афидиус entom: Aphidius granarius.
афилактический aphylactic.
афитис золотистый entom: Aphytis
chrysomphali.
афония aphonia, voicelessness.
афотическая область bio: aphotic
region.
афотический пояс aphotic zone.
афредодерус ichth: pirate perch
(Aphredoderus sayannus).
африканская болезнь African sickness, African lethargy.

африканские страусы orn: African ostriches (Struthiones).
африканский кабан zool: wart hog (Phacochoerus africanus).
~ слон zool: African elephant (Loxodon africanus).
~ страус orn: African ostrich (Struthio camelus).
африканское масляное дерево tallow tree (Pentadesma butyraceum).
африкт friction (of pleura, etc.)
афрозид pharm: afroside.
афта int: aphtha.
афтозный стоматит int: aphthous stomatitis.
аффект psych: affect, emotion, mood.
~ боязни psych: affect of anxiety.
~ страха psych: affect of fear.
аффектация affectation.
аффективная реакция psych: affective reaction.
аффективность psych: affectability.
афферентный psych: afferent, centripetal.
ахиличный path: achylous.
ахилия path: achylia.
ахиллов рефлекс physl: Achilles reflex.
ахиллово сухожилие anat: Achilles tendon.
ахолический path: acholous, acholic.
ахолия acholia.
ахондроплазия path: achondroplasia, achondroplasty.
ахромазия path: achromasia.
ахроматизм achromatism.
ахроматиновая сетка hist: linin network.
ахроматиновый hist: achromatinic.
ахроматическая фигура hist: achromatic figure.
ахроматопсия ophth: achromatopsia.
ахромия achromia, achroma.
ацетазоламид pharm: acetazoleamide.
ацетат chem: acetate.
ацетилсалициловая кислота pharm: acetylsalicylic acid.
ацетилхолин acetylcholine.
ацетон acetone.
ацетопирин pharm: antipyrine, acetylsalicylate.
ацетосалициловокислый антипирин = ацетопирин.
ацетоуксусная кислота acetoacetic acid.
ацидоз acidosis.
ацидотический acidotic.
ацидофил acidophil.
ацидофильная простокваша acidophilous soured milk.
ацидофильность acidophilism.
ацидофильный acidophilic, acidophilous.
ациклический acyclic.
~ цветок bot: acyclic (not whorled) flower.
ацинозный anat: acinous.
ацинус anat: acinus.
аэрарий platform for air baths.
аэратор aerator.
аэрация aeration.
аэренхима bot: aerenchyma.
аэрировать aerate.
аэро- aer(o)-.
аэроб mcbio: aerobion, aerobe.
аэробиоз aerobiosis.
аэробиозный aerobiotic.
аэробионт aerobion, aerobe.
аэробный aerobic, aerobian.
аэроген aerogen.
аэрозолевая бомба san: aerosol bomb.
аэроневроз av med: aeroneurosis, psychoneurosis in aviators, air pilot disease.
аэроотит av med: aerotitis.
~ среднего уха aerotitis media.
аэропатия av med: aeropathy.
аэросинусит av med: aerosinusitis.
аэротаксис aerotaxis.
аэротерапия aerotherapy, aerotherapeutics.
аэрофагия aerophagia, aerophagy.
аэрофильный aerophil(ous).
аэрофит bot: aerophyte, air plant.
аэрофобия psych: aerophobia.
аэроцеле path: aerocele.
аэроэмболия av med: aeroembolism, decompression sickness.
аяйя orn: roseate spoonbill (Ajaja ajaja).

Б

бабануха хреновая entom: leaf spot of horse-radish (Septoria armoraciae), see also листоед хреновый.
бабасу = орех бразильский.
Бабинский Babinski.
бабка chestnut, pastern (of a horse).
бабочка entom: butterfly.
~ белая американская white moth, fall webworm (Hyphantria cunea).
~ зонтичная parsley worm (Papilio asterias).
~ "мертвая голова" death's-head moth (Acherontia atropos).
~ морская = морская б.
~ ночная night moth, owlet-moth, noctuid (Noctuidae).
бабочки = чешуекрылые.
бабочколовка moth catcher (device).
бабочница entom: moth fly (Psychodidae).
бабуин = павиан.

бабье лето Indian summer.
багрэ ichth: sea catfish (Bagrus marinus)
багряник стручковый = иудино дерево.
багрянка zool: dog whelk (Purpura).
багрянки = красные водоросли.
багряные водоросли = красные в.
багульник bot: Labrador tea, marsh tea, wild rosemary (Ledum, L.)
бадан bot: Bergenia crassifolia.
бадранки = лимон бадранки.
бадриджан = баклажан.
бадьян bot: badian (Illicium verum).
бадяга пресноводная zool: fresh-water sponge (Spongilla). [Sertoli c.
базальная клетка anat: basal cell,
~ мембрана anat: basement membrane, membrana basalis. [of the cochlea.
~ часть улитки anat: basal portion
базальное тельце zool: basal granule, basal body.
базальный прицветник bot: glume.
~ угол крыла entom: humeral angle of the wing.
~ членик усиков zool: scape.
Базедов Basedow.
базедова болезнь Basedow's disease, exophthalmic goiter.
базедовизм = базедова болезнь.
базедовик Basedow's disease patient, Basedowian.
базелла-шпинат = шпинат индийский.
базидальные грибы = базидиомицеты.
~ лишайники bot: Basidiolichenes.
базидиеносный gill-bearing.
базидиомицетный bot: basidiomycetous.
базидиомицеты bot: basidiomycetous fungi (Basidiomycetes).
базидия bot: basidium.
базилик bot: basil, sacred herb (Ocimum basilicum, L.)
~ карликовый bush basil (O. minimum).
~ низкорослый = б.карликовый.
базилярный basilar. [leaf.
базипетальный лист bot: basipetal
базиспориевая сухая гниль phytp: basisporium dry rot.
базихроматин hist lab: basichromatin.
базофилик basophilic patient.
базофильная пунктация hem: basophilic stippling. [nules.
базофильные зёрнышки basophil gra-
базофильный hist: basophilic, basophi-
~ лейкоцит basophilic leucocyte. |lous.
~ эритробласт basophilic erythroblast.

байбак zool: baboc (Marmota babak, Mull.); woodchuck (Arctomys).
Байер Bayer.
байкальская нерпа zool: Lake Baikal seal (Phoca sibirica).
байкальские широколобки (сем.) ichth: Comephoridae.
байховый чай bot: beichao.
бакаут bot: lignum vitae, pockwood (Guaiacum officinale, L.)
баклажан bot: eggplant (Solanum melongena, Melongena esculenta).
баклан orn: cormorant, shag, (Phalacrocorax).
~ хохлатый shag (P. graculus).
баклановые (сем.) orn: cormorant family (Phalacrocoracidae).
бактериальная дырчатость phytp: bacterial shothole.
~ пища bacterial diet.
~ флора bacterial flora.
бактериальное заболевание bacteriosis.
~ разложение bacterial decomposition.
~ увядание паслёновых phytp: bacterial wilt. [cancer.
бактериальный рак phytp: bacterial
~ цилиндр bacterial cast (in urine).
бактериемический bacteremic.
бактериемия bacteremia.
бактериеубивающий bactericidal.
бактерии bacteria.
~ -азотособиратели nitrogen-fixing bacteria.
~ группы кишечной палочки coliform bacteria.
бактерийного происхождения bacteriogenous, bacteriogenic.
бактериоз bacteriosis.
~ огурцов bot: angular leaf spot.
бактериолиз bacteriolysis.
бактериолитический bacteriolytic.
бактериолитическое вещество bacteriolysant.
бактериолог bacteriologist.
бактериологически-чистая культура bact: pure culture.
бактериологический bacteriologic.
бактериология bacteriology.
бактериопурпурин bacteriopurpurin.
бактериоскопия microscopic examination of bacteria.
бактериостат bacteriostat.
бактериостатический bacteriostatic.
бактериотоксин bacteriotoxin (destructive to or produced by bacteria).

бактериотоксический bacteriotoxic.
бактериофаг bacteriophage.
бактериофагия bacteriophagy.
бактерицид bactericide.
бактерицидное вещество bactericide.
бактерицидный bactericidal.
бактерия bacterium.
бактероид bacteroid.
баланоглосс zool: balanoglossus (Balanoglossus kowalevskii).
балантидий zool: Balantidium.
балантидиозис vet: balantidiosis.
балата bot: balata (Mimusops balata, Mimusops globosa).
балл = отметка.
~ негодности av med: point for unfitness.
балластное вещество ballast substance.
баллистокардиограмма ballistocardiogram.
баллон bulb, shell, envelope; cylinder, drum.
~ для спринцеваний irrigation bulb.
~ Политцера Politzer bag.
баллотирование ballottement, repercussion.
*балобан orn: shrike (Gennaia).
балтийская сельдь ichth: Baltic herring (Clupea harengus membras).
бальза bot: balsa (Ochroma lagopus).
бальзам balm, balsam.
бальзамин bot: balsam, jewelweed, snapweed, touch-me-not (Impatiens, L.)
бальзамирование embalming.
бальзамический balmy, balsamic.
бальнеография balneography.
бальнеологический balneologic.
бальнеология balneology.
бальнеотерапия balneotherapy.
балянофорин balanophorin.
балянус zool: barnacle (Balanus).
бамбук bot: bamboo (Bambusa).
бамбуковые (подсем.) bot: bamboo subfamily (Bambuseae, Nees.)
бамия = гибиск съедобный.
банан bot: banana (Musa).
~ пизанг cooking banana (M. paradisiaca)
~ текстильный manila, wild plantain, Siam hemp (Musa textilis, Nees.)
банановые (сем.) bot: banana family (Musaceae).
банановый трипс entom: banana thrips.
бананоед orn: turakoo, see турако.
банг bot: bhang, bang, Indian hemp plant
бангиева водоросль bot: bangiaceous alga (Bangia).
бандаж binder.
банка 1. jar, can, tin; 2. med: cupping glass, suction cup
банка для мази ointment jar.
банкивский петух orn: Indian cock (Gallus gallus).
банный день san: bath(ing) day.
бантенг zool: banteng, Indian buffalo (Bos banteng, Bos sondiacus).
банхус entom: Banchus falcatorius.
банщик san: bathhouse (male) attendant.
банщица san: bathhouse (female) attendant.
баньян = смоковница бенгальская.
баня 1. san: bathhouse; 2. chem: bath.
баобаб bot: baobab tree (Adansonia digitata).
баобабовые (сем.) silk-cotton tree family (Bombacaceae).
барабанная вырезка anat: tympanic notch.
~ лестница anat: scala tympani.
~ перепонка anat: tympanic membrane, eardrum.
~ полость anat: tympanic cavity.
~ струна neur: chorda tympani.
~ часть anat: tympanic part, pars tympanica (of the temporal bone).
барабулевые (сем.) ichth: red mullets (Mullidae).
барабулька = барабуля.
барабуля ichth: red mullet, goatfish, surmullet.
баран ram, male sheep, he-sheep, tup (Ovis).
~ -производитель = случной б.
баранец малый bot: lamb succory, swine's succory (Arnoseris minima).
бараний горох = нут.
~ язык 1. zool: lamb tongue; 2. see баранец малый.
баранник bot: Arnica montana.
баранчики = первоцвет аптечный.
бараньи эритроциты sheep corpuscles
барашек zool: lamb, young sheep, see ягнёнок.
барбарис bot: barberry, berberis (Berberis vulgaris, L.)
барбарисовые (сем.) bot: barberry family (Berberidaceae).
барбитурат pharm: barbiturate.
барбитуровая кислота chem: barbituric acid.
барвинок bot: dogbane, Indian hemp (Apocynum, L.)
~ малый vinca, running myrtle (Vinca minor, L.)
барибал zool: Baribal bear, black bear (Ursus americanus).
барид entom: curculio Baris.
~ брюквенный = б. зеленый.
~ жеруховый Baris lepidii.
~ зеленый Baris coerulescens.
~ капустный Baris carbonaria.

барид мальвовый entom: Baris timida.
~ пёстрый Baris scolopacea.
~ рапсовый Baris chlorizans.
~ смоляно-чёрный Baris laticollis.
бариевая каша barium sulfate (roentg.)
барий chem: barium, Ba.
барокамера av med: altitude chamber.
барометрическая дезоксигенация av med: barometric disoxygenation.
барорецепторный baroreceptor.
баротравма mil: "barotrauma" (severe fluctuations of the atmospheric pressure).
барраж barrage.
барракуда ichth: great barracuda, picuda, becuna (Barracuda).
барсук zool: badger (Meles meles, M. taxus).
бартолинова железа anat: Bartholin's gland.
бархатистые чешуйки bot: velvety chaff.
бархатки bot: African marigold (Tagetes erecta, L.)
бархатная губка zool: velvet sponge (Hippospongia meandriniformis).
бархатник = амарант.
бархатное дерево bot: Amoor cork tree (Phellodendron amurense, Rupr.)
бархатные бобы bot: velvet bean (Mucuna utilis, Wall.)
бархатцы = бархатки.
бассия = орех бассия.
бастардное индиго = ложное и.
батат bot: batatas, sweet potato (Ipomoea batatas, Poir.)
батилимнион bathylimnion.
батиэмбрикс ichth: sailfin (Bathyembryx istioplasma).
батрахиозавры (подкл.) zool: Batrachiosauria (extinct reptiles).
батрахосепс zool: Batrachoseps (urodele
батрахоспермум bot: Batrachospermum (algae).
батун = лук дудчатый.
бафия яркая bot: barwood (Baphia nitida
бахия bot: bahie grass (Bahia lanata).
бахрома fringe, fimbria.
бахромка трубной воронки (яйцевод) anat: fimbria ovarica.
бахромчатокрылые = трипсы.
бахромчатый fringy, fimbrial, fimbriate; laciniated, laciniatus.
~ лист bot: laciniated leaf.
бахусник bot: sea myrtle, consumption weed, groundsel tree (Baccharis halimifolia).
бахча agr: melon field.
бацилла bacillus.
бациллобоязнь psych: bacillophobia.
бациллавыделитель bacilli isolator, bacilli separator.
бацилломицин bacillomycin.
бациллоноситель bacilli carrier.
бациллоносительство bacilli carrying.
бациллосодержащий bacilli-bearing.
бациллоубивающее средство bacillicide.
бациллоубивающий bacillicidal.
бациллофобия psych: bacillophobia.
бациллурия bacilluria.
бациллярная дизентерия bacillary dysentery.
~ инфекция bacillosis.
~ рожа свиней vet: red fever.
бациллярного происхождения bacillogenous.
бациллярный bacillar(y).
~ белый понос vet: pullorum disease.
башенковидный turretted.
башенный череп = башнеобразный ч.
башмак копыта zool: coffin.
башнеобразный череп path: steeple head, tower skull.
баянусовы органы zool: kidneys in bivalved mollusks.
бегающие птицы orn: cursorial birds, running birds, gradients (Cursorius, Ratitae, Gradientes), see also бескилевые.
бегемот zool: hippopotamus (Hippopotamus amphibius).
бегемоты (сем.) zool: hippopotamus family (Hippopotamidae).
Беггиатоа Beggiatoa (bacterium).
~ удивительная B. mirabilis.
бегония bot: begonia (Begonia).
бегунок 1. runner, roller; 2. orn: cf. зобатые бегунки.
бедное (видами) семейство bio: depauperate family.
бедреная кость (у лошади) zool: hurlbone (of a horse).
бедренная артерия anat: femoral artery.
~ вена anat: vena femoralis.
~ грыжа path: femoral hernia.
~ кость anat: thigh bone, femur.
~ фасция anat: femoral sheath.
~ шина surg: thigh splint.
бедренное кольцо anat: femoral ring.
бедренный нерв anat: femoral nerve, anterior crural nerve.
~ треугольник anat: femoral triangle.
бедро anat: thigh, hip; zool: haunch.
бедряная линия entom: coxal line.

без- see also бес-.
~ клыков zool: fangless.
~ околоцветника bot: achlamydeous.
~ шва seamless.
безазотистый nonnitrogenous, nitrogen -free, anazotic.
безалкогольный alcohol-free, soft (drink, etc.)
безбелковая пища protein-free diet.
"безбелковые" семена exalbuminous seeds
безболезненность painlessness.
безболезненный painless, indolent.
безбородый beardless.
безбрачие agamia, asexuality.
безбрачный agamic, asexual.
безводный chem: anhydrous.
безвоздушный airfree, void, vacuum, apneumatic
безволие psych: abulia.
безволосый hairless, naked, glabrate, depilous.
безвредный harmless, uninjurious, innocuous, innoxious.
безвременник осенний bot: colchicum, autumn crocus, meadow saffron (Colchicum autumnale, L.)
безвременность psych: timelessness.
безвыборное питание nonselective feeding.
безглазие path: anophthalmia.
безглазый eyeless, blind.
безгнилостное состояние asepsis.
безгнилостный aseptic.
безголовый zool: acephalous.
безгумусный humusless.
бездеятельность inactivity, torpor.
безжёлчный bilefree, acholic, acholous.
беззаботность carelessness.
беззвучное шептание mussitation.
беззвучность голоса aphonia.
беззёрный bot: cornless.
беззубка zool: fresh-water mussel Anodonta cygnea.
беззубые киты (подотр.) zool: baleen whales, whalebone whales (Mystacoceti).
беззубый toothless, edentate, fangless.
~ рот edentulous mouth.
безкрылый exalate, wingless.
безлёгочные саламандры (сем.) zool: Plethodontidae.
безлёгочный zool: lungless.
безлепестковый = безлепестный.
безлепестные bot: Apetalae.
безлепестный apetalous, petalless.
безлиственный bot: aphyllous.
безлистный bot: leafless, naked.
безлихорадочность apyrexia, absence of fever.
безлихорадочный apyretic, afebrile, apyrexial.
безлоскутная ампутация surg: chop amputation.
безматочный anat: ametrous.
~ улей entom: queenless hive.
безмикробный amicrobic.
безмякотные нервные волокна = волокна Ремака.
безмякотный pulpless.
безмясый fleshless; meatless.
безнадежное состояние hopeless condition.
безногая ящерица legless lizard.
безногие zool: apods, footless (Apoda, Gymnophiona).
безногий legless, footless, apodal, apus.
безнравственный amoral.
безоаровый козёл zool: bezoar goat (Capra aegagrus), milch g. (C. hircus).
безопасная булавка safety pin.
безостость bot: awnlessness, baldness
безостый bot: awnless, inermis, bald, beardless.
безотказный в работе faultless in operation, dependable.
безразличие (ко всему) psych: apathy, indifference.
безрёберный ecostate.
безрогий zool: hornless, hummel.
безротый bio: astomatous, lipostomatous.
безрукий armless, abrachius.
безрукость armlessness, abrachia.
безрыбный fishless.
безудержно импульсивен recklessly impulsive.
безумие psych: folly, amentia, dementia.
безусловнорефлекторный neur attr: unconditioned-reflex, natural-reflex.
безусловный рефлекс unconditioned reflex.
безусый beardless.
безухие тюлени (сем.) zool: earless seals, hair seals (Phocidae).
безухий zool: earless.
~ (урод) anotus, anotous.
безъядерная клетка hist: denucleated cell.
безъядерный bio: unnucleated, nonnucleated.
безъязыкий aglossus.
безъязычие aglossia.
безъязычный aglossus.
безымянная артерия anat: innominate artery, arteria anonima.
~ кость anat: innominate bone.
безымянный палец anat: third finger, ring finger.
бекас orn: snipe (Capella gallinago).

*бекас болотный обыкновенный orn: common snipe (Scolopax gallinago).
бекманния bot: slough grass (Beckmannia syzigachne, Steud.)
белая гниль phytp: ground rot (on water melons); pod blight, bean blight (on leguminous).
~ гниль винограда white rot on grapes
~ горячка psych: delirium tremens.
~ крыса albino rat.
~ куропатка orn: willow ptarmigan (Lagopus lagopus); white grouse (L. albus.
~ линия живота anat: linea alba, abdominal line, white line.
~ мокрая гниль phytp: sclerotiniosis.
~ почка phytp: white bud (on corn).
~ припухлость бедра gyn: white leg.
~ пятнистость phytp: white spottedness, leaf blight, leaf spot.
~ ржавчина phytp: white rust; white blister (on cabbage).
~ цапля orn: snowy egret (Leucophoyx thula).
~ чайка orn: ivory gull (Pagophila eburnea).
белёк zool: young seal.
белемниты zool: belemnites (Belemnoidea)
белена bot: henbane, hogbean (Hyoscyamus, L.)
беление bleaching, blanching.
бели gyn: leukorrhea, whites, fluor albus.
белильная известь = хлорноватисто кальциевая соль.
белить bleach, blanch.
беличьи (сем.) zool: squirrel family, marmots, squirrels & chipmunks (Sciuridae).
белка zool: squirrel (Sciurus).
~ -летяга flying s., see летяга.
~ обыкновенная common squirrel (S. vulgaris).
белки плазмы hist: plasma proteins.
белковая вода albumin water.
~ моча path: albuminous urine.
~ фракция protein fraction.
~ ~ (гемоглобина) globin fraction (of hemoglobin).
белковое вещество proteic substance.
~ кольцо albumin ring.
белковообменный proteometabolic.
белковый albinotic, albuminous, proteic.
~ обмен proteometabolism.
белладонна bot: belladonna, deadly nightshade, banewort (Atropa belladonna, L.)
белловская канюля surg: Bellocq's sound.
Белль Bell.
белобровик = дрозд-белобровик.
белобрюхий тюлень zool: monk seal (Monachus monachus).
беловатое утолщение whitish thickening.
беловенечный zool: white-crowned.
белоглазка ichth: bream Abramis sapa.
*белогрудый дрозд orn: ring ouzel (of thrush family).
белодон zool: Belodon, Phytosaurus.
белодушка = каменная куница.
белое вещество (мозга) anat: white matter, substantia alba.
~ кровяное тельце hem: white blood cell, w. b. corpuscle, leucocyte.
~ тело embr: corpus albicans.
белозернистый bot: white-grained, white-kernelled.
белозёрный = белозернистый.
белозор bot: grass-of-Parnassus, bogstars (Parnassia, L.)
белозубка (землеройка) zool: shrew Crocidura.
~ -малютка shrew Suncus etrusca.
белок 1. albumin, protein;
2. albumen, glair, white of egg.
~ глаза anat: white of the eye.
белоколоска (пшеница) bot: white-eared (wheat).
белокопытник = мать-и-мачеха.
белокровие white blood disease, leukemia.
белокрылая крачка orn: white-winged black tern (Chlidonias leucopterus).
белокрылка entom: whitefly (Aleurodes)
~ капустная cabbage w. (A. brassicae).
~ тепличная Trialcurodes vaporariorum
~ хлопковая cotton w.
белокрыльник bot: water arum (Calla).
~ болотный wild calla (C. palustris).
*белоносая гагара orn: white-billed diver.
белорыбица ichth: Stenodus leucichthys.
белотал = ива корзиночная.
белоус торчащий bot: matgrass (Nardus stricta).
белохвостый олень zool: whitetail deer.
белоцветник bot: snowflake (Leucojum, L.)
белочная оболочка anat: tunica albuginea, sclera.
~ ~ яичка tunica albuginea testis.
белошипый огурец white-spine cucumber.
белощёкая крачка orn: whiskered tern (Chlidonias h. hybrida).
белуга ichth: beluga, white sturgeon (Huso huso).

белуха zool: white whale, white dolphin, beluga, marsoon (Delphinapterus leucas).
белые мхи = торфяные мхи.
~ ольхи (сем.) bot: white alder family, pepper-bush f. (Clethraceae).
белый вазелин pharm: white petrolatum.
~ гриб bot: edible boletus (Bol. edulis).
~ кровяной шарик white cell, leukocyte.
~ медведь zool: white bear, polar bear (Ursus maritimus, Thalarctos maritimus).
~ носорог zool: white rhinoceros (Rhinoceros simus).
~ понос = бациллярный б.п.
~ сандал pharm: white sandalwood.
~ степной гриб bot: clitocybe (Clito-
~ торфяной мох = сфагн.|cybe sapida).
~ тяж (селезенки) anat: trabecula.
бель phytp: disease of roses, fungus Sphaerotheca pannosa, Lev.
бельдежур = иппомея.
бельдюга ichth: quab, ling (Zoarces), eelpout (Z. viviparus), conger eel, mutton fish (Z. anquillaris).
бельдюговые (сем.) ichth: quabs, lings (Zoarcidae).
бельевая linen storage (room).
~ сестра linen-stock nurse (in hospital).
бельмо ophth: walleye, corneal spot.
беляк = заяц-беляк.
белянка весенняя = белоцветник.
~ горчичная entom: hedge-mustard orange -tip butterfly (Synchloe daplidicae).
~ капустная entom: cabbage white butterfly (Pieris brassicae), see капустница; cf. гусеница б.к.
~ репная turnip butterfly (P. rapae).
белянки (сем.) entom: pierids (Pieridae).
бенгальский тигр zool: Bengal tiger (Felis tigris).
бенедикт аптечный = кардобенедикт.
бензанилид pharm: benzoyl anilide.
бензедрин pharm: benzedrine.
бензидин benzidine.
бензил chem: benzyl.
бензоил chem: benzoyl.
бензой bot: spicebush, Benjamin bush (Lindera benzoin, L.)
бензойная кислота benzoic acid.
бензойнокислый висмут pharm: bismuth benzoate.
~ кокаин cocaine benzoate.
~ кофеиннатрий caffeine and sodium benzoate.
~ литий lithium benzoate.
~ натрий sodium benzoate.
бензол benzene, benzol(e).

бензонафтол pharm: betanaphthol
Бенке Behneke. benzoate.
беннеттиты (пор.) bot: Bennetitales
бентамка orn: bantam fowl. (extinct)
бентический bio: benthic, bottom-
бентонический = бентонный.|living
бентонный benthic, benthonic.
бентос bio: benthos.
Бер Bert; Bear. [mia, Risso).
бергамот bot: bergamot (Citrus berga-
бергамотовое масло pharm: bergamot oil.
*береговая ласточка orn: sand martin
береговичок (улитка) zool: periwinkle (Littorina littorea).
береговой моллюск = береговичок.
береговушка entom: brinefly (Ephydra).
берёза bot: birch (Betula).
~ карликовая dwarf birch (B. nana, L.)
~ плакучая weeping b., drooping b. (B. alba, var. pendula).
берёзка bot: 1. small birch-tree; 2. see вьюнок. [(Betulaceae).
берёзовые (сем.) bot: birch family
берёзовый деготь pharm: birch tar.
~ стланец = берёза карликовая.
берека = глоговина.
беременная pregnant (woman), gravida.
~ в девятый раз nonigravida.
~ во второй раз secundigravida.
~ в первый раз primigravida.
~ в седьмой раз septigravida.
~ в шестой раз sexigravida.
~ несколько раз multigravida.
беременность pregnancy, gestation, gravidity. [gamentary pregnancy.
~ в широкой связке obstet: intrali-
~ двойней obstet: bigeminal p., twin p.
~ несколькими плодами multifetation.
~ с пузырным заносом hydatid p.
бересклет bot: spindle tree (Evonymus)
бересклетовые (сем.) bot: staff-tree family (Celastraceae).
бересклетоцветные (пор.) bot: Celastrales.
берест = карагач.
берёста bot: silver bark.
берибери path: beriberi.
беринговоморской attr: Bering-Sea.
беркелий berkelium, Bk.
беркут orn: golden eagle, (Aquila chrysaëtus). [anilin blue.
берлинская лазурь chem: Berlin blue,
бермудская трава bot: Bermuda grass, scutch grass (Cynodon, Rich.)

Бернар Bernard.
берсим-клевер = к. александрийский. [chlorate.
бертолетова соль pharm: potassium
берш ichth: perch Lucioperca volgensis.
бес- see also без-. [rhynchidae).
беседковые птицы bowerbirds (Ptilono-
бескилевые orn: ratites (Ratitae, Palaeognathae), see also бегающие птицы.
бескислородные условия anoxic conditions.
бескислотность anacidity, inacidity.
бескишечные турбеллярии (отр.) zool: Acoela.
бескорковый crustless.
бескосточковый bot: stoneless, seed-
бескризисный acritical. less.
бескровие exsanguinity, exsanguination.
бескровный bloodless, exsanguinate.
*бескрыл orn: apterix.
бескрылая гагарка = чистик.
бескрылые насекомые (подкл.) entom: wingless insects (Apterigota).
~ птицы orn: apterix (Apteriges), see
бескрылый apterous. киви
бесоодержимость psych: demonomania.
бесоодержимый psych: demonomaniac.
беспалость path: adactylia, adactilism.
беспалый path: adactyl(ous).
беспанцырные zool: Lissamphibia.
беспанцырный shell-less, armorless, nonthecate.
беспeрeгнойный humusless. [pistil.
беспестичный bot: pistilless, without
бесплатная медицинская помощь free medical care.
бесплатное лечение free treatment.
бесплодие sterility, infertility, infecundity, acyesis, barrenness.
~ после первых родов gyn: one-child sterility.
бесплодная овца yeld ewe.
~ тычинка bot: lepal, staminodium.
~ чешуя bot: sterile palea.
бесплодность infertility, sterility.
бесплодный fruitless, sterile, infecund, infertile, afetal, atokous, acyetic,
~ цветок bot: sterile flower. | barren.
беспозвоночное животное invertebrate.
беспозвоночные zool: invertebrates, invertebrata. [less.
беспозвоночный invertebrate, backbone-
беспокойное состояние = беспокой-
беспокойный restless, uneasy. ство.
беспокойство psych: anxiety, worry, apprehension, disquietude, restlessness, unrest, uneasiness, fidgetiness.
беспокровный coverless, naked, achlamydate.
бесполое размножение bio: asexual reproduction, apogamy, apogamia, apomixis, parthenogenesis, agamogony, monogony, monogenesis, agamocytogony.
~ ~ клеток путём деления agamogonia.
бесполосoсеменный bot: apomictic.
бесполый bio: asexual, nonsexual,
бесполым путём asexually. | agamic.
беспорядочное дробление embr: indeterminate cleavage. [ed.
беспрерывный continuous, uninterrupt-
беспричинный смех psych: compulsive laughter. [therate flower.
беспыльниковый цветок bot: inan-
бессвязность речи psych: lack of connectedness in speech.
бессемянный bot: seedless.
бессилие impotence, loss of strength, asthenia, see адинамия.
бессифонная личинка zool: asiphonate larva. [flower.
бессмертник bot: immortelle, straw
~ "кошачьи лапки" = цмин песчаный. [less smile.
бессмысленная улыбка psych: meaning-
бессмысленное повторение слова или движения psych: perseveration.
~ ~ слова или фразы psych: verbigeration.
бессознательное состояние psych: unconsciousness.
бессознательный unconscious.
бессолевая диета salt-free diet.
бессонница sleeplessness, insomnia, agrypnia.
бессосудистый nonvascular, avascular.
бесспоровый bot: asporous.
бесствольный bot: trunkless, exscape.
бесстебельный = нестебельчатый.
бесстебельчатые иглокожие = свободные и.
бесструктурный bio: structurless, anhistous, amorphous. [Myrientoma.
бессяжковые entom: Proturoidea,
бестужевы капли pharm: Bestucheff's mixture, etherial tincture of iron
бестычиночный instaminate. | chloride.
бесхвостая церкария helm: tailless cercaria.
бесхвостое земноводное batrachian.

бесхвостые zool: batrachians, tailless
(Anura, Ecaudata, Batrachia). [gulate.
бесхвостый tailless, ecaudate, nonvir-
~ угорь ichth: tailless eel (Cyema atrum)
бесхлорофильный bot: nonchlorophyll-
бесцветковый bot: flowerless. [bearing.
бесцветный colorless, achromatic.
бесчелюстность agnathia, agnathy.
бесчелюстные zool: Agnatha.
бесчелюстный agnathous.
бесчеренковый = бесчерешковый.
бесчерепные zool: Acrania. [sessile.
бесчерешковый bot: stipeless, stalkless,
бесчинство psych: indecorum, excess.[ness
бесчувствие insensibility, unconscious-
бесшеечная матка path: uterus acollis.
бесшерстная овца nonwooled sheep.
бесшипный bot: spineless.
бесщитковые zool: Anaspida (extinct).
бетанафтил chem: betanaphthyl.
бетанафтол chem: betanaphthol.
бетулин tox bot: betuline.
Бехтерев Bekhterev, Bechterew.
бешенка = черноспинка.
бешеное зелье = дурман. [frenzy.
бешенство 1.infect: rabies; 2. psych:
~ матки psych: uterine madness,
nymphomania.
бешеный 1. infect: rabid, rabiate;
2. psych: lyssic.
бивариантная таблица av med: bivari-
бивень zool: tusk. |ant table.
бигардия = померанец.
бигарро bot: bigarroon, see черешня.
биение (сердца) physl: throbbing
(of the heart). [buffalo.
бизон zool: bison (Bison bison), colloq:
бизонова трава bot: buffalo grass,
bison grass (Buchloe dactyloides).
бикарбонат chem: bicarbonate, acid
carbonate, HCO_3.
бикса орлеанская = аннато.
бикуспидальный bicuspid.
билатеральная симметрия bilateral
symmetry, bilaterism.
билатерально симметричный
bilaterally symmetrical, diplozoic.
билатеральный bilateral.
билиарный biliary.
билирубин bilirubin (pigment of bile).
бильгарциоз = бильхарциоз.
бильхарциоз helm: bilharziasis, schis-
бимануальный bimanual. tosomiasis.
бинарная смесь chem: binary mixture.
бинокль binocular.
бинокуляр binocular.

бинокулярная диплопия ophth:
binocular diplopia.
бинокулярное зрение binocular vision.
бинокулярный параллакс ophth:
binocular parallax.
бинт surg: bandage (roll).
бинтовать bandage.
биньония вьющеползучая bot: cross-
vine, quarter-vine (Bignonia capreo-
биогенез biogenesis, biogeny. |lata)
биогенетический biogenetic.
биогенный biogenic, biogeneous.
биогеограф biogeographer.
биогеографический biogeographic.
биогеография biogeography.
биогеохимический biogeochemical.
биоза chem: biose.
биокатализатор biocatalyst.
биокинетика biokinetics.
биокинетические пределы температуры biokinetic temperature limits
(— 273°C to approximately 150°C).
биоклиматология bioclimatology,
биоколлоид biocolloid. bioclimatics.
биолит biolith.
биолог biologist.
биологическая борьба agr:
biological control (of pests, etc.)
~ вредность rad: biological damage.
~ защита rad: biological shield.
~ опасность rad: biological hazard.
~ проба bioassay, biological assay.
~ продукция organic production.
~ реакция biological response.
~ ткань biological tissue.
~ химия biological chemistry.
~ эффективность излучения
biological effectiveness of radiation.
биологически вредный biologically
damaging, b. noxious.
биологический полупериод rad:
biological half-life.
~ процесс biological process.
~ рентген-эквивалент rad: man
roentgen equivalent, rem.
~ эквивалент рентгена =
б. рентген-эквивалент.
~ экран rad: biological shield.
~ эффект = биологическое
действие.
биологическое действие b. effect.
~ испытание bioassay, biological as-
биология biology; life history. |say.
~ организмов в межпланетном
пространстве space biology.
биолюминесценция bioluminescence.

биом biome.
биомасса biomass, standing population,
биоматематика biomathematics. s. crop
биометрика biometrics, biometry.
биометрия biometry, biometrics.
биомеханика biomechanics.
бионтизация biontization.
биопрепарат biopreparation.
биопсия biopsy.
~ с помощью иглы needle biopsy.
биосестон bioseston.
биосинтез biosynthesis.
биостатистика biostatistics.
биостерол biosterol, vitamin A.
биостратиграфия biostratigraphy.
биосфера biosphere.
биотин biotin.
биотип biotype.
биотипический biotypic.
биотический biotic.
биотоп biotope, community habitat.
биофизика biophysics.
биофотометр biophotometer.
биохимик biochemist.
биохимический biochemical.
биохимия biochemistry.
биохиморфный biochemorphic.
биохиморфология biochemorphology.
биоценоз biocoenosis, community.
биоценологический biocenotic.
биоценология biocenology.
биоценотический biocoenotic, biocenoti
биоцитин biocytin. c.
биоэкология bioecology, life history.
биоэлектрический bioelectric.
биоэлектричество bioelectricity.
биоэнергетика bioenergetics.
биполярность bipolarity.
биполярный bipolar. [vulgare).
бирючина bot: privet, prim (Ligustrum
бирючинные (пор.) bot: Ligustrales.
бирючок ichth: ruff Acerina acerina.
бисексуальность bisexuality.
бисерное дерево = тамариск.
бискайский кит zool: Nordcaper whale
(Balaena biscayensis).
бисквитообразный biscuit-shaped.
бисмал pharm: bismuth methylenedigallate
бисса zool: turtle Chelonia imbricata.
биссус zool: byssus, beard.
биссусная железа zool: byssal gland.
битиния zool: Bithynia leachi (mollusk).
бить струей spurt.
биурет chem: biuret.
биуретовая реакция chem: biuret reac-
бифуркация bifurcation. tion.

бифуркация трахеи anat: bifurcation
бич zool: flagellum. [of the trachea.
биченосцы bio: Mastigophora, see
жгутиковые.
Биша Bichat.
благовонный sweet-smelling.
благозвучие euphonia.
благоприобретенный acquired.
благородный олень zool: noble deer;
see also американский б.о.
бланшировальный blanching.
бланширование blanching.
бланшировочный = бланшировальный.
бластема genet: blastema.
бластодерма embr: blastoderm.
бластодермальный blastodermal, bla-
бластома blastoma. stodermic.
бластоматозный blastomatous.
бластомер embr: blastomere.
бластопор(а) embr: blastopore, primi-
бластула embr: blastula. tive mouth.
бластулярный blastular.
бледная немочь greensickness,
бледнеть turn pale, fade. chlorosis.
бледное ядро anat: pallidum, globus
бледножелтый цвет sallow. pallidus.
бледносиневатость pale bluish color
бледносиневатый (цвет кожи)
pale bluish (skin color).
бледнопурпурная окраска pale
purplish coloration.
бленоррея ophthalmoblenorrhea, gonorrheal ophthalmia, g. conjunctivitis.
бледность paleness, pallor.
бледный pale, pallid, pallidus.
блекота = болиголов крапчатый.
блескость glare.
блестянка bot: stonewort (Nitella).
блестянки (сем.) entom: Nitidulidae.
блестящая оболочка (яйцеклетки)
zona pellucida (of the ovum).
блефаропласт zool: blepharoplast,
kinetoplast, kinetonucleus.
блефароспазм ophth: blepharospasm.
блефароцерида entom: net-veined midge
(Blepharoceridae).
блеяние zool: bleating.
блеять zool: bleat.
блеящая овца zool: bleater.
ближайшая причина proximate cause.
~ точка аккомодации ophth: near
point of accomodation.
~ ~ конвергенции ophth: near point
of convergence. [bicular.
близкий к кругу (или шару) subor-

близкий к нейтральному circumneutral
~ к овалу subovate.
близко примыкающий osculant.
близкое заболевание allied disease.
близнецы 1. twins; 2. anat: see мышцы-близнецы.
близорукий ophth: nearsighted, myopic.
близорукость ophth: nearsightedness, short sight, myopia.
Бло cf. пилюли Бло.
блок anat: trochlea, pulley. [block.
~ ножки пучка Гиса bundle branch
блокада автономной нервной системы autonomic block.
блокирующая проба blocking test.
блоковая глазная мышца anat: trochlearis, obliquus oculi superior.
~ ость anat: trochlear spine. [lea.
блоковидное возвышение anat: troch-
блоковидный сустав anat: hinge joint, hinge articulation, gynglymus.
блоковый нерв anat: trochlear nerve, fourth cranial nerve.
блоха entom: flea (Pulex, Ctenocephalus, Xenopsylla, etc.)
~ домашней птицы sticktight f. (Echidnophaga gallinacea).
~ дубовая oak f. (Haltica seliceti).
~ земляная = б. репная.
~ индийская крысиная Indian rat f. (Xenopsylla cheopis).
~ капустная синяя cabbage f. (Psylloides chrysocephala).
~ картофельная potato f. (Psylloides affinis). [nuata.
~ конопляная hemp f. (Psylloides atte-
~ корнеплодная Psylloides cupreata.
~ кошачья cat f. (Ctenocephalus felis).
~ крестоцветная cruciferae f. (Phylotreta). [ta.
~ ~ волнистая undulating f. (P. undula-
~ ~ выемчатая P. vittata.
~ ~ светлоногая P. nemorum.
~ ~ синяя blue f. (P. nigripes).
~ ~ чёрная P. atra.
~ листовая = листоблошка.
~ льняная flax f. (Aphtona).
~ люцерновая = сминтурус.
~ малинная raspberry f. (Batophila rubi).
~ мятная mint f. (Longitarsus lycopii).
~ паразитическая parasitic f. (Aphaniptera, Siphonaptera).
~ песчаная chigoe, chigre, jigger (Sarcopsilla penetrans, Tunga p.)
~ птичья bird f. (Pulex avium).
блоха-прыгун песчаная sand hopper (Orchestidae).
~ рапсовая = б. капустная синяя.
~ репная turnip f. (Phyllotreta).
~ свекловичная beet f. (Chaetocnema concinna).
~ собачья dog f. (Ctenocephalus canis)
~ соевая разноцветная Pagria signata. [nigrobilineatus.
~ ~ чернополосая Paraluperodes
~ стеблевая злаковая grain-stem f. (Chaetocnema aridula, C. hortensis).
~ хлебная полосатая Phyllotreta vittula. [concinna.
~ хмелевая hop f. (Plectroscellis
~ человека human f. (Pulex irritans).
блохи (отр.) entom: fleas (Aphaniptera, Siphonaptera).
блоховник bot: pennyroyal (Hedeoma pulegioides, Pers.)
блошак = испанский золотой корень.
блошка земляная entom: fleabeetle, garden fleahopper (Halticus bractea-
блошница bot: fleabane (Pulicaria) tus).
~ поносная Pulicaria dysenterica.
блувал = синий полосатик.
блуждающая клетка hist: migratory cell, wandering c.
~ почка path: wandering kidney, floating k., ren mobilis.
~ рожа infect: wandering erysipelas.
~ селезенка path: floating spleen, movable s., wandering s.
блуждающий нерв anat: vagus nerve, pneumogastric n., tenth cranial n.
блюдечко zool: limpet, patella (Patella, Acmaea).
~ обыкновенное common limpet
блюдце = блюдечко. (Patella).
блюдцеобразный salverform, hypocra-
~ галл phytp: cup gall. teriform.
бляшка anat: end-plate; odont: plaque; see also моторная бляшка.
боб bot: 1. vetch, tare; bean (Vicia); 2. see боб конский; [фасоль. 3. pod, pulse; See also вика, горох,
~ арабский = фасоль многоцветковая.
~ бархатный mucuna, banana bean (Mucuna utilis, Wall.) [ignatia).
~ игнатьев Ignatian bean (Strychnos
~ индийский bonavist, lablab (Dolichos
~ какао cacao bean. lablab, L.)
~ касторовый = рицинник.

боб конский bot: broad bean, faba b., English b., tick b., straight b., horse b. (Vicia faba, var. major, L.)
~ кофейный = нут.
~ лимский = фасоль лимская.
~ мескитский mesquite bean.
~ обыкновенный = б. конский.
~ огородный = б. конский.
~ полевой = б. конский.
~ рисовый rice bean (Phaseolus calcaratus, Roxb.)
~ русский = б. конский.
~ соевый = соя.
~ сойный = соя.
~ турецкий = фасоль многоцветковая.
бобик = стручок.
бобовник bot: Amygdalus nana (of Prunoideae).
бобовое растение bot: leguminous plant, legume, pod-bearing p., pulse p., fabaceous p. (Leguminosae).
бобовые (сем.) bot: pulse family (Leguminosae); Fabaceae.
бобовый зерноед entom: bean maggot (Mylabris obtectus).
боботодобный bot: pod-like, pulse, fabaceous.
бобр zool: beaver, castor (Castor fiber)
~ болотный coypu, nutria (Myocastor coypus, Myopotamus coypus).
бобровая крыса = бобр болотный.
~ струя pharm: castoreum.
бобровник = дрок испанский.
бобровое дерево = магнолия виргинская.
бобровые (сем.) zool: beaver family (Castoridae).
бовиста bot: Bovista fungi.
богатинка bot: fleabane (Erigeron, L.)
~ канадская horseweed, hogweed, butterweed (E. canadensis).
~ оранжевая orange daisy (E. aurantiacus).
богатый бактериями bacteria-rich.
~ белками protein-rich.
богомол entom: mantis, soothsayer (Mantis religiosa).
богомолы (отр.) entom: praying mantes, soothsayers (Mantodea).
богородичная трав(к)а = богородская трава.
богородская трава bot: thyme (Thymus); creeping t., crimson t., lemon t. (T. serpyllum).
богорожник = глоговина.
бодяк bot: common thistle, plumed t. (Cirsium, Mill.); see also осот.
бодяк ланцетолистный spear thistle, pasture t. (Cirsium lanceolatum, Hiil.)
~ полевой = осот розовый.
боевое ранение mil: combat injury.
боевой автоматизм mil: combat automatism, fighting a.
божье дерево bot: southernwood, old man (Artemisia abrotanum).
божьи коровки (сем.) wntom: ladybugs (Coccinellidae).
божья коровка entom: ladybug, ladybird, lady beetle (Coccinellidae).
~ ~ точечная fleabeetle Spilachna vigintio punctata.
бойзенова ягода Boysenberry.
Бойкотт Boycott.
Бойль Boyle.
Бойнэ Boinet.
бойня slauter-house.
бойцовый петух orn: fighting cock, gamecock.
бок side, flank.
~ живота flank, barrel (of a cow).
бокаловидная клетка hist: goblet cell.
бокальчатый bot: beaker-shaped, cyathiformis.
боккония bot: plume poppy, tree celandine (Bocconia, L.)
боковая борозда мозга anat: lateral cerebral (Sylvian) fissure.
~ ветвь метелки bot: fascicle.
~ ветка bot: branch stem.
~ линия lateral line.
боковое искривление позвоночника anat: lateral curvature of the spine, scoliosis.
~ положение lateral position.
боковой anat: lateral, lateralis.
~ желудочек anat: lateral ventricle.
~ корень bot: branch root.
~ орган (круглого червя) amphid.
~ побег bot: stem shoot, sucker, soboles.
боконервные (кл.) zool: chitons, etc. mollusks (Amphineura).
бокоплав zool: fresh-water shrimp (Gammarus); beach flea (Orchestia); scud (Amphipoda).
~-блоха zool: sand hopper Gammarus.
~ прудовый Carinogammarus roeseli.
бокоплавы (отр.) zool: sand hoppers, etc. (Amphipoda).
бокоплодные мхи (подпор.) bot: Pleurocarpi.
бокошейные черепахи (подотр.) zool: turtles Pleurodira.
болевая точка pain spot.

болевая чувствительность
sense of pain. [lus.
болевое раздражение pain(ful) stimu-
болезненная идея psych: morbid idea.
~ судорога painful spasm, algospasm.
~ точка painful point.
~ эрекция path: painful erection,
chordee. [(to).
болезненное влечение (к) addiction
~ мочеиспускание path: painful
urination.
~ мудрствование psych: morbid sophis-
tication, sophistical reasoning.
~ половое побуждение morbid sexual
impulse, aidoiomania.
~ равнодушие psych: apathy.
~ состояние morbid state, sickliness;
disease, sickness.
болезненность morbidity, soreness,
sickliness.
~ в ушах av med: soreness in the ears.
болезненносудорожный algospastic.
болезненные месячные gyn: painful
menses, dysmenorrhea. [sickly, dolorous
болезненный morbid, sore, painful,
*~ тик neur: tic doloreux.
~ язык sore tongue.
болезнетворное действие света
photopathy.
~ свойство (микробов) virulence.
болезнетворность pathogenicity.
болезнетворный pathogenic, morbific,
morbiferous. [tive o.
~ организм pathogenic organism, causa-
болезнь disease, sickness, illness,
ailment, malady; obs: morbus; see also
заболевание. [abortion.
~ Банга vet: Bang's disease, infectious
~ Барлова = детский скорбут.
~ Боткина epidemic hepatitis.
~ бродяг vagrant's disease. [disease.
~ венечной артерии int: coronary
~ влагалища gyn: disease of the vagina,
colpopathy.
~ внутренних органов disease of the
viscera, splanchnopathy.
~ волос disease of the hair, trichopathy.
~ вызываемая клещами acarinosis.
~ глаз eye disease.
~ горняков miner's disease, ankylosto-
~ Гочкина = б. Ходжкина. mosis.
~ дыхательных органов respiratory d.
~ жарких стран tropical disease.
~ Иценко-Кушинга Cushing's disease.
~ Кедани Kedani disease.

болезнь кишок int: intestinal disease
~ клетки cytopathy.
~ кожи skin disease, dermopathy.
~ крови blood disease, hemopathy.
~ лёгких lung disease, pulmonary d.
~ матки gyn: uterine d., hysteropathy.
~ митрального клапана mitral d.
~ новорожденных neonatorial disease.
~ носа nasal disease.
~ носоглотки nasopharyngeal disease.
~ Ньюкасла Newcastle disease.
~ обмена веществ metabolic disease.
~ органов грудной клетки
thoracic disease.
~ кровообращения circulatory d.
~ от вдыхания (ядовитых газов
и т.п.) inhalation disease.
~ от укуса крыс ratbite fever, sodoku
~ передаваемая семенами agr:
seed-borne disease. [sputum-borne d.
~ передающаяся через мокроту
~ ~ через мух fly-borne disease.
~ ~ через насекомых insect-borne d.
~ ~ через слюну saliva-borne d.
~ печени liver disease, hepatic d.
~ подлежащая обязательной заявке
obligatory-notice disease, reportable
~ Потта = кариес позвонков. d.
~ почек kidney disease, nephropathy.
~ Рейно Reynaud's disease.
~ Риггса Rigg's disease, periodontosis
~ сердца heart disease, cardiopathy.
~ сетчатки ophth: retinal disease.
~ сжатого воздуха compressed-air
disease, caisson d.
~ сортировщиков шерсти infect:
wool-sorter's disease. [angiopathy.
~ сосудов vascular system disease,
~ спинного мозга spinal (cord) d.
~ тазовых органов pelvic disease.
~ толстых кишок colon d., colopathy.
~ точильщиков grinder's disease,
pneumoconiosis.
~ тряпичников ragpicker's disease.
~ Филатова int: infectious mononucle-
~ Ходжкина Hodgkin's disease |osis.
lymphogranulomatosis.
~ щитовидной железы thyroid disease
~ яичника gyn: ovarian disease.
болеостома ichth: Johnny darter
(Boleostoma nigrum).
болетус bot: boletus fungi (Boletus).
болеть suffer, ache, be ill, ail.
болеуспокаивающее = болеутоляющее.

болеутоляющее (средство) pain reliever, analgesic, analgetic, analgic, anodyne.
болечувствительный algesic.
боли в детском возрасте growing pains.
~ в суставах arthralgia, articular neuralgia.
болиголов bot: poison hemlock (Conium, L.)
~ крапчатый spotted h. (C.maculatum).
~ пурпурный purple thorn-apple (Datura tatula).
*болотная курочка orn: jacksnipe, marsh fowl (Porzana).
~ лихорадка malaria, marsh fever.
~ синица = с. болотная.
~ трава bot: paludal herb.
~ черепаха zool: bog-turtle (Emis orbicularis).
болотник bot: water starwort, water chickweed (Callitriche).
болотниковые (пор.) bot: Helobiae, Najadales.
~ (сем.) bot: water-starwort family (Callitrichaceae).
болотница bot: 1. spike rush (Eleocharis, R.Br.); 2. waterweed, waterthyme, ditchmoss (Elodea canadensis, Michx.)
болотное растение bot: bog plant, paludal p., helophyte.
болотноцветник bot: limnanth, floating heart (Limnanthemum nymphacoides).
болотный swampy, marshy (uliginosus).
~ бекас = бекас болотный.
~ костный шпат vet: bog spavin.
~ солёный колосок = солянка американская.
болтающийся сустав path: flail joint.
болтливость psych: loquacity, excessive talkativeness, lalomania.
боль pain, ache.
~ в верхней половине головы helmet headache.
~ в гайморовой полости pain in the antrum of Highmore.
~ в глазах pain in the eyes.
~ в груди chest pain.
~ в грудине sternal pain.
~ в желудке stomach pain, gastrodyny.
~ в животе abdominal pain, belly ache.
~ в заднем проходе anal pain.
~ в затылке occipital pain.
~ в кости bone pain, osteopic pain.
~ в крестце sacral pain, sacrodynia.
~ в области ... pain in the area of...
~ в печени hepatic pain.
~ в подвздошной области iliac pain.
~ в подложечной области epigastric pain.
~ в почках renal pain.
~ в пузыре bladder pain.
боль в сердце cardiac pain.
~ в спине backache, lumbago, lumbosacral pain.
~ в суставе pain in a joint, arthralgia, articular neuralgia.
~ в ухе (ушах) earache.
~ в червеобразном отростке appendicular colic.
~ между двумя менструальными периодами gyn: midpain.
~ натощак hunger pain.
~ от давления pressure pain.
больбарный = бульбарный.
больничная касса hospital insurance organization, medical-expense protection.
~ палата hospital room.
~ сестра hospital nurse.
больничное лечение hospital treatment, in-patient t., institutional t.
~ обслуживание hospital service.
больничный врач hospital physician.
~ служитель h. orderly, h. attendant.
~ случай h. case.
~ стаж h. training.
~ столик bedtable.
больной patient; adj: sick, ill, ailing, aching.
~ артериосклерозом int: arteriosclerotic (patient).
~ базедовой болезнью Basedow's disease patient.
~ базофилией basophilic patient.
~ бешенством hydrophobe, rabid.
~ бредом величия megalomaniac.
~ воспалением суставов arthritic.
~ ликантропией psych: lycanthrope.
~ после наркоза surg: postanesthesia patient.
~ проказой leper.
~ пункт sick point (of the cortex, etc.)
~ сапом glandered.
большая берцовая кость = большеберцовая к.
~ гагарка orn: great auk.
~ кривизна желудка anat: greater curvature.
~ многоугольная кость запястья anat: greater multangular (or multangulum) majus, trapezium bone.
~ поганка orn: grebe Podiceps cristatus.
~ полярная чайка glaucous gull, see бургомистр.
~ спайка anat: great transverse commissure, commissura magna, corpus callosum.
большеберцовая артерия anat: tibial artery.
~ кость anat: shinbone, tibia.

большеберцовая мышца (передняя, задняя) anat: tibialis (anterior, posterior).
большеберцовый tibial.
~ нерв anat: tibial nerve, medial popliteal nerve.
большеротый чёрный окунь ichth: large-mouthed black bass (Huro salmoides).
большеухая лисица zool: long-eared fox (Vulpes zerdo).
большие косицы zool: sickles.
~ кроющие перья крыла orn: wing bar, main wing coverts.
~ крылья клиновидной кости anat: great wings of the sphenoid bone, ala magna.
~ ножницы surg: shears.
~ полушария (мозга) anat: cerebral hemispheres.
*~ рулевые перья orn: main tail.
~ щипцы мозолистого тела anat: preforceps.
большой anat: great(er), magnus.
~ баклан orn: cormorant (Phalacrocorax carbo).
~ бугор anat: greater tuberosity.
~ коренной зуб anat: molar tooth.
~ кроншнеп orn: large curlew (Numenius arquatus).
~ круг кровообращения anat: greater circulatory system, systemic circulation.
~ мозг anat: cerebrum.
~ муравьед zool: great anteater (Myrmecophaga tridactyla).
~ палец ноги anat: great toe, hallux.
~ ~ руки anat: thumb.
~ пёстрый дятел orn: great spotted woodpecker (Dendrocopus major).
~ полосатик zool: sibbald's rorqual (Balaenoptera sibbaldi).
~ поморник orn: great skua (Stercorarius s. skua).
~ родничок anat: great fontanel(le), see передний родничок.
~ угорь-удав ichth: great gulper eel (Saccopharynx harrisoni).
~ эпилептический припадок neur: grand mal epilepsy.
болюс pharm: bolus, bole.
бомия = гибиск съедобный.
бонитировать judge (the soil, etc.)
бонитировочный ключ agr: soil key.
~ ключ овечьей шерсти key of wool graduation.
бор bot: 1. pine forest; 2. millet grass (Milium, L.); 3. see мышей; 4. boron, B.

бор развесистый bot: millet grass, panic (Milium effusum).
бораго bot: borage (Borago officinalis).
бордосская жидкость pharm: Bordeaux mixture.
борец bot: aconite, monkshood, wolfsbane (Aconitum, L.)
~ высокий Aconitum excelsum, Rchb.
~ жёлтый pale yellow wolfsbane (A. lycoctonum, L.)
~ синий garden monkshood, g. wolfsbane (A. napellus).
борзая zool: grayhound, borzoi (Canis familiaris).
бормашина dental engine.
бормотать mumble, mutter, maunder.
борная кислота boric acid, boracic a.
~ мазь pharm: boric acid ointment, boracic o.
борнеол pharm: borneol, Borneo camphor, Sumatra camphor.
борнобензойнокислый натрий pharm: sodium borobenzoate.
борновиннокаменнокислый алюминий pharm: aluminum borotartrate.
борнодубильновиннокаменнокислый алюминий aluminum borotannotartrate.
борнодубильнокислый алюминий pharm: aluminum borotannate.
борнокислый кальций pharm: calcium borate.
~ кокаин pharm: cocaine borate.
~ натрий = бура.
борномуравьинокислый алюминий pharm: aluminum boroformate.
борный вазелин pharm: borated petrolatum.
бор(о)- boro-, bor-.
боров agr: barrow, castrated pig, hog.
боровик = белый гриб.
бороглицерин pharm: boroglycerin.
борода beard.
бородавка wart.
бородавник bot: nipplewort (Lampsana communis).
бородавочник 1. bot: celandine, swallowwort (Chelidonium majus); 2. zool see африканский кабан.
бородавчатая трава = бородавник.
бородавчатка ichth: scorpion fish (Synanceja).
бородавчатый warty, warted, verrucose, verrucous, papillose.
бородатка orn: bearded titmouse (Panurus biarmicus, P. barbatus).
бородатый bearded.
бородач 1. orn: bearded vulture, lammergeier (Gypaëtus barbatus); 2. bot: beardgrass (Andropogon).

бородач веничный bot: broom-beard-grass, broom, wiregrass, bluestem, prairie beardgrass (A. scoparius, Michx.)

бородачёвые (подсем.) bot: beardgrass subfamily (Andropogoneae, Presl.)

бородка beard, barb; byssus (of mollusk).

~ зерна bot: fuzz.

борозда groove, furrow, fissure, sulcus, cleft.

~ аммонова рога = б. морского конька.

~ морского конька anat: hippocampal fissure.

бороздка groove, furrow; slot, riffle; stria.

~ для сонной артерии anat: carotid groove, sulcus caroticus.

бороздчатобрюхие моллюски (подкл.) zool: Aplacophora, Solenogastres.

бороздчатость fissuration, striation.

бороздчатые надкрылья entom: furrowed wing cases.

бороздчатый grooved, furrowed, fissured, sulcate, fluted, exsculptate.

~ ноготь derm: reedy nail.

боросалициловокислый натрий pharm: sodium borosalicylate.

боррерия bot: gator beads (Borreria laevis).

борьба с (вредителями, заболеваниями и т.п.) control of (pests, diseases, etc.)

~ с грызунами deratization.

~ со старостью measures against aging.

борщевик bot: cow parsnip (Heracleum).

босиком barefooted.

боталлов проток anat: ductus arteriosis Botalli.

ботанизировать botanize.

ботаник botanist.

ботаника botany.

ботанический botanic.

ботва bot: tops.

ботик zool: boatshell mollusk (Scaphander).

ботридии helm: bothridia, phyllidia.

ботридиум Botrydium (alga).

ботрии helm: bothria.

ботриомикоз vet: botriomycosis.

ботулизм tox: botulism.

Бофорт Beaufort.

бочёнкообразный barrel-shaped, dolioform.

бочка zool: side barrel (of a cow).

бочковидная грудная клетка path: barrel chest.

боязливость psych: timidity, apprehension(s), fearfullness.

боязнь psych: phobia, morbid fear; ~ ада hadephobia. | apprehension, fear.

~ бактерий bacteriophobia.

~ бацилл bacillophobia.

~ Бога theophobia.

~ болезней nosophobia.

~ боли algophobia, odynophobia.

~ брака gamophobia.

~ булавок belonephobia.

~ быть в доме domatophobia.

~ быть заживо погребённым taphephobia.

~ венерических болезней venereophobia, cypridophobia.

~ веселья cherophobia.

~ ветров anemophobia.

~ взгляда ophthalmophobia.

~ вида крови hem(at)ophobia.

~ влаги hydrophobia.

~ воды hydrophobia.

~ волос tricho(patho)phobia.

~ времени chronophobia.

~ всех и вся pantophobia.

~ вшей pediculophobia.

~ высоких предметов batophobia.

~ высоты acrophobia, hypsophobia.

~ глистов taeniophobia, helminthophobia.

~ глубины bathophobia.

~ говорить у заик lalophobia, stutter spasm.

~ голого тела gymnophobia.

~ грабителей harpaxophobia.

~ греха hamartophobia.

~ грозы astra(po)phobia, keraunophobia.

~ грома brontophobia, tonitrophobia.

~ грязи rhypophobia.

~ движения kinesophobia.

~ денег chrematophobia.

~ детей pedophobia.

~ дневного света phengophobia.

~ дождя ombrophobia.

~ домашнего очага oikophobia.

~ еды sitophobia.

~ ж-д поездок siderodromophobia.

~ женщин gynephobia.

~ животных zoophobia.

~ заболеть nosophobia.

~ заброшенных мест eremophobia.

~ загрязнений molysmophobia, mysophobia.

~ заикания lal(i)ophobia.

~ закрытых пространств claustrophobia.

~ запахов osmophobia.

~ ~ тела bromhidrosiphobia.

~ заразы molysmophobia.

боязнь заснуть hypnophobia.
~ звезд astrophobia.
~ звуков acousticophobia.
~ змей = б. пресмыкающихся.
~ зубов животных odontophobia.
~ избиений rhabdophobia.
~ известного имени onomatophobia.
~ изнурения kopophobia.
~ иметь ребенка maieusiophobia, tocophobia.
~ кала coprophobia.
~ кислого вкуса acer(b)ophobia.
~ книг bibliophobia.
~ кожных болезней dermatophobia.
~ кошек ailurophobia, galeophobia.
~ красного цвета ereuthophobia, erythrophobia.
~ левой стороны тела levophobia.
~ лекарств pharmacophobia.
~ леса hylophobia.
~ лестниц climacophobia.
~ лихорадки febriphobia, pyrexeophobia.
~ людей = б. общества.
~ мертвого тела necrophobia.
~ молнии = б. грозы.
~ моря = б. океана.
~ мужчин androphobia.
~ мыслей phronemophobia.
~ наводнений antlophobia.
~ насекомых entomophobia.
~ насмешек catagelophobia.
~ находиться в вагоне amaxophobia.
~ небесного пространства astrophobia.
~ неудач kakorrhaphiophobia.
~ новизны cainophobia, neophobia, misoneism.
~ ночи noctiphobia, nyctophobia.
~ обкрадывания kleptophobia, harpaxophobia.
~ обнажения gymnophobia.
~ обрывов cremnophobia.
~ общества anthropophobia.
~ огня pyrophobia.
~ одиночества monophobia, eremophobia.
~ океана thalassophobia.
~ осмеяния catagelophobia.
~ острых предметов aichmophobia.
~ ответственности hypengyophobia.
~ открытых пространств agoraphobia.
~ отравления toxiphobia.
~ ошибок hamartophobia.
~ падения av med: fear of falling.
~ пауков arachnephobia.
~ переходить мост gephyrophobia.
~ ~ улицу agyophobia.
~ писать graphophobia.
~ пищи cibophobia, sitophobia.

боязнь поездов = б. ж-д поездок.
~ поездок (путешествий) hodophobia.
~ пола genophobia.
~ половой любви erotophobia.
~ пустых помещений kenophobia.
~ правой стороны тела dextrophobia.
~ пресмыкающихся ophidiophobia.
~ прививок vaccinophobia.
~ прикосновений (h)aphephobia, haptephobia.
~ пчёл apiphobia, melissophobia.
~ работы erg(asi)ophobia.
~ рака cancerophobia.
~ расстройств ataxiophobia.
~ родов maieusiophobia.
~ рыб ichthyophobia.
~ самого себя autophobia.
~ света photophobia.
~ сидеть kathisophobia.
~ сифилиса syphilophobia.
~ сквозняков aerophobia, anemophobia.
~ слабости asthenophobia.
~ смерти thanatophobia, necrophobia.
~ сна hypnophobia.
~ снега chionophobia.
~ собак cynophobia.
~ собственных страхов phobophobia.
~ совокуплений coitophobia.
~ сойти с ума lyssophobia.
~ солнечных лучей heliophobia.
~ стекла crystallophobia, hyalophobia.
~ стоять stasiphobia.
~ ~ и ходить stasibasiphobia.
~ стоячего положения stasiphobia, basophobia.
~ страха phobophobia.
~ толпы ochlophobia.
~ темноты achluophobia, scotophobia.
~ тепла thermophobia.
~ тишины eremiophobia.
~ трупов necrophobia.
~ тумана homichlophobia.
~ удовольствий hedonophobia.
~ улиц agyiophobia.
~ упасть av med: fear of falling.
~ уродства dysmorphophobia, teratophobia.
~ усталости kopophobia.
~ цветов (растений) anthophobia.
~ холеры cholerophobia.
~ холода cheimaphobia, psychrophobia.
~ червей vermiphobia.
~ чужих (людей) xenophobia.
~ шума phonophobia.
~ электричества electrophobia.
~ ядов iophobia.
~ яркого света photaugiophobia.
боярышник bot: hawthorn, red haw, thorn (Crataegus).

боярышник колючий bot: May hawthorn, white thorn, haw tree (Crataegus oxyca-
~ круглоплодный = б. летний. ntha).
~ крупноплодный = б. летний.
~ летний May haw, apple haw (C. aestivalis, Torr. & Gray).
боярышница entom: whitethorn butterfly, hedge b., blackveined white (Aporia crataegi, Pieris crataegi).
брадзот vet: bradzot. [ness of the heart
брадикардия path: bradycardia, slow-
брадикинезия bradykinesia, bradykinesis.
брадикинетический bradykinetic.
бражник entom: hornworm, sphinx, hawk moth (Sphingidae).
~ виноградный grapevine sphinx, myron sphinx (Ampelophaga myron).
~ сосновый pine sphinx moth (Sphinx pinastri); pine hawk m. (Hyloicus p.)
бражники (сем.) entom: hawk-moths,
Брайт Bright. sphinxes (Sphingidae).
брайтова болезнь urol: Bright's disease, chronic nephritis.
брак между родственниками consanguineous marriage.
браковать reject, condemn. [(Braconidae)
браконилы (сем.) entom: braconids
бранхиогенная железа anat: branchiogeneous gland.
бранхиокардиальная борозда anat: branchiocardiac groove.
брасения bot: water shield (Brasenia).
браунколь bot: borecole, kale, see капуста листовая тысячеголовая.
браункресс = жеруха. [(Brachiopoda).
брахиопода zool: brachiopod, lamp shell
брахитерапия rad: brachitherapy.
брачная окраска zool: breeding color.
брачный вылет entom: bridal trip, marital flight, nuptial flyout (bees).
~ наряд zool: breeding color, spawning
~ облёт = б. вылет. | dress, s. livery.
~ период zool: mating season.
~ полёт = б. вылет.
~ танец zool: wedding dance.
бред psych: delirium; see also бредовая идея.
~ величия delirium grandiosum, megalo-
~ животными zoopsia. mania.
~ обкрадывания delusion of theft (or of burglarization).
~ отношения delusion of reference.
~ преследования delusion of persecu-
бредина = ива козья. tion.
бредить delirate. also бред.
бредовая идея psych: delusion; see

бредовая идея обнищания psych: delusion of impoverishment.
~ ~ ревности delusion of jealousy.
~ ~ ущерба delusion of losses.
бредовое состояние psych: delirious state, delirium. [like idea.
бредоподобная идея psych: delirium-
бредопорождающий psych: delirifacient, deliriant.
бригантин bot: alpine plum, briancon apricot (Prunus armeniaca, ssp. bri-
бриолог bot: bryologist. gantiaca).
бриологический bot: bryological.
бриология bot: bryology.
бриония = переступень.
бриопогон bot: Bryopogon lichens.
бриофит bot: bryophyte.
брислинг ichth: brisling.
бровь anat: eyebrow, supercilium, superciliary ridge.
бродильная способность fermenting
бродильное начало fermenter. | force.
бродильный fermentive.
~ грибок fermenter.
бродяжничество vagrancy, wandering.
бродячая форма free-ranging form, crawler (in benthos). [Errantia.
бродячие полихеты (подкл.) zool:
бродячий vagabond, wandering, vagrant,
брожение fermentation. migratory.
~ в желудке path: gastric fermentation, stomach f.
броколи bot: broccoli, see капуста
бром bromine, Br. спаржевая.
бромат chem: bromate.
бромацетат chem: bromacetate.
бромелиевые (сем.) bot: pineapple
бромид bromide. | family (Bromeliaceae).
бромистоводородная кислота hydrobromic acid.
бромистоводородный гиосцин pharm: hyoscine hydrobromide.
~ кофеин pharm: caffeine hydrobromide.
~ хинин pharm: quinine hydrobromide.
бромистый водород = бромистоводородная кислота.
~ калий pharm: potassium bromide.
~ кальций pharm: calcium bromide.
~ литий pharm: lithium bromide.
~ магний pharm: magnesium bromide.
~ натрий pharm sodium bromide.
~ стронций pharm: strontium bromide.
бромная вода pharm: bromine water.
бромоформ pharm: bromoform, methenyl tribromide.
бромсульфалеин bromosulphthalein.

броненосец zool: armadillo (Dasypus).
~ девятипоясной nine-banded a. (D. novemcinctus).
броненосцы (сем.) zool: armadillo family (Dasypodidae).
бронзовая болезнь = аддисонова б.
бронзовка венгерская entom: carabaeid Potosia hungarica.
~ зелёная Cetonia aurata.
~ зловонная Oxythyrea funestra.
~ мохнатая = олёнка.
~ рябая Oxythyrea cinctella.
бронх anat: bronchus.
бронхиальная астма int: bronchial asthma, allergic a.
~ железа anat: bronchial gland.
бронхиальное дерево anat: bronchial tree.
~ дыхание bronchial breathing.
бронхиальный слепок cast of the bronchial tube.
бронхиола anat: bronchiole.
бронхиолярный anat: bronchiolar.
бронхит path: bronchitis.
~ с плевритом path: bronchopleurisy.
бронхитный bronchitic.
бронхоаденит bronchoadenitis.
бронхография bronchography.
бронхоплевральный bronchopleural.
бронхоскоп bronchoscope.
бронхоскопия bronchoscopy.
бронхофония bronchophony.
бронхоэктаза bronchiectasis.
бронхоэктазный bronchiectatic.
бронхоэктатический = бронхоэктазный.
броуновское движение lab: Brownian movement, pedesis.
брункресс bot: yellow cress, nasturtium (Rorippa, Scop.)
бруннерова железа Brunner's gland.
брусника bot: red bilberry, red huckleberry, mountain cranberry, foxberry (Vaccinium vitis-idaea, L.)
брусничные (сем.) bot: bilberry fam. huckleberry fam. (Vacciniaceae).
бруссонеция bot: paper mulberry (Broussonetia papyrifera, Vent.)
бруцелла Brucella (bacilli).
бруцеллёз brucellosis, Malta fever, undulant fever.
бруцеллёзная инфекция brucella infection.
бруцеллёзный психоз brucellosis psychosis.
бруцеллин pharm: brucellin.
брыжеечная артерия anat: mesenteric artery.
~ беременность mesenteric pregnancy.
брыжеечная полоска anat: taenia mesocolica.
брыжейка anat: mesentery.
~ ободочной кишки anat: mesocolon.
~ поперечной ободочной кишки anat: transverse mesocolon.
~ прямой кишки anat: mesorectum.
~ сигмовидной кишки anat: mesosigmoid.
~ тонкой кишки mesenterium tenue.
~ червеобразного отростка anat: mesenteriolum appendicularis.
~ яичника anat: mesovarium.
брыж(ж)и = брыжейка.
брызгальце ichth: spiracle.
брыкаться zool: buck, kick.
брыла orn: gill.
брюзгливость psych: grouchiness.
брюзгливый grouchy, querulous, peevish.
брюква bot: Russian turnip, underground kohlrabi, swede, rutabaga (Brassica napus rapifera).
брюньон bot: brugnon (Persica laevis)
брюссельская капуста bot: Brussels sprouts.
брюхо belly, paunch, abdomen.
брюхоногие (кл.) zool: gastropods, univalve mollusks (Gastropoda).
брюхоресничные (кл.) zool: gastrotrichs (Gastrotricha).
~ (отр.) zool: Hypotricha.
брюхоресничный червь zool: gastrotrich.
брюшина anat: peritoneum.
брюшинная оболочка anat: peritoneal coat.
брюшинный мешок anat: peritoneal sac.
брюшко zool: abdomen, venter; entom: hind body.
~ мышцы anat: muscle belly, myogaster, venter.
~ (насекомого) abdomen (of an insect)
брюшная аорта anat: abdominal aorta.
~ беременность obstet: abdominal pregnancy.
~ брыжейка anat: ventral mesentery.
~ водянка = асцит.
~ грыжа peritoneal hernia.
~ мышца anat: abdominal muscle.
~ неврастения abdominal neurasthenia.
~ нервная цепь entom: ventral nerve cord.
~ ножка zool: swimmeret (of a crayfish)
~ полость anat: abdominal cavity.
~ присоска zool: ventral sucker, posterior sucker, acetabulum.
~ рана abdominal wound.
~ стенка anat: abdominal wall.
~ часть заднегруди entom: metasternum.
~ ~ среднегруди entom: mesosternum.

брюшное давление abdominal pressure.
~ дыхание abdominal respiration.
~ отверстие (маточной) трубы anat: ostium abdominale.
брюшной abdominal, ventral, coeliac.
~ крючок surg: abdominal retractor.
~ панцырь zool: ventral shield.
~ плавник zool: pelvic fin, ventral fin, hinder fin.
~ пресс abdominal pressure, prelum [abdominale.
~ рефлекс abdominal reflex.
~ тиф infect: typhoid (fever).
~ ~ с осложнением со стороны плевры pleurotyphoid.
~ ~ с осложнением со стороны селезенки splenotyphoid.
~ ~ с поражением суставов arthro- [typhoid.
~ ~ с симптомами менингита meningotyphoid.
~ шов bot: ventral suture (of a broad bean, etc.
~ щит zool: ventral shield.
брюшнотифозная палочка bact: typhoid bacillus.
брюшнотифозный больной typhoid [patient.
брюшные внутренности anat: abdominal viscera, see also внутренности.
~ покровы anat: abdominal coats.
~ поры ichth: abdominal pores.
бубон bubo, sympathetic abscess.
бубонная чума infect: bubonic plague.
бугай = выпь.
бугор bulge, protuberance, tuber(osity); thalamus; see also возвышение, вырост, отросток.
бугорок tubercle, hillock, colliculus.
~ перламутра (на раковине) zool: blister pearl.
~ (позвонка и т.п.) anat: tubercle [(of a vertebra, etc.)
~ Шассеньяка anat: carotid tubercle.
бугорчатка = жемчужница 2.
бугорчатый tuberculate, torulose.
бугристое копыто vet: convexity of sole.
бугристость anat: tuberosity.
бугристый tuberous.
бугровой attr: bulge, protuberance; adj: tuberous; thalamic.
будра плющевидная bot: ground ivy, gill-over-the-ground, runaway robin (Glechoma hederacea, L.)
буж med: bougie.
бужирование med: bouginage.
бузина bot: elder (Sambucus); pithball.
~ вонючая stinking elder (S. pubens).
~ красная red-berried elder (S. rucemosa).
~ травянистая dwarf e., danewort, Dane's blood (S. ebulus).
бузина чёрная bot: elder of Europe wallwort, bour-tree (S. nigra).
бузинник = бузина травянистая.
бузник вонючий = бузина травянистая.
буйвол zool: buffalo.
буйволова трава bot: buffalo grass (Bulbilis, Sessleria dactiloides).
буйное помешательство psych: impulsive insanity.
буйство = неистовство.
бук bot: beech (Fagus, L.)
~ белый hornbeam (Carpinus betulus).
~ европейский European beech (Fagus silvatica).
~ лесной weeping beech (F. silvatica, var. pendula).
~ ~ пурпуровый purple beech (F. silvatica purpurea, Ait.)
букарка entom: Coenorrhinus pauxillus.
букашка entom: small insect.
буквица bot: betony (Betonica officinalis, Stachys betonica, Benth.)
~ белая = первоцвет аптечный.
букет вина flavor, race of wine.
букетик bot: cyathium.
букетная трава bot: bunch grass.
буковые (сем.) bot: beech family (Fagaceae).
буковый орешек beechnut.
букоцветные (пор.) bot: Fagales.
букс = самшит.
булавница bot: coral fungus, fairy club f., staghorn f. (Clavaria, Pers.)
~ съедобная clavaria (C. pistillaris)
булавовидная английская пшеница cone wheat, rivet w. (Triticum turgidum).
булавовидн(о-вздут)ая клетка hist: mace-shaped (swollen) cell.
булавовидное утолщение path: clubbing.
булавовидный clubbed, club-shaped, mace-shaped, clavatus.
~ палец path: clubbed finger.
~ усик entom: clavate antenna, club-[shaped a.
булавоносец седой bot: grey hair-grass (Corynephorus canescens, Beauv)
буланая кошка zool: Egyptian cat.
булат-маи = усач чанари.
булёзная сыпь derm: bullous eruption.
булимический bulimic.
булимия path: bulimia, boulimia, adephagia, cynorexia, bovine hunger.
бульбарная конъюнктива bio: bulbar conjunctiva.
бульбарный anat: bulbar (pertaining to medulla oblongata).

бульбарный паралич bulbar palsy, progressive bulbar paralysis.
бульбус anat: bulb.
бульва = груша земляная.
бульверия orn: Bulver's petrel (Bulveria bulverii).
бульдог zool: bulldog (Canis familiaris bellicosus)
бульон broth, bouillon.
бульонная взвесь bact: broth suspension.
бумагопрядильщик zool: cotton spinner (Holoturia).
бумажная пластинка anat: lamina papyracea, os planum.
бумажный стаканчик paper cup.
бунгар zool: Bungarus (poisonous snake).
бундук bot: Kentucky coffee tree (Gymnocladus dioica, G. canadensis).
бура chem: borax, sodium borate.
бурав surg: drill.
буравница борщевичная entom: miner Philophylla heraclei.
~ листовая parsnip-leaf miner (Acidia fratria
бурак bot: beetroot, see свёкла.
бурачниковые (сем.) bot: borage family, bugloss f. (Boraginaceae).
бурачок = алиссум.
бурая атрофия path: brown atrophy.
~ гниль phytp: brown rot (on apples, pears, etc.)
~ индурация легких path: congestive carnification of the lungs.
~ пятнистость phytp: brown spot(tiness (tomato) leaf mold (Phyllostricta).
~ ржавчина phytp: leaf rust.
~ сердцевина bot: brown heart (of fruit
~ сердцевинная гниль phytp: firm rot heart.
*бургомистр orn: burgomaster (Larus hyperboreus).
бургундская смола pharm: Burgundy pitch.
Бурдах Burdach.
бурдаховский пучок = клиновидный п.
буревестник orn: shearwater, stormy petrel (Puffinus).
бурилка вишнёвая entom: cherry fruit fly (Rhagoletis, Spilographa cerasi).
бурильщик entom: borer.
буркун = люцерна серповидная.
буркунчик = люцерна хмелевидная.
бурманиевые (сем.) bot: burmannia family (Burmanniaceae).
бурмания bot: burmannia (Burmannia).
бурная рвота projectile vomiting.
бурное брожение stormy fermentation.
буровский раствор pharm: Burow's solution.

бурозубка (землеройка) zool: shrew
~ -крошка shrew Sorex tscherskii, Sorex.
бурса anat: bursa.
бурундук zool: chipmunk; Brit:hackee (Eutamias, Tamias).
бурые водоросли bot: brown algae (Phaeophyta).
бурый гриф orn: brown vulture (Aegypius monachus).
~ камфорный пластырь pharm: camphorated mother's plaster.
~ медведь zool: Russian bear (Ursus arctos).
~ рак капусты phytp: brown rot of cabbage.
бурьян bot: beggarweed, tickseed, knotweed, weed. See also сорняк.
бусовидный bot: moniliform.
буськи = аистник цикутолистный.
бутелуоя bot: mesquite grass, grama grass (Bouteloua, Lag.)
~ изящная Bouteloua gracilis.
бутень американский = осмориза.
~ душистый = кервель испанский.
бутерлак bot: water purslane (Peplis).
бутирин chem: butyrin, glyceryl tributyrate.
бутирометр cream gauge.
бутоксиполипропиленгликоль chem: butoxypolypropylene glycol.
бутон bot: flower bud, button.
бутонизация bot: budding.
бутоноподобное расположение соцветий bot: pompon.
бутылка для образца specimen bottle.
~ с горячей водой hotwater bottle.
бутылконос zool: bottle-nose whale (Hyperoodon).
"бутылочная щётка" bot: bottle brush (Callistemon lanceolata, DC., Metrosideros semperflorens, Llod.)
буферированный buffered.
бухарник bot: notholcus (Holcus, L.)
~ мягкий cock's tail (H. mollis).
~ шерстистый velvet grass (H. lanatus).
бухлоэ bot: buffalo grass (Buchloe dactyloides).
бушелёр boucholeur.
БЦЖ mcbio: BCG.
бык zool: bull (Bos taurus).
быки (подсем.) zool: ox subfamily (Bovinae).
былинка bot: spire, blade of grass.
быстрая заживляемость surg: disvulnerability.
~ реакция rapid reaction.
быстроопадающий bot: fugacious, caducous.

быстроосыпающийся = быстроопадающий.
быстрорастущий quick-growing.
быстрота выборочной реакции av med: selective response speed.
быстроубивающая доза rad: fast-killing dose.
быстроувядающий bot: fugacious.
быстрые роды obstet: oxytocia.
~ сокращения мышцы clonus.
бытовой сифилис ven: extragenital syphilis
~ яд household poison.
быть в охоте = быть в течке.
~ ~ течке zool: to be in rut.
~ противным nauseate, disgust.
"бычий глаз" = рудбекия волоокая.
~ солитер = б. цепень.
~ цепень helm: beef tapeworm, hookless t. (Taenia rhynchus saginatus).
~ язык bot: beefsteak fungus (Fistulina hepatica).
бычковые (сем.) ichth: Gobiidae, cf. бычок 1.
*бычок 1. ichth: bullhead, biggyhead, muddler, blob, grubby, sculpin, pigfish salpa, drummer (Cottus); goby, bigmouth (Gobiidae); sea raven (Hemitripterus americanus); 3. zool: bull calf; small bull.
~ -горлап Neogobius gorlap.
~ -кнут = б.-мартовик.
~ -кругляк Neogobius melanostomus.
~ -мартовик Mesogobius batrachocephalus.
~ -песочник Neogobius fluviatilis.
~ -рогатка bullhead Myoxocephalus.
~ -травяник Gobius ophiocephalus.
~ -ширман Neogobius syrman.
бычье сердце path: bovine heart, cor bovinum.
бычья жёлчь oxgall.
Бьюккей Bucquoy.
бэрдиелля ichth: silver perch, mademoiselle (Bairdiella chrysura).
бюретка lab: buret(te), dropping glass.

В

в бутоне bot: in bud.
~ виде безлистного стебля scapelike
~ ~ виде зонтика umbelliform.
~ ~ иглы needle-shaped.
~ ~ капель dropwise.
~ ~ клубнелуковицы cormlike.
~ ~ лестницы scalariform.
~ ~ мокрицы onisciform.
~ ~ монетных столбиков nummular.
в виде репы napiform.
~ ~ слоевища thalloid.
~ ~ усика cirriform, antenniform.
~ ~ чашелистика sepaloid.
~ ~ чашечки patelliform.
~ два ряда two-ranked.
~ живом организме in vivo.
~ зависимости от as affected by.
~ зачатке in bud.
~ месте нахождения in situ.
~ неизменном положении in situ.
~ матке anat: in utero.
~ отношении поведения behavioristically.
~ передней части спинной половины тела anat: anterodorsally.
~ пробирке in vitro.
~ стадии нимфы nymphal.
~ ~ плодоношения in crop.
~ стекле in vitro.
~ форме = в виде.
~ ~ полумесяца crescent.
вагильная форма = бродячая ф.
вагильный = бродячий.
ваготония vagotonia.
вагусная блокада сердца path: vagal heart block.
важенка zool: female deer, she-deer.
важные для жизни органы vitals.
вазелин pharm: vaseline, petrolatum, petroleum jelly.
вазодилятаторы vasodilator nerves.
вазоконстрикторы vasoconstrictor nerves.
вазомоторная неустойчивость vasomotor instability.
вазомоторный паралич angioparalysis.
~ центр anat: vasomotor center.
вазомоторы anat: vasomotor nerves.
вайда bot: woad (Isatis, L.)
~ красильная dyer's woad, asp-of-Jerusalem (I. tinctoria).
Вайль Vail.
вайт-рот phytp: white rot (on grapes).
вайя bot: frond.
вакуолизированный vacuolated.
вакуоля vacuole.
~ с клеточным соком sap vacuole.
вакуумная трубка lab: vacuum tube.
вакцина imm: vaccine.
вакцинальная лихорадка vaccinal fever.
~ сыпь vaccination rash.
вакцинация imm: vaccination.
~ против холеры cholera vaccination, cholerization.
вакцинировать imm: vaccinate.
вакциновидный vaccinoid.

вакцинотерапия vaccinotherapy.
валежник = хворост. [draceus.
валёк ichth: whitefish Coregonus cylin-
валериана bot: valerian, setwall
(Valeriana, L.) [ficinalis).
~ аптечная "garden heliotrope" (V. of-
валериан(к)а pharm: valerian.[birica).
~ каменная bot: patrinia (Patrinia si-
валерианница bot: corn salad, lamb's lettuce (Valerianella, Mill.)
~ овощная corn salad, lamb's lettuce, fetticus (V. olitoria, Moench.)
валериановая кислота chem: valeri(ani)c acid. [oil.
валериановое масло pharm: valerian
валериановокислый chem: valeri(ani)c, valer(ian)ate.
~ аммоний pharm: ammonium valerate.
~ натрий pharm: sodium valerate.
валериановые = мауновые.
~ капли pharm: valerian drops. [root.
валериановый корень pharm: valerian
валик прямой кишки anat: rectal column, anal c., columna rectalis.[lla.
валиковый сосочек anat: vallate papi-
~ шов surg: clavate suture, quilled s.
валин valine. [(Vallisneria,L.)
валлиснерия bot: tapegrass, eelgrass
валонея = дуб валонейный.
валух = выложенный баран.
вальвулотомия surg: valvulotomy.
вальвы entom: valvae, harpagones.[ticola)
вальдшнеп orn: woodcock (Scolopax rus-
вальдшнеповые (сем.) orn: woodcock family (Scolopacidae).
Ван Лир Van Liere.
Ван-Слейк Van Slyke.
ванеса ио = дневной павлиний глаз.
ваниль vanilla (Vanilla planifolia,Andr)
ванна san: 1. bath; 2. bathtub.
~ с постепенным понижением температуры graduated bath.
ванная комната bathroom.
ванный термометр bathtub thermometer.
вантуза = присосок. [олень.
вапити = американский благородный
вапоризация gyn: atmocausis.
варакушка белозвёздная orn: blue-throated warbler (Erithacus cyaneculus).
~ краснозвёздная E. suecicus.
варан zool: monitor (lizard).
варановые zool: monitors (Varanidae).
варатах bot: waratah (Telopea speciosissima, R. Br.)
вари zool: lemur (Lemur varius). [ation.
вариационный диапазон range of vari-
варикозная вена path: varicose vein, knotted vein.
варолиев мост anat: pons Varolii.
Вартон Wharton. [jelly.
вартонов студень embr: Wharton's
василёк bot: starthistle, knapweed, centaury (Centaurea, L.)
~ голубой cornflower, bluebottle, bachlor's button (C. cyanus).
~ мальтийский Napa thistle, tocalote (C. melitensis).
~ рогатый = живокость посевная.
~ синий = в. голубой. [trum).
василистник bot: meadow-rue (Thalic-
~ водосборолистный meadow-rue (T. aquilegifolium, L.)
~ жёлтый meadow-rue.
васкуляризация vascularization.
васкулярность vascularity.
васкулярный vascular.
Вассерман Wassermann. [с.-х. наук.
ВАСХНИЛ = Всесоюзная академия
вата cotton, wadding.
Ватель Watelle.
ватная подстилка surg: cotton pad.
~ пробка cotton stopper.
ватный тампон cotton pledget, c.swab
~ шарик surg: cotton ball.
ваточник bot: milkweed, silkweed, (Asclepias, L.); common milkweed, wild cotton, swallowwort (A.syriaca).
~ инкарнатный swamp milkweed, rose m., white Indian hemp (A. incarnata).
~ клубненосный butterfly weed, pleurisy root, chigger flower (A.tuberosa).
ватсония = слива американская.
вахня ichth: Far-East navaga (Eleginus gracilis). [thes,L.)
вахта bot: buckbean, bogbean (Menyan-
~ трёхлистная marsh trefoil (M. trifoliata).
~ трилистная = в. трёхлистная.
вашингтония bot: washingtonia (Wash-
вбирать = впитывать.|ingtonia)[ся.
вбуравиться p. a. of вбуравливать-
вбуравливаться drill itself into (of caterpillars, etc.)
введение в науку propaedeutics.
~ внутрь oral administration.
~ дуоденального зонда duodenal tubage.
~ жидкости в плевральную полость surg: pleuroclysis.
~ ~ под кожу hypodermoclysis.
~ катетера urol: catheterization.

введение инъекцией needle administra-
~ трубки surg: intubation, tubage. | tion.
~ через прямую кишку rectal administ
~ члена penetration (of the penis).
в-во = вещество.
вводить канюлю surg: insert a cannule, cannulate.
~ катетер urol: pass the catheter.
~ трубку surg: intubate.
вводное заболевание intercurrent dis-
вводной zool: inhalant, inhalent. ease.
вдавление depression, impression.
~ кости при переломе surg: depressed fracture.
вдавленность depression, impression; bot: locule, basin (in fruits).
вдавленный depressed, impressed.
~ ноготь spoon nail.
~ перелом (черепа) surg: depressed
"вдовица" = зубатка синяя. | fracture
вдох inspiration, aspiration; inhalation
вдохнуть p. a. of вдыхать.
вдувание insufflation, blowing into.
вдуватель insufflator. [piratory air.
вдыхаемый воздух inspired air, res-
вдыхание inspiration, aspiration; inhalation. [tory valve.
вдыхательный клапан av med: inspira-
вдыхать inspire, aspirate; inhale.
вегетарианец vegetarian.
вегетативная нервная система anat: autonomic nervous system.
вегетативно размножаемый clonal.
вегетативное размножение bio: vegetative reproduction.
вегетативный vegetative.
вегетационная верхушка bot: apical cone, apical point, vegetative cone.
вегетационный vegetational.
ведение послеродового периода obstet: management of puerperal state.
~ родов obstet: conduct of labor.
ведро для отбросов (бинтов, ваты и др.) san: waste can, refuse can.
ведущий больного = лечащий врач.
"ведьмина метла" phytp: bird's nest, witch's broom (Exoascus cerasi, E. betullinus, etc.)
веерная пальма талипот bot: talipot palm (Corypha umbraculifera, L.)
веерноскладывающийся plicate.
веерокрылые (отр.) entom: stylopids twisted-winged insects (Strepsiptera).
веерообразный fan-shaped, flabelliform flabellate. [thes.
веерохвостые orn: Ornithurae, Neorni-

вездесущий ubiquitous, ever-present.
везикулёзная сыпь derm: miliary eruption, vesicular eruption.
везикулёзный vesicular, blebby.
везикулярный vesicular.
вейник bot: reed bentgrass (Calamagrostis, Adans.); bluejoint (C. canaden-
вейнрута = рута. sis).
вейсманизм genet: weissmannism.
веко anat: eyelid, palpebra.
векодержатель surg: blepharostat.
векоподъемник ophth: eye speculum, lid retractor.
векторкардиография vector-cardio-
велигер zool: veliger. graphy.
величина аккомодации глаза ophth: range of accomodation.
~ изображения на сетчатке ophth: size of the retinal image.
~ насыщения saturation value.
величиною с боб bean-sized.
~ ~ булавочную головку pinhead-
~ ~ горошину pea-sized. sized.
~ ~ грецкий орех walnut-sized.
~ ~ ладонь palm-sized.
веллингтония bot: wellingtonia, big tree (Sequoia gigantea, DC).
вельвичиевые (сем.) bot: welwitschia family (Welwitschiaceae).
вельвичия bot: welwitschia (Welwit-
вена anat: vein. | schia mirabilis, Hook.)
~ мелкого калибра anat: small vein.
венгерка = слива обыкновенная.
венепункция surg: venipuncture.
венерин башмачок bot: lady's slipper, mocassin flower (Cypripedium, L.)
*~ бугорок anat: hill of Venus.
~ волос bot: Venus' hair, maidenhair fern (Adiantum capillus veneris, L.)
~ пояс zool: ctenophore Cestus veneris.
венерическая болезнь venereal disease.
венерический бубон venereal bubo.
венерка zool: quahog, quahaug, Venus clam (Venus).
венеролог med: venerologist.
венерологическая больница VD-hos-
венерология venerology. pital.
венесекция surg: venesection. [artery.
венечная артерия anat: coronary
~ ~ сердца (правая, левая) anat: (right, left) coronary artery. [narius.
~ борозда сердца anat: sulcus coro-
~ пазуха сердца anat: coronary sinus.
~ связка anat: coronary ligament.
~ ямка anat: coronoid fossa.

венечный галл bot: crown gall.
~ отросток anat: coronoid process.
~ шов anat: coronal suture. [rius.
веникоподобный bot: broom-like, scopa-
вено-вазомоторный рефлекс
veni-vasomotor reflex.
венография venography.
венозная кровь venous blood.
~ система anat: venous system.
венозное сплетение anat: veniplex.
венозный anat: venous, veined.
~ застой path: venous congestion, v.
~ шум venous hum. [engorgement.
венопрессорный рефлекс venopressor r
венсанов порошок Vincent's powder.
венская паста pharm: Vienna paste.
венское питье pharm Brit: black
вентилировать ventilate. draught.
вентиляция ventilation.
вентральный ventral.
вентурия phytp: Venturia (fungi).
венула anat: venule.
венус = венерка.
венцевидный crown-like, coronarius.
венчик bot: corona, crown, coronet, petal, corolla; corollet, corollule.
~ из крючьев helm: crown of hooks.
~ члена anat: corona of the penis.
вепрь zool: aper (Sus scrofa fera), see
вератрум pharm: veratrum. кабан 1.
верба bot: willow, osier (Salix, L.); white willow (S. alba); pussy willow (S. acutiflora); see also ива.
вербейник bot: loosestrife (Lysimachia).
~ луговой чай moneywort (L. nummularia)
вербена bot: vervain, verbena (Verbena).
~ аптечная European vervain (V. officinalis). [joy (V. hastata).
~ копьевидная blue vervain, simpler's
~ крапиволистная white vervain (V. urticaefolia).
~ лимонная lemon vervain (Lippa citriodora, Kunth., or V. triphilla).
вербеновые (сем.) bot: vervain family (Verbenaceae).
верблюд zool: camel (Camelus).
верблюдка entom: snakefly (Raphidia).
*верблюдки (отр.) entom: snakeflies (Raphidioptera). [(Camelidae).
верблюды (сем.) zool: camel family
верблюжёнок zool: young camel, colt.
"верблюжье сено" bot: camel's hay (Cymbopogon schoenanthus, Spreng.)
верблюжья колючка bot: alhagi, camel's thorn (Alhagi camelorum, Fisch.)
~ походка path: dromedary gait.

верблюжья трава = в. колючка.
верболоз = чернотал.
верёвчатое тело anat: restiform body.
веред vet: anbury, ancome.
вереск bot: heather, Scotch h., ling (Calluna, Salisb.); heath (Erica, L.)
~ болотный Scotch heath, fine-leaved h. (E. cinerea).
~ декоративный heath.
~ древовидный brierwood (E. arborea)
~ крупный средиземноморский = в. древовидный.
~ обыкновенный = вереск.
вересковое bot: heath, ericaceous.
вересковые (сем.) bot: heath family (Ericaceae).
верескоцветные (пор.) bot: Ericales
веретеница zool: anguine lizard (Anguis fragilis); blindworm, slowworm (Coronella laevis). [idae).
веретеницевые zool: anguines (Angu-
веретенник orn: ringneck (Limosa melanura).
~ гудзонский barge (L. hudsonica).
веретено spindle; columella; see also ядерное веретено.
веретеновидный spindle-like, spindle -shaped, fusiform, spindly.[dle cell.
веретенообразная клетка hist:spin-
~ мышца anat: fusiform muscle.
веретенообразное расширение семявыносящего протока anat: ampulla of the ductus deferens.
веретенообразноклеточная саркома path: spindle-cell sarcoma.
веретенообразноклеточный hist: fusocellular.
веретенообразный = веретеновидный.
~ буж fusiform bougie, bellied b.
веретёнце bot: ear's spindle.
верещатник bot: heathland.
верльгофова болезнь idiopathic thrombocytopenic purpura, land scurvy, Werlhof's disease.[2. vermouth.
вермут 1. bot: see полынь горькая;
веронал pharm: veronal, barbital, diethylbarbituric acid;Brit:barbitone
~ -натрий pharm: barbital sodium.
вероника bot: speedwell (Veronica, L.)
~ американская American brooklime (V. americana, Schwein.) [tis).
~ пашенная field speedwell (V. agres-
~ плющелистная ivy-leaved speedwell (V. hederaefolia, L.) [beccabunga,L)
~ -поточник European brooklime (V.

вероника ручейная bot: brooklime (Veronica beccabunga, L.)
вероятная продолжительность жизни expectation of life.
веррукозный verrucose, verrucous, see бородавчатый.
версенат tox: versenate, edathamil, calcium-disodium.
вертел (большой, малый) anat: (greater, lesser) trochanter.
вертельный anat: trochanteric.
вертеться entom: wiggle.
вертиголовка = вертишейка.
вертикальное косоглазие ophth: upward strabism.
~ положение erect position, upright p.
вертикальный нистагм ophth: vertical nystagmus.
вертициллёзное увядание bot: verticillium wilt.
вертишейка orn: wryneck (Junx torquilla) Cf. дятловые.
вертлуг trochanter.
вертлужная впадина anat: acetabulum.
вертлужный anat: acetabular.
вертляница bot: sweet pinesap, Indian pipe (Monotropa hipopitys).
вертляницевые (сем.) bot: sweet pinesap family (Monotropaceae).
вертунья листовая entom: moth Recurvaria nanella (fam. Gelechiidae).
~ почковая bud moth (Tmetocera ocellana fam. Tortricidae).
вертячка 1. entom: gyrinid, whirligig beetle (Gyrinidae); 2. vet: turnsickness, avertin, gid, blind staggers.
верхневисочное поле зрения ophth: upper temporal field of vision.
верхнегубные щупальца entom: maxillary palpi.
верхнедевонский Upper Devonian.
верхнее жвало entom: upper jaw.
~ устье желудка anat: esophageal orifice of the stomach, cardia.
верхненосовое поле зрения ophth: upper nasal field of vision.
верхнечелюстная кость anat: maxillary bone.
~ пазуха anat: maxillary sinus, sinus maxillaris, sinus Highmori.
верхнечелюстной нерв anat: maxillary nerve
верхние колоски bot: tip spikelets.
~ рожки щитовидного хряща anat: superior cornua of the thyroid cartilage.
~ челюсти entom: upper jaws, mandibles, mandibulae.
верхний upper, top; anat: superior.
~ клык anat: eye tooth.
верхний край клюва orn: culmen.
~ крыловой треугольник entom: supratriangle.
~ отросток лопатки anat: acromion.
~ расширенный конец яйцевода entom: egg calix.
~ рот ichth: upward-pointing mouth.
~ свод ophth: superior fornix.
~ щит carapace (of a turtle).
верхняя (внутренняя) колосковая чешуя upper empty glume.
~ губа upper lip; zool: labrum, hypostoma (of invertebrates).
~ доля anat: upper lobe.
~ завязь bot: superior ovary.
~ конечность anat: upper extremity.
~ косая глазная мышца anat: obliquus oculi superior (trochlearis).
~ носовая раковина anat: superior nasal concha, superior turbinate bone, concha nasalis superior.
~ оболочка яйца entom: chorion.
~ полая вена anat: precava, vena cava superior.
~ прямая глазная мышца anat: rectus oculi superior (muscle).
~ стенка глазной впадины anat: roof of an orbit.
~ часть бедра anat: upper thigh.
~ ~ живота anat: upper abdomen.
~ челюсть anat: maxilla, superior maxilla, upper jaw.
верховка ichth: Leucaspius.
верхогляд ichth: Erythroculter erythropterus.
верхоплодные мхи (подпор.) bot: Acrocarpi.
верхушечная каверна apical cavity.
~ клетка bot: apical cell.
~ почка bot: terminal bud.
верхушечный apical, of top.
~ бронх anat: bronchus apicalis.
~ толчок physl: apex beat (of the heart)
верхушка apex, summit, top, vertex, peak; zool: beak (of bivalve shell).
~ корня bot: crown, shoulder of a root.
~ лёгкого anat: apex of the lung.
~ сердца anat: apex of the heart.
~ створки раковины zool: umbo.
вершина = верхушка.
~ головы anat: vertex.
вершинный побег bot: leading shoot.
~ угол крыла entom: apex of the wing.
вес weight.
~ выше нормы overweight.
~ тела body weight.
веселость gaiety, hilarity, exhilaration.

веселящий exhilarant, exhilarating.
~ газ exhilarant gas.
весенний катарр ophth: vernal conjunctivitis.
~ облёт пчёл flight time of bees.
~ паралич entom: spring sickness, May sickness, black robbers (of bees).
весенняя пятнистость phytp: early leaf blight.
~ ржавчина early leaf rust.
веслоногие 1.orn: web-footed birds (Steganopodes); 2. zool: copepods (very small crustaceans Copepoda).
~ раки (отр.) zool: Copepoda.
веслонос ichth: great spoonbill, paddlefish (Polyodon).
веслоносы (сем.) ichth: great spoonbill family (Polyodontidae).
веснушка derm: freckle.
веснянка entom: stonefly.
веснянки (отр.) entom: stoneflies (Plecoptera).
весовой ponderal.
~ анализ gravimetric analysis.
вести запись температуры и т.п. keep record of temperature, etc.
вестибулярная функция vestibular function.
вестибулярное раздражение vestibular stimulation.
вестибулярный аппарат anat: vestibular apparatus, v. mechanism.
весы balance, scales.
весьма резкий peracute.
ветвистороговые губки (отр.) zool: dendritic horny sponges (Dendroceratida, Darwinellidae).
ветвистоусое ракообразное zool: daphnid (Daphnidae).
ветвистоусые рачки (отр.) zool: water fleas (Cladocera).
ветвистоусый рачок zool: water flea.
ветвистый boughy, ramified.
ветвиться ramify.
ветвление branching, ramification.
ветвь branch, bough, twig, ramus, limb, ramification, offshoot, see отросток.
~ аорты anat: aortic ramus.
~ артерии anat: arterial branch.
~ лонной кости anat: ramus of the pubis.
~ фурки zool: furcal ramus.
~ щипцов forceps blade.
ветвящийся branching, ramified, ramigerous.
ветеринар veterinarian, veterinary officer.
~ -практик veterinary practitioner.
ветеринария veterinary medicine.
ветеринарная фармация zoopharmacy.
ветеринар(ный врач) = ветеринар.
ветка bot: branch, see ветвь.
ветла white willow (Salix alba).
веточка bot: ramule, branchlet.
ветренница = анемон.
~ дубравная white windflower (Anemone nemorosa, L.)
~ лесная wood anemone (A. silvestris)
~ лютичная A. ranunculoides, L.
ветрогонное (средство) pharm: antiflatulent, carminative.
ветроопыляемое растение wind-pollinated plant, anemophilous p.
"ветры" windiness, see пучение.
ветряная оспа infect: chickenpox, varicella.
вех bot: hemlock (Cicuta).
~ пятнистый cowbane, water h. (C. virosa).
~ ядовитый = в. пятнистый.
вечернее повышение температуры evening temperature rise.
вечерница see 1.bot фиалка ночная; 2.zool: кожан обыкновенный.
вечерняя еда evening meal.
~ моча evening urine.
~ температура evening temperature.
вечнозёленый bot: evergreen.
вещество matter, substance, stuff.
~ отпугивающее насекомых insect repellent.
~ печени anat: hepatic substance.
~ усталости kenotoxin.
взаимная зависимость interdependence.
взаимнотормозящий interinhibitive.
взаимодействие interaction.
взаимодействия хищника и жертвы zool: predator-prey interactions.
взаимопроникновение interpenetration.
взбалтывание shaking, shake-up, agitation.
взбалтыватель agitator.
взбалтывать shake up, stir, agitate.
взбитый fluffy.
взболтать p.a. of взбалтывать.
взвесь suspension; slurry; detritus.
взвешенное вещество suspended matter.
взволнованный agitated, jittery.
вздуваться swell (up).
вздутие flatulence, distension, swelling, inflation, bloating, turgidity, intumescence, tympanism, windiness, bulb; see also опухание.
~ желудка path: gastric flatulence.
~ живота abdominal distention, celiectasia
~ на корне phytp: root swelling.
~ на средней линии головы zool: glabella.
вздутия (на стенке кишки) anat: haustra, sacculations of the colon.

вздутость = вздутие.
вздутый flatulent, distended, swollen, inflated, bloated, turgid, intumescent, tympanous, puffed up; see опухлый.
вздуться p.a. of вздуваться.
взмах крыла orn: wing beat.
взморник = зостера.
взмутить p. a. of взмучивать.
взмучивание roiling, stirring up.
взмучивать roil, stir up.
взойти p. a. of всходить.
взрослая особь zool: adult.
~ стадия entom: imago.
взрослое состояние adulthood.
взрослый adult.
взрывная декомпрессия av med: explosive decompression.
взрывной невроз mil: blast neurosis.
взятие икры ichth: stripping of eggs.
~ крови blood taking.
~ пробы sampling.
~ части из пробы subsampling.
вибрационный массаж vibratory massage
виброин mcbio: Vibrio (of family Spirillaceae).
вибрисса zool: mustacial bristle.
виварий zool: vivarium, retainer.
виверра zool: viverrine, civet cat (Vi-
~ азиатская zibet (V. zivetta). verra).
~ африканская African civet cat.
~ настоящая = в. азиатская.
виверры (сем.) zool: civet family (Vi-
вивисектор surg: vivisector.| verridae).
вивисекционист vivisectionist.
вивисекция vivisection, biotomy.
~ без наркоза sentisection.
~ под наркозом callisection. [(Vigna).
вигна bot: cow pea, black-eyed pea
~ катьянг catjang (V. catjang, Walp.)
вид bio: species.[psychovisual sensation.
видéние psych: vision, mental image,
вѝдение vision, sight, seeing.
~ как сквозь туман hazy vision.
~ предметов в жёлтом свете ophth: yellow vision, xanthopsia.
~ радужных кругов rainbow vision.
видимый visible, visual.
~ в микроскоп microscopic.
~ простым глазом macroscopic.
видовой bio: specific.
~ иммунитет specific immunity.
видоизменение modification, variety.
видообразование bio: formation of spe-
визирующий глаз dominant eye, |cies.
sighting eye.

ВИЗР [Всесоюзный Институт Защиты Растений] All-Union Institute of Plant Protection.
вика bot: vetch, tare (Vicia, L.). See also: боб, горох, фасоль.
~ венгерская Hungarian vetch (Vicia pannonica, Grantz).
~ мохнатая woollypod vetch, villous v., Russian v. (Vicia villosa, Roth.)
~ нарбоннская Narbonne vetch, French v. (Vicia narbonensis, L.)
~ опушенная = в. мохнатая.
~ пурпурная purple v. (V.atropurpurea)
~ сочевниковидная bitter vetch (Vicia orobus). [cana, Muhl)
~ степная prairie vetch (Vicia ameri-
~ французская = в. нарбоннская.
викарная менструация gyn: vicarious menstruation.
викарный bio: vicarious.[of vitamin K)
викасол pharm: vicasol (a preparation
викунья zool: vicuña (Lama vicugna).
виллёра ichth: brown darter (Villora edwinni, Hubbs & Cannon). [lis.
виллизиев круг anat: circle of Wil-
виллизиево кольцо = виллизиев круг.
вилок капусты bot: cabbage head.
вилообразно раздвоенный dichotomous
вилообразное деление (bi)furcation.
вилообразный отросток forked appendage. [(Xema sabini).
вилохвостая чайка orn: Sabine's gull
вилохвостка entom: springtail, collembola (Collembola).
~ грибная fungus s. (Achorutes armatus)
вилохвостые pl. cf. вилохвостка.
вилохвостый коршун orn: swallow-tailed kite (Elanoides furcatus).
вилочка orn: wishbone.
вилочковая железа anat: thymus.
вилт phytp: wilt.
~ кольчатый verticullum wilt.
~ хлопчатника cotton wilt.
вилтоустойчивый bot: wilt-resistant.
Вилхелми Willhelmy.
вильсонов бекас orn: Wilson's snipe (Gallinago delicata).
вильчатый bifurcated, biramous.
виндийская система Vindhyan system.
винная пальма bot: bamboo, wine palm (Raphia vinifera, Beauv.)
~ ягода bot: fig, see инжир.
винное брожение vinous fermentation.
виннокаменная кислота tartaric acid.

виннокаменнокислый магний pharm: magnesium tartrate.
винносурьмянокалиевая соль pharm: antimony and potassium tartrate.
винные дрожжи bot: wine yeast (Saccharomyces ellipsoides, S. cerevisiae).
винный камень odont: salivary calculus, dental c., tartar, argol, odontolith.
виноград bot: grape, vine (Vitis).
~ американский foxgrape, pigeon g. (V. labrusca).
~ амурский Amoor vine (V. amurensis).
~ дикий foxgrape (V. labrusca); ampelopsis.
~ мускатный bullace grape (V. rotundifolia, Michx., V. muscadina, Muscadinia rotundifolia, Small).
виноградная лоза bot: grapevine (V. vinifera).
~ улитка zool: Roman snail (Helix pomatia).
виноградные (сем.) bot: vine family (Vitaceae).
виноградный бражник = бражник виноградный.
~ сахар grape sugar, glucose.
винт для раздвигания челюстей vet: oral screw.
винторогий козел zool: goat Capra falconeri.
винтриховское изменение звука Wintrich's change of pitch.
виомицин pharm: viomycin.
виоцин = виомицин.
випера zool: asp (Vipera aspis).
вираж turn, reversal.
вирзинг bot: Savoy cabbage.
вирилизм virilism.
вирильность virility.
вирильный virile.
вирсунгов проток anat: duct of Wirsung, pancreatic duct.
вирулентность virulence.
вирулентный virulent.
вирус virus.
~ бактерий phage (Phagus).
~ бешенства vet: rabic virus.
~ курчавости верхушки phytp: curly top virus.
~ млекопитающих mammalian virus.
~ мозаичной болезни табака phytp: tobacco mosaic virus.
~ уличного бешенства street rabies virus.
вирусное заболевание viral disease.
вирусный viral, viruliferous.
~ препарат virus preparation.
вирусолог virologist.
вирусология virology.
вирусоноситель virus carrier.
вирусоносительство virus carrying.
висение вниз головой av med: hanging head downward.
вискозный viscous.
вислозадый zool: goose-croup, drooping-croup (of a horse).
вислокрылка entom: orlfly, dobson (Sialis); fishfly (Chauliodes).
вислокрылые (отр.) entom: sialids (Megaloptera).
вислоухий zool: lop-eared.
висмут bismuth, Bi.
висмутил chem: bismuthyl.
висмутовый chem: bismuthal.
висок anat: temple.
височная артерия (глубокая, поверхностная, средняя) anat: (deep, superficial, middle) temporal artery.
~ вена anat: temporal vein.
~ доля anat: temporal lobe.
~ извилина anat: temporal gyrus.
~ кость anat: temporal bone.
~ мышца anat: temporal muscle, temporalis.
~ область anat: temporal region.
~ половина сетчатки ophth: temporal retina.
~ ямка anat: fossa temporalis.
височно-мостовой temporopontile.
~ -нижнечелюстная связка anat: temporomandibular ligament.
височный отросток anat: temporal process.
вистерия bot: wisteria (Wisteria, Nutt.)
~ китайская Chinese w. (W. sinensis).
висцерального происхождения viscerogenic.
висцеральное состояние visceral condition.
висцеральный листок anat: peritoneum viscerale.
висцеро(ре)цептивное ощущение av med: visceral sensation.
висцеро(ре)цепция av med: splanchnic and visceral sense.
висячая капля hanging drop.
витализм vitalism.
виталист vitalist.
виталистический vitalistic.
витальное угнетение vital inhibition.
витальный краситель vital dye.
витамин vitamin.
~ -A-подобный vitamin A-like.
~ B_{12} vitamin B_{12}, LLD factor, cobalamin.
~ P vitamin P, permeability v., citrin.
~ проницаемости = витамин P.
витилиго derm: vitiligo, white leprosy.

виток (одностворчатой раковины) whorl (of a univalve mollusk).
виттова пляска = хорея.
вить гнездо orn: nidificate.
виться bot: climb.
витютень = голубь дикий.
вишнёвая камедь cherry gum.
~ косточка cherry stone.
~ муха = бурилка вишнёвая.
вишнёвый клей cherry gum.
~ пилильщик zool: cherry slug.
вишнеслива bot: cherry plum (Prunus cerasifera, Ehrh.)
вишня bot: cherry (Cerasus, Prunus, L.)
~ ананасная = физалис перуанский.
~ дикая wild c. (P.demissa, Walp.)
~ душистая mahaleb c., perfumed c., St.Lucie c. (P. mahaleb, L.)
~ кислая sour c., pie c. (C. austera, (P. cerasus, L.)
~ любовная Jerusalem c. (Solanum pseudocapsicum).
~ мараскиновая marasca.
~ обыкновенная common c. (Cerasus vulgaris, Mill.)
~ перуанская = физалис перуанский
~ пёсья = физалис.
~ садовая = в. обыкновенная.
~ чернильная = в. душистая.
~ шпанская = черешня.
вкалывать иголочку surg: insert the needle (into a tumor, etc.)
ВКК = врачебно-контрольная комиссия.
вкладывание ватки insertion of a plug of cotton.
включение inclusion, enclave.
~ кислоты incorporation of an acid.
~ клетки дающее жировой шарик hist: spherome.
вкожный endermic.
вколоченный перелом surg: impacted fracture.
вкус taste.
вкусный tasty, palatable, savory.
вкусовая клетка hist: taste cell.
~ луковица hist: taste bulb.
~ почка hist: taste bud, calyculus gustatorii.
вкусовой gustatory.
~ нерв anat: gustatory nerve.
~ сосочек anat: gustatory papilla.
вкусовоспринимающий psychogeusic.
вкусовые качества tastiness, palatability.
вкусозапах flavor.
влага moisture, damp(ness).
~ глазной камеры aqueous humor.

влагалище 1. anat: vagina; 2. bot: sheath, axil, vagina, ocrea (of a leaf); volva (of a mushroom).
~ початка кукурузы bot: hose.
~ хобота zool: rhynchocoel (of a nemeretine).
~ хорды (noto)chordal sheath.
влагалищная грыжа gyn: colpocele.
~ оболочка (общая) anat: vaginal tunic, tunica vaginalis (communis).
влагалищное зеркало gyn: colposcope.
~ отверстие anat: introitus, entrance to the vagina.
влагалищный лист bot: sheathing leaf.
~ наконечник gyn: vaginal nozzle.
~ отросток брюшины anat: vaginal process of the peritoneum.
~ свод anat: vaginal vault.
влажная гангрена path: moist gangrene.
~ камера moist chamber.
влажное обертывание phys-ther: wet pack, flipping with wet towels.
~ ~ под одеялами blanket bath.
влажность humidity, dampness, moistness.
влажный humid, damp, moist.
~ кашель productive cough.
~ хрип path: moist rale.
власоглав = человеческий в.
власоед = пухоед.
влево завитый sinistral.
вливание infusion.
~ в вену surg: venoclysis.
~ (физиологического раствора) поваренной соли surg: saline infusion.
вливать по капле instill.
влияние наследственности hereditation.
вменяемость legl: sanity, soundness of mind, responsibility; imputability.
вменяемый legl: sane, sound-minded, (one who can be held) responsible; imputable.
вместилище capacity, tank, reservoir, container, receptacle.
~ спор bot: sporocarp.
~ спорангиев bot: sporocarp.
вместимость capacity, hold.
вмешивающееся заболевание intercurrent disease.
внебольничная помощь out-of-hospital care.
внебрюшинный anat: extraperitoneal.
вневременность psych: timelessness.

внегрудные хрипы path: extrathoracic rales.
внедрение instillation, inculcation, implantation, embedding, intrusion; invagination, introversion, intussusception; adoption, spread, colonizing; see also введение.
~ одной кишки в другую surg: intussusception.
~ ~ (части) кишки в другую intussusception, intestine invagination.
внедриться p. a. of внедряться.
внедряться intrude, implant, invaginate; colonize.
внезапная смерть sudden death, mors subita.
внезапное проявление outbreak.
внезапный прилив крови blush, flush.
внезародышевая мезенхима extraembryonic mesenchyme.
внезародышевый целом extraembryonic coelom.
внекапсулярная плазма zool: extracapsular (cyto)plasm.
внекишечный anat: extraenteric, abenteric.
внеклеточный hist: extracellular.
внекостный ectosteal.
внематочная беременность obstet: extrauterine pregnancy.
внеобонятельный extraolfactory.
внеплодник bot: epicarp.
внеполовой extragenital.
внесение удобрения agr: fertilization.
внесердечный exocardial.
внесуставной abarticular.
внетрубный extratubal.
внеутробный extrauterine.
внечерепное ранение mil: extracranial wound.
внешнее торможение psych: unconditioned inhibition, natural inhibition.
внешнесекреторный physl: exacrinous.
внешний облик habitus, appearance.
~ покров zool: perisome.
~ слой гаструлы hist: epiblast, ectoblast.
внешняя инфекция exogenous infection.
внеядерный extranuclear.
внимание attention.
ВНИХФИ = Всесоюзный научно-исследовательсикй химико-фармацевтический институт.
внутреннее измерение anat: endometry.
внутреннее основание черепа anat: basis cranii interna.
~ паховое кольцо anat: abdominal inguinal ring.
~ торможение = условное т.
~ ухо anat: internal ear.
внутреннемыщелковый anat: entocondylar.
внутренние органы anat: viscera.
внутренний геморрой path: internal hemorrhoids.
~ зернистый слой (мозга) anat: internal granular layer.
~ кожный нерв плеча anat: medial cutaneous nerve of arm, lesser internal cutaneous nerve.
~ ~ нерв предплечья anat: medial cuteneous nerve of forearm, internal cutaneous nerve.
~ крыловой треугольник entom: subtriangle.
~ маточный зев anat: internal orifice of the uterus.
~ мыщелок anat: entocondyle.
~ ~ плеча anat: epitrochlea.
~ орган anat: viscus.
~ поворот obstet: internal version.
~ слуховой проход anat: internal acoustic meatus.
внутренности viscera, entrails, insides, guts; numbles, nombles, umbles; giblet.
внутренностный anat: visceral, splanchnic.
~ жир anat: mesenterial fat.
~ листок плевры anat: pulmonary pleura, visceral pleura.
внутренность internal part, viscus, see внутренности.
внутренняя болезнь internal disease, medical disease.
~ жевательная лопасть entom: lacinia.
~ зародышевая оболочка embr: hypoblast.
~ оболочка (сосуда, органа) anat: intima.
~ пленка (яйца) zool: inner shell membrane (of an egg).
~ прямая глазная мышца rectus oculi medialis (internus).
~ секреция physl: internal secretion, incretion.
~ цветковая чешуйка (или чешуя) bot: palea.
~ челюстная артерия anat: internal maxillary artery.

внутренняя шишка (геморроидальная) surg: internal pile.
внутри inside.
~ варолиевого моста anat: intrapontine.
~ кровяного тельца intraglobular.
~ мозговой извилины anat: intragyral.
~ предсердия anat: intraatrial.
~ сильвиевой борозды anat: entosylvian.
~ сосуда intravasal, intravascular.
~ толстых кишок intracolic.
внутриартериальный intraarterial, endarterial.
внутрибронхиальный intrabronchial.
внутрибрюшинный intraperitoneal.
внутрибрюшной intraabdominal.
внутривенное вливание intravenous infusion, venoclysis.
внутривидовой bio: intraspecific.
внутривлагалищный anat: intravaginal.
(внутри)глазное давление physl: intraocular pressure.
внутригрудное давление physl: intrathoracic pressure.
внутридолевой intralobular.
внутридольковый intralobular.
внутрижелудочковый anat: intraventricular.
внутризёренный intragranular.
внутрикапсульный intracapsular.
внутрикапсулярная плазма hist: intracapsular (cyto)plasm.
внутриклеточный intracellular.
внутриклубочковая ткань hist: intraglomerular tissue.
внутрикожный intracutaneous, endermatic, intradermal.
внутрикомплексное соединение = клешневидное соединение.
внутрикристаллический intracrystalline.
внутрилёгочный intrapulmonary, intrapulmonic.
внутриматочная беременность obstet: uterogestation, normal pregnancy.
внутриматочный anat: intrauterine, intrametrical.
~ соскоб surg: endometrial biopsy.
внутримозговой anat: intracerebral, intramedullary.
внутримолекулярный intramolecular.
внутримышечный intramuscular.
внутринервный hist: endoneurial.
внутриорбитальный intraorbital.
внутриплодник bot: endocarp.
внутриполостный intracavitary.
внутрипорошицевые мшанки zool: Kamptozoa, Calyssozoa (class of Nemathelminthes).
внутрипочечное давление physl: renal pressure.
внутрипоясничный intralumbar.
внутрипузырный intravesical.
внутриродовой bio: intrageneric.
внутриротовой intraoral.
внутрисвязочный intraligamentous.
внутрисекреторный incretory.
внутрисердечное давление physl: endocardial pressure.
внутрисердечный intracardiac.
внутристен(оч)ный intramural, intraparietal.
внутрисумочный intracapsular.
внутрисуставный interarticular.
~ перелом surg: joint fracture.
внутритканевый interstitial.
внутритрахеальный intratracheal.
внутриутробное дыхание fetal respiration.
внутриутробный intrauterine, prenatal.
~ перелом intrauterine fracture.
внутриушной entotic.
внутрихрящевой hist: intracartilaginous.
внутричерепной intracranial.
внутриягодичный intragluteal.
внуриядерный intranuclear.
внушать psych: suggest.
~ отвращение nauseate, disgust.
внушение psych: suggestion.
внушить p. a. of внушать.
вобла ichth: 1. vobla (Rutilus rutilus caspicus); 2. see плотва аральская.
вобрать p. a. of вбирать.
вовлечение матки в страдание gyn: uterine involvement.
~ плевры в страдание pleural involvement.
вогнутая линза concave lens.
вогнутость бедра twist (of a cow).
вогнутые внутрь ноги path: knock-knee, genu valgum.
вогнутый лист bot: depressed leaf.
~ спереди и выпуклый сзади procelous.
вода water, aqua.
~ горьких миндалей pharm: bitter-almonds water.
~ корицы pharm: cinnamon water.
~ перечной мяты pharm: peppermint water.

водная макрофлора larger aquatic vegetation.
водное растение water plant, aquatic plant, hydrophyte.
водорастворимый water-soluble.
водососудистая система zool: water vascular system.
водохозяйственный aquicultural.
водные организмы aquatic life.
водный aquatic, watery.
~ гриб bot: water mold.
~ обмен water metabolism.[infect:rabies.
водобоязнь path: 1. hydrophobia; 2.
водокрас американский bot: American frogbit (Limnobium spongia, Bosc.)
~ лягушечный frogbit (Hydrocharis morsus-ranae).
водокрасовые (сем.) bot: frogbit family (Hydrocharitaceae).
водолаз = ньюфаундлендская собака.
водолазный скафандр diving dress.
водолечебный balneologic.
~ курорт watering place.
водолечение balneotherapy.
водолюб water scavenger (Hydrophilidae).
водолюбы (пор.) bot: Helobiae (ord.)
водомерка entom: water measurer, water skater (Hydrometridae).
~ палочковидная marsh treader.
водонасыщенная почва aqueous soil.
водоотвод(ная труба) drain (pipe).
водоотводный ров san: drain ditch.
водоперица = уруть.
водоплавающая птица diver.
водопровод улитки anat: aqueduct of the cochlea.
водопроводная вода san: tap water.
водопрочность agr: water stability (of soils).
водорез orn: scissorbill, skimmer, (Rhynchops).
водород hydrogen, H.
водорослевая клетчатка bot: algulose.
~ растительность algae vegetation.
водорослевый bot: algal.
водоросль bot: alga; seeweed.
~ живущая в иле silt-alga.
~ обрастающая животных epizoic alga.
водосбор обыкновенный bot: garden columbine, European c., aquilegia (Aquilegia vulgaris, L.)
водосвинка zool: "water pig" (Hydrochoerus).
водоснабжение san: water supply.
воды obstet: waters, amniotic fluid; vet: fetal fluids.

водяная баня water bath.
~ блоха = дафния.
~ змея zool: aquatic snake. Cf. водяной уж, морская змея.
~ крыса zool: water rat (Arvicola amphibius).
*~ курочка orn: moor hen, European gallinule (Gallinula chloropus).
~ мозоль soft corn, soft clavus.
~ плесень bot: water mold, downy mildew (Phycomycetes).
~ постель water bed.
~ сеточка bot: water net (Hydrodictyon reticulatum, L.) alga.[vulgaris].
~ сосенка bot: horsetail (Hippurus
~ трава bot: watergrass (Paspalum, L.); see also шерстяк раскидистый.
~ черепаха zool: turtle.
~ чума = элодея.
водяника bot: crowberry (Empetrum, L.)
~ чёрная bot; black crowberry, curlewberry (E. nigrum).
водянистая влага глаза aqueous humor.
~ жидкость = в. влага глаза.
водянистость aquacity.
водянка path: dropsy; hydrops.
~ беременных hydrops gravidarum.
~ влагалища hydrocolpocele.
~ глаза hydrophthalmia, buphthalmia.
~ головы hydrocephaly.
~ жёлчного пузыря hydrops of the gallbladder.
~ живота abdominal dropsy, hydroperitoneum, ascites.
~ околосердечной сумки hydropericardium.
~ почечных лоханок hydronephrosis.
~ сердечной сорочки hydropericarditis.
~ яичка hydrocele.
водяное перо bot: water violet, featherfoil (Hottonia palustris).
водяной костюм av med: water suit.
~ ослик (ракообразное) zool: aquatic sow-bug (Asellus).
~ папоротник bot: 1. water-clover fern (Marsilea quadrifolia); 2. see селагинелла.
~ жук entom: water spider.
~ побег bot: watersprout, succulent spring, water shoot, epicormic branch.
~ пузырь bleb.
~ рак path: water cancer, see нома.
~ скорпион entom: water scorpion (Ranatra).
~ уж zool: (nonpoisonous) water snake (Natrix).

водяночный path: dropsical; hydropic.
водяные орехи (сем.) bot: water-chestnut family (Hydrocaryaceae).
~ папоротники (пор.) bot: water ferns (Hydropteridales).
~ птицы waterfowl.
~ устьица bot: water stomata.
военврач medical officer (physician or surgeon).
военная медицина military medicine; war medicine.
~ травма combat trauma, war trauma.
~ хирургия military surgery, war s.
военно-санитарная служба army medical service.
~ санитарное дело military sanitation
военный врач military physician, army medical officer, army physician, army surgeon.
~ госпиталь army hospital.
~ невроз war neurosis.
~ психоневроз war psychoneurosis.
~ тиф = сыпной т.
возбудимость physl: excitability, irritability.
возбудимый excitable, irritable.
возбудитель stimulus, causative agent, incitant.
~ болезни pathogenic agent.
~ брожения fermenter.
~ инфекции infection causative agent, virus.
возбуждать excite, stimulate, provoke.
возбуждающая причина exciting cause.
возбуждающее средство excitant, stimulant, stimulator, irritant.
возбуждающий exciting, stimulating.
~ аппетит appetizer, orectic, orexigenic.
~ сонливость somnolescent.
возбуждение excitation, stimulation.
возбужденный excited, stimulated.
возврат return.
~ болезни relapse.
~ метки zool: tag return.
~ признаков genet: filial regression.
возвратный нерв anat: recurrent laryngeal nerve.
~ теплообмен в сосудах counter-current vascular heat exchange.
~ тиф infect: relapsing fever, recurrent fever, remittent fever.
возвышение eminence, mons, prominence, protuberance; see also бугор, вырост, отросток.
~ большого пальца anat: palm prominence, thenar.
возвышение гортани = адамово яблоко.
~ пятого пальца anat: hypothenar.
воздействие influence, effect.
воздержание abstinence, continence, self-restraint.
воздерживающийся abstinent, abstemious, continent.
воздух air.
воздухо- aer(o)-, air-.
воздухобоязнь psych: aerophobia.
воздухонепроницаемая дверь av med: air-tight door.
вохдухоносная ткань zool: air-cell layer.
воздухоносный aeriferous.
~ пузырь ichth: air bladder.
~ путь anat: air-passage.
~ сосуд bot: trachea, aerenchyma.
воздушная болезнь av med: airsickness.
~ ванна air bath.
~ камера air cell.
~ клубнелуковица cormlet.
~ луковка bot: bulblet, bulbil.
~ опухоль на шее aerial goiter.
~ перспектива av med: aerial perspective.
~ подушка air pillow, a. cushion.
~ полость bot: air vessel.
~ трубка entom: trachea.
~ эмболия av med: aeroembolism.
~ ячейка anat: air cell.
воздушное лечение aerotherapeutics, aerotherapy.
воздушный корень aerial root.
~ мешок orn: air sac, pneumatocyst.
~ пузырёк air bubble; air vessel.
~ пузырь air bladder.
возможность скрещивания interbreeding opportunity.
возмужалость puberty, pubescence.
возмужалый puberal, pubescent.
возникновение уродств path: teratogeny.
возраст полового созревания puberal age.
возрастная группа age group.
возрастной состав age(-class) composition.
войлочная болезнь = чёрная парша.
вокруготовой circumoral.
вол zool: ox, bullock, castrated bull.
волдырь path: bleb, bulla, blister; wheal, pomphus, urtica.
волевая деятельность psych: willfulness, volitional activity.
волевое действие psych: volition(al action).
волевой психоз volitional psychosis.
волжанка bot: goat's beard (Aruncus, Adans).

волк zool: wolf (Canus lupus).
~ пчелиный entom: bee wolf (Philanthus triangulum).
~ -самец dog wolf.
волкодав zool: wolfdog, wolfhound.
волна возбуждения excitatory wave (in nerve).
~ -спайк wave-spike.
волнение psych: agitation, emotion, commotion, excitement.
волнистый undulatory, undulate, flexuous.
волнообразная лихорадка = бруцеллёз.
~ перепонка zool: undulating membrane.
волнообразные мышечные сокращения кишок physl: peristalsis.
волнушка bot: Lactarius torminosus, Schaff. (mushroom).
волнянка entom: tussock moth (Orgyia); moth Lymantria mathura.
~ ивовая satin moth (Stilpontia salicis)
волнянки (сем.) entom: tussock moths (Orgyidae).
"воловий язык" bot: oxtongue, see румянка.
воловик = румянка.
воловья трава = стальник.
вологлодка = румянка.
володушка bot: thoroughwax (Bupleurum, L.)
~ круглолистная hare's ear (B. rotundifolium).
волок = бабочколовка.
волокна Пуркинье anat: Purkinje fibers.
~ Ремака hist: fibers of Remak.
волокнина крови fibrin.
волокнистая опухоль fibroma; see also невринома.
~ соединительная ткань hist: fibrous connective tissue.
волокнистое строение fibration, fibrous structure.
волокнистость fibration, fibrillation, stringiness.
волокнистые связки bot: fibrous bundles.
волокнистый fibred, fibrous, fibrillar, stringy, nemaline.
~ хрящ anat: fibrocartilage, fibrous cartilage.
волокно fiber, filament; staple.
~ кальмара axon of squid.
волоконце fibril(la).
волос hair, capillus.
~ усов = вибрисса.
волосатик zool: hairworm (Gordiacea).
~ обыкновенный zool: gordian worm (Gordius aquaticus).
волосатиковые (кл.) zool: hairworms, gordian worms (Nematomorpha, Gordiacea), see нематоподобные.
волосатость pilosity. Cf. ненормальная волосатость.
волосатый pilous, hirsute, shaggy.
~ носорог zool: Rhinoceros tichorinus.
волосень coronet (of a horse).
волосистая часть головы scalp.
волосистокрылые = ручейники.
волосистость hairiness, pubescence.
волосистый hairy, hair-covered, hirsute.
волоски entom: pili.
волосковидный capilliform, piliform.
волоснец bot: 1. wild rye, lyme grass (Elymus, L.); 2. see рудбекия волосокая.
~ высокий giant rye grass (E. giganteus, Vahl.)
~ канадский Canada lyme grass (E. canadensis).
~ песчаный sea lyme grass, strand wheat (E. arenarius).
волосность capillarity.
*волосный anat: minute (blood) vessel, capillary.
волосок bot: filament, trichome, root fibril.
волосоносый piliferous.
волосохвостовые (сем.) ichth: Trichiuridae.
волосы бороды anat: hair of the beard.
~ в подмышечной впадине anat: armpit hair.
волосяная железа anat: hair gland.
~ луковица anat: hair bulb.
~ фолликула hair follicle.
волосянка = овсяница овечья.
волосяное влагалище anat: hair sheath.
волосяной мешочек anat: hair sac, saccule of a hair.
~ сосочек anat: hair papilla.
~ язык path: hairy tongue, black tongue.
волочащаяся походка path: dragging gait, paraparetic gait.
волчанка derm: lupus (exedens).
волчаночный lupoid, lupiform.
волчец bot: sow thistle, milk t. (Sonchus, L.); spiny-leaved sow t., prickly sow t. (S. asper, L.)
~ кудрявый blessed thistle (Cnicus benedictus, L.)
волчеягодник bot: daphne, common spurge olive (Daphne mezereum, L.)
~ лавролистный spurge laurel (D. laureola).
волчий аппетит wolfish appetite, canine a., lycorexia.
волчица zool: female wolf, bitch-wolf (Lupus).

"волчок" = боковой побег, водяной побег, жировой побег.
волчье лыко = волчеягодник.
волчьи ягоды = волчеягодник.
волчья пасть path: wolfjaw, cleft palate, fissured palate.
волынская лихорадка infect: Volhynia fever, trench fever.
вольвокс bot: Volvox (alga).
вольвоксовые (пор.) bot: Volvocales order (algae).
вольная пастьба agr: continuous grazing.
~ случка zool: wild pairing.
вольнопрактикующий врач private practicing physician.
вольфов проток embr: Wolffian duct, mesonephric duct.
~ ход = вольфов проток.
вольфово тело embr: Wolffian body, primordial kidney.
вольфрам tungsten, W.
вольффия bot: water meal, rootless duckweed (Wolffia).
волютин bot: volutin (algal substance).
воля psych: will, volition.
~ к работе psych: will to do work.
вомбат zool: wombat (Phascolomys).
вонючая смола asafetida.
вонючий stinking, fetid, malodorous.
вонючка zool: stinker, see скунс.
вооруженный цепень helm: armed tapeworm, pork tapeworm (Taenia solium).
ворвань blubber oil.
"воркующий" шум (сердца) "dove-coo" (cardiac) murmur.
воробей orn: sparrow (Passer).
~ домашний orn: house sparrow, common s. (Passer domesticus).
~ -самец cock s.
~ -самка hen s.
воробейник bot: pigeonweed (Lithospermum arvense, L.)
~ аптечный gromwell (L. officinale).
воробьиные orn: passerines (Passeres).
воробьиный passerine.
ворон orn: raven (Corvus corax).
ворона orn: crow (Corvus).
воронец bot: baneberry, necklaceweed cohosh (Actaea, L.)
~ колосистый baneberry (A. spicata).
вороний глаз четырёхлистный bot: herb Paris, four-leaved grass (Paris quadrifolia, L.)
вороника = водяника.
ворониковые (сем.) bot: crowberry family (Empetraceae).
Воронин Woronin, Wor.
воронка funnel; zool: infundibulum.
воронкообразная грудь anat: foveated chest, funnel chest.
воронкообразный funnel-shaped, bell-mouthed, infundibuliform.
~ орган zool: infundibulum.
~ цветок bot: funnel-shaped flower.
воронок = ласточка городская.
ворота anat: hilus, hilum, porta; gate.
~ инфекции infection atrium, i. gate.
~ органа anat: hilus.
~ печени anat: porta of the liver.
~ почки anat: hilus renalis.
воротная вена anat: portal vein.
воротник collar.
воротничковая жгутиковая клетка zool: collared flagellate cell.
воротничковые жгутиковые (сем.) choanoflagellates (Craspedomonadidae).
воротничковый рябчик orn: ruffled grouse (Bonasa umbellus).
воротничок collar.
воротный anat: hilar, portal.
ворс naps.
ворсинка nap, lint, villus, setule.
ворсинчатая оболочка зародыша zool: chorion.
ворсинчатость = ворсистость.
ворсинчатый = ворсистый.
ворсистость nappiness, villosity, etc., see ворсистый.
ворсистый nappy, linty, villiferous, setulose, tomentose, woolly, fluffy.
ворсовальная шишка = ворсянка сукновальная.
ворсянка bot: teasel (Dipsacus, L.)
~ сукновальная fuller's teasel, teasel bur (D. fullonum).
ворсянковые (сем.) bot: teasel family (Dipsacaceae).
воск wax; beewax.
восковая пальма bot: wax palm (Copernicia cerifera; Ceroxylon andicola).
~ чашечка = восковница.
восковидная бледность waxy pallor.
~ гибкость psych: flexibilitas cerea.
восковидный waxy, ceraceous.
~ цилиндр mcscop: waxy cast.
восковица = восковник.
восковник bot: 1. wax myrtle, candleberry, bayberry (Myrica cerifera, L.); sweet gale, "meadow fern", (M. gale); 2. see восковое дерево.
восковниковые (сем.) bot: wax-myrtle family, sweet-gale family (Myricaceae).

восковница (рабочей пчелы) entom: wax-yielding membrane, w.-y. mirrors.
восковобледный path: tallowfaced.
восковое дерево bot: wax plant (Hoya carnosa, R. Br.)
*восковой waxy, cereous.
~ налёт bot: powdery coating, bloom.
восконосная пальма = карнауба.
воскообразный = восковидный.
воскоотделительные железы entom: wax glands (of bees).
воспаление path: inflammation.
~ аорты aortitis.
~ апоневроза aponeurositis.
~ артерии arteritis.
~ брюшины peritonitis.
~ вен vein inflammation, phlebitis.
*~ венчика копыта vet: coronary frog-band.
~ верхушки apicitis.
~ внутреннего уха otitis interna.
~ внутренней оболочки артерии endarteritis.
~ ~ оболочки матки endometritis, inflammation of the endometrium.
~ ~ оболочки сердца endocarditis, inflammation of the endocardium.
~ вымени vet: inflammation of the udder, gerget.
~ глаза ophthalmia.
~ головного мозга encephalitis, inflammation of the brain.
~ дёсен gingivitis, inflammation of gingiva.
~ жёлчного пузыря cholecystitis.
~ заднего прохода sphincteritis, anus inflammation.
~ зева pharingitis.
~ кишок enteritis.
~ костного мозга osteomyelitis, inflammation of marrow.
~ краев века ophth: blepharitis.
~ крайней плоти posthitis.
~ лёгких с охватом доли lobar pneumonia.
~ ~ у свиней vet: swine plague.
~ лимфатических узлов lymphadenitis, inflammation of lymph nodes.
~ ~ узлов у бронхов bronchoadenitis.
~ матки gyn: metritis.
~ мозговых оболочек meningitis.
~ ~ покровов (у лошадей) vet: blind staggers.
~ мочевого пузыря cystitis, inflammation of the urinary bladder.
~ надкостницы periostitis.
~ надпочечных желез adrenalitis.

воспаление наружного уха otitis externa.
~ наружной оболочки бронха peribronchitis.
~ околосердечной сумки pericarditis, inflammation of the pericardium.
~ паутинной оболочки мозга arachnoiditis.
~ печени hepatitis, inflammation of the liver.
~ поджелудочной железы pancreatitis.
~ позвонков spondylitis, inflammation of vertebrae.
~ почек nephritis.
~ почечных клубочков glomerular inflammation.
~ ~ лоханок pyelitis.
~ придатка яичка epididymitis.
~ придатков матки gyn: adnexitis.
~ пупка vet: navel ill.
~ сальных желез acne.
~ сердечной мышцы myocarditis, inflammation of the myocardium.
~ серого вещества спинного мозга poliomyelitis.
~ сетчатки ophth: retinitis, retinal inflammation.
~ скелетных мышц myositis.
~ слизистой оболочки catarrh.
~ ~ оболочки рта stomatitis.
~ сосудистой оболочки choroiditis.
~ спинного мозга myelitis, inflammation of the spinal cord.
~ среднего уха otitis media, inflammation of the middle ear.
~ сустава arthritis.
~ тазобедренного сустава coxitis, hip-joint inflammation.
~ толстой кишки colitis, inflammation of the colon.
~ угла глаза canthitis.
~ яичника oöphoritis.
воспаленный path: inflamed.
воспалительная припухлость path: inflammatory swelling.
воспалиться p. a. of воспаляться.
воспаляться path: inflame.
воспитательная психотерапия no-restraint system.
восполнить население bio: repopulate.
восприимчивость susceptibility, receptivity.
~ к опылению bot: receptivity.
восприимчивый susceptible, receptive.
восприниматель receptor.
воспринимать perceive.

воспринимающий орган anat: receptor.
воспринять p.a. of воспринимать.
восприятие perception, esthesia.
~ глубины av med: depth perception.
~ положения предметов в пространстве av med: perception of positions of objects in space.
~ света light perception.
~ цвета color perception.
воспроизведение reproduction.
восстанавливающий энергию bio: anakinetic.
восстановление просвета repatency.
~ функции functional restoration.
восточная язва = пендинка.
востробрюшка ichth: Hemiculter.
восходящая аорта anat: ascending aorta.
~ артерия глотки anat: ascending pharyngeal artery.
~ ободочная кишка anat: ascending colon.
восходящий ток physl: ascending current.
восьмилепестной bot: octapetalous.
восьмилучевой коралл zool: sea whip (Muricea).
восьмилучевые кораллы (подкл.) zool: alcyonarian polyps (Alcyonaria, Octocorallia).
восьминогие моллюски (отр.) zool: eight-armed millusks (Octopoda).
восьмиобразная повязка figure-8 bandage.
восьмиобразный пессарий gyn: figure-8 pessary.
~ шов surg: transfixion suture, figure-of-8-suture.
восьмитычиночный цветок bot: octandrous flower.
вошерия bot: Vaucheria (algae).
вошь entom: 1. louse; 2. crawler.
~ воловья = вошь свиней.
~ головная head louse (Pediculus capitis).
~ гороховая pea louse (Nectarophora destructor).
~ долгоносая рогатого скота long-nosed ox louse (Haematopinus vituli).
~ животных biting louse (Trichodectes scalaris).
~ карповая carp-louse (Argulus foliaceus).
~ книжная book louse (Troctes divinatorius).
~ лобковая crab louse (Phthirius pubis).
вошь платяная body louse (Pediculus vestimenti, P. corporis).
~ птичья bird's louse (Mallophaga).
~ пчелиная bee's louse (Braula coeca, Nitzsch.)
~ рыбья fishlouse (Caligus), see рыбьи вши.
*~ свиней swine louse (Hoematorinus urius).
~ травяная Anaplura.
вощаная бумага waxed paper, oilpaper.
вощаной = восковой.
~ спуск pharm: cerate.
впадать в бессознательное состояние lapse into unconsciousness.
впадение в детство puerilism, degenerative psychosis.
впадина anat: depression; socket.
~ на грудине path: sternal concavity.
впалая грудь path: funnel breast.
впалый sunken, hollow (cheek, etc.)
впасть p.a. of впадать.
впечатление impression.
~ рельефности ophth: impression of relief.
впитать p.a. of впитывать.
впитывать imbibe, absorb, take up, take in.
вполне развитый fully-developed.
вправимая грыжа surg: reducible hernia, free hernia.
вправить p.a. of. вправлять.
вправление surg: reposition, reduction, redressment.
~ вывиха вытяжением и противовытяжением distraction.
вправленный вывих surg: reduced dislocation.
вправлять surg: reposition, reduce, redress.
впрыскивание injection.
впрыскивать inject.
впускание капель instillation.
впускать капли instill.
впячение = ротовое впячение.
впячивание anat: invagination.
врановые (сем.) orn: corvine family (Corvidae).
врастание ingrowth, intussusception.
~ ногтя path: ingrowing of a nail, acronyx.
врастающий ноготь path: ingrowing nail, unguis incarnatus.
врасщеп = прививка врасщеп.
врач physician (also surgeon).
~ -диететик dietarian.
~ лётной службы av med: flight surgeon.
~ -специалист medical specialist (physician).
~ части mil: unit surgeon.

врачебная комиссия mil: medical commission.
~ наука medicine.
врачебное наблюдение medical supervision.
врачебно-контрольная комиссия medical control commission.
~ -трудовая экспертная комиссия psych: medical-and-labor examination c.
вращательная радиотерапия rotation radiotherapy.
вращательное движение rotatory motion, gyration.
вращающаяся пробирка lab: roller tube.
вращающееся кресло turning chair.
вращение rotation, turning, gyration.
~ влево sinistrogyration.
~ внутрь internal rotation.
~ вправо dextrogyration.
~ кверху ophth: sursumversion.
~ кнаружи external rotation.
вред от голодания hunger injury.
вредитель agr: blight, pest, destructive insect, crop-eater.
~ растений blight, pest, blast.
вредное биологическое действие rad: noxious biological effect, biological damage.
~ вещество tox: injurious substance, noxious s.
вредные воздействия полета av med: deleterious effects of flight.
вредный harmful, injurious, noxious, deleterious, unwholesome.
~ для здоровья insalubrious.
временная искусственная нога orthop: pillion.
~ пломба odont: temporary filling, provisional filling.
~ слепота temporary blindness, spell of blindness.
временное облегчение remittence, temporary abatement of symptoms.
~ ослабевание симптомов = временное облегчение.
временные жабры zool: caducibranchiate
временный зуб temporary tooth.
время активного сознания av med: time of useful consciousness.
~ выборочной реакции av med: discrimination reaction time.
~ вызывающее заболевание rad: induction time.
~ вымирания 50-и процентов rad: median lethal time, MLT.
~ задержки дыхания breath-holding time.
~ лёта entom: flight time.
~ полувыведения rad: biological halflife.
время потери сознания av med: time of unconsciousness.
~ реакции reaction time.
~ свертывания hem: clotting time.
~ сознания av med: time of consciousness.
~ цветения bot: blooming period.
врожденная высотная устойчивость av med: inherent altitude tolerance.
~ неспособность congenital inability.
~ способность inherent ability.
~ устойчивость av med: inherent tolerance.
врожденное отсутствие фаланг(и) path: hypophalangism.
~ ~ пигмента path: albinism.
~ укорочение уздечки языка path: ankyloglossia, tongue-tie.
~ уродство congenital malformation.
врожденный congenital, inherent, innate, inborn, inbred.
~ вывих surg: congenital dislocation.
~ иммунитет congenital immunity.
~ птоз ophth: congenital ptosis.
~ сифилис ven: congenital syphilis, prenatal s.
123 вросший ноготь path: ingrowing nail.
всаливание salting-in.
всасываемость absorbability.
всасываемый absorbable.
всасывание absorption, suction, imbibition, sucking up, taking in.
~ в кишечнике intestinal a.
~ воды water a.
~ питательных веществ nutritive a.
~ через кожу cutaneous a.
всасывающая способность absorption capacity, a. power.
всасывающее средство pharm: absorbent.
всасывающий absorbing, absorptive.
всеведущий omniscient.
всемогущество omnipotence.
всесветное распространение cosmopolitanism.
всесветный cosmopolitan.
Всесоюзная академия с.-х. наук All-Union Academy of Agricultural Sciences.
Всесоюзный научно-исследовательский химико-фармацевтический институт All-Union Scientific Research Chemical and Pharmaceutieal Institute.
всеядное животное omnivore.
всеядный omnivorous.

вскармливание ped: feeding, nourishing.
вскармливать грудью ped: nurse (at the breast), suckle.
вскипание жидкостей организма av med: boiling of the body fluids.
вскипятить p. a. of кипятить.
вскормить p. a. of вскармливать.
вскрывать surg: cut open, open, cut up, incise, lance.
~ ланцетом lance.
вскрытие surg: autopsy; opening (of a vein, etc.)
~ артерии surg: arteriotomy, opening of an artery.
~ вены проколом surg: venipuncture.
~ ~ разрезом surg: venesection.
~ живота surg: celiotomy, opening of the abdominal cavity.
~ нарыва surg: incision of an abscess.
~ сустава surg: incision into a joint, arthrotomy.
~ цветков bot: tripping of flowers.
~ черепа surg: cephalotomy.
вскрытый цветок bot: tripped flower.
вскрыть p. a. of вскрывать.
вспаивать (о животных) agr: raise, breed, rear (animals).
всплывание chem: flotation.
вспоить p. a. of вспаивать.
вспотеть p. a. of потеть.
вспухание inflation, see also опухание.
вспучивание flatulence, etc., see вздутие; bulging, swelling, intumescence, buckling.
вспыльчивый short-tempered, quick-t.
вспыхивать flash, scintillate, flicker, blink.
вспыхнуть p.a. of вспыхивать.
вспышка аффективного возбуждения psych: emotional outburst.
~ (болезни) flareup (of a disease), outbreak, outburst.
~ гнева psych: tantrum, fit of temper.
~ моторного возбуждения motor outburst.
~ эпидемии и т.п. outbreak of an epidemic, etc.
вставлять между... intercalate.
вставочное кольцо = вставочный ободок.
вставочный ободок bot: intercalary band (of diatoms).
~ рост bot: intercalary growth.
встречаемость frequency of occurrence.
встречающийся в кале zool: coprozoic (protozoans).
встряхивание shaking, shake-up, succussion.
встряхивать shake up, scramble.
встряхнуть p. a. of встряхивать.

всход bot: sprout, germination.
всходить bot: germinate, sprout.
всхожесть bot: germination.
всхожий bot: germinative.
втереть p. a. of втирать.
втирание inunction, rubbing in.
~ (жидкой) мази embrocation.
втирать rub in, embrocate.
вторая пара крыльев entom: second wings.
~ рудиментарная семядоля bot: epiblast, ectoblast.
~ сигнальная система second signaling system (Pavlovian cortical system in man associated with thinking and speaking). Cf. первая сигн. сист.
вторжение сорняков bot agr: weed encroachment.
вторичная бактериальная культура на разводке lab: subculture.
~ ветка bot: secondary branch.
~ инфекция secondary infection, consecutive infection.
~ катаракта ophth: secondary cataract, aftercataract.
~ обертка соцветия bot: involucel.
~ ось bot: rhachilla.
~ поимка zool: recapture, recatch.
~ полость тела c(o)elom.
~ причина secondary cause.
~ сегментация annulation.
~ чешуйка bot: second glume.
вторично разветвляющийся subbranching, subdichotomous.
вторичное зарастание regrowth.
~ ребро entom: secondary keel.
вторичнопокровные (подкл.) bot: Metachlamydeae.
вторичноротые (подразд.) zool: Deuterostomia.
вторичные паразиты hyperparasites.
~ половые признаки secondary sexual characters.
вторичный зонтик bot: umbellet.
~ киль entom: secondary keel.
~ колос bot: spikelet.
~ лист bot: pinna.
~ прицветник bot: bractlet.
~ шок secondary shock.
второй отдел желудка zool: reticulum, see сетка.
~ тон аорты aortic second sound.
~ шейный позвонок anat: second cervical vertebra, epistopheus, axis.
второстепенный симптом minor symptom.

ВТЭК = врачебно-трудовая экспертная комиссия.
втягивающий мускул retractor muscle.
втяжение retraction, drawing back.
втяжной retractile.
втянутость барабанной перепонки otolar: retraction of tympanic membrane
втянутые бока zool: tucked flanks.
втянутый живот retracted belly.
вульва zool: vulva.
вход entrance, ostium; anat: aditus, introitus.
~ в гортань anat: aditus laryngis.
~ в желудок anat: cardia.
входное отверстие раневого канала surg: entry wound.
входные ворота portal of entry, site of entry.
вши (отр.) pl.of вошь, entom: true lice (Anolpura).
вшивая трава = вшивица.
вшивица bot: lousewort (Pedicularis, L.)
~ американская = мытник американский.
вшивость lousiness, pediculosis.
вшивый lousy, pediculous.
выбеливание растений bot: etiolation, blanching of plants.
выборочная реакция av med: selective response, discrimination reaction, choice reaction.
~ стерильность intersterility.
выбрасывание кисти (при цветении) bot: tasseling.
~ кресла av med: seat ejection.
~ султана = в. кисти.
выбрасывать стрелку bot: spear, bolt, shoot out, beat.
выбрасывающееся кресло av med: ejection seat.
выбрасывающий семяпроток anat: ejaculatory duct.
выброс стрелки cf. выбрасывать стрелку.
выбросить p.a. of выбрасывать.
выбухание = выпячивание.
~ барабанной перепонки path: bulging of the drum.
~ пупка path: exumbilication.
вываривать 1. seethe, boil; 2. thicken, inspissate, condense; extract.
выварить p.a. of вываривать.
выведение breeding, hatching.
~ матки в нормальное положение = выправление матки.
~ породы agr: breeding.
выведенный bred, hatched.
вывернутый everted; path: ectropic; bot: resupinate.
вывести p. a. of выводить.
выветривание weathering.
выветрившийся weatherworn.
вывих sprain, dislocation, luxation, wrench, abarticulation, snap.
~ нижней челюсти jaw fall.
~ плеча shoulder slip.
вывихнуть surg: sprain, dislocate, luxate, wrench.
выводить agr: breed, raise, hatch, incubate.
выводковая камера zool: brood case.
~ сумка zool: brood pouch.
выводной exhalent, efferent.
~ проток anat: efferent duct; excretory duct.
~ ~ молочной железы lactiferous duct.
~ ~ почки zool: kidney duct (in amphibians).
~ свищ odont: evacuating sinus.
выводок zool: brood, hatch.
выводящий канал anat: excretory duct.
выворачивание век ophth: eversion of the eyelid, ectropionization.
~ стрекательной нити zool: eversion of the stinging thread.
выворачивать веко ophth: evert the eyelid, ectropionize.
выворот eversion, ectropion, extroversion, evagination, outpouching.
~ века ophth: ectropion.
~ губы path: eversion of the lip, eclabium.
выгребная яма san: cesspool.
выдавливание pressing out, expression, squeezing (out), extrusion.
~ сальных пробок derm: comedo expression.
~ трахоматозных зерен ophthalmoxysis, scrattage.
выдавливать (икру и молоки) ichth: strip.
выдалбливать surg: hollow out, chisel out.
выдвижной protractile, protrusible.
выделение 1. secretion, discharge; excretion; 2. isolation, isolating, separation; singling out. Cf. отделение.
~ белка в моче path: albuminuria.
~ гноя с мочёй path: pyuria.
~ железы physl: secretion.
~ из глаза sebum palpebrale.
~ кислорода oxygen evolving.
~ крови через кишечник melena.
~ мокроты expectoration.
~ молока грудной железой lactation.
~ пластинчатыми разводками mcbio: isolation by plating.

выделение сахара с мочой path: glycosuria.
~ семени с мочой path: seminuria.
~ слюны physl: salivation.
~ соков bot: secernment.
~ через кишечник physl: intestinal elimination.
~ ~ почки physl: renal elimination.
выделения discharge; excreta.
~ из матки gyn: uterine discharge.
~ тлей и щитовок entom: honey-dew.
выделительная клетка zool: renette.
~ система excretory system.
выделить p.a. of выделять.
выделять 1. secrete, discharge; excrete; 2. isolate, separate; single out.
~ сок bot: secern, secret (juice, sap).
выделяющий ядовитую слюну zool: venomosalivary.
выдергивание диафрагмального нерва surg: avulsion of the phrenic nerve, phrenicoexeresis.
выдерживать без пищи starve.
выдолбить p. a. of выдалбливать.
выдох expiration, exhalation.
~ в средней его части midexpiratory flow.
выдохнуть p. a. of выдыхать.
выдра zool: otter (Euchydris, Lutra).
выдыхаемый воздух expired air.
выдыхание breathing forth, expiration.
выдыхательный клапан av med: expiratory valve.
выдыхать breathe forth, exhale.
выедать пластинку листа bot entom: skeletonize the leaf.
выезд на место field trip.
выездная лекция guest lecture.
выемка 1. anat: diverticulum, pouch; hilus; 2. recess, pit, excavation.
выемчатокрылые cf.моли.
выёмчатый sinuate, dedalous, emarginate.
выжечь p. a. of выжигать.
выживаемость bio: percentage survival, survival rate.
выживание survival.
~ наиболее приспособленных survival of the fittest.
выживать survive.
выжигание burning out, cauterization.
выжигать burn out, cauterize.
выжидательная терапия expectant treatment, temporization.
выжимание = выдавливание.
выжить p. a. of выживать.
вызванный кокками coccigenic.
вызванный ожогом ambustial.
~ паразитами parasitogenic.
~ склерозом sclerogenous.
вызвать p. a. of вызывать.
выздоравливать recover, recuperate, convalesce.
выздоравливающий recovering, recuperating, convalescent.
выздороветь p. a. of выздоравливать.
выздоровление recovery, recuperation, convalescence, anastasis.
вызов к больному house call.
вызревание agr bot: ripening, maturing.
вызревающая клетка hist: maturing cell.
вызывать provoke, cause, give rise, produce.
~ опухоль tumefy, cause to swell.
~ послабление mildly purge.
~ тошноту nauseate.
вызывающий аборт obstet: abortient, abortifacient, ecbolic.
~ альбуминурию path: albuminuretic.
~ астму path: asthmogenic.
~ бессонницу path: agrypnotic.
~ бешенство psych: rabific.
~ боль dolorogenic.
~ бредpsych: delirifacient, deliriant.
~ брожение fermentative.
~ водянку path: hydropigenous.
~ воспаление path: causing inflammation, phlogogenic.
~ гниение putrifactive.
~ диабет path: diabetogenic.
~ желтуху path: icterogenic.
~ зоб path: goitrogenic.
~ зуд urticant.
~ иммунитет immunogenic, immunifacient.
~ истерию hysterogenic, hysterogenous.
~ кашель cough-exciting.
~ кровотечение path: hemorrhagenic.
~ легкое послабление mildly purgative, eccoprotic.
~ летаргию path: lethargogenic.
~ лихорадку path: febrifacient.
~ нагноение path: suppurant, suppurative.
~ невралгическую боль algogenic.
~ некроз в опухоли tumor-nectrotizing.
~ ожирение path: steatogenous.
~ опорожнение pharm: evacuant.
~ ороговение keratogenous.
~ осаждение chem: precipitant.
~ паралич paralyzant.
~ пеллагру path: pellagragenic.
~ плеврит path: pleuritogenous.

вызывающий половое возбуждение erogenous, erogenic.
~ развитие опухоли path: oncogenous.
~ рассасывание кости path: ossifluent
~ расслабление relaxant.
~ расширение зрачка ophth: mydriatic.
~ рвоту emetic, vomitive.
~ ~ и понос emetocathartic.
~ рефлекс physl: reflexogenic.
~ сонливость somnolescent.
~ ссадины abrasive.
~ сужение зрачков ophth: myotic.
~ ~ сосудов vasoconstrictive.
~ сыпной тиф infect: typhogenic.
~ тошноту nauseant, qualmish.
~ уремию path: uremigenic.
~ чихание sternutatory.
~ экзему derm: eczemogenous.
~ энцефалит path: encephalitogenic.
~ эпилепсию neur: epileptogenic.
выйная линия (верхняя, нижняя) anat: nuchal line (superior, inferior).
~ связка nuchal ligament.
выйти p. a. of выходить.
выкачать p. a. of выкачивать.
выкачивание pumping out.
выкачивать pump out.
выкидывать стрелку = выбрасывать стрелку.
выкидыш 1. obstet: miscarried fetus; miscarriage; 2. zool: slink, warp.
~ (нежизнеспособного плода) obstet: immature delivery, miscarriage.
выкинуть p. a. of выкидывать.
выкладывать = холостить.
выклёвываться orn: hatch, exclude.
выклюнуться p. a. of выклёвываться.
выколачивать beat, percuss.
выколашивание bot: earing.
выколашиваться bot: come into ear.
выколоситься p. a. of выколашиваться.
выколотить p. a. of выколачивать.
выкупать p. a. of купать.
вылавливание fishing out.
вылет entom: emergence.
вылечивать cure (completely, thoroughly), heal up.
вылечить p. a. of вылечивать.
вылов caught.
выложенный agr zool: castrated, gelded.
~ баран gelded ram, wether.
вылупившийся orn: hatched, emerged.
вылупиться p. a. of вылупляться.
вылупление orn: hatching, emergence.
вылупляться orn: hatch, emerge, escape.
вылущать = вылущивать.
вылущение = вылущивание.
вылущивание 1. surg: enucleation, skinning, flaying; 2. bot: dehusking, shelling out.
вылущивать 1. surg: enucleate, skin, flay; 2. bot: dehusk, shell out.
вылущить p. a. of вылущать, вылущивать.
вымачивание retting, soaking.
вымереть p.a. of вымирать.
вымерзание winterkilling (of plants).
вымерзать winterkill.
вымерзнуть p. a. of вымерзать.
вымерший extinct.
выметать p. a. of вымётывать.
вымётывать (икру) ichth: cast out (eggs)
вымирать die out, become extinct.
вымораживание freezing thoroughly.
вымораживать freeze thoroughly.
выморозить p. a. of вымораживать.
вымывание из крови углекислоты av med: washing of carbon dioxide out of the blood.
~ кислорода из крови av med: washing of oxygen out of the blood.
вымыть p. a. of мыть.
вымышленная история psych: confabulation.
вымя zool: udder.
вынашивать obstet: to be pregnant.
вынесенные (на берег) водоросли bot: wrack.
вынести p. a. of выносить.
вынимание кишок = потрошение.
выносить endure, bear, take, tolerate.
выносить p. a. of вынашивать.
выносливое растение hardy plant.
выносливость endurance, stamina, hardiness, tolerance, toleration.
выносливый hardy, durable.
выносящий канал zool: excurrent opening, osculum (in sponges).
~ канальец (яичка) anat: efferent ductule.
~ проток anat: efferent duct.
вынужденное движение neur: forced movement.
вынырнуть reemerge.
выпадать в виде хлопьев flocculate, flake.
выпадение falling (down), descent, descensus, prolapse, procidentia; shedding.
~ бровей derm: eyebrow shedding.
~ влагалища vet: falling of the vagina.
~ матки gyn: uterine prolapse.
~ прямой кишки path: rectal prolapse, prolapsus ani.

выпадение пуповины obstet: prolapse of the umbilical cord.
~ **ресниц** ophth: shedding of cilia, deplumation, ptilosis.
~ **ручки плода** obstet: arm procidentia, arm prolapse, presenting arm.
выпалывание agr bot: weeding.
выпаривание evaporation, vaporization.
выпаривать evaporate, vaporize.
выпаритель vaporizer.
выпарительная чашка lab: evaporation bowl.
выпарительный змеевик vaporizer coil.
выпарить p. a. of **выпаривать.**
выпереть p. a. of **выпирать.**
выпирать из орбиты (о глазах) shove from the orbits (of eyes).
выписка из больницы discharge from a hospital.
выплаживание entom: breeding.
выплёвывать spit out.
выплод entom: breeding.
выплюнуть p. a. of **выплёвывать.**
выполаскивать rinse out, flush.
"выполняющая" чечевичку ткань bot: complementary tissue.
выполоскать p. a. of **выполаскивать.**
выпот path: exudate, effusion.
выпотевание exudation.
выпотевать exude, exudate.
выпотный exudative.
~ **плеврит** int: serous pleurisy.
выпотрошить p. a. of **потрошить.**
выправление матки gyn: basculation, replacing a retroverted uterus.
выпревание (растений) bot: damping out.
выпрямитель anat: erector (muscle).
выпрямление straightening out, extension.
выпрямляющая волос мышца anat: arrectores pilorum.
выпрямляющий мускул = **выпрямитель.**
выпуклость tumidity; bulla; convexity, camber, crowning, bulge.
выпуклый tumid; convex.
выпуск discharge; tapping; planting (of larval fish
выпускание жидкости = **парацентез.**
~ **мочи посредством катетера** urol: catheter drainage.
выпускать жидкость surg: tap.
~ **кровь** surg: bleed.
выпускная труб(к)а discharge tube, d. tubing.
выпустить p. a. of **выпускать.**
выпучивание = **вспучивание.**

выпь orn: bittern (Botaurus, Ixobrychus, etc.)
~ **американская** American b. (B. lentiginosus).
выпяченная перепонка bulging membrane.
выпячивание evagination, protrusion, bulging (out), protuberance, outpouching.
~ **внутренностей через брюшную стенку** path: eventration.
~ **глаз(ного яблока)** path: exophthalmos, ophthalmoptosis.
выработка навыков habit formation.
выравнивание equalization.
~ **отправлений** physl: compensation.
выражение лица при болезни disease countenance.
~ **тревоги** anxious expression.
выраженная мания psych: hypermania.
выраженность degree of evidence, of symptoms, manifestation.
~ **акцента** degree of accentuation.
~ **разницы изображений** ophth: amount of difference in the (retinal) images.
выраженный одним симптомом monosymptomatic.
~ **стоматит** path: marked stomatitis.
~ **тремор** path: marked tremor, pronounced tremor.
выращивание bot: raising, growing.
~ **бактерий** bacterial cultivation.
~ **в термостате** incubation.
выращивать raise, grow, cultivate; incubate.
вырвать p. a. of **рвать.**
вырезание surg: excision.
вырезать surg: excise.
вырезать p. a. of **вырезать.**
вырезка cut, incisure, cleft, notch, crena, recess, pit, hilus.
~ **вертлужной впадины** anat: acetabular notch.
вырезуб ichth: roach Rutilus frisii.
вырезывание surg: excision.
~ **почек** bot: disbudding.
выродившийся degenerate(d), deteriorated, dysgenic.
выродиться p. a. of **вырождаться.**
вырождаться degenerate.
вырождающийся degenerating, dysgenic.
~ **вид** degenerate species.
вырождение degeneration.
~ **народа** cacogenics, dysgenics.
вырост excrescence, evagination, apophysis, outgrouth; diverticulum; see also бугор, возвышение, отросток
выростить p. a. of **выращивать.**

вырывание surg: avulsion.
высаливание salting-out.
высверливание drilling.
высвобождение disentanglement, disengagement, release, liberation.
высев seeding, sowing, dissemination.
выселение (клеток) hist: emigration (of cells).
высидеть p. a. of высиживать.
высиженный zool: hatched, incubated.
высиживание orn: hatching, incubation.
высиживать orn: hatch, brood, incubate.
выскабливание surg: 1. curettage, scraping away, abrasion; 2. abortion.
~ ложкой scooping (out), removal by spoon.
~ матки gyn: uterine curettage.
выскабливать surg: 1. curet, scrape (away); 2. make abortion, abrade.
~ ложкой scoop out, remove by spoon.
выскоблить p. a. of выскабливать.
выслушать p. a. of выслушивать.
выслушивание auscultation.
~ стетоскопом mediate auscultation.
выслушивать auscult(ate).
высокая клизма high enema.
высокий bot: taller (elatior).
высокое давление high pressure.
~ содержание белка high protein content.
~ ~ жира high fat content.
высококалорийный high-caloric.
высокорослый bot: tall-growing.
высокоствольный bot: long-boled, standard (tree).
высокотоксичный highly toxic.
высота (тела) при сидячем положении height-sitting.
~ ~ при стоячем положении height-standing.
высотная акклиматизация av med: altitude acclimatization.
~ болезнь av med: altitude sickness.
~ устойчивость av med: altitude tolerance
высотное косоглазие = вертикальное косоглазие.
высотный полет av med: high-altitude flight.
выстилка lining.
выстланный хитином chitin-lined.
выстукивание percussion, tapping.
выстукивать percuss, tap.
выступ prominence, see возвышение.
~ на рубчике (семени) bot: caruncle, strophiole.
выступание ключицы prominence of the clavicle.
~ поверхностных сосудов path: prominence of superficial (blood) vessels.
выступательное движение (плода) obstet: expulsion movement.
выступать наружу (о сыпи) erupt.
выступить p.a. of выступать.
выступающие лопатки path: winged scapulae.
выступление крови (из сосудов) path: blood extravasation.
высунутый язык protruded tongue.
высушивание drying (off), desiccation, exsiccation.
высушивающий dessiccant, exsiccant, exsiccative.
высыпание eruption, efflorescence, exanthem(a), rash, crop.
высыпать erupt, break out, effloresce (of rash).
высыпать p. a. of высыпать.
высыпь = высыпание
~ изнутри enanthem(a).
высыхание drying (off), desiccation, exsiccation.
высшая психическая функция higher mental function.
высшее животное higher animal.
~ млекопитающее zool: placental monodelphian, eutherian.
~ ракообразное zool: malacostracan.
~ растение higher plant.
высшие звери zool: higher mammals (Eutheria), see плацентарные.
~ раки zool: malocostracans (subclass Malacostraca).
~ ракообразные (подкл.) zool: higher crustaceans: lobsters, crayfishes, crabs, etc. (Malacostraca).
высший организм higher organism.
выталкивание ejection, expulsion.
выталкивающее движение expulsive movement, forcing out movement.
вытаскивать (зуб) draw (the tooth).
вытащить p. a. of вытаскивать.
вытеснение displacement, crowding out.
вытирание wiping dry, rubbing dry.
вытирать тампоном surg: swab out, dab up.
вытравить p. a. of вытравлять.
вытравление etching.
вытравлять etch.
вытягивать stretch, extend.
вытягивающая ручная шина surg: extension arm splint.
вытяжение stretching, extension, traction.
~ нерва nerve stretching, neurectasy.

вытяжение ноги surg: leg traction.
вытяжка 1. bio chem: extract(ion); 2. see вытяжение.
вытянутые пальцы рук extended fingers.
выуживание колоний bact: colony fishing.
выучка learning.
выход 1. exit, egress, outlet, vent; 2. yield, output, product(ion).
~ **в трубку** = **стеблевание.**
~ **из цисты** excysting, excystment.
~ **пыльцевой трубки** bot: hilum.
~ **цыплят** agr production of chickens.
выходить в колос come into ear.
~ **в лист** bot: foliate.
~ **в трубку** bot: spike.
~ **(из яйца)** hatch, issue.
выходное отверстие exit, outlet.
выходные щипцы obstetric forceps.
выхолощенный agr zool: emasculated, castrated, see выложенный.
~ **бык** castrated bull, bullock, ox.
выхухоль zool: desman (Desmana moschata).
выцветший bot: glaucous.
выцедить p. a. of **выцеживать.**
выцеживать = **отцеживать.**
вычерпать p. a. of **вычерпывать.**
вычерпывать scoop out.
вычерчивание поля зрения ophth: plotting the field of vision.
вычислитель сухих веществ в молоке milk solids calculator.
вычленение surg: disarticulation; Brit: dearticulation.
вычленять surg: disarticulate, disjoint.
выщепление липоидов liberation of lipoids.
выщипать p. a. of **выщипывать.**
выщипывать (волосы) pick, pull, remove (hair), depilate.
выя anat: nape, nucha.
вьюн ichth: Misgurnus.
вьюнковые (сем.) bot: convolvulus family (Convolvulaceae).
вьюновые (сем.) ichth: Cobitidae.
вьюнок bot: bindweed (Convolvulus, L.)
~ **заборный** hedge bindweed, wild morning glory (C. sepium).
~ **полевой** field bindweed (C. arvensis).
~ **пурпурный** = **ипомея.**
вьюрки = **вьюрковые.**
вьюрковые (сем.) orn: finch family, siskin family (Fringillidae).
вьюрок orn: brambling. (Fringilla montifringilla).
~ **американский** snowbird (Junco hyemalis)
вьющееся растение bot: climber.
вьющеползучее растение bot: tendril-climber plant, vine.
вяжущее свойство astringency.
~ **средство** pharm: astringent.
вяжущий astringent; styptic.
вяз bot: elm (Ulmus, L.); slippery elm, red elm (U. rubra).
~ **бурокрасный** Ulmus fulva.
~ **горный** wych elm (U. glabra, Huds.)
~ **шершавый** = **вяз горный.**
вязель(ник) bot: crown vetch (Coronilla, L.); see also **чина.**
вязиль = **клевер луговой.**
вязкий viscous, viscid.
вязкость viscosity.
вязовое растение ulmaceous plant.
вязовые (сем.) bot: elm family (Ulmaceae).
вяло заживающая язва path: weak ulcer.
~ **реагирующий зрачок** ophth: sluggish pupil.
вялое свисание ручной кисти path: wrist drop.
~ ~ **стопы** path: foot drop.
вялость flaccidity, flabbiness, anergy, limpness, laxity, lassitude; apathy, lethargy; indolence.
~ **кровообращения** path: circulatory inefficiency.
вялый flaccid, flabby, anergic, limp, lax; apathetic, lethargic; indolent; bot: wilt(ing), wilted, withered.
вянуть wilt, wither, droop.
вяхирь = **голубь дикий.**

Г

габитус habit(us), body build.
гаверсовы каналы hist: Haversian canals.
гавиал zool: gavial (Gavialis).
гага orn: eider (Somateria).
~ **обыкновенная** common e. (S. mollissima).
гагара orn: loon, Brit: great northern diver (Gavia, Urinator).
гагарка orn: razorbill (Alca).
гагары orn: loons (Gaviae).

гагачий пух eider down.
гад zool: reptile.
гадюка zool: adder, viper (Vipera); asp [V. aspis).
~ **обыкновенная** common a., common v. (V. berus).
гадюковые zool: adders, vipers (Viperidae).
газация agr entom: fumigation.
газель zool: gazelle (of Antilocapridae).
газированная вода carbonated water.
газовая вакуоль pseudovacuole (of blue-green algae).
~ **горелка** lab: gas burner.
~ **эмбола** gas embolus.
газовый обмен bio: gaseous interchange
газометрический анализ gasometric analysis.
газообмен = газовый обмен.
газообразование gas formation, gasification.
газоотводная трубка colonic tube.
газы в кишечнике flatus.
~ **крови** av med: gases of the blood.
гаичка бурая = синица болотная.
гайана windmill grass, Rhodes grass (Chloris gayana).
гайлюссация bot: huckleberry (Gaylussacia).
гайморова пазуха = г. полость.
гайморова полость anat: antrum of Highmore, maxillary sinus.
гайно zool: squirrel nest.
галазон pharm: halazone.
галактит vet: milkstone.
галактоген galactogen.
галактолит vet: milkstone.
галакторрея path: galactorrhea.
галеа entom: galea.
галеновы препараты pharm: Galenicals.
гализитоидный коралл halysitoid coral.
Галилей Galileo.
галипланктон bio: haliplankton.
*****галка** orn: daw, jackdaw, a kind of European crow (Colaeus monedula).
галл bot: gall; purples, earcockle (on wheat).
галлица entom: gall midge.
~ **берёзовых семян** birch-seed gall midge (Semutobia betulae).
~ **буковая** beech-tree midge (Cecidomyia fagi).
~ **ивы** willow-tree midge (Rabdophaga saliciperda).
~ **листовая смородинная** currant-leaf gall midge (Perrisia tetensi).
~ **малинная** raspberry gall midge (Lasioptera rubi).
галлица цветочная смородинная currant-flower gall midge (Contarinia ribis).
галлицы (сем.) entom: gall midges (Cecidomyidae, Itonididae).
галловая изозома = изозома галловая.
~ **нематода** zool: root-knot eel-worm (Heterodera radicicola).
галлообразователь gall-producing insect, see комарик, орехотворка
галлораговые = сланоягодниковые.
галлусовокислая иодокись висмута pharm: bismuth iodosubgallate.
галлусовокислый висмут (основной) pharm: bismuth subgallate.
галлюцинации на почве алкоголизма psych: alcoholic delirium.
галлюцинация psych: hallucination.
~ **общего чувства** bodily h.
галлюцинировать psych: hallucinate.
галлюцинозное состояние psych: hallucinosis.
галоид chem: halogen.
галоидгидрокортизон halohydrocortisone.
галоидная водородная кислота chem: hydracid.
~ **соль** chem: halide.
галоидоводородная кислота chem: halogen acid.
галопирующая чахотка = скоротечная чахотка.
галопирующий паралич galloping paralysis.
~ **пульс** path: running pulse.
галофильный halophilic.
галофит halophyte.
*****галстучник** orn: ringed plover.
Галь Gal.
гальванокаустика surg: galvanocautery.
гальванотаксис surg: galvanotaxis.
гальванотерапия med: galvanotherapy.
гальванотропизм bio: galvanotropism.
гальванохирургия galvanosurgery.
гама = сезамовая трава.
гамбузия mosquito-fish (Gambusia affinis).
гамета genet: gamete.
гаметангий bot: gametangium.
гаметическое сцепление генов genet: gametic linkage.
гаметогенез genet: gametogenesis.
гаметоноситель genet: gamete carrier.
гаметофит bot: gametophyte.
гаметоцит genet: gametocyte.
Гамильтон Hamilton.

гамма gamma.
~ -глобулин imm: gamma globulin.
~ -рентген rad: gamma roetgen.
~ -установка, терапевтическая rad: therapeutic gamma-ray source.
гамсбок zool: gamsbok (antelope).
ганглий hist: ganglion.
~ над пищеводом zool: archicerebrum.
ганглиозная клетка hist: ganglion cell.
ганглиозный gangliar, ganglionic.
гангрена path: gangrene.
гангренесцирующая язва path: carious ulcer.
ганоидный ichth: ganoid.
ганоиды ichth: ganoids; see also костные ганоиды, хрящевые г.
гаолян bot: kaoliang (Sorghum chinense).
гаплоид(ный) genet: haploid.
гаплоспоридии (подкл.) zool: Haplosporidia.
гаплостемонный bot: haplostemonous (flower).
гаптен hapten.
гармоничный шов anat: sutura harmonica.
гарпия тополевая большая entom: prominent Dicranura vinula.
гаррупа ichth: blackgrouper, warsaw (Garrupa nigrita).
Гартман Hartmann.
*гаршнеп orn: small snipe, half-snipe (Scolopax gallinula).
гастральгия gastralgia.
гастральная полость (гидры и т.п.) zool: gastric cavity, stomach c. (of a hydra, etc.)
гастрит int: gastritis.
гастритовый gastritic.
гастрическая лихорадка gastric fever
гастрический gastric.
гастрозоид zool: gastrozooid.
гастролит 1. path: see желудочный камень; 2. zool: gastrolith, see раковые камешки.
гастромаляция path: gastric softening.
гастромицеты bot: gastromyces (Gastromycetales).
гастропликация surg: stomach reefing.
гастропора zool: gastropora.
гастроптоз path: gastroptosis.
гастротриха zool: gastrotrich (phylum Gastrotricha).
гастрофилёз vet: gastrofilosis.
гастроцель 1. path: gastrocele; 2. embr see первичная кишка.
гастроэктазия path: gastrectasis.
гастроэктомия surg: gastrectomy.
гастроэнтерит path: gastroenteritis.
гастроэнтеростомия surg: gastroenterostomy, gastroduodenostomy, gastrojejunostomy.
~ по поводу язвы желудка gastroenterostomy for relief of gastric ulcer.
гаструла embr: gastrula.
гаструляция embr: gastrulation.
гастрэктомия surg: gastrectomy.
гаультерия bot: wintergreen (Gaulteria procumbens, L.)
гаустеллум entom: haustellum.
гашиш pharm: hashish, hasheesh, cannabis; bot: churrus, see банг.
гашишизм hashish addiction.
гвайюла bot: guayule (Parthenium argentatum, Gray).
гваяковая настойка pharm: tincture of guaiac.
гваяковое дерево = бакаут.
гваяколсульфонокислый калий pharm: potassium-guajacol sulfonate.
гвизоция bot: Guizotia, Cass.
гвинейский червь helm: guinea worm (Filaria medinensis).
гвоздика bot: carnation, pink (Dianthus, L.); clove.
~ кустистая = гвоздика перистая.
~ перечная pimento, allspice, bayberry (Pimenta officinalis, Berg.)
~ перистая garden pink, grass pink (D. plumarius).
~ садовая carnation, clove pink (D. caryophyllus, L.)
~ трехгранная maiden pink (D. deltoides, L.)
~ турецкая sweet William (D. barbatus).
~ шотландская = г. перистая.
гвоздичная кислота eugenic acid.
гвоздичник = армерия.
гвоздичное дерево bot: allspice (Pimenta officinalis, Berg.); clove tree (Eugenia caryophyllata, Thumb.)
~ масло pharm: clove oil.
~ растение bot: caryophyllaceous plant.
гвоздичные (сем.) bot: pink family (Caryophyllaceae).
гебефренический psych: hebephrenic.
гебефрения psych: hebephrenia.
гевея bot: seringueira, para rubber tree (Hevea brasiliensis, Muell.Arg.)
~ гвианская = г. каучуконосная.
~ каучуконосная seringa (H. guianensis, Aubl.)
гезарол = ДДТ.
гейлардия bot: blanket flower, gaillardia (Gaillardia).

гекконы zool: geckos (Geckonidae lizards)
гексаметоний pharm: hexamethonium.
гексахлоран = ГХЦГ.
гексаэтилтетрафосфат chem: hexaethyl-tetraphosphate.
гексобарбитал pharm: hexobarbital.
гексобарбиталовый наркоз hexobarbital narcosis.
гектическая лихорадка path: hectic fever.
гектический румянец hectic flush.
геленин helenin.
гелениум bot: sneezeweed (Helenium, L.)
гелеопланктон heleoplankton.
гелидиум bot:red algae Gelidium; tengusa (Gelidium corneum).
гелий helium, He.
гелиопсис bot: oxeye, orange sunflower (Heliopsis helianthoides, H. laevis).
гелиотаксис bio: heliotaxis.
гелиотерапия heliotherapy, sun treatment.
гелиотроп bot: turnsole, heliotrope (Heliotropium, L.)
гелиотропизм bio: heliotropism.
гелиотропичный heliotropic.
гелихризум = цмин.
гелофит bot: helophyte.
гельминт helminth.
гельминтоз path: helminthiasis, helminthism.
гельминтокариоз vet: brusone, Helminthosporium
гельминтология helminthology.
гельминтоспориоз helminthosporiosis, falla.
гельминтофауна helminth fauna.
гельминтофобия psych: helminthophobia.
гемагглютинация hemagglutination.
гемальная дуга zool: hemal arch.
гемангиома oncol: hemangioma.
гемангиоперицитома hemangiopericytoma.
гематемезис path: hematemesis.
гематинный hematinic.
гематогенный hematogenic, hematogenous.
гематококк дождевой bot: Hematococcus pluvialis (alga).
~ снежный H. nivalis.
гематоксилин chem: hematoxylin.
гематологический hematological.
гематология hematology.
гематома path: hematoma, blood boil.
гематохром bio: hematochrome.
гемато-энцефалический барьер hematoencephalic barrier, blood-brain barrier.
гематурия path: hematuria.
гемерокаллис = лилейник.
гемианопия ophth: hemianop(s)ia, half-vision.

гемипарез path: hemiparesis.
гемиплегический path: hemiplegic.
гемиплегия path: hemiplegia.
гемиптерологический hemipterological.
гемисиндром hemisyndrome.
гемлок bot: hemlock, hemlock spruce (Tsuga, Carr.)
геммула gemmule, hibernaculum (of sponges).
гемоглобин hemoglobin.
гемоглобинный индекс blood quotient.
гемоглобинообразующий hemoglobiniferous.
гемоглобинурийная лихорадка = острая г. л.
гемоглобинурия path: hemoglobinuria.
гемограмма hemogram.
гемодинамика hemodynamics.
гемодинамический сдвиг hemodynamic shift.
гемоконии hemoconia, chylomicrons, blood dust.
гемокультура bact: blood culture.
гемолиз hemolysis.
гемолизин hemolysin.
гемолизировать(ся) hemolyze, lake.
гемолимфа hemolymph.
гемолитическая анемия hemolytic anemia.
~ желтуха = г. анемия.
гемопаразит hemoparasite.
гемоперикард hemopericardium.
гемопоэз hemopoiesis, hematosis.
гемопоэтический hemopoietic.
геморрагическая корь hemorrhagic measles, black measles.
~ оспа hemorrhagic smallpox.
геморрагический hemorrhagic.
геморрагия hemorrhage.
геморроидальные шишки path: hemorrhoids, piles.
гемор(р)ой hemorrhoids, piles.
гемосидерин hemosiderin.
гемостаз hemostasis.
гемостатический hemostatic.
гемоторакс hemothorax.
гемофилик path: hemophiliac, bleeder.
гемофилия path: hemophilia.
гемофильный hemophilic.
гемофусцин hemofuscin.
гемоцит entom: hemocyte.
гемоцитобласт hist: hemocytoblast.
гемоцитометр hemocytometer.
ген bio: gen(e).
Гендерсон Henderson.
генеалогический коэффициент genet: fractional percentage coefficient.

генеалогия genealogy, line of descent.
генез(ис) genesis.
генерализованный generalized.
генеративный generative.
генерация generation.
генетик geneticist.
генетика genetics.
генетический genetic.
генетта zool: genet (Genetta genetta).
гензеновский узелок embr: Hensen's node.
гениталии anat: genitalia.
генитально-кишечный канал zool: genito-intestinal canal.
генитальный genital.
Генле Henle.
генный genet: factorial.
генотип bio: genotype.
генуинная эпилепсия neur: genuine epilepsy.
генциана = горечавка.
геобиоз geobiosis, terrestrial life.
геоботаник geobotanist.
геоботаника geobotany.
геогельминт geohelminth.
географическое распространение geographic range.
георгин(а) bot: georgina, dahlia (Dahlia).
геотропизм geotropism.
геофагия path: geophagy, geophagia, dirt eating.
геофильный bio: geophilous, earth-loving.
геофит bot: geophyte.
геохимия geochemistry.
гепарин hem: heparin.
гепатизация path: hepatization.
гепатит path: hepatitis.
гепатопанкреас zool: hepato-pancreas.
геранецветные (пор.) bot: geranium order (Geraniales).
гераниевые (сем.) bot: geranium family (Geraniaceae).
герань bot: cranesbill (Geranium).
~ ароматическая nutmeg geranium (Pelargonium odoratissimum, Ait., or G. odoratissimum, L.)
~ мягкая dovesfoot cranesbill (G. molle)
гербаризация herbarization.
гарбарий herbarium.
гербарный herbarial.
~ экземпляр herbarium specimen.
гербицид bot: herbicide, weed-killer.
гербицидное действие herbicidal effect.
гербицидный herbicidal, weed-killing.
гередитарный hereditary.

гермафродитизм path: hermaphrodi(ti)sm, androgynism, androgyny.
гермафродитический hermaphroditic.
гермафродитная железа zool: hermaphroditic gland, ovotestis.
гермафродитный = гермафродитический.
~ проток zool: hermaphroditic duct.
герметизированная кабина av med: pressure cabin, pressurized c.
герметизованная одежда = med:
герметизованный комбинезон av med: pressure suit.
~ костюм av med: pressure suit, antiblackout suit.
герметически закрытая кабина av med: sealed cabin.
герминативный germinal.
герниотом surg: hernia knife.
героин pharm: heroin, diacetylmorphine.
героинизм heroinism, heroin addiction
геронтизм gerontism.
геронтический gerontic.
геронтология gerontology.
геронтонтальный gerontal.
геронтотерапия gerontotherapy.
геронтофилия gerontophilia.
герпетиформный дерматит path: dermatitis herpetiformis.
герпетолог herpetologist.
герпетологический zool: herpetological.
герпетология zool: herpetology.
гесперидин hesperidin.
гессенка = муха гессенская.
гетерогамета heterogamete.
гетерогамный heterogamous.
гетерогемагглютинин heterohemagglutinin.
гетерозиготный genet: heterozygous.
гетерозис crossbred vigor.
гетерологический geterologous.
гетероморфизм heteromorphism.
гетероморфный heteromorphic.
гетеронимная гемиопия ophth: crossed hemianopsia.
гетеропода zool: heteropod.
гетероспецифический heterospecific.
гетероталлизм heterothallism.
гетеротрансплантация heterotransplantation.
гетеротрихальный heterotrichous.
гетеротропия ophth: heterotropia.
гетеротрофная бактерия heterotrophic bacterium.
гетерофильный heterophyllous.
гетерофория ophth: heterophoria.

гетероциста bot: heterocyst.
гетол = коричнокислый натрий.
геухера bot: alumroot (Heuchera americana, L.)
гиалин hist: hyalin.
гиалинизироваться hyalinize.
гиалиновое перерождение path: hyalinosis, vitreous degeneration.
гиалиновый слой bot: hyaline layer.
~ хрящ hist: hyalin cartilage.
~ цилиндр urol: hyaline cast.
гиалуронидаза hyaluronidase, invasin. [acid.
гиалуроновая кислота hyaluronic
гиацинт bot: hyacinth (Hyacinthus).
~ водяной water h. (Eichornia, Kunth.)
гиббон zool: gibbon (Hylobatus).
гиббоны (сем.) zool: gibbon family (Hylobatidae).
гибель death.
~ хромосомы genet: chromosome deletion.
гибкий flexible.
гибиск bot: rose mallow (Hibiscus, L.)
~ кустарниковый shrubby althea, rose-of-Sharon (H. syriacus, L.)
~ мускусный bot: swamp rose, mallow r., wild cotton (H. moscheutos, L.)
~ сирийский = г. кустарниковый.
~ съедобный okra, gumbo (H. esculentus)
гибитан pharm: hibitane.
гибогнатус ichth: brassy minnow (Hybognathus hankinsoni, Hubbs).
гибралтарская лихорадка = мальтийская лихорадка.
гибрид hybrid.
гибридизация hybridization, crossbreeding.
гибридность hybridism, hybridity.
гибридный adj: hybrid.
гигантизм gigantism.
гигантоклеточная саркома oncol: giant-cell sarcoma.
гигантская акула ichth: basking shark, bone s. (Cetorhinus maximus).
~ древесная оса = рогохвост еловый.
~ клетка hist: giant cell.
~ крапивница path: giant urticaria.
~ саламандра zool: giant salamander (Megalobatrachus).
гигантские броненосцы = глиптодонты.
гигантский кенгуру zool: great gray kangaroo (Mactopus giganteus).
гигантский скребень helm: spiny-headed pig's worm (Macracanthorhynchus hirudinaceus).
гигартина bot: red algae Gigartina; batters (G. stellata); catanari (G. teedii).
гигиена hygiene.
~ во время полёта av med: in-flight hygiene.
~ рта oral hygiene.
~ труда hygiene of work.
гигиенический hygienic. [cotton.
гигроскопическая вата absorbent
гигроскопичность hygroscopicity.
гидергин hydergine.
гидра zool: hydra (Hydridae).
~ обыкновенная common hydra (Hydra vulgaris).
гидракарина entom: water mite (Hydracarina).
гидрамнион obstet: dropsy of the amnion.
гидрант zool: hydranth.
гидраргирол = парафенилсульфонокислая ртуть.
гидрартроз path: hydrarthrosis.
гидрастика bot: orangeroot, yellow puccoon (Hydrastis, Ellis); golden seal, "tumeric" (H. canadensis).
гидрастис = гидрастика.
гидратационная вода chem: water of hydration.
гидрахнида entom: hydrachnid.
гидремический hydremic.
гидремия hydremia.
гидробиология hydrobiology. [rida).
гидровые (отр.) zool: hydras (Hyd-
гидродиктиевые (сем.) bot: Hydrodictyaceae algae.
гидроид zool: hydroid, hydrozoan.
гидроидная медуза zool: hydromedusa
гидроидные (кл.) zool: hydrozoans, hydroids & craspedote medusae (Hydrozoa).
~ (подкл.) zool: hydroids (Hydroidea).
~ полипы (отр.) zool: hydrozoan polyps (Leptolida).
гидроиды без чашечки (подотр.) zool: tabularian hydroids (Athecata, Anthomedusae, Gymnoblastea)
~ с чашечкой (подотр.) zool: campanularian hydroids (Thecaphora, Leptomedusae, Caliptoblastea).
гидроксиламин hydroxylamine.
гидролиз hydrolisis.
гидролизованный hydrolized.
гидронефроз path: hydronephrosis.
гидронефрозный hydronephrotic.

гидроперикард path: hydropericardium.
гидропс path: hydrops.
гидросальпинкс gyn: hydrosalpinx.
гидротерапия hydrotheraphy, hydrothera-
гидроторакс path: hydrothorax.| peutics.
гидрофилляциевые (сем.) bot: waterleaf family (Hydrophyllaceae).
гидрофильный hydrophilic.
гидрофит bot: hydrophyte.
гидрофитный hydrophytic.
гидрофобия path: hydrophobia.
гидрофобный path: hydrophobic.
гидрохинон pharm: hydroquinone.
гидроцефалическая идиотия psych:
hydrocephalic idiocy.
гидроцефалия path: hydrocephaly.
гидроцефалус = гидроцефалия.
ГИДУВ = Государсвенный институт
для усовершенствования врачей.
гиена zool: hyena (Hyaena).
гиены(сем.) zool: hyena family
(Hyaenidae).
гиккори bot: hickory (Carya, Nutt.);
bitternut (C. amara).
~ болотный water hickory, bitter pecan,
swamp h. (C. aquatica).
~ яйцевидный твердокорый shagbark
h., shellbark h. (C. ovata).
гиллихтис ichth: mudsucker (Gillichthys
гилус anat: hilus. mirabilis).
гималайский енот zool: giant panda
(Aeloropus melanoleucus).
~ медведь zool: bear Ursus torquatus.
гимениальная пластинка bot: gill-
shaped plate, gill, sporogenous layer.
гимений bot: hymenium.
гименомицеты (пор.) bot: Hymeno-
mycetales (fungi).
гимнастика gymnastics, calisthenics.
гимнастический gymnastic.
гимнелис ichth: Gymnelis.
гимногобиус ichth: Gymnogobius.
гимнокладус канадский = бундук.
гимносарда ichth: striped tuna (Gymno-
sarda pelamis); dogtooth t. (G. nudu).
гимноспора bot: gymnospore, naked
spore. [morphism.
гинандроморфизм zool: gynandromor-
гингивит odont: gingivitis.
гинеколог gynecologist.
гинекологическое кресло
gynecological (examination) chair.
гинекология gynecology.
гинекофорный канал (у шистозомид)
helm: gynecophoric groove.
гинецей bot: gynoecium, see пестик.

гини = черешня.
гинкго bot: Ginkgo biloba.
~ (пор.) bot: Ginkgoales.
гинофора bot: gynophore. [lingual a.
гиоидная дуга embr: hyoid arch,
гиосциамин pharm: hyoscyamine.
гиосцин pharm: hyoscine.
гипербулия psych: hyperbulia.[lation.
гипервентиляция av med: hyperventi-
гипервитаминоз hypervitaminosis.
гипергликемический hyperglycemic.
гиперэзофория ophth: hyperesophoria.
гиперемированный hyperemic.
гиперемичный hyperemic.
гиперемия hyperemia.
~ лёгких path: pulmonary engorgement,
pulmonary congestion. [gestion.
~ спинного мозга neur: spinal con-
гиперестезия чувств psych:
emotional hyperesthesia.
гиперестетический hyperesthetic.
гиперкапния hypercapnia.
гиперкинез path: hyperkinesis.
гиперкинетический hyperkinetic.
гиперметаморфоза entom:
hypermetamorphosis.
гиперметроп ophth: hypermetrope.
гиперметроп(ич)ный hypermetropic.
гиперметропия hypermetropia.
гипермнезия psych: hypermnesia.
гипернефрома path: hypernephroma,
Grawitz tumor.
гиперостоз path: hyperostosis, bony
overgrowth.
гиперплазия hyperplasia, numerical
hypertrophy.
гиперпластический path: hyperplas-
гиперпноэ hyperpnoea. tic.
гиперрефлексия hyperreflexia.
гиперсекреция hypersecretion.
гиперсеротонемия hyperserotonemia.
гиперстенический path: hypersthenic.
гиперстения hypersthenia.
гипертимия psych: hyperthymia.
гипертиреоз path: hyperthyroidism.
гипертоник hypertensive patient.
гипертонический hypertonic.
гипертоничность hypertonicity.
гипертоничный = гипертонический.
гипертония path: hypertonia.
гипертропия ophth: hypertropia.
гипертрофия path: hypertrophy.
~ почки hypernephrotrophy.
~ сердца hypercardia.
~ с одновременным расширением
сердца eccentric hypertrophy (heart).

гиперфорический hyperphoric.
гиперфория ophth: hyperphoria.
гиперфункция hyperfunction.
гиперхроматоз hyperchromatosis.
гиперхромия hyperchromia, hypercro-
matism. [anemia.
гиперхромная анемия hyperchromic
гиперэкзофория ophth: hyperexophoria.
гиперэстезия path: hyperesthesia.
гипноз hypnosis.
гипнонаркоз psych: hypnonarcosis.
гипнотерапия psych: hypnotherapy.
гипнотизация psych: hypnotization.
гипнотизёр psych: hypnotist.
гипнотизировать psych: hypnotize.
гипнотизирующий psych: hypnotizing.
гипнотизм psych: hypnotism.
гипнотик psych: hypnotic, hypnotized
гипнотический psych: hypnotic. | person.
гиповитаминоз path: hypovitaminosis.
гипогенитализм path: hypogenitalism.
гипогенный bot: hypogenous.
гипогликемическая кома =
сахарный диабет.
гипогликемический hypoglycemic.
гипогликемия hypoglycemia.
гипоглицин hypoglycin.
гиподерма hypoderma, hypodermis,
subcuticula. [paralysis.
гипокалиемия hypopotassemia, periodic
гипокинез hypokinesis, hypokinesia.
гипокотиль bot: hypocotyl.
гипоксидация hypoxidation.
гипоксидоз hypoxidosis.
гипоксия path: hypoxia.
гиполимнион hypolimnion.
гипоманиакальный psych: hypomanic.
гипомания psych: hypomania.
гипомнезия psych: hypomnesia.
гипопатия psych: hypopathy.
гипопигий entom: hypopygium.
гипоплазия path: hypoplasty,
hypoplasia. [convertinemia.
гипопроконвертинемия hem: hypopro-
гипопротромбинемия hypoprothrombine-
гипопус entom: hypopus. mia.
гипоспадия path: hypospadia.
гипостаз genet: hypostasis.
гипостатический genet: hypostatic.
гипостенический hyposthenic.
гипостения hyposthenia.
гипоталамус anat: hypothalamus.
гипоталасса hypothalassa.
гипотеза hypothesis.
~ мишени rad: target theory, hit t.
гипотензивный hypotensive.
гипотермия hypothermia.
гипотоничность path: hypotonicity.
гипотоничный hypotonic.
гипотония hypotonia.
гипотропия ophth: hypotropia.
гипофаринкс entom: hypopharynx.
гипофиз anat: hypophysis.
гипофизный hypophyseal.
гипофизэктомированный surg:
hypophysectomized.
гипофория ophth: hypophoria.
гипофункция hypofunction.
гипохлорит hypochlorite.
гиппокамповый hippocampal.
Гиппократ Hippocrates.
гиппократовское лицо path:
Hippocratic countenance.
гиппол = метиленгиппуровая
кислота.
гиппурия path: hippuria.
гиппуровая кислота hippuric acid.
гипс gypsum, plaster-of-Paris.
гипсовая болезнь шампиньонниц
phytp: plaster mold disease.
~ пилка surg: gypsum saw.
~ повязка surg: plaster cast.
~ шина surg: plaster splint. [jacket.
гипсовый корсет orthop: plaster
гирелля ichth: greenfish, opal-eye
(Girella nigricans).
гирка bot: awnless wheat. лон.
Гиршпрунг Hirschprung. Cf. мегалоко-
Гис His. [atrioventricular bundle.
гисов пучок anat: bundle of His,
гистамин histamine.
гистаминовый histaminic.
гистаминоподобный histamine-like.
гистеромания psych: hysteromania.
гистидин histidine.
гистиоцит histiocyte.
гистиоцитоз histiocytosis.
гистиоцитома oncol: histiocytoma.
гистобласт histoblast.
гистогенез histogenesis.
гистоид histoid.
гистолиз histolysis.
гистолитический histolytic.
гистолог histologist.
гистологическая химия
histological chemistry.
гистология histology.
~ нервной системы neurohistology.
гистопатологический histopatholo-
гистопатология histopathology. gical.
гистоплазминовая проба
histoplasmin test(ing).

гистотоксическая гипоксия path: histotoxic hypoxia.
гистотрофический histotrophic.
гистохимический histochemical.
гистохимия histochemistry.
гиф = гифа.
гифа bot: hypha (of a fungus).
гич(ка) bot: sugar-beet tops.
главный агглютинин imm: major agglutinin, chief agglutinin.
~ врач chief physician, head physician.
~ корень bot: taproot.
~ побег bot: leading shoot.
~ стебель bot: axis.
гладиолус bot: gladiolus, gladiole (Gladiolus).
гладкая мышечная ткань hist: smooth muscle tissue.
~ мышца anat: smooth muscle, unstriated muscle.
~ сардина ichth: smooth sardine (Sardinella anchovia).
~ часть хориона embr: chorion laeve, chorion avillosum.
~ чешуйка bot: glabrous glume.
гладкий bot: smooth, glabrus.
~ уж zool: smooth snake (Coronella austriaca).
гладко протекающее выздоровление uneventful recovery.
гладкое семя bot: flattened seed.
гладконосые (сем.) zool: typical insect-eating bats (Vespertilionidae).
гладыш entom: back swimmer (Notonectidae).
глаз eye.
~ на стебельке zool: projecting eye.
глазки zool: ocelli.
глазная больница eye hospital.
~ ванночка eye bath, ophthalmic bath.
~ влага aqueous humor.
~ впадина orbit(al cavity), eyesocket.
~ камера chamber of the eye.
~ клиника eye clinic, ophthalmoclinic.
~ мышца anat: eye muscle.
~ ось eye axis.
~ плева orn: orbit.
~ подагра path: gout in the eye.
~ примочка eyewash, collyrium.
~ щель anat: palpebral fissure.
глазница = глазная впадина.
глазничная артерия anat: ophthalmic artery.
~ часть anat: orbital part.
~ щель anat: orbital fissure, fissura orbitalis.
глазничный нерв anat: ophthalmic nerve.
~ отросток anat: orbital process.

глазное дно anat: ocular fundus, fundus oculi.
~ зеркало ophthalmoscope.
~ яблоко anat: eyeball, globe of the eye.
глазной ocular, of the eye.
~ белок white of the eye.
~ бокал embr: eyecup, optic cup.
~ зонд ophth: eyeprobe.
~ зуб anat: eye tooth.
~ камень pharm: aluminated copper.
~ компресс eye compress.
~ кубок = глазной бокал.
~ магнит Mellinger magnet.
~ нерв anat: ophthalmic nerve.
~ нистагм path: ocular nystagmus.
~ пузырь embr: optic vesicle, eyecup.
~ стебелёк zool: eyestalk.
~ ток physl: eye current.
~ щит eye shade, eye shield.
глазные капли pharm: eye drops.
глазодвигательный нерв anat: oculomotor nerve, third cranial nerve.
~ паралич path: oculomotor paralysis.
*глазок 1. bot: bud, oculus, escutcheon; stigma; 2. zool: eyespot, ocellus.
~ (крыла насекомого) stigma.
~ со щитком bot: bud shield.
глазомер sizing up by the eye.
глауберова соль = сернокислый натрий.
глаукома ophth: glaucoma.
глеба bot: mush (of a fungus)
гледичия bot: honey locust (Gleditsia)
~ сладкая = г. трехшипная.
~ трехшипная honey shuck, three-thorned acacia (G. triacanthos, L.)
глеокапса bot: Gleocapsa (colonial algae).
глеотрихия bot: Gleotrichia (colonial algae)
глиадин gliadin.
глиальная дисплазия glial displasia.
гликемия hem: glycemia.
гликоген glycogen.
гликогенный glycogenous.
гликогенолитический glycogenolytic.
гликозид pharm: glycoside.
глинистые испражнения clay-colored stools.
глиоз neur: gliosis.
глиптаухен ichth: goblin (fish) (Glyptauchen panduratus).
глиптодонт zool: glyptodont.
глиптодонты (сем.) zool: extinct family Glyptodontidae.
глист(а) intestinal worm, helminth.
~ печёночный овечий sheep liver fluke (Fasciola hepatica, Distoma

hepaticum).
глистная болезнь helminthiasis,
~ инвазия = г. болезнь. helminthism.
глистогонное лечение vermifuge treatment.
~ средство vermifuge, anthelmintic, taeniafuge.
глистопечёночная болезнь vet: liver-fluke disease, fascioliasis.
глистоубивающее средство vermicide, helminthicide.
глицерин pharm: glycerin, glycerol.
глицериноборнонатриевая соль pharm: sodium glyceroborate.
глицериновый glyceric.
~ бульон mcbio: glycerin broth.
глицеринофосфорнокислый кальций pharm: calcium glycerophosphate.
~ хинин pharm: quinine glycerophosphate.
глицерия bot: manna grass (Glyceria).
глициния китайская = вистерия китайская.
глобин globine.
глобулин globulin.
глобулиновые зёрна hist: globulin edestin.
глог = кизил.
глоговина bot: checker-tree (Sorbus torminalis); service-tree (Pyrus sorbus).
глоксиния bot: gloxinia (Sinningia speciosa, Bernth & Hook.)
глотание swallowing, deglutition.
~ воздуха path: air swallowing.
глотательное движение swallowing motion.
глотательный deglutitive, deglutitory.
глотать swallow.
глотка anat: pharynx, gullet.
глоточная миндалина anat: pharyngeal tonsil.
~ мышца anat: pharyngeal muscle.
~ перепонка embr: pharyngeal membrane.
глоточное отверстие anat: pharyngeal orifice.
глоточнонёбная дужка anat: pharyngopalatine arch.
глоточные зубы ichth: pharyngeal teeth
глоточный бугорок anat: pharyngeal tubercle.
~ шов anat: raphe of the pharynx.
глохидий zool: glochidium.
глубина дыхания depth of breathing.
глубинная доза rad: depth dose.
~ часть профундали euprofundal.
глубинное восприятие psych: depth perception.
глубокая артерия бедра anat: deep femoral artery.
глубокая артерия плеча anat: arteria profunda brachii.
~ пальпация dipping.
~ спячка psych: sopor.
~ фасция шеи anat: deep cervical fascia.
~ язва path: hollow ulcer.
глубокий вдох deep breath.
~ гипнотический сон psych: deep hypnotic sleep, hypnonarcosis.
~ сгибатель пальцев anat: flexor digitorum profundus.
глубоководная креветка zool: deep-water prown (Pandalus borealis).
~ чёрная рыба deep-sea black fish (Melanostomias valdiviae).
глубоководный adj: deep-sea.
глубокое дыхание deep breathing.
~ прижигание surg: inustion.
~ чувство av med: deep sensibility.
глубьевой adj: deep-sea.
*глупыш orn: 1. fulmar, mallie (Fulmarus g. glacialis); 2. gannet (Moris bassana, family Sulidae).
глутаминовая кислота glutamic acid.
глухарь orn: capercaillie, capercailzie, great grouse, cock of the woods (Tetrao urogallus).
~ -кокон entom: dead cocoon.
глухой deaf.
~ тон thudding sound (of the heart).
глухонемой deafmute.
глухонемота deafmutism.
глухота deafness
~ котельщиков boilermaker's deafness.
~ на низкие тона bass deafness.
~ у летчиков av med: aviation deafness.
глыбка small block, tiny lump.
глюкоза glucose.
глюкозидуроновая кислота glucosiduronic acid.
глюкозурия glycosuria.
глюкокортикоидный glucocorticoid.
глюкуроновая кислота glucuronic acid.
глютенин glutenin.
глянцевый glossy.
гнев psych: wrath, anger.
гнездарь orn: nestling.
гнездо zool: nest, nidus.
~ из пузырьков воздуха ichth: bubble-nest.
~ (лосося) ichth: redd.
~ раковых клеток hist: cancer nest.
гнездование nestling, nidification.
гнездовиковые (сем.) bot: bird's nest fungi (Nidulariaceae).

гнездовой nesting, nidulate.
~ домик zool: nesting house.
гнездовье zool: nesting ground, breeding site, b. place.
гнездующая птица nester.
гнетовые (сем.) bot: Gnetaceae.
гнетум bot: Gnetum.
гнида entom: nit.
гниение putrefaction, rotting.
гнилец пчёл foul brood (bee disease).
~ ~ американский American f.b. (Bacillus larvae.
гнилое дерево punk.
гнилой putrid, rotten, decayed, putrefied.
гнилостное брожение в кишечнике path: intestinal putrefaction.
~ разложение putrefaction, decay, decomposition.
гнилостный putrescent, putrefactive, ichorous, ichoroid.
гниль rot.
~ древесины phytp: white rot.
~ конца цветочной ветви phytp: blossom-end rot.
~ корневой шейки phytp: crown rot.
~ шейки phytp: neck rot (on rice).
гниющий putrescent, rotting.
гноевидный puruloid, puriform.
гноекровие path: pyemia.
гноеотделяющее средство pharm: digerent
гноеродный path: pus-forming, pus-producing, pyogenous, pyoge(et)ic.
~ стафилококк mcbio: Micrococcus pyogenes
гноетечение purulent discharge, pyorrhea.
гной path: pus.
гнойная клетка path: pyocyst.
~ масса purulent substance.
гнойничковая сыпь derm: impetigo.
гнойничковое заболевание кожи pyoderma.
гнойничковый impetiginous, impetiginoid
гнойничок path: pustule.
гнойное воспаление path: empyema.
~ ~ дёсен odont: alveolar pyorrhea, periodontosis.
~ заражение крови path: pyemia.
~ отделяемое path: suppurative discharge, purulent d.
гнойный аппендицит path: suppurative appendicitis.
~ очаг path: suppurative focus.
~ периостит path: suppurative periostitis.
~ плеврит int: purulent pleurisy.
~ пузырёк pustule.
~ тендовагинит surg: thecal abscess.
~ энцефалит path: suppurative encephalitis.

гну zool: gnu, brindled gnu, wildbeest (Connochaetes taurinus).
гнус = мошкара.
гнусавость twang, rhinolalia.
гнусавый выговор = гнусавость.
гнюс = электрический скат.
гоацин orn: hoatzin, hoactzin (Opisthocomus hoazin).
гобиоморфус ichth: bully (Gobiomorphus).
гобиус ichth: Gobius.
Говард Howard.
Говадр-Дольмен Howard-Dolman.
говорунчик = славка полевая.
говорящий во сне psych: somniloquist.
говядина beef.
гоготанье (гусей) cackling (of geese).
гоготать cackle.
год отрождения молоди zool: brood year.
~ урожая ichth: survival year.
годен mil: fit.
годичный слой bot: growth ring.
годный для питья potable.
годовалое животное yearling.
годовик zool: yearling, one-year-old.
~ макрели ichth: blinks.
годовой класс zool: year class.
гойя мясная = восковое дерево.
голавль ichth: bullhead, chut, chub, roach back (Leuciscus cephalus).
голая амёба zool: naked amoeba.
голенастая птица wader.
голенастое растение leggy plant.
голенастые orn: gressorial birds (Gressores).
голеностопный сустав anat: talocalcaneal joint, articulatio talocruralis.
голень anat: shinbone, tibia, shank; zool: lower leg; gaskin (of a horse); hock joint (of a cock).
голец ichth: 1. brook trout (Salvelinus alpinus); 2. loach, beardie (Nemachilus strauchi).
~ -губач = голец 2.
голлев пучок anat: slender column.
Голль Goll, Holl.
голобазидиальные грибы (подкл.) bot: Holobasidiomycetes.
голобазидиомицеты = голобазидиальные грибы.
голобластическое яйцо embr: holoblastic egg.
голобрюхие рыбы apodes.
голова head.
головастик zool: tadpole.
головач 1. zool: humpback whale (Megaptera nodosa); 2. entom: see кравчик;

3. ichth: see бычок-горлап.
головешка ichth: Percottus glehni.
головешковые (сем.) ichth: Eleotridae
головка (small) head, capitulum; bot:
~ клитора anat: glans clitoridis.|crown
~ (ленточного червя) zool: scolex.
~ мака bot: poppyhead.
~ ребра anat: rib head, capitulum cos-
~ сперматозоида sperm head. tae.
~ члена anat: glans penis.
головль = голавль.
головная боль headache, cephalalgia.
~ кишка embr: head gut.
~ кривизна embr: cephalic flexure.
~ лопасть zool: prostomium (of segmented worms).
~ повязка surg: head bandage.
~ почка embr: head kidney.
~ складка embr: cephalic fold.
головнёвое вздутие phytp: smut boil.
головнёвые грибы bunt fungi (Tilletiaceae); smut fungi, blisters (Ustilaginaceae).
головнёвый шарик phytp: bunt ball.
головное предлежание obstet: cepha-
головной cephalic. lic presentation.
~ ганглий brain ganglion.
~ мозг anat: brain, encephalon.
~ отросток embr: head process.
~ сегмент (у членистоногих) zool: cephalomere.
головня phytp: smut (Ustilago, Tilletia).
~ вонючая stinking smut (Tilletia tritici, T. foeteus).
~ каменная = г. вонючая.
~ колбовидная Ustillago panici milia-
~ кукурузы corn smut (U. zeae). cei.
~ лука onion smut (Urocystis cepulae).
~ мокрая = г. вонючая.
~ пузырчатая white blister (Ustilago maydis).
~ пыльная wheat smut (Ustilago tritici); oat smut (U. avenae); barley s.(U. nuda)
~ сорго whole-head smut (Phacelotheca reiliana). [ta).
~ стеблевая rye smut (Urocystis occul-
~ твёрдая covered smut: wheat smut (T. tritici); oat smut (Urocystis laevis); barley smut (U. hordei). [al.
головоглоточный zool: cephalopharinge-
головогрудный zool: cephalothoracic.
~ панцырь zool: carapace (of a crusta-
головогрудь zool: cephalothorax. |cean).
головокружение path: dizziness, giddiness; vertigo.

головокружение в связи с заболеванием глаз path: ocular vertigo.
~ ~ связи с заболеванием матки gyn: uterine vertigo. [fear.
~ от страха psych: dizziness from
~ при подагрическом диатезе path: lithemic vertigo.
~ ~ смотрении с большой высоты height vertigo.
головоногие (кл.) zool: cephalopods: nautili, squids, octopuses (Cephalo-
головоногий моллюск calamary,|poda). squid, cephalopod (Cephalopoda).
головоногое zool: cephalopod.
головотрубка entom: beak.
головохордовые zool: cephalochordates (Cephalochorda).
головчатая кость запястья anat: capitate, os magnum.
головчатое соцветие bot: head (a dense cluster of sessile flowers).
головчатый zool: cephalate.
~ рак phytp: nail-head canker.
голод 1. hunger; 2. famine.
голодание starvation.
голодать starve.
голодная боль hunger pain.
~ диета starvation diet.
голодный отёк path: nutritional edema, starvation e., famine dropsy.
~ психоз famine psychosis, p. induced by starvation.
~ тиф = сыпной тиф.
голое ядро hist: naked nucleus.
голожаберный моллюск zool: nudibranchiate; see also морской сли-
голозёрный bot: hull-less. зень.
голозойное питание holozoic nutrition, phagotrophy.
голокринная железа anat: holocrine gland, holocrinous g.
голомянковые (сем.) ichth: Comepho-
голорепа = кольраби. ridae.
голосемянные bot: gymnosperms (Gymnospermae).
голосемянный bot: gymnosperm(ous).
голосовая связка anat: vocal fold, true v. cord, plica vocalis.
~ щель anat: glottis, rima glottidis.
голосовое дрожание physl: tactile fremitus.
голосумчатые грибы bot: gymnoasci.
голотелки (сем.) entom: Psilidae.
голотелый zool: gymnosomatous.
голотурии zool: holothurians, sea cucumbers (Holothurioidea).

голотурия zool: holothurian, sea cucumber.
~ съедобная edible h. (H. edulis).
голофитное питание zool: holozoic nutrition.
голофитный bot: holophytic.
голоцветный bot: nudiflorous.
голубая акула zool: ground shark (Carcharhinus).
~ плесень blue mold, (Penicillium glaucum).
~ ползучая трава blue couch grass (Cynodon incompletus, Nees).
~ рыбка blue chromis (Demoisellea cyanea).
*голуби (отр.) orn: columbs (Columbae).
голубика bot: Alpine bilberry, bog bilberry (Vaccinium uliginosum, L.)
голубиные (сем.) orn: doves and pigeons (Columbidae).
голубиный помет pigeon dung.
голубки = водосбор.
голубой коралл zool: blue coral (Heliopora).
~ краб zool: blue crab (Callinectes sapidus).
голубок = голубь.
голубь orn: dove, pigeon (Columba livia).
~ бухарский = голубь-трубач.
~ веерохвостый = г. трубастый.
~ дикий wood pigeon, ringdove (C. palumbus).
~ зобастый cropper.
~ каролинский траурный mourning dove, turtledove (Zenaidura macroura, Z. carolinensis).
~ лесной = голубь дикий, клинтух.
~ -самец male pigeon.
~ трубастый fantail (Sphenocercus).
*~ -трубач trumpet.
~ флорентийский runt.
~ хохлатый jacobin (Chalcoptera).
~ чистый runt.
голубянка entom: blue butterfly, copper b. (Polyommatus virgaureae).
голый naked.
Гольджи Golgi.
Гольмгрен Holmgren.
гольян ichth: Phoxinus.
гоматропин pharm: homatropine.
гомбо = гибиск съедобный.
гомеопат homeopath(ist).
гомеопатический homeopathic.
гомеопатия homeopathy.
гомеостазис homeostasis.
гоми = просо итальянское.
гомогамный bot: homogamous.
гомогенизированное молоко homogenized milk.
гомогенизировать homogenize.
гомогенитальность path: homogenitality.
гомогенитальный path: homogenital.
гомогенный homogeneous.
гомозигоз genet: homozygosis.
гомозигота genet: homozygote.
гомозиготный homozygous.
гомойотермный homoiothermal.
гомологическая перевивка homograft.
гомологический = гомологичный.
гомологичный homologous.
гомология homology.
гомосексуализм path: homosexuality.
гомосексуалист homosexual.
гомосексуальный (субъект) homosexual.
гомоспецифический homospecific.
гомоталличный homothallic.
гомотрансплант surg: homoplastic graft, homograft.
гомотрансплантация кожи skin homograft.
гомоцистеин homocysteine.
гомфозус ichth: beaked wrasse (Gomphosus); akilolo (G. varius).
гомфонема bot: Gomphonema (algae).
гон = течка.
гонада bio: gonad.
гонадный gonadal.
гонадотропин gonadotropin.
гонадотропный gonadotropic.
гонидиальный gonidial.
гонидий gonidium.
гонка = течка.
гонобобель = голубика.
гонозоид zool: gonozooid (of a medusa)
гонококк gonococcus.
гонококковая инфекция gonococcal infection, gonococcic infection.
гонорейный артрит gonorrheal arthritis.
~ ревматизм gonorrheal rheumatism.
гонорея ven: gonorrhea.
гонофор zool: gonophore.
гончая zool: coursing dog (Canis familiaris vulpicapus).
~ -лисья foxhound.
~ на коротких ногах beagle (C. familiaris irritans).
горб path: hump, hunch; humpback.
горбатка = шипоноска.
горбатость path: gibbosity.
горбатый humpbacked, gibbous.
~ бык (индийский) = зебу.
горбач = головач 1.
горбуша humpback salmon, pink s. (Oncorhynchus gorbuscha).
горбушка ichth: Erythroculter oxycephalus.

горбылёвая рыба thunder pumper (Haplonotus grunniens);black drum (Pogonias
горбылёвые (сем.) Sciaenidae.|cromis).
горбыль светлый ichth: yellowfin croak
er (Umbrina cirrosa).
~ чёрный Corvina nigra.
горгонида zool: gorgonid (of the
phylum Coelentrata).
гордовик сливолистный =
гордовина сливолистная.
гордовина bot: viburnum, arrow-wood,
laurestinus (Viburnum, L.)
~ сливолистная bot: black haw, sweet
haw, stagbush (V. prunifolium, L.)
горение combustion.
~ сена = самосогревание сена.
~ яблок phytp: apple scald.
горец bot: knotweed, smartweed, joint-
weed (Polygonum).
~ аптечный = горец змеиный.
~ вьющийся black bindweed, wild buckwheat (P. convolvulus, L.) [bium, L.)
~ земноводный water smartweed (P.amphi
~ змеиный bistort (P. bistorta, L.)
~ кустарниковый false buckwheat
(P. dumetorum, L.)
~ почечуйный lady's thumb, heart's
ease (P. persicaria, L.) [lare).
~ птичий knotgrass, knotweed (P. avicu-
горечавка bot: gentian (Gentiana, L.)
~ конская feverwort (Triosteum).
~ крестовидная cruciate gentian
(Gentiana cruciata, L.) [L.)
~ мыльная soapwort gentian (G. saponaria
~ синяя march g. (G. pneumonanthe, L.)
~ эндрью closed g. (G. Andrewsii,Griseb)
горечавковые (сем.) bot: gentian family (Gentianaceae).
горечи pharm: bitters.
горизонтальное положение horizontal
posture, decubitus. [G. savagei).
горилла zool: gorilla (Gorilla gorilla,
горихвостка(-лысушка) orn: redstart
(Phoenicurus phoenicurus).
~ садовая icterine warbler
(Hypolais icterina).
горицвет весенний adonis (Adonis
vernalis, L.) [Desf.)
~ кожистый lychnis (Lychnis coronaria,
горичник bot: masterwort (Imperatoria
ostruthium, Peucedanum ostruthium,Koch)
"горка" anat: monticle, monticulus.
горлица orn: turtledove
(Streptopelia turtur).
горло anat: throat.

горловой gular, guttural.
горловые хрипы path: guttural rales.
горлюха bot: yellow succory (Picris,L.)
горляная трава = колокольчик
крапиволистный.
горлянка = тыква горлянка.
~ сухоцвет = цмин песчаный.
гормидиум bot: Hormidium. [um.
гормогоний bot: hormogone, hormogoni-
гормон physl: hormone.
~ надпочечников arterenol, norepine-
гормональный = гормонный.|phrine.
гормонный hormonic, hormonal.
гормонообразующий hormonogenic, hor-
гормоциста bot:hormocyst.|monopoietic.
горная антилопа rock-jumper.
~ болезнь mountain sickness.
горностаевые cf. моли.
горностай zool: ermine, stoat, winter
weasel (Mustela erminea). [dae.
горные сомики (сем.) ichth: Sisori-
горный лев zool: mountain lion, see
~ лён asbestos. кугуар.
городской врач city physician, town
городчатый лист bot:crenate leaf.|p.
горох bot: pea (Pisum sativum).
~ австралийский = макадамия.
~ бараний = нут.
~ в "стручках" pea pod.
~ голубиный pigeon pea, grandul arhar
(Cajanus indicus); see вигна катьян
~ земляной hog peanut (Amphicarpa). г.
~ коровий = вигна.
~ кофейный = нут.
~ лущильный shelling pea (P.sativum).
~ мозговой marrow pea (P. sativum,
L. var. medullare). [мозговой.
~ морщинистый wrinkled pea, see г.
~ огородный garden pea, eating p.
(P. sativum, L. var. vulgare, Pahl.)
~ полевой field pea, (P. sativum).
~ прерийный prairie pea (Lathyrus
venosus, Muhl.)
~ сахарный sugar pea, honey p., edible
podded p. (P. sativum saccharatum).
~ спаржевый asparagus p. (Lotus tetra-
~ степной = г. прерийный.|gonolobus).
~ турецкий chick-pea, mother pea,
see нут.
гороховидная кость (запястья)
anat: pisiform bone.
горошек bot: vetch, pea, tare.
~ воробьиный tufted vetch, Canada pea,
bird's tare (Vicia cracca, L.)
~ гусиный = г. воробьиный.

горошек душистый lady pea, sweet p. (Lathyrus odoratus).
~ журавлиный vetchling, wild pea (Lathyrus, L.)
~ зелёный green pea (Pisum sativum).
~ мышиный = г. воробьиный.
~ одноцветковый one-flowered tare (Vicia articulata, Horn.)
~ полевой maple pea, dun p., Austrian winter p. (Pisum arvense, L.)
~ сорный wild vetch, spring v. (Vicia segetalis, Thuill.)
горошина bot: grain of pea.
~ (моллюск) zool: bivalve mollusk Pisidium amnicum.
горошковидный pisiform.
гортанное зеркало laryngeal mirror.
гортанный laryngeal, guttural.
~ желудочек anat: sinus of the larynx.
гортань anat: larynx.
гортензия bot: hydrangea (Hydrangea, L.)
~ садовая hydrangea (H. opuloides, Koch.)
горчак 1. ichth: Rodeus sericeus; 2. bot: see горечавка.
горчица bot: mustard (Sinapis).
~ белая white mustard (S. alba, L., Brassica hirta, Moench.)
~ дикая = г. полевая; рокет-салат.
~ индийская Indian mustard, conringia (Conringia orientalis, Brassica juncea).
~ китайская Chinese mustard, leaf mustard (Brassica juncea, Coss., or Sinapis juncea, L.)
~ полевая field mustard (Brassica arvensis, L., or B. sinapistrum, Boiss.)
~ сарептская = г. китайская.
~ чёрная black mustard (Brassica nigra, Sinapis nigra).
~ шпинатная tendergreen, mustard spinach (Sinapis juncea, L.)
горчичник pharm: sinapism, mustard plaster, m. paper, charta sinapis.
горчичный газ mustard gas.
~ спирт pharm: spirit of mustard.
горькая настойка pharm: bitter tincture.
~ (слабительная) соль = английская соль.
~ ямчатость phytp: bitter pit (on fruits).
горький миндаль pharm: bitter almond.
горькушка bot: Lactarius rufus, Scop. (mushroom).
горячая ванна hot bath.
~ примочка med: stupe.
госпитализация hospitalization.
госпитализировать hospitalize.
госпиталь hospital (predominantly military).
госпиталь для выздоравливающих convalescent hospital.
~-изолятор isolation hospital.
госпитальная гангрена hospital gangrene, nosocomial gangrene.
госпитальное лечение h. treatment.
~ судно mil: hospital ship, ambulance boat.
госпитальный больной in-patient.
государственная медицина state medicine, federal m., socialized m.
Государственный институт для усовершенствования врачей State Institute for Improving (the Knowledge of) Physicians.
готтентотский фартук = срамный фартук.
гофманские капли pharm: Hoffmann's drops, spirit of ether.
гофрированный фильтр lab: goffered filter.
Гочкин Hodgkin.
граафов пузырёк hist: Graafian follicle.
граб bot: hornbean, ironwood (Carpinus, L.)
~ американский American hornbeam, bluebeech, waterbeech (Carpinus caroliniana, var. virginiana).
~ виргинский bluebeech (C. virginiana) hop hornbeam, leverwood (Ostria v.)
~ европейский European hornbeam (C. betulus, L.)
грабельки = живокость посевная.
граберов орган entom: Graber's organ.
граблик = аистник цикутолистный.
гравида gravida, pregnant wooman.
гравилат bot: avens (Geum).
~ городской avens, herb bennet (G. urbanum, L.)
~ прибрежный = г. речной.
~ речной water avens, purple avens (G. rivale, L.)
градинка chalaza (of an egg).
градусник collq: thermometer.
гражданский авиационный врач civilian flight surgeon.
грамицидин pharm: gramicidin.
грамова трава = бутелуоя.
грамотрицательный mcbio: gram-negative.
грамположительный gram-positive.
гран pharm: grain (weight).
гранат(ник) bot: pomegranate (Punica granatum, L.)
гранатное дерево = гранатник.
гранатовые (сем.) bot: pomegranate family (Punicaceae).

гранулёзоклеточная миобластома granular-cell myoblastoma.
гранулёма granulation growth.
гранулировать granulate.
гранулобластома granuloblastoma.
гранулопения granulopenia.
гранулоцит granulocyte.
грануляционная ткань hist: granulation tissue.
грануляция hist: granulation.
граптолитовые zool: class Graptolithoidae (of the subphylum Hemichorda).
грателупия bot: red algae Grateloupia; tamba-nori, mukade-nori, limu pakaelewaa (G. filicina); cemenori (G.affinis).
граус orn: grouse.
~ красный = куропатка шотландская.
грацилярия bot: red algae Gracilaria; limu manauea (G. coronopifolia); Ceylon moss (G. lichenoides, G. confervoides).
грач orn: rook (Corvus frugilegus).
гребенник bot: dog's-tail (Cynosurus cristatus, L.)
~ обыкновенный crested dog's-tail (C. cristatus).
гребенчатый усик entom: pectinate antenna.
гребенщик bot: tamarisk (Tamarix, L.)
~ французский French tamarisk, salt cedar (T. gallica).
гребень crest, comb; see also гребешок.
~ винограда bot: stalk of grapevine.
~ грудной кости orn: carina.
гребешковая мышца anat: pectineous muscle.
гребешковый pectinate, cristate, cristal.
гребешок 1. crest, crista, comb; 2. zool: pecten, comb, ctene, scallop, squim, frill (Pecten gibbus, P. irradiatus).
~ большеберцовой кости anat: tibial crest.
~ морской zool: scallop, pecten (Pecten)
~ ~ исландский P. islandicus.
~ ~ черноморский P. ponticus.
~ обыкновенный common scallop (P. maximus).
гребляк entom: water boatman (Corixa).
гребная пластинка zool: comb, ctene.
гребневидный усик entom: pectinate antenna, comb-like a.
гребневики (кл.) zool: comb jellies, sea walnuts, ctenophores, clenophorans (Ctenophora).
грегарины (отр.) zool: gregarines (Gregarinida).
грейпфрут grapefruit (Citrus grandis).
грелка heater, hot-water bottle, h.-w.bag
гремучая змея zool: rattlesnake (Crotalus).
грена entom: silkworm eggs.
гренадилла = страстоцвет.
гренландский кит zool: Greenland whale, arctic right w., bowhead w. (Balaena mysticetus).
~ тюлень zool: Greenland seal, harp s. (Histriophoca groenlandica, Phoca g.)
грецкая губка = греческая г.
греческая губка = сотовая губка, туалетная губка.
гречиха buckwheat (Fagopyrum esculentum, Moench., or F. sagittatum, Pilib., or Polygonum fagopyrum, L.)
~ двухрядная = горец птичий.
~ земноводная water smartweed (P. amphibium)
~ птичья = горец птичий.
~ сахалинская sacaline (P. sachalinense).
~ татарская Indian b., duck wheat, Kangra b. (P. tataricum, L.)
гречихоцветные (пор.) bot: Polygonales order.
гречишка вьюнковая = горец вьющийся.
гречишные (сем.) bot: buckwheat family (Polygonaceae).
гречка расширенная = паспалум.
гриб bot: fungus; mushroom.
~ -зонтик пёстрый parasol mushroom (Lepiota procera, Fr.)
~ на длинной ножке bot: leggy mushroom.
~ -навозник = навозник.
грибки bot: fungi (molds, rusts, yeasts, etc.)
~ -фузарии phytp: fusaria.
грибковая болезнь fungus disease.
грибкового происхождения mycetogenous.
грибковое заболевание fungus disease, fungus infection, mycosis.
~ начало fungin.
~ поражение path: mycotic lesion.
~ растение mycetogenous plant.
грибковый fungous, fungal, fungic.
грибная муха entom: mushroom fly (Sciaridae).
грибница bot: mycelium, spawn.
грибное отравление muchroom poisoning.
грибной bot: fungal.
грибовидно разрастаться fungate.
грибовидное разрастание рака oncol: cancer mushroom, c. fungosity.
~ разращение = грибовидное разрастание.
грибовидный fungiform, fungoid, muchroom-like.

грибовидный микоз path: mycosis fungoides.
~ сосочек anat: fungiform papilla.
грибок fungus, see грибки.
~ стригущего лишая thread fungus.
грибокорень bot: mycorrhiza.
грибообразный fungiform, fungoid.
грибоподобный = грибообразный.
грибы bot: fungi (phylum Fungi).
~ -водоросли bot: algae-like fungi, see фикомицеты.
грива zool: hackle, mane, crest.
гризли zool: grizzly bear (Ursus horribilis).
гринда grind whale, pilot w. (Globicephalus melas).
гринделия bot: gum-plant, gumweed, tarweed, sticky-heads (Grindelia).
гриот griott, see морель.
грипотерий zool: Grypotherium (a species of Gravigrada, cf. тихоходы).
грипп infect: grip(pe), influenza.
гриппозное состояние cold misery.
гриппозный психоз influenza psychosis.
гриф orn: vulture, Brit: griffon (Vultur)
*грифовые (сем.) orn: vultur family (Vulturidae).
гроздевидное сплетение anat: pampiniform plexus.
гроздевидный racemose.
гроздовник = ключ-трава.
гроздь bot: fascicle, bunch, cluster.
громадная рыба-фонарь giant lanternfish (Mystophum affine).
громкоголосый stentorophonous.
громкость звука loudness of sound.
грубое изменение gross change.
~ повреждение molar lesion.
грубозернистый coarse-grained.
грубые и густые волосы shag.
грубый тремор path: coarse tremor.
грудина anat: breastbone, sternum.
грудинная линия anat: midsternal line, linea sternalis.
грудинный anat: sternal.
грудино-ключичная связка anat: sternoclavicular ligament.
~ -ключично-сосцевидная мышца anat: sternocleidomastoid muscle.
~ -ключичный сустав anat: sternoclavicular joint.
~ -подъязычная мышца anat: sternohyoid muscle.
~ -щитовидная мышца anat: sternothyroid muscle.
грудная аорта anat: thoracic aorta.
~ артерия anat: mammary artery.
~ жаба int: breast pang, angina pectoris.
~ клетка anat: thorax, chest.
~ кость 1. anat: see грудина. 2. zool: brisket (of a cow); orn: keel bone.
~ мышца (большая, малая) anat: pectoralis muscle (major, minor).
*~ нога zool: peraepod, trunk leg (of a crustacea).
~ полость anat: thoracic cavity.
~ чешуйка entom: antisquama.
грудник = канатник.
грудника bot: Indian mallow, flowering maple (Abutilon, Gaert.)
грудница med: mastitis, mammitis; vet: inflammation of udder.
грудное дыхание physl: thoracic respiration.
грудной лимфатический проток = грудной проток.
~ отдел спинного мозга anat: thoracic cord.
~ плавник zool: pectoral fin; ichth: wing (of flying fish).
~ проток anat: thoracic duct, ductus thoracicus.
~ ребёнок suckling, nursling.
~ сбор pharm: pectoral species.
~ сосок anat: breast nipple, papilla.
~ чай pharm: breast tea.
грудноспинной нерв anat: thoracodorsal nerve, long subscapular nerve.
грудные позвонки anat: thoracic vertebrae, dorsal v., vertebrae thoracales.
грудоакромиальная артерия anat: thoracoacromial artery.
грудобрюшная преграда anat: diaphragm, midriff.
грудобрюшный anat: phrenic.
грудь anat: breast, thorax, pectus.
груздь bot: peppery lactarius, pepper cap (Lactarius piperatus, Fr.)
групер ichth: grouper (Epinephelus, Lobotes surinamensis).
группа гифов bot: group of hyphae, mycelium.
~ крови blood group.
~ разновидностей bio: convarieties.
~ сообществ bio: formation.
группоспецифический mcbio: group-specific.
груша bot: pear (Pyrus communis, L.)
~ анжуйская Anjou pear.
~ бергамотная bergamot pear (P. bergamota).

груша-бессемянка seedless pear.
~ -долговетка long-stalked pear.
~ дынная melon pear (Solanum muricatum, Ait.)
~ земляная girasole, American artichoke Jerusalem artichoke (Helianthus tuberosus, L.)
~ -скороспелка jargonel(le), early harvest pear, hasting pear.
грушанка bot: pyrola, wintergreen, shinleaf (Pyrola, L.)
грушанковые (сем.) bot: wintergreen family, shinleaf family (Pyrolaceae).
грушевидная мышца anat: piriformis muscle.
грушевидное углубление anat: piriform recess.
грушевидный pear-shaped, pyriform (pyriferus).
грушеобразный = грушевидный.
грыжа path: hernia, rupture.
~ брюшной стенки ventral hernia, abdominal hernia, epigastric hernia.
~ матки gyn: metrocele, hysterocele.
~ печени surg: hepatocele.
~ прямой кишки surg: rectal hernia, rectocele.
~ пузыря surg: bladder hernia, cystocele
~ селезенки surg: lienocele.
грыжевое кольцо surg: hernial ring.
грыжевой hernial, herniary.
~ бандаж truss.
~ мешок surg: hernial sack.
грызун zool: rodent, gnawer (Rodentia).
грызуны zool: rodents, gnawing mammals (Rodentia).
грызущая боль gnawing pain; av med: "aviator's stomach".
грызущие насекомые sawfly insects, mandibulate insects.
грюнколь bot: borecole, kale, see капуста листовая тысячеголовая.
грязевая ванна phys-ther: mud bath, moor-bath.
~ припарка mud poultice.
грязеед = илоед.
грязелечение phys-ther: pelotherapy.
гуава bot: guava (Psidium guajava, L.)
гуайява = гуава.
гуанако zool: guanaco (Lama huanachus).
гуанин guanin(e).
гуано bird dung, guano.
губа lip.
губа шейки матки anat: labium cervicis uteri.
губан ichth: tautog, moll, oyster fish (Tautoga onitis); wrasse.
~ зубчатый Crenilabrus.
губановые (сем.) ichth: tautogs (Labridae).
губернакулум helm: accessory piece.
губительная температура deadly temperature.
губка zool: sponge (Spongia).
~ лиственичная bot: white agaric (Polyporus laricus).
~ растительная vegetable sponge, see люфа.
×~ "слоновое ухо" elephant's sponge.
губки (тип) zool: sponges (Porifera, Spongia).
губной labial.
~ лишай derm: coldsore, herpes, facialis.
губоногая многоножка zool: centipede (Chilopoda).
губоногие zool: chilopods (subclass Chilopoda).
~ многоножки (отр.) zool: centipedes (Chilopoda).
губоцветные (сем.) bot: mint family, salvia f., ringents, labiate (Labiatae).
губоцветный bot: labiate(d), ringent.
губчатое костное вещество anat: diploe, cancellous bone.
губчатость cancellation, sponginess.
губчатый cancellous, cancellate, spongy, see ноздреватый.
гудсония bot: hudsonia (Hudsonia, L.); golden heather (H. ericoides).
гузка orn: croup.
гулявник bot: tumbling mustard (Sisymbrium, L.); hedge m. (S. officinale).
~ чесночный Jack-by-the-hedge (S. alliaria).
гумай bot: beardgrass (Andropogon, L.); Johnson grass (A. halepensis, Brot.).
гуманность humanism, humanity.
гумбо = бамия.
гумин humine.
гуминовый humic.
гумма ven: gumma.
гуммиарабик gum arabic, acacia [mucilage.
гумм(и)оз phytp: gum flow, gummosis.
гуммозный узел ven: gummatous node.
гуморальный humoral.
гумус agr: humus.
гумусо-железистая почва agr: humic ferruginous soil.
гумусовый humic.

гумусообразовательный humus-forming.
ГУТ = гамма-установка, терапевтическая.
гуппи guppy, mosquito fish; see also гамбузия.
гура = кола.
гурахаро = даман.
гусак orn: gander, he-goose.
гусеница entom: caterpillar, crawler, lepidopterous larva.
~ бабочки сезия borer (Sesia).
~ белянки капустной cabbage worm.
~ изозомы пшеничной галловой wheat-straw worm.
~ капустной мухи radish maggot.
~ моли морковной parsnip webworm.
~ -пяденица looping caterpillar, inchworm; see also землемер, пяденица.
~ редечной мухи radish maggot.
~ совки озимой cutworm, surface-feeding caterpillar (Euxoa segetum, Hadena, Agrotis).
~ стеклянницы смородинной = г. бабочки сезия.
гусеницеловка agr: caterpillar-collecting device.
гусеницеобразный grublike.
гусёнок zool: gosling.
гусиная кожа goose flesh, anserine skin, cutis anserina.
~ лапка 1. zool: goose's foot; 2. bot: see лапчатка гусиная.
~ походка path: waddling gait.
"гусиные лапки" bot: good king Henry, mercury (Chenopodium Bonus-Henrichus, L.)
гусиный жир goose grease, g. fat.
густая культура bact: crowded culture.
~ сетчатость close netting.
густера ichth: Blicca bjoerkna.
гусь orn: goose (Anser anser).
~ белый white-fronted (A. albifrons).
~ дикий = гусь серый.
~ серый gray goose, greylag (A. cinereus).
гусята pl. of гусёнок.
гусятина goose meat.
гусятник = горец птичий.
гуща mash.
ГХЦГ (гексахлорциклогексан) chem: hexachloro-cyclohexan.
ГЭТК (гексаэтилтетрафосфат) chem: hexaethyl-tetraphosphate.

Д

давать (лекарство) administer (the drug).
~ наркоз surg: anesthetize.
~ почки bot: bud.
~ ростки germinate, sprout.
~ сильное слабительное vet: drench.
~ эфир (для наркоза) etherize.
давление pressure.
~ столба спинномозговой жидкости physl: intrathecal pressure.
давящее чувство psych: incubus, nightmare.
дазия bot: red algae Dasya; cherille weed (Dasya pedicillata).
дайкон = редька японская.
дактилёспарус jackass fish, morwong (Dactylosparus macropterus).
дактиломегалия path: dactylomegaly.
дактилоскопия legl: fingerprinting.
далеко зашедший случай path: advanced case.
далия = георгин(а).
даллиевый (сем.) ichth: Alaska blackfishes (Dalliidae).
даллия = чёрная рыба.
дальневосточная сардинка = иваси.
дальнейшая точка ясного зрения ophth: far point.
дальнейшее заражение mcbio: subinoculation.
дальнейший пассаж mcbio: subpassage.
дальнозоркий ophth: farsighted, hypermetropic, presbyopic, presbyope.
дальнозоркость ophth: farsightedness, far sight, hypermetropia, presbyopia.
дальтонизм ophth: Daltonism.
дальтоник ophth: achromate.
дамальихтис surf-fish (Damalichthys argyrosomus).
даман zool: daman (Hyrax).
даманы (отр.) zool: hyracoids (Hyracoidea).
"дамские пальчики" bot: lady's fingers (grapes).
Данлэп Dunlap.
данные data, findings, specification.
~ анализа analysis, findings.
~ аускультации auscultation findings.
~ вскрытия autopsy findings.
~ исследования findings.
~ лабораторного исследования laboratory findings.

данные операции surg: operative findings.
~ о питании nutritional data.
~ рентгеновского исследования x-ray findings.
дантист dentist.
дантония bot: wild oat grass (Danthonia).
Дарвин Darwin.
дарвинизм Darwinism.
дарвинистская точка зрения Darwinian point of view.
дарвинов бугорок anat: Darwin's tubercle.
дать p. a. of давать.
дафиля orn: pintail (Dafila acuta).
дафния zool: water flea (Daphnia).
дача administration (of a drug).
~ эфира для наркоза surg: etherization
дающий низкую температуру cryogenic.
~ подземные побеги bot: stoloniferous.
два раза в день twice daily, bis in die, b.i.d.
дважды изогнутый biangular.
~ рожавшая женщина bipara.
~ тройчатый лист bot: biternate leaf.
двенадцатиперстная кишка anat: duodenum.
двенадцатиперстно-тощая кривизна duodenojejunal flexure.
двенадцатиперстный duodenal.
двигательная реакция motor response.
~ функция neur: efferent function.
двигательное ощущение physl: kinesthetic sensation, muscle sense.
~ расстройство neur: motor disturbance
двигательный motor, locomotive, locomotory.
~ аппарат организма anat: motor apparatus, locomotorium.
~ нерв anat: motor nerve.
~ параллакс ophth: motion parallax.
движение movement, motion, travel.
~ больных patient turnover.
~ вправо ophth: dextroduction.
~ глаз ocular movement(s).
~ кзади dorsiduction.
~ книзу ophth: subduction.
~ лимфы lymph flow.
~ соков bot: circulation of sap.
движения плода obstet: fetal movements.
движущая сила moving force, agent.
двоение в глазах ophth: double vision, diplopia.
двойная гиперфория ophth: double hyperphoria.
~ гипофория ophth: double hypophoria.
~ матка path: uterus duplex, u. didelphys, dimetria.
~ окраска lab: double staining.
двойная чашка lab: double dish.
двойное изображение ophth: double image.
~ оплодотворение bot: double fertilization.
~ преломление birefringence.
~ сознание psych: double consciousness.
двойнозуб = морской кольчатый карась.
двойной набор хромосом genet: diploid.
~ переворот av med: snap roll.
~ пульсовой удар dicrotism.
~ слух double hearing.
~ урод double monster.
двойственное сознание psych: double consciousness.
двойчатый didymous.
двояковогнутый 1. zool: amphicelous; 2. biconcave.
двоякодышащие zool: dipnoans (Dipnoi).
~ рыбы lungfishes.
двоякодышащий zool: dipnoan.
двоякозубчатый лист bot: doubly serrate leaf.
двояконогий рак zool: scud (Amphipoda); see also бокоплав.
двоякоперисторассечённый bot: bipinnatifid.
двоякоперистый bot: bipinnate.
дву- di-, bi-, ambi-, ampho-, duo-, two- twin, twice, double, see also двух-.
двубоковая симметрия bilateral symmetry.
двубратственный bot: diadelphous.
двубрюшная мышца anat: digastric muscle.
двувалентный divalent.
двуветвистый bot: two-branched, biramose, biramous.
двугаметный genet: digametic.
двуглавая мышца anat: bicipital muscle.
~ ~ бедра anat: biceps femoris (muscle).
~ ~ плеча anat: biceps brachii.
двуглавый anat: bicipital.
двугнёздный bio: bilocular.
двугорбый верблюд zool: two-hump camel, Bactrian c. (Camelus bactrianus).
двугубый bilabiate.
двудольное растение dicotyledon.
двудольные (кл.) bot: dicotyledons (Dicotyledoneae).
двудольный bot: dicotyledonous, diclinous, bilobate.
двудомный bot: dioecious, dioicous.
двудырчатый two-hole, biforate.
двужгутиковый bio: biflagellate.
двузернянка культурная = эммер.

двузиготный genet: dizygotic.
двузубчатый = двузубый.
двузубый bidental, bidentate.
двуионный потенциал bio: bi-ionic potential.
двукамерный bilocular.
двукисточник тростниковидный = канареечник тростниковый.
двукрылое насекомое dipterous insect, dipteron, two-winged fly.
двукрылые (отр.) entom: dipterons, flies (Diptera).
двукрылый dipterous.
двулёгочные (отр.) zool: Dipneumones.
двулепестковый bot: dipetalous.
двулистный bot: bifoliate.
двулопастный bot: bilobed, bilobate.
двуногие zool: biped, bipedal.
двуногое (животное) biped.
двуокись углерода chem: carbon dioxide.
двуосный сустав anat: biaxial joint.
двупалость path: didactylism.
двупарноногие zool: diplopods (Diplopoda.
двупарнорезцовые грызуны (подотр.) zool: rodents of the suborder Duplicidentata.
двупарноусые zool: Teleiocerata, see жабродышащие.
двуперистая мышца anat: bipennate muscle.
двуперисторазрезанный bot: bipinnatifid.
двупильчатый bot: double serrate.
двупластинчатый лист bot: binary leaf.
двуполостная матка path: uterus bilocularis, u. septus, bipartite u.
двуполостный two-cavity, two-chambered
двуполость bisexuality.
двуполосчатый bivittate.
двуполый bisexual.
двупредсердные моллюски (отр.) zool: Diotocardia.
двураздельный bipartite, biseptate, divaricate, bifid, bilobed, bilobate.
двуразовый two-dose.
двурезцовые zool: Diprotodontia.
двуресничный zool: biciliate.
двурогая матка path: uterus bicornic.
двурогий bicornate, bicornu(a)te, bicornuous.
двуродовой bio: bigeneric.
двуручное исследование bimanual examination.
двуручный поворот obstet: bimanual version, combined version.
двурядный bio: bifarious, distichous.
двусеменодольные bot: dicotyledonous, diclinous.
двусернокислый хинин pharm: quinine bisulfate.
двуслойный two-layer, bistratal, bistratose.
двуспоровый bot: disporous.
двустворчатая ракушка = д. моллюск.
двустворчатое зеркало gyn: duckbill speculum.
двустворчатые zool: bivalves (Bivalva, Lamellibranchiata), see пластинчатожаберные.
~ моллюски (кл.) = пластинчатожаберные.
двустворчатый bicuspid, mitral, bivalve.
~ клапан anat: bicuspid valve.
~ моллюск zool: bivalve mollusk: clam (Spisula, Venus, Mya, etc.), mussel, scallop, lamellibranch, razor shell.
двустебельное растение double stem plant.
двусторонне-симметричные (разд.) zool: bilaterally symmetrical animals, acelomate bilateria (Bilateria, Bilateralia).
двусторонний bifacial; two-way, bilateral, ambilateral.
~ плеврит double pleurisy.
двусторонность bilateralism.
двусторонняя одноименная диплопия ophth: bilateral homonymous diplopia.
~ перекрестная диплопия ophth: bilateral crossed diplopia.
~ пневмония double pneumonia.
~ симметрия bilateral symmetry.
двутычиночный bot: two-stamen, diandrous.
двуугленислый chem: bicarbonate.
двуузловой binodal.
двуустка zool: distome, two-mouth fluke.
~ кошачья cat fluke (Opistorchis falineus).
~ сибирская = д. кошачья.
двуухий binaurial, binotic.
~ стетоскоп binaurial stethoscope.
двухгодичный biennial.
двухгодовалый biennial.
двухгодовик biennial; ichth: two-year-old.
двухгрупповые тычинки bot: diadelphous stamens.
двухдетная obstet: duipara.
двухкамерный желудок binocular stomach.
двухконтурный double-contoured.
двухлетний biennial.

двухлетник bot: biennial.
двухлеток птицы second-summer bird.
двухлористый chem: bichloride.
двухлучевой корень bot: diarch root.
двухмускульный bimuscular.
двухотверстный biforate.
двухпластинчатый bot: bilamellate.
двухромовокислый chem: bichromate.
двухфазный two-phase, biphase.
двухходовой катетер two-way catheter, Bozeman's c.
двучленистый biarticulate.
двуядерный hist: binucleate.
двуячеистый bilocular.
ДДТ (дихлордифенилтрихлорэтан) chem: DDT.
деанестетическое средство pharm: deanesthetisant.
дебил psych: moron.
дебильность mental debility, moronity.
"девица в зелени" = чернушка полевая.
девичье зеркало bot: Venus'-looking glass (Specularia speculum, DC.)
девичья трава bot: feverfew (Chrysanthemum parthenium).
девонский Devonian.
девственная плева anat: hymen, virginal membrane, maidenhead.
девственник male virgin.
девственница virgin.
девственное размножение bio: parthenogenesis, virgin birth.
девственность virginity, maidenhood.
девственный virginal.
девясил bot: elecampane, scabwort (Inula helenium, L.)
девясильная камфора helenin.
девятибальная система av med: stanine system.
девятииглая колюшка ichth: nine-spined stickleback (Pungitius).
дегазация degassing.
дегазировать degas.
дегельминтизация = глистогонное лечение.
дегенерат degenerate.
дегенеративный degenerative.
дегенерация degeneration.
дегидраза chem: dehydrogenase.
дегидроаскорбиновая кислота dehydroascorbic acid.
дегидроизоандростерон dehydroiso-androsterone.
дегидрохолат chem: dehydrocholate.
дёготь tar.
дегра degras.
дегтярная вода pharm: tar water.
дегтярное масло pharm: oil of tar.
~ мыло tar soap.
дедалия bot: dedalia fungi (Daedalia).
~ дубовая phytp: D. quercina, Pers.
дееспособность capacity for acting, activity.
дежурная сестра nurse on duty (in a hospital).
дезинсекция disinsection, disinsectization.
дезинтоксикация detoxication.
дезинфекция disinfection.
дезинфицировать disinfect.
дезинфицирующее средство disinfectant.
дезоксигенация av med: disoxygenation.
дезоксикортикостерон(ацетат) desoxycorticosterone(-acetate).
дезоксирибоза desoxyribose.
дезоксирибонуклеиновая кислота desoxyribonucleic acid.
дезориентация disorientation.
дезоровская личинка zool: Desor's larva (in heteronemertines).
деионизированная вода deionized water.
действие action, function, effect.
~ змеиного яда envenomation.
~ лекарства effect of a drug.
~ по врачебной технике manipulation.
действующее начало pharm: agent; principle
действующий совместно synergistic.
дейтеранопия ophth: deuteranopia.
дейтомерит zool: deutomerite.
декальцинация decalcification.
декальцинировать decalcify.
декантация decantation, defusion.
декантирование = декантация.
декапитатор obstet: decapitator, decollator.
декапитационный крючок obstet: decapitating hook.
декапитация obstet: decapitation, decollation.
декапода zool: decapod (crustacean).
декапсуляция surg: decapsulation.
декаптерус ichth: cigar-fish, scad, round robin (Decapterus punctatus).
декодон bot: swamp loosestrife (Decodon).
декокт pharm: decoction.
декомпенсация decompensation.
декомпрессионная болезнь av med: decompression sickness.
декомпрессия av med: decompression.

декоративное растение ornamental plant.
декортикация surg: decortication.
дексиотропный = противозакрученный.
декстральный dextral.
декстрозоазотный коэффициент urol: dextrose-nitrogen ratio, D:N ratio.
декубация imm: decubation.
декубитус decubitus ulcer, bedsore.
деламинация embr: delamination.
делать аборт gyn: perform an abortion.
~ анализ analize.
~ венесекцию surg: perform a venesection, phlebotomize.
~ нечувствительным anesthetize, make numb, deaden.
~ обратное титрование lab: restandardize.
~ поворот obstet: turn.
~ повторный разрез surg: reincise.
~ поперечный разрез surg: transect.
~ прививку 1. imm: inoculate, vaccinate; 2. bot: engraft.
~ посев bact: inoculate, seed.
~ ~ на пластинке bact: plate.
~ припарки foment, stupe.
~ трахеотомию surg: tracheotomize.
~ укол inject (hypodermically), give shot
деление division, fission, cleavage.
~ клетки cell division, cell fission.
~ на две части bipartition.
~ ~ сегменты genet: merotomy.
~ ядра genet: nuclear cleavage.
делессерия bot: Delesseria (alga).
делинт bot: delint.
делирий = бред.
делириозный синдром psych: delirious syndrome
делириум = бред.
делительная воронка = капельная в.
дельтовидная бугристость anat: deltoid tuberosity.
~ мышца anat: deltoid muscle.
~ связка anat: deltoid ligament.
дельфин zool: dolphin (Delphinus).
~ -касатка grampus.
~ обыкновенный common dolphin (D. delphis).
демаркационная линия line of demarcation.
демаркация demarcation.
деменция psych: dementia.
демерсальный demersal.
деминерализация demineralization.
демиэлинизация demyelinization.
демография demography.
демойнезианский desmoinesian.
демономаниак psych: demonomaniac.
демономания psych: demonomania.
демоноропс bot: rattan (Daemonorops).
демонофобия psych: demonophobia.
демонстративный demonstrative.
демонстрация demonstration; presentation (of patients).
демпинг-синдром dumping syndrome.
демьянка = баклажан.
денаркотизованный denarcotized.
денатур(из)ация denaturization.
денатурированный спирт denatured alcohol.
денге infect: dengue, dandy fever, breakbone f.
дендрит neur: dendrite,
дендроид dendroid.
дендроидный dendroid, dendritic.
дендроика orn: myrtle warbler (Dendr. coronata)
дендрология bot: dendrology.
дендрохимия dendro-chemistry.
денежник = ярутка полевая.
денервация surg: denervation.
денитрификаторы denitrifying bacteria.
денитрификация denitrification.
денитрифицировать denitrify.
денитрифицирующий denitrifying.
денсиметр densimeter.
дентин hist: dentin, ebur.
~ клыков моржей walrus ivory.
дентинная клетка dentinal cell.
дентинный каналец dentinal tubule.
день после облучения rad: postradiation day.
деонтология deontology.
деперсонализация psych: depersonalization.
депигментация depigmentation.
депилировать depilate.
депиляционный depilatory.
депиляция depilation.
деплазмолиз deplasmolysis.
депрессивный depressive.
депрессия depression.
депрессорный рефлекс depressor reflex.
дератизация san: deratization.
дербенник bot: loosestrife (Lythrum).
~ иволистный spiked loosestrife (L. salicaria).
дербенниковые (сем.) bot: loosestrife family (Lythraceae).
дёргание jerking, twitching, tug(ging)
дэргач = коростель.
дереализация psych: derealization.
деревей = стотысячник обыкновенный.
дерево жизни = туя.
~ смерти = анчар.

деревоподобный = древовидный.
деревянистый woody. [peg.
деревянная нога orthop: wooden leg,
деревянное масло pharm: sweet oil.
дереза bot: matrimony vine, boxthorn (Lycium, L.)
дереизм psych: dereism.
дёрен = кизил. [(Carnaceae).
дёренные (сем.) bot: dogwood family
держи-дерево Christ's thorn, Jerusalem thorn (Paliurus spina-Christi, Mill., or Rhamnus paliurus, L.)
дериват derivative.
дермальная мембрана dermis.
дермальный dermal, dermatic.
дерматит path: dermatitis. [sue.
дерматоген bot: dermatogen, cover tis-
дерматол pharm: bismuth subgallate.
дерматолог dermatologist.
дерматологический dermatological.
дерматология dermatology.
дерматома embr: dermatome.
дерматофит mcbio: dermatophyte.
дермографизм dermographia, dermography
дёрн sod, turf, sward.
дерновидный turflike, cespitose.
дернообразный = дерновидный.
деррис derris (insecticide).
деряба 1. orn: see дрозд-деряба; 2. bot: ecballium (Ecballium elaterium, A.Rich., or Momordica elaterium, Hort.)
дерябка bot: hedge bedstraw (Gallium mollugo); blue burr (Echinospermum lappula, Lehm.) [desaturation.
десатурация азота av med: nitrogen
дёсенный gingival, uletic.
десенсибилизация desensitization.
десенсибилиз(ир)овать desensitize.
десквамация derm: desquamation. [alga.
десмидиевая водоросль bot: desmid
десмидиевые (сем.) bot: desmids (Desmidiaceae).
десмургия surg: desmurgy.
десна odont: gingiva, gum.
деструктивный destructive.
деструкция destruction.
десятиногие моллюски (отр.) zool: ten-armed mollusks (Decapoda).
десятиногие раки (отр.) zool: ten-legged crustaceans (Decapoda).
десятиногое ракообразное zool: decapod (Decapoda).
десятирёберный decemcostate.
детёныш зверя zool: cub.
детерминированное дробление embr: determinate cleavage.

детка 1. entom: grub, brood (bees); 2. bot: multiplier; ratoon (in a bulb)
детоненавистничество psych: misope-
детородный genital, generative. dia.
~ член anat: penis; zool: pizzle.
деторождение childbearing.
детоубийство legl: infanticide.
детоубийца legl: murderer of an
детрит detritus. infant.
детритизация smallpox vaccination.
детритный detrital.
детритофаг zool: detritus eater.
детритояд(ное животное) detritus
детритоядный detritus-consuming.|eater.
детрокаж detrocage (of oysters).
детская болезнь childhood disease.
~ матка path: infantile uterus.
~ острица = острица.
~ площадка children's playground.
~ псевдолейкемия ped: infantile pseudoleukemia.
детские весы baby scale.
~ ясли children's creche, day nursery.
детский врач pediatrist (physician).
~ манежик creeping pen.
~ паралич infantile paralysis.
~ сад kindergarten.
~ скорбут infantile scurvy.[placenta.
детское место obstet: afterbirth,
детскость psych: childishness.
дефекат lime cakes.
дефекация defecation, egestion.
дефект defect, lack, failure.
~ верхней стенки мочеиспускательного канала epispadias.
~ глазных мышц deficiency of ocular
~ зрения deficiency of vision.|muscles.
дефензонат defensonat.
дефибрилляция defibrillation.
дефибринирование defibrination.
дефибринированная кровь defibrinated blood.
дефибринировать defibrinate.
деформация deformation.
децентрирование decentration.
децентрированный decentered.
децинормальный chem: decinormal, tenth-normal.
деятельная сила active force.
деятельность головного мозга cerebration, mental activity.
~ листьев bot: leaf activity.
джейран zool: Central Asian gazelle (Gazella subgutturosa).
джексоновская эпилепсия neur: Jacksonian epilepsy, focal e.

джем jam.
джеммель = одногорбый верблюд.
Джемс James.
джигетай zool: dziggetai, culan (Asinus hemionus).
джизлан = цикада хлопковая.
джиттер = джиттери.
джиттери vet: jittery (sex-linked nervous disorder in the chick).
джиу-джитсу j(i)ujitsu, judo.
Джонс Jones.
джонсонова трава = гумай.
джунгли jungles.
джут bot: jute (Corchorus olitorius, C. capsularis).
~ -нальта nalta jute.
джуфиш jewfish (Garrupa nigrita; Promicrops guttatus; Tarpon atlanticus).
дзелква bot: zelkova, zelkwa (Zelkova crenata, Spach.)
диабет diabetes (mellitus).
диабетик path: diabetic.
диабетическая кома = сахарный диабет.
диагноз diagnosis.
~ при выписке больного discharge diagnosis.
диагност(ик) diagnostician.
диагностика diagnostics.
диагностирование diagnostication, diagnosis.
диагностировать diagnose, diagnosticate.
диагностическая рентгеновская трубка diagnostic x-ray tube.
диаграмма diagram, chart, graph.
~ пульса med: sphygmogram.
диазоальбумин diazo albumin.
диазотируемый метаболит tox: diazotizable metabolite.
диализат dialyzate.
диализатор dialyzer.
диализ(ир)ованная среда dialized medium.
диаметр артерии anat: artery caliber.
диамокс pharm: diamox.
диапауза diapause.
диапедез path: diapedesis.
диапедетический diapedetic.
диарея diarrhea.
диартроз anat: diarthrosis.
диастер hist: diaster.
диастола diastole.
диастолический шум path: diastolic murmur.
диастолическое давление diastolic pressure.
диатез diathesis, constitution.
диатермия phys-ther: diathermy.
диатетический path: diathetic.
диатомея bot: diatom.
диатомин diatomin.
диатомит diatomite, diatomaceous earth
диатомовая водоросль bot: diatom alga.
диатомовые водоросли bot: diatoms (Diatomeae).
диатомовый diatomaceous.
диафаноскоп diaphanoscope.
диафиз anat: diaphysis.
диафиз(ар)ный anat: diaphyseal.
диафрагма diaphragm, midriff.
диафрагмальная артерия phrenic artery.
~ грыжа surg: diaphragmatocele.
~ плевра anat: diaphragmatic pleura.
~ поверхность anat: diaphragmatic surface, facies diaphragmatica.
диафрагмально-рёберная пазуха anat: phrenicocostal sinus.
диафрагмальный нерв anat: phrenic nerve.
диафрагмо-рёберный phrenocostal.
дивергентное косоглазие ophth: divergent strabismus.
дивергенция divergence.
дивертикул anat: diverticulum
дигенез digenesis, digenism.
дигенетические сосальщики (подкл) zool: digenetic trematodes (Digenea, Malacocotylea).
дигенетический сосальщик zool: fluke (Trematoda).
дигидрострептомицин dihydrostreptomycine.
дигиталис bot: digitalis, foxglove (Digitalis purpurea, L.)
дидимоприум bot: didymoprium (alga).
диета diet.
~ для подагриков gout diet.
~ с низким содержанием соли low-salt diet.
~ ~ преобладанием жиров ketogenic d.
диетврач dietist (physician).
диететика dietetics.
диететическое лечение dietetic treatment.
диетик diet-observing person.
диетический режим dietary regimen.
диетотерапия dietotherapy, alimentotherapy, dieting, dietary treatment.
дизентерийная амёба zool: Entamoeba histolylica.
дизентерийный path: dysenteric.
дизентерия path: dysentery; vet: scours.
дизмнезия psych: dysmnesia.
дизурия dysuria.
дикая кошка zool: wild cat (Felis silvestris, Schreb.)
~ ~ Центральной Америки = оцелот.
~ свинья zool: wild sow, see кабан 1.
дикетогулоновая кислота diketogulonic acid.

дикие животные wildlife.
~ травы native grasses. [livia).
*дикий голубь orn: turtledove (Columba
~ козёл zool: wild goat, ibex (Capra ibex, C. sibirica, etc.)
~ кролик zool: wild rabbit (Lupus cuni-
~ лук bot: wild onion. culus).
~ осёл = онагр.
дикобраз zool: Hystrix leucura.
дикобразы (сем.) zool: Hystricidae.
дикое деревцо bot: wild tree, wildling, wilding.
~ животное wild animal, wildling.
~ мясо path: proud flesh.
дикорастущая трава wild grass.
дикорастущий wild-growing. [recoil w.
дикротическая волна dicrotic wave,
дикротический пульс dicrotic pulse.
дикротия path: dicrotism.
диктиосома dictyosome.
диктиота bot: Dictiota (algae).
диктиотовые bot: Dictyotales (algae).
диктокаулёз vet: dictiocaulosis.
дилатация dilatation.
диморфант bot: dimorphantis (Dimor-
диморфизм dimorphism.|phanthus elatus).
диморфный dimorphous.
динамика 1. dynamics; 2. course, trend.
~ веса тела body weight curve, body weight changes. [psychology.
динамическая психология dynamic
динатрий chem: disodium.
динитронафтол dinitronaphtol.
динитроортокрезол dinitro orthocresol.
динобрион bio: Dinobryon (chrysomonadic flagellate organisms).
динозавр zool: dinosaur (Dinosauria).
диоксидиэтилстильбен dioxydiethyl stilbene.
дионея bot: Venus' flytrap (Dionaea).
диоптрия ophth: diopter.[(Dioscoreaceae
диоскорейные (сем.) bot: yam family
диоспировые (пор.) bot: Diospyrales, see эбеновые.
диплёдус pinfish (Diplodus holbrooki).
диплобактерии diplobacteria.
диплобациллы diplobacilli, double bacilli.
диплодиевая сухая гниль phytp: diplodia dry rot.
диплодий genet: diplodium.
диплоид genet: diploid.
диплоидия = диплоид.
диплоидный diploid.
диплококк mcbio: diplococcus.

дипломированная сестра graduate nurse.
диплопиометр ophth: diplopiometer.
диплопический ophth: diplopic.
диплопия ophth: diplopia. [lum stage.
диплостомидная стадия diplostomu-
дипсомания psych: dipsomania.
дипсофобия psych: dipsophobia.
Дирингсхофен Diringshofen.
дисахарид chem: disaccharide, biose.
диск disk.
дисковидное расширение bot: stylopodium (in pistil).
дискоидальное дробление embr: diskoid division. [sae.
дискомедузы (отр.) zool: Discomedu-
дискомицетные лишайники bot: Disolichenes. [menses.
дисменорея gyn: dysmenorrhea, morbid
дисомический genet: disomic.
диспансер dispensary.
диспепсия int: dyspepsia.
диспептическое расстройство int: dyspeptic disorder, dyspepsia.
диспергированный трипсином trypsin-dispersed.
дисперсность dispersity.
дисперсный dispersive, disperse.
диспное dyspnea.
диспонирующий disposing, inclining.
диссеминированный disseminated.
диссимиляционная редукция dissimilatory reduction.
диссимиляция dissimilation.
диссимуляция psych: dissimulation,
диссоциация dissociation. |feigning.
дистальная часть хоботка entom:
дистальный distal. |distiproboscis.
дистиллированная вода distilled w.
дистихлис bot: spike grass, alkali g., salt g. (Distichlis).
дистонический dystonic.
дистония dystonia.
дисторсия distorsion.
дистрофикация dystrophication.
дистрофия path: dystrophy, dystrophia.
дистрофный path: dystrophic.
дисфагия dysphagia.
дисфотическая зона disphotic zone.
дисфункция dysfunction.
дисцизионная игла ophth: discission
дисциплина discipline. needle.
дитион = дитиосалициловокислый натрий.
дитиосалициловокислый натрий sodium dithiosalicylate.

✻дитиосалициловый вистум pharm: bismuth dithiosalicylate.
дитриховские пробки Dittrich's
диурез path: diuresis. plugs.
диуретик path: diuretic.
дифиллоботриоз path: diphyllobothri-
дифтерит = дифтерия. asis.
дифтеритный некроз path: diphteritic necrosis.
дифтерия infect: diphteria.
дифференциальная скорость восстановления rad: differential recovery rate.
дифференциально-диагностические признаки differential diagnosis indications.
дифференциальное счисление лейкоцитов differential blood count.
дифференциальный диагноз differential diagnosis.
~ коэффициент поглощения rad: differential absorption ratio.
~ счет белый шариков hem: differential white count.
~ ~ лейкоцитов по Шиллингу hem: Schilling count.
дифференциация differentiation.
диффузная эритема derm: diffuse ery-
диффундируемость diffusibility.|thema.
дихлорэтан chem: ethylene chloride.
дихогамия bot: dichogamy.
дихотермический dichothermic.
дихотомический dichotomous.
дихроический dichroic.
дихромат ophth: dichromat.
дихроматопсия ophth: dichromatopsia.
дициклически dicyclically.
дичок bot agr: wild tree, wilding.
~ для прививок bot agr: matrix tree
~ черешни bot agr: mazzard. |stock.
~ шпанской вишни mazzard.
диэлдрин chem: dieldrin.
диэта и т.п. = диета и т. п.
диэтилбарбитуровокислый натрий pharm: sodium diethyl barbiturate.
дланевидная нервация bot: palmate venation (of a leaf).
дланевидно-лопастной bot: palmately lobed (leaf).
~ -рассечённый лист bot: palmately
дланевидный bot: palmate.|parted leaf.
~ сложный лист bot: palmately compound leaf.
длина тела body length.[snout-to-vent l.
~ туловища anat: trunk length; zool:
длинная кость anat: long bone.

длинная мышца головы anat: longus capitis (muscle), rectus capitis anticus major.
~ ~ шеи anat: longus colli (muscle), longus cervicis.
~ ножка наковальни anat: long crus of the incus.
длинноволновая диатермия phys-ther: long-wave diathermy.
длинноволокнистый long-stapled.
длинноклювая кайра orn: common guillemot (Uria aalge), gwylog.[beaked.
длинноклювый orn: longirostral, long-
длиннокрылые orn: martins, swifts, colibri, etc. order (Macrochires).
длиннолицый anat: dolichofacial.
длинномордый тюлень zool: grey seal (Halichoerus gripus).[schnederi.
длинноногий сцинк zool: Eumeces
длинноносый баклан orn: green cormorant (Phalacrocorax a. aristot.)
длиннопестичный (цветок) bot: pin-eyed (flower).
длинноплавниковый zool: long-finned.
длинностебельчатая гидра zool: brown hydra (Pelmatohydra oligactis).
длинностебельчатый bot:long-stalked.
длиннотычинковый bot: long-stamened.
длинноусые двукрылые entom: straight-seamed flies with long antennae (Nematocera, Diptera). See also комары.
~ мухи (подотр.) entom: long-antenna flies (Nematocera).
длиннохвостые раки (подотр.) zool: Macrura.
длиннохвостый поморник orn: long-tailed skua (Stercorarius longicaudus)
длинношёрстный long-haired,
~ бык = як. long-wooled.
длинный нерв грудной клетки anat: long thoracic nerve.
длительность жизни life span.
~ пребывания на высоте av med: duration of exposure to altitude.
дневная слепота path: day blindness, hemeralopia.
~ спячка zool: diurnation.
дневной павлиний глаз entom: peacock butterfly (Vanessa io).
дневные хищники orn: accipiters
~ ясли ped: day nursery. |(Accipitres).
дно bottom, base, fundus.
~ глазницы anat: orbital floor.
~ желудка anat: fundus ventricoli.
~ матки anat: fundus uteri.

✱ дно пузыря anat: vesical base.
ДНОК = динитроортокрезол.
дночерпатель bio: bottom sampler, bottom grab.
до before, preceding, prior to, ante- .
~ еды before meals, ante cibum.
добавочная железа anat: appendicular gland, accessory gland.
~ олива anat: parolive.
~ пища supplementary food.
~ полунепарная вена anat: accessory hemiazigos vein.
добавочное кольцо ichth: supernumerary annulus.
~ сокращение сердца extrasystole.
добавочные кольца zool: disturbance rings.
добавочный additional, accessory, | adventitious; bot: appense.
~ нерв anat: (spinal) accessory nerve, eleventh cranial nerve.
~ сгибатель anat: accessiflexor.
дображивание after-fermentation.
доброкачественная опухоль benign tumor.
доброкачественный benign, benignant, nonmalignant, innocent.
~ гной laudable pus.
добывание пищи food getting.
добыча zool: quarry, prey.
доверов порошок pharm: Dover's powder.
додаивание agr: after-milking.
дождевая лужа rainpool.
дождевик 1. bot: puffball (fungus Lycoperdon, Batsch.); 2. entom: Chrysozona.
~ бокальчатый beaker-shaped puffball, lilac p. (L. cyathiforme).
~ -великан giant puffball (L. giganteum, Calvatia giganteum).
~ гигантский = д. великан.
~ шаровидный Bovista nigrescens, Per.
~ шиповатый gemmed p. (L. gemmatum).
дождевой душ shower.
~ червь = червь дождевой.
доза dose, d.
~ лекарства dose of a drug.
дозиметр rad: dosimeter.
дозиметрический комплект rad: dosimeter kit.
~ контроль monitoring (radioactivity, radiation).
дозировка dosage, assignment of dose.
доказательный proving, demonstrative, conclusive.
доклеточное вещество precellular matter.
доклеточный precellular.
доклинический preclinical.
долголетие longevity.
долгоножка entom: leather jacket, | cranefly.
~ вредная Tipula paludosa.
~ льняная = д. вредная.
долгоножки (сем.) entom: typical craneflies (Tipulidae).
долгоносик entom: curculio, snout beetle; see слоник, скрытнохоботник, смолёвка.
~ амбарный granary weevil (Calandra granaria).
~ бататовый sweet-potato weevil (Cylas formicarius).
~ бахчёвый black vine weevil (Brachyrhinchus sulcatus, Fab.)
~ веткорез Rhynchites coeruleus.
~ вишнёвый cherry weevil (Rhynchites auratus).
~ водяной water weevil (Lissorhoptrus simplex).
~ волосистый листовой Polydrossus inustus.
~ горчаковый Phytonomus arator.
~ грушевый pear weevil (Rhynchites giganteus).
~ желудёвый acorn weevil (Balaninus glandium).
~ земляничный strawberry root weevil, s. crown girdler (Brachyrhinchus ovatus).
~ ильмовый Magdalis armigera.
~ капустный cabbage and turnip gall weevil (Centorhynchus sulcicollis).
~ клеверный clover-seed w. (Apion).
~ ~ стеблевой clover-stem w. (Apion seniculum).
~ клубеньковый клеверный sweet-clover w. (Sitona sulcifrons).
~ ~ люцерновый Sitona inops.
~ ~ полосатый striped pea weevil (Sitona lineatus).
~ ~ светлобокий Sitona humeralis.
~ ~ узколобый Sitona cilindricollis.
~ ~ щетинистый Sitona crinitus.
~ -короед bark weevil (Magdalis ruficornis).
~ кукурузный maize billbug (Calendra zea-mays).
~ листовой leaf weevil (Polydrosus obliquatus).
~ ~ грушевый pear-leaf weevil (Phyllobius pyri).
~ ~ продолговатый Phyllobius oblongus.
~ люцерновый большой alfalfa weevil (Otiorhynchus ligustici).
~ ~ листовой alfalfa-leaf weevil (Phytonomus variabilis).
~ морковный carrot-leaf weevil (Liparus coronatus).

долгоносик овощной entom: vegetable
weevil (Listroderes obliquus).
~ оливковый olive weevil (Dacus oleae)
~ ольховый Cryptorrhynchus lippathi.
~ ореховый hazelnut weevil (Balanus
nucum, Bobtusus).
~ почковый bud weevil (Sciaphobus squa-
~ прыгун Rhamphus pulicarius. lidus)
~ рисовый rice weevil (Sitophilus oryzae
Calandra oryzae). [hoptrus simplex).
~ ~ водяной rice-water weevil (Lissor-
~ сафлорный safflower greater weevil
(Larinus syriacus).[groicus petraeus).
~ ~ корневой safflower-root w. (Meso-
~ ~ малый safflower lesser w. (Banga-
sternus orientalis). [punctiventris).
~ свекловичный beet pest (Bothynoderes
~ ~ восточный = д. с. малый.
~ ~ малый Bothynoderes foveicollis.
~ ~ серый Tanymecus palliatus.
~ ~ чёрный Psalidium maxillosum. [zeri.
~ семеед кленовый Bradibatus creut-
~ ~ ясеневый Lignyodes enucleator.
~ сливовый plum curculio (Rhynchites
cupreus). [bius abietus).
~ сосновый большой pine chafer (Hylo-
~ ~ малый = смолёвка точечная.
~ -трухляк Codiosoma spadix.
~ узколобый клубеньковый =
д. клубеньковый клеверный.
~ урюковый Rhynchites auratus.
~ фасолевый bean weevil (Bruchus
obtectus, Sitones lineatus). [ris).
~ хлебный corn weevil (Colandra grana-
~ хлопковый cotton-boll weevil (Anthonomus grandis)
~ ~ аризонский Arizona cotton-boll w.
(A. grandis thurberiae).
~ ~ мексиканский = д. хлопковый.
~ ~ южноамериканский South-American
cotton-boll w.(A. vestitus).
~ широкохоботный Caulophilus latinasus
~ яблонный = цветоед яблонный.
~ ~ краснокрылый Coenorrhinchus
aequatus.
долгоносики (сем.) entom: curculios,
typical snout-beetles (Curculionidae).
долгопят zool: tarsier (Tarsius spect-
долгоцветущий bot: long-flowering.| rum.
долиннеевский pre-Linnaean (time).
долото chisel; see also желобоватое д.
~ для перегородки (носа) septum
chisel. [scalpellum.
долотовидный передний резец zool:
долька lobule, lobulus.

долька плода bot: coccus.
дольковый lobular, lobulated.
Дольмен Dolman.
дольный lobed, pedate, cleft.
дольчатость lobulation.
дольчатый bot: lobed, lobulated, lobu-
доля lobe. |lar; bot: cleft (leaf).
дом для престарелых asylum for the
~ отдыха rest home. aged.
домашнее средство med: home remedy.
домашний уход med: home care.
домашняя медицина domestic medicine
~ мышь house mouse.
~ птица poultry, fowl.
домик zool: house, case, lorica.
доминанта bio: dominant.
доминантный dominant, prepotent.
доминирование dominance, prepotency.
доминирующая идея psych:
dominating idea. [musculus).
домовая мышь zool: house mouse (Mus
домовые отбросы household refuse,
household garbage.
домовый гриб bot: house fungus,
dry-rot fungus.
донашивать (ребёнка) obstet: carry
to full time.
донести p. a. of доносить 1.
донная рыба ground fish.
донник bot: melilot, sweet clover
(Melilotus, L.) [nalis).
~ аптечный yellow melilot (M. offici-
~ белый white melilot, Bokhara clover
(M. alba).
~ жёлтый лекарственный =
д. аптечный.
~ мелкоцветный bitter melilot, sour
clover (M. indica).
донники bio: benthos.
донный bio: bottom-dwelling, fundic;
attr: bottom; see бентический.
донор hem: donor. [шивать.
доносить 1. report; 2. p.a. of дона-
доношенный obstet: mature, carried to
full time. [onion).
донце bot: bottom, disk, stem (of
дополнительная окраска bact:
counter staining.
дополнительный supplementary, complementary, extra, accessory.
~ самец zool: complemental male.
дорзальный = дорсальный.
~ край крыла = анальный к. к.
дориден pharm: doriden. [phus).
дорирамфус ichth: pipefish (Doryram-

дородовой antenatal, prenatal, antepartum, prepartal.
дорозома ichth: winter shad, stink s., nanny s., mud s. (Dorosoma cepedianum).
дороник bot: leopard's cane (Doronicum, L.)
дорсальная пястная артерия anat: dorsal metacarpal artery.
дорсально dorsally, dorsad.
дорсальный dorsal.
дорсовентральный anat: dorsoventral, postoanterior.
досада psych: annoyance, fret, irritation.
достигший полного роста fullgrown.
доступность для облова fishability.
доступный для сбора harvestable.
~ осязанию palpable.
дочерние звёзды (две) hist: diaster.
дочерняя звезда hist: daughter aster.
~ клетка genet: daughter cell.
драконник bot: Dracontium.
драконовые (сем.) ichth: weevers (Trachinidae).
дракункулёз helm: Dracunculus-worm disease, guinea-worm disease.
драм ichth: drum (Pogonias cromis, Sciaenops ocellatus).
драмамин pharm: dramamine.
драпарнальдия bot: Draparnaldia (algae
драхма pharm: drachm, dram (weight).
драцена bot: dragon tree (Dracaena draco); see also кордилина.
драчливость pugnaciousness.
древесина bot: xylem, woody tissue.
древесинник entom: ambrosia beetle (Xyleborus, Xyloterus).
древесная вата wood wool, lignin.
~ кобра zool: tree cobra (Naja dendraspis).
~ лягушка zool: peeper (Hyla crucifer); tree frog (Dendrobates); see квакша.
~ оса entom: horntail (Sirex gigans).
древеснеть bot: lignify.
древесница zool: 1. see древесная лягушка; 2. entom: arboreal moth.
~ въедливая entom: leopard moth (Zeuzera aesculi, Zeuzera pyrina).
древесное растение arboraceous plant, wood plant, ligneous plant.
древесный woody, ligneous, arboreal.
~ клоп entom: box elder bug.
~ сосуд bot: wood vessel.
~ спирт wood alcohol, methyl alcohol.
~ уголь charcoal.
~ уксус pharm: woodvinegar.

древнекрылые насекомые Palaeoptera.
древовидность arborization.
древовидный treelike, arboreal, arboreaous, arborescent, dendritic, dendroid, dendriform.
~ кустарник bot: arbuscle.
древоводство arboriculture.
древогубец вьющийся bot: waxwork, climbing bittersweet (Celastrus scandens).
*древолаз orn: tree creeper (Certhia brachydactyla).
древоразрушающий гриб wood-rotting fungus.
древосек осиновый entom: poplar longicorn (Saperda carcharias).
древостой (pole)wood stand, growing stock (trees).
древоточец entom: wood borer (Scolytidae, Cossidae); see also муравей древоточец, жучок-точильщик.
~ ивовый = д. плодовый.
~ пахучий carpenter moth, goat m.(Cossus).
~ плодовый shot-hole borer (Scolytus rugulosus).
древоточцы (сем.) entom: carpenter moths (Cossidae)
дрейфующие водоросли bot: driftweed.
дрёма bot: campion (Lychnis, L.); German catchfly (L. viscaria); ragged robin, cuckoo flower (L. flos-cuculi).
~ белая white cockle, w. campion, evening lychnis (L. alba).
~ венцевидная rose campion, mullein pink (L. coronaria).
~ липкая catchfly (Melandrium viscosum).
дремать dose, nap, drowse, slumber.
дремлик = ятрышник мужской.
дренаж drain(age).
дренажная трубка surg: drainage tube.
дренировать drain.
дриада восьмилепестковая bot: dryas (Dryas octopetala).
дробление division, fission, cleavage; breaking up, subdividing; crushing; bact: scission.
~ дозы rad: dose fractionation.
~ яйца embr: blastulation, segmentation, cleavage.
дробная доза pharm: divided dose.
~ стерилизация bact: discontinous sterilization, intermittent s.
дробный fractional.
дробянка bact: fission fungus.
дробянки bot: schizophytes (Schizophyta).
дровосек = усач 1.
дрогист druggist.
дрожание tremor, trembling, jarring, shivering, trepidation, thrill.

дрожание глазного яблока nystagmus.
дрожательный паралич paralysis agitans, Parkinson's disease.
дрожать tremble.
дрожащий почерк tremulous handwriting.
дрожжевой yeasty.
~ грибок bot: yeast fungus.
дрожжи bot: yeast (Saccharomyces).
дрожь tremor, trembling, shiver(ing).
дрозд orn: thrush, blackbird, ouzel, robin (Turdus, Hylocichla, etc.)
~ -белобровик Brit: redwing.
~ -деряба missel thrush.
~ -рябинник fieldfare.
*~ чёрный blackbird (Merula merula).
дроздовые (сем.) orn: thrush family (Turdidae).
дрозофила entom: pomace fly (Drosophila).
дрок bot: woadwaxen, whin, cytisus (Genista).
~ испанский Spanish broom (Spartium junceum).
~ красильный dyer's greenweed, dyeweed (G. tinctoria).
дромадер = одногорбый верблюд.
дронт orn: dodo (extinct).
*дрофа orn: species Otis tarda.
дрофы (отр.) orn: Otides.
дряква 1. orn: shooting star (Dodecatheon); 2. bot: see цикламен.
~ американская American cowslip (Dodecatheon maedia).
дряхлеть cf. дряхлый.
дряхлость decrepitude, infirmity from age.
дряхлый decrepit.
дуб bot: oak (Quercus).
~ американский шерлаховый scarlet oak (Q. coccinea).
~ бархатный black oak, yellow-bark oak, quercitron (Q. velutina, Lam.)
~ белый white oak (Q. alba).
~ валонейный valonia oak (Q. cerris Valonea, Kotscy).
~ виргинский live oak (Q. virginiana).
~ густолистный = пазания.
~ жёлтый = дуб бархатный.
~ живой = дуб виргинский.
~ каменный English oak, sessile oak, stalkless-flowered oak (Q. petraea, Liebl., or Q. sessiflora, Salisb.)
~ карликовый dwarf oak, bear oak, scrub oak (Q. ilicifolia, Wang.)
~ летний pedunculate oak (Q. robur, Q. pedunculata, Ehrh.)
~ лировидный overcup oak, swamp-post oak (Q. lyrata).
~ пробковый cork oak (Q. suber).
дуб с крупными жолудями bur oak (Quercus macrocarpa, Michx.)
~ сидячелистный = дуб каменный.
~ сидячецветный = дуб каменный.
~ скальный = дуб каменный.
~ турецкий Turkey oak (Q. cerris).
~ шерлаховый = дуб американский.
дубильная кислота tannic acid.
дубильновиннокаменнокислый алюминий pharm: aluminum tannotartrate.
дубильнокислая ртуть pharm: mercury tannate.
дубильнокислый алюминий pharm: aluminum tannate.
~ свинец pharm: lead tannate.
~ хинин pharm: quinine tannate.
дублинская креветка zool: Dublin prawn (Nephrops norvegicus).
дубник bot: hawkbit (Leontodon hispidus); see also кульбаба.
дубовая кора pharm: oak bark.
дубовый лишайник bot: Evernia prunastri, Ach. (lichen).
дубонос orn: grosbeak; Brit: hawfinch (Pheucticus, Hesperiphona, etc.)
~ красногрудый grosbeak Hedymeles virginianus.
дубровка bot: 1. bugleweed (Ajuga); 2. see ветреница лесная.
дубровник bot: germender (Teucrium).
~ шалфейный wood sage, germander sage (T. scorodonia).
дубянка = омела белая.
дуга anat: arch, arcus.
~ аорты anat: arch of the aorta, arcus aortae.
~ зубов anat: dental arch.
~ крыла zool: wing-bow.
~ позвонка anat: vertebral arch, neural a.
Дуглас Douglas.
дугласово пространство anat: pouch of Douglas, see карман прямая кишка – матка.
дуговой индекс arcadal index.
дугообразная артерия anat: arciform artery, arcuate artery.
дугообразное возвышение anat: arcuate eminence.
~ искривление ног path: bowlegs, genu varum.
дугопозвонковые = апсидоспондили.
дудак = дрофа.
дудник = ангелика.
дужка 1. orn: wishbone; 2. entom: arculus.
дум-пальма bot: palm Hyphaene.
дуоденальный зонд med: duodenal sound.
~ сок physl: duodenal secretion.

дуотал pharm: duotal.
*дупель orn: double snipe, great s. (Scolopax major).
дурашливость path: silly behavior, [silliness.
дуриан(с) bot: durian (Durio zibethinus.
дурио = дуриан.
дурман bot: stramonium, Jimsonweed, thorn apple (Datura).
~ вонючий thorn apple (D. stramonium).
дурная болезнь collq: bad disease (syphilis).
~ привычка bad habit.
дурнишник bot: cocklebur, clotbur, burdock (Xanthium).
дурное самочувствие discomfort, indisposition, see also недомогание.
дурной запах изо рта ill-smelling breath, stomatodysodia.
дурнопахнущий evil-smelling, bad-[smelling.
дурнота qualm, faintness, nausea.
дурра bot: durra, see дурро.
дурро bot: sorghum, broomcorn (Sorgum vulgare, Pers.)
~ белое rice corn, Jerusalem c.
~ бурое brown durra.
~ египетское brown durra.
дусен bot: doucin, dwarf apple (Malus pumula paradisiaca).
дуст agr: dust, powder.
дутые сливы = кармашковая болезнь.
душ shower.
душевная болезнь psych: mental disor-[der, insanity.
~ глухота neur: mind deafness, psychic d., auditory amnesia, word deafness.
~ слепота neur: psychic blindness.
~ тревога mental anxiety.
душевнобольной psych: insane, see психопат.
душевное расстройство psych: mental derangement, alienation.
душевный покой mental rest.
душение (за шею) legl: garrotting.
душистый odorant, odoriferous, aromatic.
~ колосок bot: sweet vernal grass (Anthoxanthum odoratum).
душица bot: 1. marjoram, origano (Origanum vulgare); 2. see базилик карликовый.
душки = базилик.
дующий шум souffle, blowing sound.
ДХЭ = дихлорэтан.
дымчатое дерево smoke tree, see скумпия кожевенная.
дымянка bot: fumitory, earth-smoke [(Fumaria).
~ аптечная common fumitory (F. officinalis).
~ лекарственная = д. аптечная.

дынное дерево melon tree, see папайа.
дыня bot: melon (Cucumis melo).
~ -канталупка = канталупа.
~ -кассаба cassaba, winter melon.
~ манго mango melon.
~ мускусная muskmelon, see канталупа.
~ сетчатая = дыня мускусная.
~ цукатная chito melon, orange m.
дырчатость presence of holes; see also бактериальная дырчатость.
~ вишнёвых листьев phytp: shot-hole disease of cherry (Coccomyces).
дырчатый holey, cribiform, perforated, see продырявленный.
~ перелом surg: puncture fracture, [buttonhole f.
дыхало zool: blow hole.
дыхальце zool: spiracle, stigma, breathing opening.
дыхание 1. breathing, respiration; 2. [breath.
~ куколки zool: pupal respiration.
~ через рот mouth breathing.
дыхательная гимнастика respiratory gymnastics.
~ деятельность respiratory activity.
~ пауза respiratory pause.
~ поверхность anat: respiratory [surface.
~ судорога path: respiratory spasm.
~ трубка entom: breathing tube.
дыхательное горло anat: windpipe, trachea.
~ движение respiratory movement.
~ отверстие breathing opening, see дыхальце.
~ упражнение respiratory exercise.
дыхательные пути anat: air passages, respiratory tract.
дыхательный respiratory; spiracular.
~ аппарат 1. anat: respiratory apparatus; 2. av med: rebreather a.
~ коэффициент respiratory quotient.
~ объем vital capacity, respiratory c.
~ паралич respiratory paralysis.
~ полип breathing polyp.
~ центр anat: respiratory center, |panting c.
~ шум respiratory murmur.
дышать breath, respire.
~ с присвистом path: wheeze.
~ с трудом pant.
дышащий жабрами zool: gill-breathing
Дэмант Damant.
дюгонь zool: Indian sea cow, dugong (Halicore dugong).
Дюрозье Duroziez.
дягиль bot: angelica (Angelica).

дягиль лекарственный bot: garden angelica (Angelica archangelica).
~ лесной Angelica silvestris.
дягильник = дягиль.
дятел orn: woodpecker (Picidae).
~ белоклювый yellow-bellied w., sapsucker (Dryocopus principalis).
~ вертлявый middle spotted w. (Dendrocopus).
~ златокрылый flicker (Colaptes auratus).
~ золотистый golden w.see дятел златокрылый. [laptes formicivorus).
~ калифорнийский California w. (Co-
~ красноголовый red-headed w. (Colaptes erythrocephalus). [viridis).
~ настоящий зелёный green w. (Picus
~ пёстрый spotted w. (Dendrocopus major, D. medius, D. minor).
дятлина = клевер.
дятловые (сем.) woodpecker family (Picidae). [(Piciformes, Picariae).
дятлы (отр.) woodpecker order

Е

евгеника eugenics.
евгенический eugenic.
евгения = яблоко розовое.
евгенол = гвоздичная кислота.
евдошка = умбра.
евнух path: eunuch.
евнухоидизм eunuchoidism.
евнухоидный eunuchoid.
евнушество eunuchism.
евстахиева заслонка anat: Eustachian valve.
~ труба anat: Eustachian tube, auditory tube.
Егер Jaeger.
египетская цапля orn: cattle egret (Bubulcus ibis).
единица unit.
~ активности rad: activity unit.
~ облучения rad: rad unit.
единичный цветок bot: single flower.
единорог 1.zool: narwhal, sea unicorn (Monodon monoceros); 2.ichth: see рыба-е.
едкая щёлочь caustic alkali.
едкий caustic, acrid, pungent.
~ аммиак chem: ammonia water. [xide.
~ калий caustic potash, potassium hydro-
~ натр caustic soda, sodium hydroxide.
~ натрий = едкий натр.
едкий щёлок chem: caustic lye.
едкое кали chem: caustic potash, see едкий калий.
~ средство pharm: escharotic.
едкость causticity. [urchin.
ёж zool: hedgehog (Erinaceus europaeus);
~ -рыба porcupine fish, globefish (Diodon).
ежа bot: orchard grass (Dactylis).
~ сборная dew grass, cocksfoot (D. glomerata).
ежевика bot: European dewberry (Rubus caesius, Rubus villosus).
~ американская black raspberry, thimbleberry (R. occidentalis).
ежеголовка = ежеголовник.
ежеголовник bot: bur reed, burweed (Sparganium). [ramosum).
~ ветвистый branched bur reed (S.
ежеголовниковые (сем.) bot: bur-reed family (Sparganiaceae).[mella)
ежемуха entom: tachina fly (Tachina
ежемухи (сем.) entom: tachina-flies (Larvaevoridae).
ежовик bot: Hydnum (fungus).
ежовиковые bot: Hydnaceae (fungi).
ежовник bot: Echinochloa, Beauv.
~ безлистный anabasis (Anabasis aphylla). [(E. crusgalli).
~ петушье просо barnyard grass
~ хлебный Japanese millet, billion-dollar grass (E. frumentacea, Link.)
~ японский = е. хлебный.
ежовое копыто vet: convexity of sole
елевзина = елеузина.
Еленкин Elenkin, Elenk.
елеузина bot: goose grass, yard grass (Eleusine, Gaertn.)
~ индийская wiregrass (E. indica).
елец ichth: dace (Leuciscus leuciscus).
еловые (сем.) = сосновые (сем.)
елоха = ольха серая.
ель bot: spruce (Picea, Dietr.)
~ белая канадская white spruce (P. canadensis). [excelsa, Link.)
~ обыкновенная Norway spruce (P.
~ чёрная марианская black spruce, bog s. (P. mariana, BSP. or P. nigra, Link.)
емкость capacity, capacitance.
енот zool: raccoon (Procyon lotor).
енотовая собака zool: raccoon dog (Nyctereutes procyonides).
енотовидная собака = енотовая с.
еноты (сем.) zool: raccoon family (Procyonidae).

ёрник обыкновенный = водяника
чёрная. [rina cernua).
ёрш ichth: ruff(e), striped perch (Ace-
ёршик lab: test-tube brush. [manda).
ершоватка ichth: yellowtail, dab (Li-
естественная история natural history.
~ передача natural transmission.
~ случка zool: wild pairing.
~ смерть natural death.
естественник naturalist. [ral seeding.
естественное обсеменение bot: natu-
естественнонаучный natural-science.
естественный отбор genet: natural
~ распад physiolysis. selection.
естество nature.
естествознание natural science, n. hi-
естествоиспытатель naturalist. |story
есть eat.
еуаструм bot: Euastrum (algae).
ехидна zool: echidna, spiny anteater
(Tachyglossus).

Ж

жаба zool: toad, see жабы.
~ -повитуха Alytes obstetricans.
жаберная дуга zool: gill arch, bran-
~ камера = ж. полость. chial a.
~ киста path: branchial cyst, branchio-
genic c., cervical c. [chiostegite.
~ крышка zool: gill cover, opercle, bran-
~ палочка zool: gill rod, gill bar.
~ пластинка zool: branchial plate.
~ полость zool: gill cavity, branchial
~ пóра zool: atriopore. chamber.
~ тычинка zool: gill raker.
~ улитка zool: gilled snail.
~ щель zool: gill slit, branchial cleft;
embr: visceral cleft.
жаберный branchial, branchiferous, gil-
~ лепесток gill fringe. led.
~ мешок zool: branchial pouch.
~ сегмент zool: branchiomere.
~ сифон zool: incurrent siphon, inha-
жабра zool: gill, branchion. lant s.
жабрей bot: hedgehog (Galeopsis tetrahit); hemp nettle (G. ladanum).
жабродышащие (подтип) zool: crustaceans and trilobites (Branchiata).
жаброног zool: fairy shrimp, branchipod,
foot-gill cancriform (Branchiopoda).

жаброногие раки (отр.) zool:
Branchiopoda
жаброногое ракообразное =
жабры zool: gills. жаброног.
~ с икрой gravid gills (of mollusks).
жабы zool: toads (Bufonidae). [udidae).
жаворонковые (сем.) orn: larks (Ala-
жаворонок orn: skylark, Old World
lark (Alauda).
~ лесной woodlark (A. arborea,
Lullula arborea).
~ луговой skylark (A. arvensis).
~ полевой = ж. луговой
~ степной = ж. хохлатый.
~ хохлатый tufted lark (Galerita,
A. cristata).
жадно есть eat greedily, gobble.
*~ проглатывать shark up.
жажда thirst.
жако orn: African lovebird (Psittacus).
жалить zool: sting (bee, wasp), bite
(poisonous snake).
жало zool: sting (bee, wasp), dart
(insect), onchus (roundworm).
жалоба complaint.
жалоносное насекомое stinger.
жалоносные (подотр.) entom:
aculeate insects, stingers (Aculeata)
жалящий stinging, biting; cf. жалить.
жар fever, heat.
жаровое повреждение heat injury.
жаропонижающее действие
antipyresis. [algogenic.
~ (средство) antifebrile, antipyretic,
жаростойкий heat-resisting,
tolerant to heat.
жароустойчивый bio: thermophylic.
жасмин bot: mock orange, syringa,
jasmine (Philadelphus coronarius).
жатвенная лихорадка harvest fever.
жвало entom: jaw, bill.
жвачка rumination; cud.
жвачное (животное) ruminant.
жгут surg: tourniquet.
жгутик flagellum, cilium, lash.
жгутиковая камера zool: flagellated
chamber. [lata), see биченосцы.
жгутиковые zool: flagellates (Flagel-
жгутоногие (отр.) zool: whip
scorpions (Pedipalpi). [smart(ing).
жгучая боль burning pain, causalgia,
жевание chewing, manducation, masti-
~ резинки chewing the gum. cation.
жевательная лопасть entom: chewing
lobe (galea, lacinia).

жевательная мышца anat: masseter, mastication muscle.
~ судорога path: masticatory spasm, trismus.
~ тёрка = радула.
жевательные зубы anat: masticating teeth, grinding t. (molar and bicuspid)
жевательный masticatory, manducatory.
~ аппарат zool: jaws, trophi (of rotifers).
~ выступ zool: gnathobase.
~ желудок zool: masticatory stomach.
жевать chew, manducate, masticate.
~ жвачку zool: chew the cud, ruminate.
желатин gelatin, isinglass.
желатиновая пластинка bact: gelatin plate.
желатинозный gelatinous.
желвак path: scirrhus, hard carcinoma.
желвачный scirrhous.
железа anat: gland.
~ без выводного протока ductless g.
~ века ophth: Meibomian g., tarsal g.
~ внутренней секреции endocrine g.
~ выделяющая ушную серу wax g.
~ луковицы мочеиспускательного канала anat: bulbourethral g., Cowper's g.
~ наружной секреции exocrine g.
~ подмышечной впадины anat: axillary g.
~ преддверия влагалища (большая, малая) (major, minor) vestibular g.
железистая клетка hist: adenoblast.
~ лихорадка glandular fever.
~ ткань hist: glandular tissue.
железистого происхождения adenogenous, adenogenic.
железистый adenic, adeniform, adenoid, glandlike, glandiform, glandular.
~ волосок glandular hair.
~ желудок orn: fore-stomach, proventriculus, glandular stomach.
~ клубок anat: gland coil.
~ эпителий hist: adenose epithelium.
железка anat: glandule.
железница vet: red mange.
железнодорожная болезнь railway-car sickness.
железнодорожный врач railway medical officer.
железное дерево southern celtis, late tree (Celtis occidentalis); lignum vitae (Ixora ferrea); see тисс, бакаут.
~ ~ вестиндское West Indian greenheart (Colubrina ferruginosa).
железные воды ferruginous waters, chalybeate waters.
железный препарат pharm: chalybeate.
железняк клубневой = зопник клубненосный.
железо iron, Fe.
железобактерия iron (depositing) bacterium.
желёзы дна желудка fundic glands.
~ краев век ciliary glands, Moll's g.
желеобразный jelly-like.
желобобрюхие zool: Solenogastres (class of the phylum Molluska).
желобоватое долото surg: gouge.
желобоватый зонд surg: grooved director.
жёлтая губка zool: yellow sponge (Euspongia agaricina).
~ листовая ржавчина phytp: yellow rust (Puccinia glumarum).
~ лихорадка yellow fever.
~ (ртутная) мазь pharm: yellow salve.
~ хинная кора yellow cinchona.
желтизна листьев bot: yellow disease.
желтобрюх = желтопуз.
желтоголовый yellow-headed.
желтогузка entom: moth Euproctis similis.
~ туркестанская E. karghalica.
жёлтое пятно ophth: yellow spot, see центральная ямка.
~ тело hist: yellow body, corpus luteum.
~ ~ беременных c.l. of pregnancy, true c.l.
~ ~ менструации c.l. of menstruation, false c.l.
жёлтозелёная плесень phytp: yellow-green dusty mold.
жёлто-зелёного оттенка glaucous.
желток zool: yolk, vitellus.
желтокорень = гидрастика.
желтокрылка ichth: Cottocomephorus grewingki.
жёлтолихорадочный комар entom: yellow-fever mosquito, stray m. (Stegomyia fasciata).
желтолозник bot: purple osier, basket willow (Salix purpurea).
желтопуз zool: legless lizard Ophisarius apus.
желторотый птенец orn: unfledged nestling, squab.
желтофиоль bot: lipfern, wallflower (Chelianthes, Sw.)
желтохвостка ichth: yellowtail Bairdiella chrysura, etc.
желточная клетка hist: yolkcell, vitelline cell.
~ оболочка embr: vitelline membrane.
~ пробка embr: yolk plug.
желточник zool: yolk gland, vitellarium.

желточное кровообращение embr: vitelline circulation.
~ ядро hist: yolk nucleus.
желточный канал embr: vitelline duct.
~ мешок embr: yolk sac, vitellicle.
~ проток helm: yolk duct.
~ пузырь = желточный мешок.
~ сосуд embr: vitelline vessel.
желтощёк ichth: Elopichthys.
желтуха 1. int: jaundice, icterus; 2. phytp: yellows.
~ гиацинтовая phytp: yellow disease [of hyacinth.
~ еловой хвои phytp: spruce-needle | rust
~ листьев персика peach yellows.
~ новорожденных ped: jaundice of the newborn, icterus neonatorum.
~ от закупорки желчного протока obstructive jaundice, mechanical j.
желтушка = кульбаба осенняя.
желтушная окраска path: icteric discoloration.
желтушник bot: treacle mustard (Erysimum); wormseed mustard (E. cheiranthoides); coast-wall flower (E. capitatum, Greene).
желтушно окрашенный bile-stained.
желтушный icteric; icteroid, bile-stained.
желтый корень pharm: yellow root.
~ кровяной сгусток chicken-fat clot.
~ оттенок кожи yellowish discoloration of skin, xanthochromia.
~ пластырь pharm: rosin cerate, basilicon salve.
~ суслик zool: yellow suslik (Citellus fulvus).
желудок anat: stomach; see also мускульный желудок.
~ в виде песочных часов path: hour-glass stomach.
~ крупной дичи zool: paunch.
желудочек anat: ventricle.
~ головного мозга anat: cerebral ventricle, v. of the brain.
желудочковая связка anat: ligamentum ventricularia.
~ экстрасистола ventricular extrasystole.
желудочковый градиент ventricular gradient.
желудочная артерия anat: gastric artery.
~ железа gastric gland.
~ секреция physl: gastric secretion.
~ ямка anat: gastric pit.
желудочно- gastro-.
~ -двенадцатиперстная артерия anat: gastroduodenal artery.
~ -диафрагмальный anat: gastrophrenic.
желудочно-кишечное заболевание gastro-intestinal disturbance.
~ ~ пищеварение physl: gastrointestinal digestion, primary d.
~ -кишечный тракт anat: gastrointestinal tract.
~ -ободочный anat: gastrocolic.
~ -сальниковая артерия anat: gastroepiploic artery.
~ -селезёночный anat: gastrosplenic
~ -сосудистая полость zool: gastrovascular cavity.
желудочного происхождения gastrogenic.
желудочное ведерко int: stomach bucket.
~ кровотечение int: hematemesis.
~ пищеварение physl: gastric digestion.
~ содержимое stomach contents.
желудочные оводы (сем.) entom: botflies of horses (Gastrophilidae).
желудочный gastric, stomachal, stomachic.
~ жом surg: stomach clamp.
~ зонд stomach tube.
~ камень path: gastric concretion, gastrolith.
~ сок physl: gastric juice.
~ червь helm: stomach worm (Strongylidae).
желчегонное действие cholagogic action.
~ средство cholagog(ue).
желчегонный bile-expelling, bile-flow stimulating, cholagog.
жёлчеобразующий cholepoietic.
желчн- bili-, chol(o)-.
жёлчная кислота bile acid, cholic a.
~ среда bact: bile medium.
желчнокаменная болезнь cholelithiasis.
жёлчный камень path: biliary calculus.
~ пигмент bile pigment.
~ проток anat: common bile duct, ductus choledochus.
~ пузырь anat: gall bladder, vesica fellea.
~ путь biliary tract.
~ ход = желчный проток.
жёлчь bile.
жемчуг pearl.
жемчужина pearl.
~ приросшая к раковине bouton pearl.
жемчужная банка pearl bank.
~ опухоль = холестеатома.
~ раковина zool: pearl shell.
~ ракушка zool: white shell (Margaritifera).
~ рыба pearl fish (Emmelichthys nitidus).
жемчужница 1. zool: pearl shell; 2. vet: grape disease, pearl d. tuberculosis.

жемчужница пресноводная zool: pearly mussel (Margaritana margaritifera.
жемчужный pearly.
Женевская конвенция Geneva convention.
женоненавистник misogynist.
женоненавистничество psych: misogyny, hatred of women.
женская болезнь gynecopathy.
~ палата female ward (in a hospital).
~ подставка bot: female receptacle.
женский female; bot: pistillate.
~ мочеприемник female urinal.
женское молоко human milk.
~ отделение female department (of a hospital).
~ растение bot: pistillate plant, female plant.
~ ~ конопли bot: pistillate hemp.
~ ядро embr: female pronucleus.
женственность femininity, muliebrity, womanliness.
женщина woman, female.
~ беременная в первый раз obstet: primigravida. See also беременная.
~ -врач lady-doctor, woman-doctor.
~ рожавшая восемь раз octipara.
~ ~ десять раз decemipara.
~ ~ несколько раз multipara.
~ ~ один раз unipara.
~ ~ семь раз septipara.
~ ~ три раза tripara.
~ ~ четыре раза quadripara.
~ ~ шесть раз sextipara.
жень-шень bot: ginseng, sang, manplant (Panax quinquefolius).
жерёбая кобыла zool: pregnant mare.
жеребёнок zool: colt, foal.
жеребец zool: stallion, studhorse.
жеребиться give birth (of a mare).
жерёбость zool: pregnancy (of a mare).
жерёбчик = жеребёнок.
жерех ichth: Aspius aspius.
~ южнокаспийский South-Caspian fish A. a. taeniatus.
жерлянка zool: Bombina (batrachian).
жерновка zool: gastric mill.
жеруха bot: watercress (Nasturtium, R.Br.)
~ аптечная true w., roripa nasturtium (N. officinale).
~ болотная = сердечник луговой.
жерушник bot: yellow cress (Rorippa, Scop.)
жест gesture.
жёсткая вода hard water.
~ ракушка hard clam, round c., bullnose cherry stone (Venus mercenaria).
~ флора coarse vegetation.
жёсткие хрипы path: coarse rales.
жёсткий шум path: rasping murmur.
жестковатое дыхание slightly harsh breathing.
жёстковолосистая трава bot: bent grass.
жёсткое дыхание harsh breathing, rough b., rude b.
жёсткокрылое насекомое entom: hebrid (Hebridae); mesoveliid.
жёсткокрылые entom: coleopters, see жуки.
жёсткокрылый entom: coleopterous.
жёсткость (воды) hardness (of water).
жестокая боль severe pain.
~ головная боль severe headache.
жжёная магнезия pharm: calcined magnesia, magnesium oxide.
жжение burning (pain), scalding.
~ в легких burning sensation in the lungs.
~ кожи burning of the skin.
~ при мочеиспускании urol: scalding, chaudepisse.
жжёные квасцы pharm: burnt alum, dried a.
живая ткань living tissue.
живица bot: sap.
живое living things.
живой вес agr zool: live weight.
~ организм living organism.
живокость bot: larkspur, delphinium (Delphinium).
~ высокая perennial larkspur (D. elatior).
~ посевная rocket larkspur (D. consolida).
живоловный отлов live trapping.
живоловушка live trap.
живородящая бельдюга ichth: viviparous blenny (Zoarces).
~ карпозубая рыба mayfish (Poeciliidae).
~ рыба viviparous fish.
~ ящерица viviparous lizard (Lacerta vivipara).
живородящий окунь ichth: minny, moharra, blue surf fish (Embiotocidae)
~ папоротник bot: viviparous spleenwort (Asplenium viviparum).
живорождение zool: live-bearing, viviparity.
живость psych: liveliness, animation.
живот anat: abdomen, belly, paunch.
~ петуха orn: fluff (of a cock).
животная жизнь animal life.
~ клетка hist: animal cell.
~ пища carnivorous diet.
животновод cattle raiser, animal husbandman.
животноводство cattle raising, animal breeding.

животное animal.
~ впадающее в зимнюю спячку hibernating animal.
~ питающееся донным илом bottom ooze feeder.
~ ~ у дна bottom feeder.
~ тепло animal heat.
царство animal kingdom.
животноядный bio: zoophagous.
животный крахмал animal starch.
~ магнетизм psych: animal magnetism.
~ микроорганизм microzoon.
~ организм animal organism.
~ паразит zooparasite, animal parasite.
~ ~ кожи dermatozoon.
~ ~ крови hemozoon.
~ уголь animal charcoal.
~ эктопаразит parazoon.
~ эндопаразит entozoon.
живучка bot: marsh elder (Iva frutescens).
~ кровельная old-man-and-woman (Sempervivum tectorum).
~ ползучая bugle (Ajuga reptans).
живущее bio: living things.
живущий в иле zool: mud-living.
~ ~ крови bio: blood-inhabiting, hematobious.
~ ~ почве soil-inhabiting.
~ ~ тканях растений endophytous.
~ внутри организма endobiotic.
~ на других организмах epizoic.
~ ~ саргассуме sargassum-borne.
~ ~ цветах anthophilous.
живчик = сперматозоид.
жигалка = муха-жигалка.
жидкая драхма pharm: fluidra(ch)m.
~ мазь liniment.
~ облиствённость bot: sparse foliage.
~ питательная среда mcbio: culture fluid.
~ унция pharm: fluidounce.
~ туляремийная вакцина liquid tularemia vaccine.
~ часть протоплазмы hist: plasmasol.
жидкий liquid, fluid; thin, sparse.
вазелин pharm: liquid petrolatum.
~ травостой bot: loose grasses.
жидкое содержимое кисты path: cystic fluid.
жидкость liquid, fluid, liquor, humor.
~ для промывания irrigant, wash.
жизнедеятельность vital activity.
жизненная емкость (лёгких) vital capacity.
~ потребность vital requirement.

жизненная сила vital power.
~ энергия bio(e)nergy.
жизненное дерево = туя.
жизненность vitality, vital power, vigor.
жизненный vital, biotic, life.
~ цикл bio: life cycle, life history.
жизнеспособность viability.
жизнеспособный viable.
жизнь пресных вод fresh-water biology.
жи́ление tenesmus, straining.
жилистый veined.
жи́литься strain (oneself).
жилищная норма floor-space ration (in USSR).
жилка 1. anat: small vein, venule; 2. entom: vein.
~ внутри семядольки bot: intercotyledonary axis
~ (листа) bot: nerve, rib.
жилкование venation, veining.
~ крыльев entom: venation of the wings, neuration, nervuration, venatio.
жилковатый veiny, venous.
жимолостные (сем.) bot: honeysuckle family (Caprifoliaceae).
жимолость bot: honeysuckle (Lonicera).
~ душистая L. caprifolium.
~ немецкая вьющаяся woodbine (L. periclymenum).
жир- fat-, adipo-, lipo-.
жир grease, fat.
~ из тресковой печени cod-liver oil.
жираф zool: giraffe (Giraffa camelеopardalis).
жирафы (сем.) zool: giraffe family (Giraffidae).
жиреть take on fat, get fatty.
жирная кислота fatty acid.
жирное сердце path: fatty heart.
жирноперерожденная клетка hist: fatty cell.
жирность fat content.
жирный fat(ty), adipose, greasy, unctuous, pinguid.
осадок lab: fat scale.
жировая долька hist: fat lobule.
~ капля mcscop: fat drop.
~ капсула anat: fatty capsule, capsula adiposa.
~ клетка hist: fat cell.
~ опухоль path: fatty tumor, adipoma, lipoma.
~ ткань hist: fatty tissue, adipose t.
~ эмболия path: fat embolism, oil e.
жировидный fatlike, lardaceous, lipoid.
жировик path: lipoma, wen, cebaceous cyst.
жировиковый lipomatous.
жировичок ophth: pinguecula.

жировое отложение lipopexia.
~ перерождение fatty degeneration.
~ тело zool: fat body.
жировой комок anat: fat pad.
~ ~ Биши anat: buccal fat pad.
~ обмен fat metabolism, lipometabolism.
~ плавник zool: adipose fin, flesh fin.
~ побег bot: nourishing shoot, sucker, suckling.
~ шарик hist: fat globule.
жировоск (трупный) adipocere.
жировосковой adipoceratous.
жирообменный lipometabolic.
жирообразующий lipogenetic.
жиропот lanolin, wool fat, oily secretion.
жирорастворимый liposoluble, fat-soluble.
жирорасщепляющий fat-splitting, steatolytic.
жиряк 1. orn: oilbird (Steathornis caripensis); 2. see даман.
жирянка bot: butterwort, white rot (Pinguicula vulgaris).
житник = полевая мышь.
житняк гребенчатый bot: crested wheat grass (Agropyron cristatum).
жминда = амарант.
Жолли Jolly.
жолобоватая шина surg: gutter splint.
жом 1. surg: clamp, compressor, crushing forceps; 2. pulp.
жостер = крушина слабительная.
жужелица entom: ground beetle, carabus, carabid (Carabidae).
~ золотисто-зелёная entom: gilt ground beetle (Carabus auratus).
~ просяная millet b. (Pardileus calceatus).
~ семенная seed b. (Amara similata).
~ хлебная grain b. (Zabrus tenebrioides).
жужелицы (сем.) entom: ground beetles (Carabidae).
жужжала (сем.) entom: bee-flies (Bombyliidae).
жужжальце entom: balancer, halter, poiser.
жужжание hum, buzz, drone.
жужжать hum, buzz, drone.
жужжащее насекомое dor.
жук entom: beetle (Coleoptera).
~ айвовый quince curculio (Coleoptes humeralis).
~ белокаёмчатый Pantomorus leucoloma.
~ ветчинный Necrobia rufipes.
~ водяной water b. (Dytiscidae).
~ золотой rose chafer (Scarabeus auratus).

жук карапузик chafer, black b. (Hister), see карапузики.
~ колорадский картофельный Colorado potato b. (Leptinotarsa decemlineata).
~ -красун Anisoplia segetum.
~ -крестоносец Anisoplia agricola.
~ -кузька Anisoplia austriaca.
~ майский = хрущ майский.
~ малинный raspberry b., raspberry bug (Byturus unicolor, B. tomentosus)
~ мексиканский фасолевый Mexican bean b. (Epilachna).
~ морковный carrot b. (Ligyrus gibbosus).
~ музейный museum b. (Anthrenus museorum).
~ мучной = хрущак мучной.
~ -навозник dung-b. (Copris), dor (Geotrupes stercorarius).
~ -нарывник blister b. (Meloidae).
~ -носорог unicorn b., rhinoceros b. (Oryctes nasocornis).
~ -олень stag b. (Lucanus cervus).
~ -рогач stag b. (Lucanus).
~ спаржевый common asparagus b. (Crioceris asparagi).
~ сухофруктовый Carpophilus hemipterus.
~ табачный Lasioderma serricorne.
~ -усач long-horned b., capricorn b., cerambycid (Cerambycidae), see усачи (сем.) and усач 1.
~ хлебный 1. beetle of genus Anisoplia, fam. Scarabaeidae, see жук-красун, жук-крестоносец, жук-кузька; 2. drug b. (Sitodrepa panicea); see also долгоносик хлебн.
~ щелкун clickbeetle, elater.
~ японский Japanese b. (Popillia japonica).
жуки (отр.) entom: beetles, coleopters (Coleoptera).
~ -чернотелки (сем.) entom: darkling beetles (Tenebrionidae).
~ -щелкуны (сем.) entom: clickbeetle family (Elateridae).
жуколовка agr: beetle-catching device.
жулан orn: red-backed shrike (Lanius collurio).
журавельник = герань.
журавли orn: cranes (Grues).
журавль orn: crane (Gruidae).
Журдане Jourdanet.
журнал для записи больных patients registry.

журчалка бугорчатая entom: lesser bulbfly (Eumerus tuberculatus).
~ луковая onion syrphus (E. strigatus).
журчалки (сем.) entom: syrphus-flies (Syrphidae).
жучок entom: small beetle.
~ картофельный fleabeetle (Crepidodera cucumeris).
~ пчелиный bee beetle (Trichodes apiarius).
~ -точильщик wood fretter (Xylophaga).

З

забегание вперёд overshoot.
забеременеть become pregnant.
забивание сорняками agr bot: crowding by weeds.
забинтовать p. a. of бинтовать.
заболеваемость morbidity (rate), disease r., case r.; admission r. (to a hospital).
~ малярией malaria rate.
~ туберкулёзом tuberculosis rate.
заболевание disease, sickness, affection, see болезнь.
~ глаз ocular affection.
~ желёз внутренней секреции endocrinopathy.
~ ленточным глистом taeniasis.
~ мочевых органов urosis.
~ мышц myopathy.
~ новорожденного от молозива colostration.
~ плевры pleuritic disease.
~ почек renal disease.
~ слёзного аппарата lacrimal disease.
~ слухового нерва otolar: acoustic nerve disease.
заболевать fall ill.
заболеть p. a. of заболевать.
заболонник entom: scolytid beetle (Scolytus).
~ берёзовый birch-bark b. (S. ratzeburgi).
~ дубовый oak-bark b. (S. intricatus).
~ морщинистый fruit-tree bark b., shot-hole b. (S. rugulosus).
заболонники (подсем.) entom: scolytids (Scolytinae); see also короеды.
заболонь bot: cambium, sapwood.
заборный bot: of hedges, sepium.
забракование mil: rejection; disqualification.
забрушенный сот capped comb.
забрюшинное пространство anat: retroperitoneal space.
забурьянение agr bot: invasion of weeds, weed encroachment.
завал кишок vet: intestinal constipation.
заведение institute, institution, establishment, asylum.
завёрнутый вверх или вниз bot: revolute.
завивать(ся) curl.
~ в кочан bot: head.
завивающийся внутрь involute.
завируха болотная = славка полевая.
завирушка лесная orn: hedge sparrow (Accentor modularis).
зависящий от питания nutrition-dependent, alimentary.
завитой circinate, curled, involute.
завиток whorl, spire.
~ ушной раковины anat: helix.
завитый влево sinistral.
~ вправо dextral.
завить(ся) p. a. of завивать(ся).
завоз болезни "importation" of disease, spread of disease.
завозный сорняк bot: imported weed.
заворачивать веко ophth: entropionize.
заворот век(а) ophth: entropion, inversion of eyelid(s).
~ кишок ileus.
завороченный reflexed.
завроптеригиа zool: Sauropterygia (extinct).
завядание = увядание.
завязанные глаза blindfolding.
завязывание bot: setting.
*завязывать плоды (семена) bot: det the fruits (seeds).
завязь bot: ovary, young fruit, button.
~ огурцов bur, cuke, gherkin, young cucumber.
~плодов fruit set.
загар sunburn, tan.
загипнотизированный hypnotized, hypnotic.
заглазничный anat: postorbital.
заглатывание ingestion, swallowing.
заглатывать ingest, swallow.
заглотать p. a. of заглатывать.
заглоточный anat: postpharyngeal.
загниваемость putrescibility.
загнивание корней фиалок phytp: violet root rot.
загниватель san: septic tank.
загнутый кзади recurved.
загон agr zool: pound, pen.
загонная пастьба agr: rotational grazing.
заграждение obstruction, obstructing.
загривок zool: nape, withers.
загрудинное пространство anat: afterbreast.

загрудинный зоб path: substernal goiter.
загрязнение contamination.
~ из воздуха aerial c.
загрязнить p. a. of загрязнять.
загрязнять contaminate, pollute, soil.
загрязняющее вещество contaminant, pollutant.
загущённая культура agr bot: crowded crop.
зад anat: hindquarters, buttock(s).
заделать p. a. of заделывать.
заделка lab: embedding, mount(ing).
~ в парафин lab: paraffin embedding.
~ в целлоидин hist: celloidin e.
заделывать (препарат) lab: embed, mount.
задержавшиеся роды obstet: protracted labor.
задержание holding, inhibition, arresting.
задержанное развитие microplasia.
задерживать дыхание hold the breath.
задерживающий inhibitory.
~ нерв anat: inhibitory nerve.
~ пищеварение antidigestive.
~ приступ истерии neur: hysterofrenic
~ секрецию secreto-inhibitory.
~ фактор inhibitor.
~ центр anat: inhibitory center.
задержка 1. retention, inhibition, delaying; suppression, enclavement; 2. zool: retinaculum (of collembolae).
~ дыхания breath holding.
~ мочи ischuria, urinary retention.
~ остатков плода (после выкидыша) missed abortion.
~ по Биллсу av med: Bills' "block".
~ развития arrest of development.
~ роста бактерий bacteriostasis.
~ умершего плода obstet: missed labor.
задернение grassing down.
задернённость turfness.
заднебоковой anat: posterolateral.
заднебрюшие entom: metasoma.
заднебрюшной zool: metasomatic.
задневнешне anat: posteroexternad.
задневнешний anat: posteroexternal.
задневнутренне anat: posterointernad.
задневнутренний anat: posterointernal.
заднегрудь entom: afterbreast, metathorax.
заднее крыло entom: posterior wing, hind wing.
заднежаберники = заднежаберные моллюски.
заднежаберные моллюски (подкл.) zool: Opistobranchia.
~ (мягкотелые) zool: opistobranchia (malacozoans).
заднемозговой anat: metencephalic.

заднепередний posteroanterior, dorsoventral.
заднеплечевой postbrachial.
заднепроходная мышца anat: anal sphincter.
заднепроходное отверстие anus.
~ ~ (у простейших) zool: vent, cell-anus, cytopyge, cytoproct.
заднепроходный плавник anal fin.
~ треугольник anat: anal triangle.
заднеротовой anat: retrobuccal.
заднеспинка entom: scutellum, metatergum.
задний back, rear, hind; posterior.
~ боковой posterolateral.
~ брюшной posteroventral.
~ дворик устьица bot: stomatal back cavity.
~ жгутик zool: trailing flagellum.
~ кожный нерв бедра anat: posterior cutaneous nerve of thigh.
~ корешок (нервов) anat: posterior root (of nerves), dorsal r., sensory r.
~ мозг anat: afterbrain, hindbrain, metencephalon.
~ отдел кишечника anat: endgut.
~ палец orn: claw.
~ проход anat: anus.
~ рог (спинного мозга) dorsal cornu, dorsicornu.
~ спинной posterodorsal.
~ ~ плавник ichth: second dorsal fin.
~ (спинномозговой) корешок anat: dorsal root, posterior r.
~ столб (спинного мозга) anat: posterior column, dorsicolumn.
задняя (верхняя, нижняя) зубчатая мышца anat: serratus posterior (superior, inferior).
~ грудь = заднегрудь.
~ дуга позвонка posterior arch of the vertebra.
~ камера глаза anat: posterior chamber of the eye.
~ кишка entom: hindgut.
~ лапа zool: hindpaw, posterior leg.
~ лапка = з. лапа.
~ нога hind leg, haunch.
~ присоска subanal sucker, caudal s.
~ синехия ophth: posterior synechia.
~ срединная борозда anat: posterior median sulcus (of spinal cord).
~ сторона posterior aspect.
~ центральная извилина anat: ascending parietal gyrus, postcentral g., g. centralis posterior.
~ часть брюшка entom: postabdomen.
~ ~ вымени zool: hind udder.
~ ~ наличника entom: postclypeus.
~ ~ основной кости anat: postsphenoid.

задняя часть тела entom: hind body.
~ ямка черепа anat: postcranial fossa, posterior cranial fossa.
задохнуться p. a. of задыхаться.
задушающая плесень phytp: choke.
задушение suffocation. [overlying.
~ ребёнка собственным телом legl:
задыхаться 1. choke, suffocate; 2.pant, breathe hard, grasp for breath.
заживать heal.
~ вторичным затяжением surg: heal by second intention.
~ первичным затяжением surg: heal by first intention, h. by immediate
заживление healing (up), |union. closing, scarring (of a wound).
~ под струпом surg: healing by a scab.
~ раны surg: wound healing.
заживо сгореть to be burned alive.
зажим clamp, pinch clamp, clip,forceps, shut-off, pinch cock, thumb cock. Cf. надевать на нос зажим. [вать.
зажить heal completely; p. a. of зажи-
зазубренность crenulation.
зазубренный indented, serrated, crenated, jagged, nicked.
~ кзади retroserrate.
~ лист bot: serrated leaf, lacerated l.
зазубрина crena.
замес kneading.
заика path: stammerer, stutterer.
заикание path: psellism, stammering, stuttering, anarthria literalis,batta-
заикаться path: stammer, stutter.|rism.
зайцы (сем.) zool: rabbits and hares
зайчиха zool: she-hare. |(Leporidae).
заказник wildlife preserve.
закаливание hardening, inurement, habi-
~ растений plant hardening. tuation.
закалить(ся) p. a. of закалять(ся).
закалка = закаливание.
закалять(ся) harden, increase resistance, inure, habituate.
закапывание 1. burying, interment; 2. dripping, instillation.
закапываться bury oneself, burrow,
закваска leaven. embed.
закипание жидкостей организма av med: boiling of the body fluids.
закисание souring.
закисление acidulation.
закислить p. a. of закислять.
закислять acidulate.
закладка establishment, start, laying.
заклинатель змей snake charmer.

заключающий тело оборот body whorl (of a gastropod shell).
заключённый в оболочку sheathed,
~ в цисту encysted. thecate.
заковка vet: prick.
закомлеватость = корневая з.
закон регрессии genet: law of filial regression.
~ сцепления и перекрёста genet: law of linkage and crossing-over.
*законы патологии pathonomy.
~ тканей histonomy.
закопаться p. a. of закапываться.
закостренный лён bot: chaffy flax.
закрутка vet: artery clamp.
закрученный intorted, involute.
закручивание involution.
закручивающая листья гусеница entom: leaf-rolling caterpillar.
закручивающийся stranding.
закрывать close, shot, cover, occlude.
закрытая пыльная головня phytp: closed smut (on oat).
закрытие closure, shutting, covering, occlusion, obturation.
~ пищевода path: esophageal closure.
~ привратника желудка int: pyloric obstruction. [mous blooming.
~ трубы path: tubal occlusion.
закрытое цветение bot: cleistoga-
закрытоплодные = пиреномицеты.
закрытый ватной пробкой lab: cotton-plugged. [simple f.
~ перелом surg: closed fracture,
закукливаться entom: pupate.
закуклиться p.a. of закукливаться.
закупоривание occluding, obstructing. closing, shutting up, clotting.
закупоривать occlusion, obstruct, clot, plug, cork.
закупорить p. a. of закупоривать.
закупорка occlusion, obstruction, in-
~ артерии arterial occlusion. farct.
~ бронха bronchial obstruction.|sion.
~ венечной артерии coronary occlu-
~ вены occlusion of a vein, venous stasis, v. congestion.
~ верхнего отдела кишок high intestinal obstruction.
~ канала сгустком clottage. [sis.
~ кишок intestinal obstruction, i. sta-
~ кровеносного сосуда blood-vessel stasis.
~ мочевых путей urinary obstruction.
~ мочеточника ureteral obstruction.

закупорка носа nasal obstruction.
~ носовых ходов = з. носа.
~ пазухи sinus obstruction.
~ прохода blocking of a canal (duct).
~ тощей кишки jejunal obstruction.
~ трахеи tracheal obstruction.
~ труб(ы) gyn: tubal occlusion.
~ эмболом embolic occlusion.
залёжка rookery (of seals, etc.)
заложение цветка bot: vernation.
заложенность в ушах av med: "full and stuffy" feeling in the ears.
~ носа path: nasal obstruction, rhinocleisis.
залом = черноспинка.
замазка putty, cement; agr bot: covering
замедление slowing down, retardation.
~ родов obstet: bradytocia.
~ сердечной деятельности bradycardia
замедленная диастола path: bradydiastole, bradydiastolia.
~ перистальтика path: bradydiastalsis.
~ речь neur: bradyphasia, bradyglossia, bradyarthria.
замедленное мышление psych: sluggish mental activity, bradyphrenia.
замедленный рефлекс delayed reflex.
замедлять рост retard the growth, stunt
замедляющий рост stunting.
замена ткани другой transsubstantiation.
заменитель крови blood substitute.
заменяющий substituting, vicarious.
заметная хромота́ perceptible lameness
заметное потение perceptible perspiration, diaphoresis.
замещающая терапия replacement therapy.
замещающий substituting, replacing, vicarious.
~ врач locum tenens.
замирание червы = застуженная детка.
замия bot: zamia (Zamia).
замковая часть переднего крыла entom: clavus.
замок lock.
~ раковины zool: hinge, hinge teeth.
замор killing, suffocation.
~ рыб fishkill.
замораживание freezing.
замораживающий микротом hist: freezing microtome.
замороженный срез hist: frozen section.
заморская свинка = морская свинка.
замочка retting.
замутнение roiling.
замыкание заднего прохода path: closure of anus.
замыкательное сокращение closing contraction.
замыкающая клетка bot: guard cell.
~ ~ устьица bot: stomatal guard cell.
замыкающий мускул closing muscle, adductor, eye (of a mollusk).
занимающий правильное положение entopic.
занклюс ichth: Moorish idol (Zanclus cornutus).
заннихеллия bot: horned pondweed (Zannichellia).
заново культивированный recultivated.
занозка = манник.
занос obstet: mole.
~ сорняков = забурьянение.
заносный ecdemic.
заоболочечная беременность membranous pregnancy.
заострённый mucronate, acuminate.
~ на обоих концах bio: biacuminate.
~ нос pinched nose.
запавшие виски path: hollow temples.
~ черты лица path: sunken features.
запавший sunken, hollow.
~ живот retracted belly.
~ сосок crater nipple, retracted n.
западание sinking (back), retraction, deepening.
запаздывающее торможение psych: delayed inhibition.
запаздывающий delayed, tardy, tardive.
~ условный рефлекс psych: delayed conditioned reflex.
запал 1. zool: broken wind, pursiness, chest foundering (in horse); 2. bot: scorch; wind burn.
запалённая лошадь brokenwinded horse.
запас производителей brood stock.
запасание корма zool: hoarding.
запасная почка bot: supernumerary bud.
запасной желудок entom: food reservoir.
запекаться clot (of blood).
запёкшаяся кровь gore, cruor.
запечатанный сот = забрушенный сот.
запинание stuttering.
запирание obstruction, obturation.
запирательная артерия anat: obturator artery.
~ мышца (внутренняя, наружная) anat: obturator (internus, externus) muscle.
запирательное отверстие anat: obturator foramen, f. obturatum.
запирательный жёлоб anat: obturator groove, sulcus obturatorius.
~ нерв anat: obturator nerve.
заплесневелость mustiness, moldiness.
заплесневелый musty, moldy, fusty.
запломбировать p. a. of пломбировать.

запоздалая реакция delayed reaction.
запоздалые роды obstet: postponed labor, tardy l., partus serotinus.
запой psych: dipsomania; see also периодический запой.
запойный пьяница dipsomaniac.
запоминание psych: memorizing.
запоп bot: zapupe (Agava zapupe).
запор path: constipation. [gles.
запотевшие очки av med: fogging gog-
запредельное торможение = охранительное т. [tion.
запрещение алкоголя alcohol prohibi-
запрокидывание головы назад path: retraction of the head.
запупе = запоп.
запустевать obliterate.
запустеть p. a. of запустевать.
запущенное состояние (болезни) advanced state (of disease). [case.
запущенный случай path: neglected
запылённость лёгких pneumonoconiosis.
~ кремнистой пылью silicatisis.
запыхавшийся breathless, panting.
запястная связка anat: carpal ligament. [pometacarpal joint.
запястно-пястный сустав anat: car-
запястный anat: carpal. [horse).
запястье anat: wrist, carpus; knee (of
запятовидная бацилла mcbio: comma bacillus, vibrio comma.
запятовидный mcbio: comma-shaped. [tion.
заражаемость susceptibility to infec-
заражать 1. infect, communicate a disease; 2. bact: inoculate; 3. rad: con-
~ малярией malarialize. taminate.
~ растения головнёй phytp: smut.
~ туберкулёзом tuberculize.
заражаться contract an infection, contract a disease.
заражение 1. infecting, infection; 2. bact: inoculation; 3. rad: contamina-
~ большим количеством |tion. bact: heavy inoculation.
~ глистами invermination, helminthiasis
~ крови path: blood poisoning, septicemia, sepsis. [area c.
~ местности rad: ground contamination,
~ насекомыми insect infestation.
~ оспой imm: variolation.
~ радиоактивными веществами radiocontamination.
~ саккулиной sacculinization (of crabs)
~ финнами helm: cysticercosis.
заражённость 1. infected condition; 2. bact: inoculated c.

заражённость трихинами = трихиноз.
~ хетерофиес helm: heterophyiasis.
заражённый клещами tick-infested.
~ чумой plague-infested. [ous matter.
зараза infection, contagion; infecti-
~ водяная = болотница 2.
зараз(итель)ность contagiousness, infectiousness, infectivity.
зараз(итель)ный contagious, infectious, infective.
заразить(ся) p.a. of заражать(ся).
заразиха bot: broom rape (Orobanche).
заразиховое растение bot: orobanchaceous plant.
заразиховые (сем.) bot: broom-rape family (Orobanchaceae).
заразная болезнь infectious disease, communicable d.
~ больница contagious hospital. [giosa.
~ гнойничковая сыпь impetigo conta-
заразное начало imm: infectious matter, contagious m. [tive.
заразный contagious, infectious, infec-
~ выкидыш infectious abortion.
~ период period of communicability.
~ ринит vet: malignant rhinitis [нение.
зарастание сорняками = забурья-
заращение anat: atresia, imperforation, closure, obliteration (of lumen).
зародыш embryo; germ; bot: seed bud, corcle, corcule.
~ листа bot: leaf primordium.
~ раковой опухоли oncol: cancer
~ стебля bot: plumule. germ.
зародышевая камера zool: brood case.
~ клетка embr: germ cell; obs: geno-
~ оболочка embr: blastoderm. blast.
~ плазма embr: germ plasm.
~ почка bot: gemma.
~ трубка germ tube.
~ хрящевая ткань embr: precartilage.
зародышевое пятно embr: germinal macula, nucleolus.
~ состояние embryoism. [(of flukes).
зародышевые шары zool: germ balls
зародышевый embryonic, embryonal, germinal.
~ диск embryonic disk, blastodisk.
~ корень bot: radicle (in a seed).
~ листок embr: germ layer, blastophyl-
~ мешок bot: embryo sac. |lum.
~ мочевой проток anat: urachus.
~ пузырёк embr: germ bladder, blastula, blastocyst, germ vesicle.

зародышевый рубчик germinal disk.
~ эпителий germinal epithelium.
зарождение inception, conceiving.
заросль bot: copse, coppice, thicket.
~ растений vegetation bed.
заросток bot: gametophyte.
заросший grown over; weedy, weed-filled
~ лесом forested.
~ пруд plant-filled pond.
~ растениями plant-filled.
~ тростником reedy.
зарубцевание = рубцевание.
зарубцеваться p. a. of рубцеваться.
зарыбленный пруд stocked pond.
зарянка orn: robin (Erithacus).
засадка (пруда рыбой) stocking.
засадчик zool: ambuscader.
засевание mcbio: inoculating.
засевать mcbio: inoculate.
засекать время note the time.
засекаться vet: overreach, cut, interfere (of a horse).
заселение bio: stocking, colonization.
заселённый bio: stocked, colonized.
засечка vet: attaint, crepance (in horses.
заслонить p. a. of заслонять.
заслонка valve; see also клапан.
~ аорты anat: aortic valve.
~ между предсердием и желудочком сердца anat: atrioventricular valve.
~ нижней полой вены anat: (inferior vena) caval valve.
заслонять свет (be)dim.
заслуженный член fellow (of a society)
засорение глаз dust in the eyes.
застаиваться congest, stagnate; engorge, choke, form an infarct.
застарелая язва path: long standing ulcer.
застарелый old, long-time.
застой path: stagnation, congestion, stasis, infarct(ion), engorgement.
~ в зрительном сосочке ophth: choking of the disk.
~ во внутренних органах path: visceral congestion.
~ крови hemostasis.
застойный stagnated, congested, engorged
~ сосочек ophth: choked disk, engorged papilla.
застонать p. a. of стонать.
застояться p. a. of застаиваться.
застрахованный insured.
застуженная детка cold structure (of bees).
~ расплод = застуженная детка.
застывшая поза psych: fixed posture.

засуховыносливый bot: drought-enduring.
засухоустойчивость bot: drought-resistance.
засухоустойчивый drought-resisting.
засушливый xeric, droughty.
засыпание psych: predormition.
засыхание побегов груши phytp: pear-blight.
затампонировать p. a. of тампонировать.
затвердевание solidification.
затвердевать solidify.
затвердевшее вымя vet: caked breast
затвердевший = затверделый.
затверделый hardened, indurated.
затвердение hardening, induration, sclerosis.
~ вымени vet: mastitis, garget; see also грудница.
~ груди path: mastoscirrhus.
~ грудной железы path: puerperal mastitis, caked breast.
затемнение dimming, darkening, screening off, diaphragming.
затемнённая комната darkened room.
затемнить p. a. of затемнять.
затемнять (be)dim, darken, screen off.
затихание abatement, subsidence, remission, defervescence, lysis.
затруднение глотания path: dysphagia.
~ дыхания difficulty in breathing.
~ мочеиспускания urinary difficulty, retention of urine.
~ оттока aggravation of outflow.
затруднённое дыхание difficult breathing, hard b., pant(ing), dyspnea; vet: roaring.
~ мочеиспускание strangury.
затруднённость сосредоточения psych: difficulty in concentration.
затруднённые роды obstet: difficult labor, dystocia.
затуманенное зрение blurred vision.
затуманенный глаз blear-eye, lippitudo, lippitude.
затухание attenuation.
затхлый запах moldy odor.
затыкание уха plugging of the ear.
затылок anat: occiput; poll (of horse).
затылочная артерия anat: occipital artery.
~ бороздка zool: cervical groove (of crustacea).
~ доля (мозга) anat: occipital lobe.
~ извилина anat: occipital convolution.
~ кость anat: occipital bone, os occipitale.

затылочная область anat: occipital
region. [cal.
затылочно-шейный anat: occipitocervi-
затылочное отведение occipital-area
take-off (for electrical measurements
of brain currents, etc.) [sentation.
~ предлежание obstet: occipital pre-
затылочный бугор anat: occipital
protuberance.
~ гребень anat: occipital ridge.
~ гребешок anat: occipital crest.
~ изгиб embr: cervical flexure.
~ нерв (большой, малый, третий)
(greater, lesser, third) occipital
nerve.
затяжной persistent, lasting, sustain-
ed, long-time, long-standing. [sis.
затянувшийся кризис protracted cri-
затянутость во времени time delay,
time lag.
заурурус bot: lizard's tail (Saururus).
заурурусовые (сем.) bot: lizard's
tail family (Saururaceae).
заусеница agnail, hangnail.
заушница infect: mumps.
захват bot: wind burn.
захиревшее дерево stunted tree.
захождение (костных отломков)
друг за друга surg: overriding.
зацвёлый = заплесневелый.
зацветание щиткового соцветия
bot: cymose inflorescence.
зацепка entom: retinaculum.
зачатие embr: conception.[ment, germinant
зачаток embr: bot: somite, bud; rudi-
~ конечности embr: limb bud.
~ корня bot: root primordium.
~ крыла entom: wing bud.
~ лёгкого lung bud.
~ листа bot: leaf rudiment.
~ пятого пальца dewclaw (of cow).
зачаточная полость тела embryonic
body cavity, c(o)elom.
~ пора bot: germ pore, micropyle.
~ предсердие anat: primitive atrium.
зачаточный primordial, somatic; rudi-
~ корешок bot: radicle. mentary.
зачать embr: conceive.
зашивание surg: suturation, suturing.
~ грыжи surg: herniorrhaphy.
зашивать surg: suture.
зашить p. a. of зашивать.
защита организма infect: phylaxis.
защитительный = защитный. [tion.
защитная окраска bio: cryptic colora-
защитная повязка surg: protective
dressing.
~ реакция imm: defense reaction.
~ способность imm: defense ability.
защитные очки goggles, protective
glasses.
~ силы physl: defense forces.
защитный zool: aposematic.
~ рефлекс defense reflex.
защищенный от мух fly-proof.
заяц zool: hare (Lepus). [dus).
~ -беляк white h., blue h. (L. timi-
~ -русак common h., gray h., brown h.
(L. europaeus).
заячий zool: leporine.
заячьи лапки bot: see 1. клевер
пашенный; 2. пушица.
заячья губа path: harelip, cleft lip,
cheiloschisis.
~ капуста = капуста заячья.
звезда star; aster; hist : see
центросома.
звездовик bot: earthstar (Geaster).
звездообразная повязка surg:
stellate bandage.
звездообразный star-shaped, stellate,
astroid. [pus).
*звездочёт ichth: stargazer (Astrosco-
звездочёты (сем.) ichth: stargazers
(Uranoscopidae).
звёздчатая камбала ichth: great
flounder (Platichthys stellatus).
~ клетка hist: stellate cell.
звездчатка bot: chickweed, starwort
(Stellaria, L.) [tea).
~ лесная greater stitchwort (S. holos-
~ средняя common chickweed (S. media).
звездчатый stellate.
~ анис pharm: star anise (Illicium
verum). [starred f.
~ перелом surg: stellate fracture.
звери zool: beasts; see also
млекопитающие. [cum, L.)
зверобой bot: St. John's wort (Hyperi-
~ виргинский marsh St-John's wort
(H. virginicum, L., or Elodea
companulata, Pursh).
~ чашечный bot: Aaron's beard
(H. calycinum).
зверобойные (сем.) bot: St. John's-
wort family (Guttiferae).
зверозубые пресмыкающиеся zool:
Theriodontia (extinct). [tinct).
зверообразные zool: Therapsida (ex-
звероподобные zool: Theromorpha,
Pelycosauria (extinct).

звон в ушах path: ringing in the ears.
~ ~ ушах от телефона path: telephone tinnitus. [harlequin fly (Chironomus).
звонец entom: chironomid midge, true m.,
звонкие хрипы ringing rales, sonorous rales.
звук sound.
~ Скода Skoda's resonance, tympanitic r.
~ треснутого горшка cracked-pot sound.
звуковая боль otolar: odynacousis.
звуковысотный слух pitch hearing.
звукопроводный sound-conducting.
звучные хрипы = звонкие хрипы.
здоровая ткань healthy tissue.
здоровый healthy, healthful, salubrious.
~ взрослый healthy adult.
здоровье health, salubrity.
здравница health station, health resort.
здравое суждение sound judgment.
здравый смысл common sense.
зебра zool: zebra (Hyppotigris, Equus chapmani).
зебрина bot: spiderwort, wandering Jew (Tradescantia zebrina, Hort.)
зебу zool: zebu, East Indian ox (Box indicus).
зебувидный скот zebu cattle.
зев anat: 1. mouth, os, ostium, orifice; see also отверстие; 2. fauces, isthmus faucium.
~ матки (внутренний, наружный) anat: os uteri (internum, externum).
зевание yawning.
зевный anat: faucial.
зевота 1. physl: yawning; 2. orn: gapes. Cf. нематода зевоты кур.
зейдлицкий порошок pharm: Seidlitz powder, compound effervescing powder.
зелёная водоросль bot: green alga, chlorophyte.
~ гидра zool: green hydra (Chlorohydra viridissima).
~ устрица green oyster.
~ черепаха zool: green turtle (Chelonia mydas).
зеленец = завязь огурцов.
зелёнка bot: masked tricholoma (Tricholoma personatum).
зелёноглазка = муха зелёноглазая.
зелёное мыло green soap.
зелёномясый bot: greenfleshed.
зеленуха = зелёнушка.
зелёнушка 1. ichth: Crenilabrus tinca; 2. orn: see зелёный вьюрок.
зелёнушковые = губановые.
зелёные водоросли bot: green algae, chlorophytes (Chlorophyta).
~ водоросли, собственно Euchlorophyceae.
~ жгутиковые bio: green flagellated organisms.
~ мхи (пор.) bot: true mosses (Bryales).
зелёный green; bot: verdant.
~ вьюрок orn: greenfinch (Ligurnus chloris).
~ краб zool: shore crab (Carcinus).
~ хлоропласт hist: green chloroplast.
зелень bot: greens, top; green scum (on water).
землеедство = геофагия.
землемер entom: geometer, see пяденица.
~ крыжовниковый currant measuring worm (Cymatophora ribearia).
землерой zool: digger, digging animal.
землеройка zool: shrew (Sorex).
~ водяная water s. (Neomys fodiens, Sorex palustris).
~ короткохвостая short-tailed s. (Blarina brevicauda).
~ обыкновенная common s., masked s. (Sorex araneus, S. cinereus).
землеройки (сем.) shrews, borrowing animals (Soricidae).
землистый цвет лица path: muddy complexion.
земляная звездочка bot: earth star (Geaster) fungi.
земляника bot: strawberry (Fragaria); wild s. (F. vesca).
земляничник крупноплодный = земляничное дерево.
земляничное дерево bot: strawberry tree (Arbutus unedo).
земляной волк = протел.
~ рак phytp: collar rot.
~ червь = червь дождевой.
земляные орешки = лабазник шестилепестный.
земноводное zool: amphibian.
~ с постоянными жабрами perennibranch.
земноводные zool: amphibians (Amphibia), see амфибии.
зенитный прицел av med: pedestal sight(ing station).
зеркало mirror, speculum.
~ для ректоскопии anal speculum.
зеркальное письмо neur: mirror writing.
зёрна пыльцы bot: pollen grains.

зернистость graininess, granularity.
зернистый granular, granulous, granulated, granulative; bot: seedy.
~ распад rad: granular disintegration.
~ цилиндр urol: granular cast.
зерно 1. grain; 2. bot: seed.
зерновик entom: seed beetle (Bruchus seminarius). [bot: caryopsis.
зерновка 1. entom: bruchid weevil; 2.
~ акациевая Kytorrhinus quadriplagiatus
~ бобовая broad-bean weevil (Bruchus rufimanus).
~ вьюнковая Euspermophagus sericeus.
~ гороховая pea weevil (Bruchus pisorum). [chinensis).
~ китайская Chinese w. (Callosobruchus
~ соевая bean w. (Acanthoscelides obtectus).
~ фасолевая Acanthoscelides obsoletus.
~ четырехпятнистая Callosobruchus quadrimaculatus.
~ эспарцетная Bruchidius unicolor.
зерновки (сем.) entom: bruchid weevils (Bruchidae).
зерноед maggot; cf. кукурузный з.
зернофуражная культура fodder grain.
зёрнышко granule, granula; acinus; bot: small seed, pip, stone.
~ в клетках бурых водорослей bot: fucosan vesicle.
зернящий granulating, granulative.
зигаденус мухоубивающий bot: fly-poison (Zygadenus muscaetoxicus, Reg.)
зигнема bot: Zygnema. [(algae).
зигнемовые (сем.) bot: Zygnemaceae
зигомицеты bot: zygomycetes (Zygomyce-
зигоспора bot: zygospore. tales).
зигота embr: zygote.
зизания bot: zizania (Zizania).
зильберсальварсан pharm: silver
зимаза zymase. arsphenamine.
зимин zymin.
зимняя почка bot: hibernaculum.
~ спячка zool: hibernation.
зимование = зимовка.
зимовка wintering; zool: hibernation.
зимовник = безвременник осенний.
зимовочное приспособление bio: hibernating device.
зимоген zymogen, proferment.
зимнее яйцо zool: winter egg.
зимний зуд path: winter itch, frost i., pruritus hiemalis. [ca)
зимокка zool: zimocca (Euspongia zimoc-
зимология zymology.
зимолюбка bot: wintergreen, checkerberry (Chimaphila, Pursh.)
зимородок orn: kingfisher, halcyon (Alcedo). Cf. ракши. [tea).
*~ -великан kinghunter (Dacelo gigan-
~ -хохотун laghing jackass, see з-великан.
зимостойкий winterhardy.
зимостойкость winterhardyness.
зимующая культура bot: overwintering crop.
зимующее бобовое bot: winter legume
зимующий (over)wintering; hibernating.
зиять gape.
зияющий gaping.
злак bot: grain, cereal, corn, grass.
злаки (сем.) bot: grass family (Gramineae).
злаковые = злаки (сем.)
~ мушки (сем.) entom: Chloropidae.
злаковый bot: gramineous, of the grass family.
злакоцветные bot: graminales.
златка entom: metallic wood-borer, buprestid (Buprestidae).
~ дубовая oak borer (Agrilus angustutus, Illig.) [ens.
~ ильмовая зелёная Lampra decipi-
~ люцерновая Sphenoptera montana.
~ осиновая Poecilonota variolosa.
~ плоскоголовая flat-headed borer (Chrysobothris femorata).
~ синяя сосновая Phaenops cyanea).
~ смородинная зелёная green currant borer (Agrilus viridis).
~ стеблевая кунжутная Acmaeodera ballioni.
~ узкотелая sinuate borer (Agrilus sinuatus, Oliv.)
златки (сем.) entom: metallic wood-borers (Buprestidae).
златоглазка entom: golden-eyed fly, aphis lion (Chrysops).
златоглазки (сем.) entom: lacewing flies, aphis lions (Chrysopidae).
златогузка entom: brown-tailed moth (Euproctis chrysorrhoea, Nygmia phoeorrhoea).
*златок bot: king's speer (Asphodelus, Asphodelina lutea, Recsh.)
златоцвет bot: 1. corn marigold (Chrysanthemum segetum); see also хризантема; 2. see ромашка далматская. [mum frutescens).
~ канарский marguerite (Chrysanthe-

злая корча path: spasmodic ergotism.
злокачественная анемия path: pernicious anemia.
~ опухоль oncol: malignant tumor.
~ оспа infect: malignant smallpox.
злокачественное новообразование oncol: malignant growth.
злокачественность malignancy.
злокачественный malignant, pernicious.
~ гной malignant pus.
~ насморк malignant rhinitis.
~ отёк malignant edema; vet: bradzot.
злонравие maliciousness, malignancy, ill-temper.
злостный сорняк bot: worst weed.
злоупотребление abuse, wrong use, misuse, excessive use.
~ алкоголем alcohol abuse, excessive use of alcohol.
змеевик coil (pipe).
змееголовник bot: dragonhead (Dragocephalum, L.)
~ молдавский Moldavian d. (D. moldavicum).
змееголовые (сем.) ichth: Ophiocephalidae.
змеезвезды zool: brittle stars (Ophiuroidea).
змеёныш zool: snakelet.
змеехвостки = змеезвезды.
змеи (подотр.) zool: snakes (Ophida, Serpentes).
змеиный корень bot: birthwort, Virginia snakeroot (Aristolochia serpentaria)
~ яд snake venom.
змейка zool: small snake.
змея zool: snake, serpent, ophidian.
знак "Rp" в начале рецепта pharm: superscription.
знахарка woman quack.
знахарское средство quack medicine, nostrum.
знахарство quackery.
знахарь quack, medicaster.
значащийся в списке больных sick-listed.
значительное врожденное уродство path: monstrosity.
зоб 1. orn: crop, gorge, craw, glandular stomach, see железистый желудок; 2. mastax (of a rotifer); 3. path: goiter, goitre.
зобатые бегунки orn: Thinocori.
зобная железа = вилочковая ж.
"зобное сердце" path: goiter heart.
зобный path: goitrous, strumous.
зоеа zool: zoea.
зола ash.
~ водорослей kelp-ashes, varec.
золеподобное превращение chem: solation.
золотарник bot: goldenrod (Solidago virga aurea, L.)
золотая печать pharm: golden seal, hydrastis canadensis.
~ пломба odont: gold filling.
~ розга = золотарник.
~ рыбка goldfish (Cyprinus auratus, Carassius auratus).
золотистый заяц = агути.
~ окунь rosefish, hemdurgan (Sebastes marinus).
золото gold, Au.
золотое дерево bot: aucuba (Aucuba japonica, Thunb.)
"золотой дождь" bot: bean tree, catalpa, carob, etc. (Cytissus laburnum, L.); golden shower (Cassia fistula).
~ фазан orn: golden pheasant (Thumalea picta).
золототысячник bot: centaury (Erythrea centaurium, Pers.)
золотуха path: scrofula, king's evil.
золотушный scrofulous.
золотянка стенная bot: Xanthoria parietina (lichen).
зольник bot: cineraria (Senecio cineraria, DC).
зона́ = головня.
зона zone.
~ ламинарий bot: laminarian belt.
~ фукусов bot: fucoid belt.
зональное распределение zonation.
зональность zonation.
зонд sound, sonde, probe.
~ для искусственного кормления feeding tube.
~ ~ мозга brain probe.
зондаж sounding, probing.
зондирование = зондаж.
зондировать sound, probe.
зонотрихия orn: white-crowned sparrow.
зонтик bot: umbel.
зонтикообразный bot: umbelliform.
зонтикоцветные (пор.) bot: parsley order (Umbelliflorae).
зонтичное растение bot: umbelliferous plant. (Umbelliferae).
зонтичные (сем.) bot: parsley family
зоогеограф zoogeographer.
зоогеографический zoogeographical.
зоогеография zoogeography.

зооглейный zoogloeic.
зоогонидий zoogonidium.
зоодермический zoodermic.
зооид zooid.
зооксантелла zool: zooxanthella.
зоолит zoolite.
зоолог zoologist.
зоологический zoological.
зоология zoology.
~ беспозвоночных invertebrate zoology.
~ ископаемых paleozoology.
~ позвоночных vertebrate zoology.
зооноз zoonosis, zoonotic disease.
зоонозный zoonotic.
зоопалеонтология paleozoology.
зоопланктон zooplankton.
зооспора zoospore.
зооспорангий zoosporangium.
зоостерин zoosterin.
зоотехник zootechnician.
зоотехнический zootechnic.
зоофит zoophyte.
зоохимия animal chemistry.
зопник клубненосный bot: Jerusalem sage (Phlomis tuberosa, L.)
зóря = любастик.
зостера bot: grass-wrack, eelgrass (Zostera marina, L.)
зрачковая пленка ophth: pupillary membrane.
~ реакция pupillary reaction.
зрачковый край anat: pupillary margin.
зрачок ophth: pupil.
зрелая завязь bot: mature ovary, pericarp.
зрелость maturity, ripeness.
зрелый mature, ripe.
зрение sight, eyesight, vision.
зрительная аура neur: visual aura.
~ галлюцинация visual hallucination.
~ иллюзия движения av med: visual illusion of motion.
~ ~ от облаков av med: optical illusion from cloud.
~ ориентация av med: visual orientation.
~ ось ophth: optic axis.
~ палочка = рабдом.
~ память eye memory.
~ способность visual power.
зрительное восприятие visual perception.
~ отверстие anat: optic foramen.
~ ощущение visual sense.
зрительный visual.
~ бугор anat: thalamus opticus.
~ нерв anat: optic nerve, second cranial nerve.
зрительный порог visual threshold.
~ пурпур hist: visual purple, retinal red.
~ сосочек anat: optic disk, optic papilla.
зуб tooth.
~ держащий мостик abutment, abuttal.
~ мудрости wisdom tooth.
~ на штифте odont: pivot crown.
~ с коронкой jacket crown tooth, crowned tooth.
~ ~ расходящимися корнями odont: barred tooth.
зубастый карп ichth: sac-a-lait (Poeciliidae).
зубатка ichth: Anarhichas.
~ пёстрая A. minor.
~ полосатая wolf fish (A. lupus).
~ пятнистая A. minor.
~ синяя A. latifrons.
зубатковые (сем.) ichth: Anarhichadidae.
зубатые киты (подотр.) zool: toothed whales (Odontoceti).
~ птицы orn: Odontognathae (extinct).
зубатый zool: dentigerous.
~ кит zool: toothed whale.
зубец tooth; entom: canine.
~ T T-wave (of heart).
~ на зерне пшеницы wheat beak.
зубная болезнь odont: tooth disease.
~ боль toothache, odontalgia, dentalgia.
~ бороздка embr: dental furrow.
~ коронка odont: crown of a tooth.
~ пилка odont: dental file, tooth f.
~ пломба tooth filling.
~ профилактика dental prophylaxis.
~ пульпа anat: dental pulp.
~ формула zool: dental formula.
~ щетка toothbrush.
~ ячейка anat: tooth socket.
зубное дерево = ясень колючий американский.
~ зеркало odont: dental mirror, odontoscope.
зубной аппарат dentition.
~ врач dentist.
~ зачаток embr: tooth bud.
~ корень anat: tooth root, fang.
~ мешочек embr: tooth sac.
~ налет odont: dental deposit.
~ отросток = альвеолярный о.
~ порошок pharm: tooth powder, dentifrice.
~ сосочек anat: dental bulb.
~ шприц dental syringe.
зубные щипцы odont: dental forceps, denticeps.
зубовидная связка anat: dentate ligament.

зубовидная фаза dented stage.
зубовидный dentiform, tooth-shaped, toothlike, odontoid.
~ отросток anat: dens (of the vertebra)
зубоврачебное дело dentistry.
~ кресло dental chair.
зубоврачебный кабинет dental department, dental office.
зубоврачевание dentistry.
зубок 1. little tooth, jag; 2. bot: chive, clove, bulbil (a segment of the bulb).
зубр zool: aurochs, European bison (Bos bonasus), urus (B. primigenius).
~ американский = бизон.
зубровка bot: holy grass (Hierochloe, R. Br.)
~ душистая vanilla grass, Indian grass, sweet g., (H. odorata, Beauv.)
зубчатая мышца (передняя) anat: serratus (anterior) muscle, serratus anticus, serratus magnus.
~ связка anat: denticulate ligament.
~ тура bot: notched wrack (Fucus serratus).
зубчатка mcscop: rack and pinion.
зубчатое ядро anat: nucleus dentatus.
зубчатость dentation, etc.
зубчатый dentate, toothed, serrate, denticulate; see also мелкозубчатый, пильчатый.
~ лист bot: serrate leaf, dental leaf.
~ шов anat: dentate suture, sutura dentata.
зубчик denticle.
зубы морского ежа = аристотелев фонарь.
~ разделенные большими интервалами odont: rake teeth.
зуд itching, pruritus.
~ в заднем проходе path: anal itching.
~ дровосеков derm: lumbermen's itch.
зудень = клещ, клещик.
зудовый pruritic.
зудящий pruritic, urticant.
зуёк orn: plover.
~ долгоногий stiltbird (Himantopus himantopus).
~ полулапчатый killdeer (Aegialitis semipalmata).
зюзник bot: water horehound, bugleweed (Lycopus, L.)
~ европейский gypsywort (L. europaeus).
зябкий chilly, algid.
зяблик orn: chaffinch (Fringilla coelebs)
зябра = жабрей.

И

иатрогения iatrogenia.
иатрохимия iatrochemistry.
ибис orn: ibis (Threskiornithidae, Ibididae).
ива willow (Salix); see верба.
~ вавилонская = ива плакучая.
~ жёлтая golden osier (S. vitellina).
~ златолистная kinghead, marsh elder (S. xanthiifolia).
~ золотистая = ива златолистная.
~ козья goat willow (S. caprea).
~ корзиночная bot: basket willow, osier (S. viminalis).
~ ~ пурпурная red osier (S. purpurea)
~ ксантифольная great ragweed (Iva xantifolia).
~ ломкая crack willow, brittle w., (S. fragilis).
~ миндальная Spaniard rod (S. triandra).
~ плакучая weeping willow, witch w., osier twig (S. babylonica).
~ поникшая = ива плакучая.
~ прутьевидная = ива корзиночная.
Иван-чай = чай капорский.
ивановский побег bot: Lammas shoot.
иваси ichth: Far-East pilchard (Sardinella melanostica).
ивасиевый полосатик zool: fish whale, sei w., (Balaenoptera borealis).
ивняк osiery, osier bed.
ивовая шелкопряд-листовёртка = челночница ивовая.
ивовые (сем.) bot: willow family (Salicaceae).
ивовый древоточец = крушень-д.
ивоцветные (пор.) bot: Salicales.
игла needle; stylus; zool: spicule, mucro.
~ для взятия крови blood needle, spring lancet.
~ ~ посева bact: planting wire.
~ ~ пробной пункции surg: exploring needle.
~ ~ спинномозговой пункции surg: spinal tap needle.
~ ~ шейки матки gyn: cervix needle.
~ -рыба pipefish (Syngnathus).

игла с радием radium needle (implant).
~ ~ радиокобальтом oncol: radiocobalt needle (implant).
~ Франка hem: Francke's spring lancet.
иглистый = игольчатый.
игло- acu-, needle-.
иглоголовое zool: needle head(Rhabdosoma).
иглодержатель surg: needleholder, needle forceps.
иглокожее zool: echinoderm.
иглокожие zool: echinoderms (Echinodermata).
иглошёрст zool: porcupine (Erithizon dorsatum).
иглошёрсты (сем.) zool: porcupines (Erithizontidae).
игобрюх ichth: Spheroides.
игольчатый acerous, acicular, acerate, spicular, spiculate, echinate.
~ душ needle bath.
игристое вино sparkling wine.
игрунковые (сем.) zool: tamarins Hapalidae.
игрунок zool: tamarin.
~ серебристый tamarin (Hapale argentata).
игуана zool: iguana lizard (Iguana tuberculata).
игуанодон zool: Iguanodon (extinct).
игуаны (сем.) zool: iguana family (Iguanidae).
идеализация psych: idealization.
идентификация identification.
идея преследования idea of persecution.
идиоглоссия psych: idioglossia.
идиопатическая анемия idiopathic anemia, primary a., essential a.
идиопатический idiopathic, self-existing, essential.
идиопатическое заболевание idiopathy.
идиосинкразический idiosyncratic.
идиосинкразия idiosyncrasy.
идиот psych: idiot.
идиотизм idiocy.
идиотия idiocy.
идиотский idiotic.
идиохромидии bio: idiochromidia.
идущий к коре corticipetal.
~ ~ спинному мозгу spinipetal.
~ от коры corticifugal.
~ ~ нерва abnerval.
~ ~ спинного мозга spinifugal.
*избегающий света bio: lucifugal.
избирательное сродство elective affinity.
избирательный (s)elective.
избыток липазы в крови path: hyperliposis.
избыточное действие (мышцы) overaction (of a muscle).
~ отложение жира excessive adipose deposits.
~ сокращение глазных мышц ophth: overaction of the external ocular muscles.
избыточный вес overweight.
извержение семени ejaculation.
известковая вода pharm: lime water.
~ жидкая мазь pharm: carron oil, lime liniment.
~ игла zool: calcareous spicule (in sponges).
~ капсула zool: calculus.
известковое перерождение плодного заноса obstet: stone mole.
известковые губки (отр.) zool: calcareous sponges (Calcarea, Calcispongiae).
известковый calcic, calcareous, calcigerous.
известь lime.
извив coil.
извилина sinuous curve, tortuous curve, convolution.
~ мозга anat: gyrus, cerebral convolution.
~ морского конька anat: hippocampal gyrus.
извилины Рейлиева островка anat: insular convolutions.
извилистость tortuosity, etc.
извилистый tortuous, sinuous, meandrous, meandering, flexuous, repand (leaf, etc.)
извитой coiled, convoluted, spiral, winding, gyrose; see also извилистый.
~ каналец anat: convoluted tubule, tubulus contortus (renal).
~ ~ второго порядка distal convoluted tubule.
~ ~ первого порядка proximal convoluted tubule (near the glomerulus).
извитость = извилистость.
извлечение drawing out, extraction, pulling out
~ зуба odont: tooth pulling.
извнутри кнаружи entoectad.
извращение perversion.
извращённая наклонность perverted craving.
извращённое восприятие illusion.
извращённый аппетит perverted appetite, pice, parorexia.
~ вкус perverted taste.
~ половой инстинкт psych: erotopathy.
~ субъект pervert.
изгиб flexure.
~ матки вперёд anat: anteflexion of the uterus.

изгибание дугой arching.
~ корней bot: bending of roots.
изглаживание obliteration.
изгнание expulsion.
~ глистов expelling intestinal worms.
~ плода gyn: causing abortion; obstet: expulsion of the fetus.
изгнать p. a. of изгонять.
изгонять expel , drive away.
~ плод obstet: expel the fetus; gyn: cause abortion.
изгоняющие родовые схватки obstet: expulsive pains.
изготовление мостика odont: bridge-
~ муляжей ceroplasty. [work.
~ тотальных препаратов lab: mounting in toto. [pyrosis.
изжога (water)brash, heartburn, gastric
изидий bot: isidium (of lichens).
ИЗИФ = Институт прикладной зоологии и фитопатологии.
излечение complete recovery, complete cure, healing up.
излечимость curability.
излечимый curable, healable.
излияние effusion, suffusion.
излом breaking off; infraction.
излюбленная локализация path: site of predilection, seat of predilection.
изменение границ поля зрения ophth: perimetric change. [change.
~ кровообращения path: circulatory
~ перкуторного звука int: impairment of resonance.
~ печени path: hepatic change.
~ психического статуса mental change
~ сетчатки ophth: retinal change.
~ цвета discoloration.
изменчивость mutability; variability, unsteadiness, changeability.
изменчивый mutable; variable, unsteady,
изменяемость changeability. | changeable.
изменяемый alterable, changeable.
изменяющийся со временем tempolabile
измерение measurement, measuring, mensuration.
~ напряжения радиации actinometry.
~ поля зрения ophth: campimetry.
~ силы выдоха measurement of expiratory force.
~ таза obstet: pelvimetry. [metry.
~ ~ и головки obstet: pelviencephalo-
~ температуры под мышкой axillary measurement of temperature.
измеритель поля зрения ophth: campimeter.

измерительная лента measuring tape.
~ рулетка = и. лента.
~ штанга measuring rod. [ture
измерять температуру take tempera-
изможжение weariness, exhaustion, emaciation, prostration, phthisis.
изможждённый fatigued, exhausted, emaciated, prostrate. [violation.
изнасилование legl: rape, raping,
изнасиловать rape, violate.
изначальный primordial.
изнашивание (организма) wearing out (of organism).
изнеможение от жары path: heat
износ wear(ing out). | prostration.
изношенность degree of wear.
изношенный outworn, wornout.
изнурение wearing (oneself) out, wasting away, enervation.
изнурительная болезнь consumptive disease, debilitating d., wasting d.
изнурить p. a. of изнурять.
изнурять wear out, exhaust, emaciate, enervate. [oneself.
изнуряться wear oneself out, exhaust
изоагглютинин isoagglutinin.
изобилующий водорослями algae-rich
изображение на сетчатке ophth:
изогалина isohaline. | retinal image.
изогамета bio: isogamete.
изогамия bio: isogamy.
изогамный isogamous.
изогемагглютинин isohemagglutinine.
изогнутый в виде крючка = крючковатый. [positor.
~ яйцеклад entom: scimitar-shaped ovi-
изозома галловая entom: jointworm, wheat midge (Harmolita). [ci, I. hordei).
~ пшеничная jointworm (Isosoma triti-
~ ячменная = и. пшеничная.
изолейцин isoleucine.
изолепис изящный bot: isolepis gracilis (Scirpus cernuus, S. gracilis).
изолецитальный embr: isolecithal.
изолизинный isolytic.
изолированный ацидоз тканей path: outlying acidosis.
~ корень bot: excised root.
изолировать isolate.
изолятор infect: isolation ward, probationary ward.
изоляция инфекционных больных contagious isolation.
изоморфный isomorphous, isomorphic.
изониазид pharm: isoniazid.

изоникотиновая кислота pharm: isonicotinic acid.
изопода zool: isopod.
изопропаноламин pharm: isopropanolamine.
изотерма isotherm.
изотермическая линия isothermal line.
изотонический isotonic.
изотропный isotropic.
изохроматидное расщепление genet: isochromatid break.
изувечить maim, mutilate, disfigure.
изучение личности personality study.
~ признаков болезней semiotics.
изъязвление path: arrosion, erosion, ulceration, exulceration, pitting.
~ желудка int: gastric ulceration.
~ кожи derm: cutaneous ulceration.
~ роговицы ophth: corneal ulceration.
изъязвляться path: ulcerate, etc.
изъятие withdrawal.
~ (вида из сообщества) bio: exclosure.
~ хлористого натрия (из пищи) dechloridation.
изюбр zool: wapiti (Cervus canadensis lugdorfi).
изюмный виноград bot: raisin grape.
икота path: hiccup, hiccough, singultus, singultation.
икотный path: singultous.
икра 1. ova, roe; 2. caviar.
~ ноги anat: sura, calf (of the leg).
икринка ichth: ovum, berry.
икрометание ichth: spawning.
икрометать ichth: spawn, shed the eggs.
икромечущая рыба egg-shedding fish.
икроножная мышца anat: gastrocnemius (muscle).
икряная рыба hard-roed fish, gravid f.
икрянка = икряная рыбы.
икряной anat: sural.
иксодид entom: black-legged tick, cattle t. (Ixodes ricinus scapularis).
иктидозавр zool: Ictidosauria (extinct)
иктиобус ichth: mongrel, black buffalo (Ictiobus niger); smallmouth buffalo (I. bubalus).
ил silt, ooze, muck.
илео-цекальный угол ileo-caecal junction.
илеус path: ileus.
иллит illite.
иллюзия illusion.
~ противовращения av med: illusion of reversal of motion.
иловатый uliginous.
иловая лихорадка mud fever.
илоед zool: mud-eater.
ильм = вяз.
ильная рыба single fish (Amia); bowfin, dogfish (A. calva).
ильные рыбы = амии.
имагинальная фаза entom: imaginal phase.
имагинальные диски imaginal buds.
имаго entom: imago.
имбецил psych: imbecile.
имбецильность psych: imbecility.
имбецильный psych: imbecilic.
имбирные (сем.) bot: ginger family (Zingiberaceae).
*имбирь bot: ginger, zinziber (Zinziber officinale, Roscoe).
~ жёлтый turmeric, curcuma (Curcuma longa).
иметь выкидыш obstet: miscarry, abort.
имеющий обёртку bot: involucrate.
~ прицветники bot: bracteate.
~ таллом polystichous, haplostichous.
~ твёрдую оболочку hard-shelled.
~ усики capreolate.
иммерсионная линза mcscop: immersion lens.
иммобилизация immobilization.
~ переломов surg: immobilization of fractures.
иммобилизирующая повязка surg: fixation dressing.
иммортель bot: immortelle.
иммунизация immunization.
иммунизировать immunize.
иммунитет immunity.
~ вызванный облучением rad: immunity due to irradiation.
иммунная сила phylactic power.
~ сыворотка antiserum.
иммунное вещество phylactic agent.
~ прилипание immune adherence.
~ тело immune hemolysin, i. body.
иммунный immune.
иммунобиологический immunobiological.
иммуногенный immunogenic.
иммуноконглютинин immuno-conglutinin.
иммунологический immunological.
иммуно-физиологический immuno-physiological.
иммунохимический immuno-chemical.
иммунохимия immunochemistry.
императа bot: cogon grass (Imperata cylindrica koenigi, I. exaltata).
императивный imperative.

импетиго derm: impetigo.
имплантация implantation.
импотент path: impotent.
импотенция path: impotence, impotency.
импрегнация impregnation.
импульс impulse, drive, impetus.
импульсивный impulsive.
импульсы от внешних источников neur: exteroceptive impulses.
~ ~ внутренних органов neur: enteroceptive impulses.
инактивация inactivation.
инактивировать inactivate.
инвагинация invagination.
инвазия invasion; infestation.
инвалид invalid, disabled, incapacitated, handicapped (person); see also нетрудоспособный.
~ труда (old-age) retired person.
инвалидность disability, invalidism.
инверсия inversion.
инвертаза invertase.
инвертный сахар invert sugar.
инволюционный психоз involutional psychosis.
инволюция involution.
ингалятор inhaler.
ингаляционный наркоз inhalation anesthesia.
ингаляция inhalation.
индау посевной = рокет-салат.
индейка orn: turkey (Meleagris), turkey hen. Cf. индюк.
~ дикая США wild turkey (M. gallopavo).
индейский adj: American Indian. Cf. индийский.
индекс работоспособности av med: efficiency index.
~ Шнейдера Schneider index.
индивидуализация individualization.
индивидуальная психология individual psychology.
индивидуальное развитие ontogeny.
индивидуальный перевязочный пакет mil: first-aid dressing package.
~ санитарный пакет mil: first-aid packet.
индивидуум individual.
индиго bot: indigo (Indigofera, L.)
~ дикое = и. ложное.
~ ложное false indigo, bastard i., indigo bush (Amorpha fruticosa, L.)
индигоноска bot: indigo (Indigofera tinctoria, L.)
*индийская конопля pharm: bang, beng.
индийский Indian, of the East Indies. Cf. индейский.
~ буйвол zool: Indian buffalo (Bubalus bubalus).
~ слон zool: Indian elephant (Elephas indicus, Elephas maximus).
индийский шелковичный червь entom: tussur (Antheraca, Attacus).
индийское розовое дерево bot: Burmese rosewood (Pterocarpus indicus)
индикатор indicator; rad: tracer.
индолилмасляная кислота indolebutyric acid.
индолилуксусная кислота indoleacetic acid, indolylacetic acid.
индолилуксусный нитрил indolylacetonitrile.
индри zool: lemur Lichanotus brevicaudatus.
индукция induction.
индурация induration.
индюк zool: turkey cock, gobbler, tom. Cf. индейка.
индюшата pl. of индюшонок.
индюшка = индейка.
индюшонок turkey chick.
инжир bot: fig (Ficus carica, L.)
инкапсулирование = инкапсуляция.
инкапсулированный encapsulated, sacculated, insheathed.
инкапсуляция encapsulation, sacculation.
инквилинизм entom: inquilinism.
инкрет incretion (substance).
инкреторный incretory.
инкубатор incubator.
~ для недоносков ped: infant incubator.
инкубационный incubative.
~ период incubation period; latency.
инкубация incubation.
инкудатный incudate.
иннервационный аппарат anat: innervational apparatus.
иннервация anat: innervation.
иннервировать innervate.
инокулирование = инокуляция.
инокулировать inoculate.
инокуляция inoculation.
иноперабельный surg: inoperable.
инородное тело foreign body.
иностранцевия zool: Inostrancevia alexandri (exinct).
инотропный эффект inotropic effect.
инсектарий insectary, insectarium.
инсектицид insecticide.
инсоляция insolation.
инспекция inspection.
инспирометр inspirometer.
инстилляция instillation.
инстинкт instinct.
~ самосохранения instinct of self-preservation.
инстинктивное действие psych: instinctive action.
инстинктивный instinctive, instinctual.

инстинктивный страх instinctive fear.
Институт прикладной зоологии и фитопаталогии Institute of the Applied Zoology and Phytopathology (Leningrad, USSR).
инструмент tool, device, instrument.
~ для введения тампона surg: packer.
~ ~ извлечения инородных тел surg: probang, extractor.
~ ~ исследования explorer.
~ ~ прививки inoculator.
~ ~ производства ампутации surg: ablator.
~ ~ расколки черепа anat: skull breaker.
~ ~ рассечения стриктур surg: stricture cutter.
~ ~ удаления зубного камня odont: scaler.
~ ~ удаления инородных тел surg: extractor, probang.
инсулин insulin.
инсулиназа insulinase.
инсулино-шоковая терапия psych: insulin shock therapy.
инсульт insult.
инсуфициенция insufficiency.
интактный intact.
интегумент integument.
интеллект intellect, mental power.
интенсивность дыхания respiration intensity.
~ фотосинтеза bot: photosynthetic rate
интенционное дрожание neur: intention tremor, volitional tremor.
интерглобулярное пространство hist: interglobular space.
интердуральное пространство anat: interdural space.
интеркалярный рост bot: intercalary growth.
интеркаляция bot: intecalation.
интеркурентное заболевание intercurrent disease.
интермедин intermedine.
интермитирующий intermittent.
интернатура internship.
интерорецептивный interoceptive.
интерорецептор anat: interoceptor.
интерстициальная беременность obstet: interstitial pregnancy, intermural p.
~ клетка hist: interstitial cell.
~ пневмония path: interstitial pneumonia.
интерстициальный кератит ophth: interstitial keratitis.
интерфазное ядро hist: interstage nucleus.
интима entom: intima.
интоксикация intoxication.
интонация (голоса) intonation.
инторзия intorsion.
интраверзия psych: introversion.
интраназальный intranasal.
интраспинальный intraspinal.
интрогрессивный introgressive.
интродуцировать introduce.
интубация surg: intubation.
интуиция intuition.
интуссусцепция surg: intussusception.
инулин inulin.
инулиновое пространство inulin space.
инфантилизм половых органов infantilism of the genital organs.
инфантильная грудь path: infantile chest.
инфантильность infantilism.
инфанторий infantorium.
инфаркт path: infarct.
инфекциозность infectivity.
инфекционная болезнь infectious disease.
~ желтуха vet: leptospirosis.
инфекционный белый понос = бациллярный б. п.
инфекция infection.
инфильтрационный attr: infiltration.
инфильтрация infiltration.
~ лейкоцитов leucocytic infiltration.
инфицировать infect.
инфицирующий infecting.
инфранейстон bio: infraneuston.
инфузории (кл.) zool: infusorians, ciliates (Infusoria, Ciliopora).
инфузория zool: infusorian; see also ресничные инфузории.
инфузорная земля diatomaceous earth.
инфузорный infusorial.
инцизия surg: incision.
инцистировавшийся encysted.
инцистирование cyst formation, encystment.
инцистированная форма zool: encysted form.
инцистироваться encyst.
инъекция injection.
иод iodine, I.
иодистый калий pharm: potassium iodide.
~ коллодий pharm: iodized collodion.
~ литий pharm: lithium iodide.
~ натрий pharm: sodium iodide.
~ стронций pharm: strontium iodide.
иодокись висмута pharm: bismuth oxyiodide.
иодоформ pharm: iodoform.
иодоформенная марля surg: iodoform gauze.
Ионгблад Jongbloed.
ионотерапия medical ionization.
ионтофорез iontophoresis.

иохимба bot: yohimba (Paussinystalia yohimba).
иохимбин yohimbine.
ипекакуана bot: ipecac(uanha); pharm: ipecac.
ипомея bot: morning glory (Ipomoea).
ипохондрический бред psych: hypochondriac delirium.
ипохондрия psych: hypochondria(sis).
ипрониазид iproniazid.
ипсилон = совка-ипсилон.
ирга bot: Juneberry, sugarplum, shadbush, serviceberry, sarviceberry (Amelanchier, Medic.); see also кизил.
иридотомия ophth: coretomy.
иридо-циклит ophth: iridocyclitis.
иридэктомия ophth: iridectomy.
ирис bot: iris, see касатик.
ирисовые = касатиковые.
ирит ophth: iritis.
иритный ophth: iritic.
ирландская форель ichth: gillaroo (Salmo stomachius).
ирландский мох bot: Irish moss, carrageen (Chondrus crispus) red alga.
иррадиация irradiation.
~ болей neur: reference of pain.
иррадиирующая боль referred pain.
иррадиирующе-болевой synalgic.
иррациональность psych: irrationality.
ирригатор fountain syringe.
ирритация irritation.
иррумация psych: irrumation, fellatio.
искажение distortion.
искажённые непроизвольные движения athetosis.
искажённый distorted.
исключительный случай exceptional case.
исковерканное тело mangled body, disfigured body.
ископаемое животное fossil animal, zoolite.
ископаемый мох fossil moss.
искоренить p. a. of искоренять.
искоренять extirpate, eradicate, uproot, stamp out.
искривление curvature.
~ большого пальца ног внутрь (к другим пальцам) path: hallux valgus.
~ ~ пальца ног кнаружи hallux varus.
~ длинной кости curvature of the long bone.
~ кзади recurvation.
~ кнаружи excurvation.
~ кпереди procurvation.
~ ногтей gryposis.
искривление нормальной оси предплечья deviation of the normal axis of the forearm.
~ носовой перегородки path: deviation of the nasal septum.
~ позвоночника curvature of the spine
~ ~ вперед forward curvature of the lumbar spine, lordosis, hollow back.
~ ~ в стороны scoliosis.
~ спины от велосипедной езды path: bicycle back.
~ стопы path: talipes, clubfoot, foot distortion.
искривленная перегородка носа path: deflected nasal septum.
искривленное копыто zool: wry hoof.
искривленный кнаружи excurved.
~ лист bot: retrorse leaf.
искусственная пиявка mechanical leech.
искусственно вызванная овуляция zool: induced ovulation.
~ вызванные роды obstet: induced labor.
~ заражать bact: inoculate.
искусственное дыхание artificial respiration.
~ оплодотворение artificial fertilization, a. impregnation.
~ опыление bot: artificial pollination
~ разведение artificial breeding; a. culture.
искуственные роды obstet: artificial labor. [controlled p.
искуственный выкидыш obstet: artificial abortion, induced a.
~ зуб odont: dummy tooth, false tooth, artificial crown.
~ перелом surg: refracture.
иснардия bot: water purslane (Isnardia palustris).
испанская макрель ichth: Spanish mackerel, cero (Scomberomorus).
испанский бородатый мох = мох луизианский.
~ золотой корень bot: golden thistle, Spanish oyster plant (Scolymus hispanicus).
~ сальсифи = испанский золотой корень.
испарение evaporation, vaporization.
~ воды через лёгкие pulmonary transpiration.
испещренный бороздками furrowed, grooved.
~ линиями lineolate, striated.
~ мелками бороздками strigose.
испорченное мясо spoiled meat, tainted meat.

испорченный продукт spoiled foodstuff.
исправление ненормального искривления surg: detorsion.
испражнение defecation, passage, evacuation of the bowels, bowel movement; vet: motion.
испражнения feces; zool: casting(s).
~ в виде горохового супа infect: pea-soup stools.
испытание test(ing), assay, trial.
~ иммунитета к... challenge for ... immunity.
~ умственных способностей psych: mental test; intelligence test.
иссекать surg: exsect.
иссечение surg: exsection. [omy.
~ ахиллова сухожилия achillot(enot)-
~ варикозного узла cirsotomy.
~ омертвевших частей necrotomy.
~ (отрезка) толстых кишок colectomy.
~ рубцовой ткани ulectomy.
~ хряща chondrectomy.
~ части брюшной стенки laparectomy.
~ ~ губы cheilotomy.
~ ~ нерва neurectomy.
исследование investigation, exploration, examination, studies. [studies.
~ в опытной установке pilot plant
~ испражнений stool examination.
~ мочи examination of urine, uroscopy.
~ невооруженным глазом macroscopy.
~ обмена веществ metabolic investigation.
~ питания nutritional investigation.
~ по годовым кольцам стволов bot: tree-ring analysis.
~ прямой кишки rectal examination.
~ состояния здоровья physical examination. [nation.
~ с помощью зеркала speculum exami-
~ умственных способностей = испытание у. с.
~ языка glossoscopy. [student.
исследователь investigator, researcher,
исследовательская работа research work, investigation(s). [mine.
исследовать investigate, explore, exa-
исследуемый субъект examinee.
иссоп анисовый bot: anise hyssop (Agastache anethiodora).
истерик psych: hysteriac (he).
истерика psych: hysterics.
истерическая амблиопия psych: hysterical ambliopia.
истерическая аура neur: aura hysterica.
~ потеря голоса hysterical aphonia, apsithyria, apsithurea. [sy.
~ эпилепсия neur: hysterical epilep-
истерический паралич hysterical paralysis. [tion.
~ смех hysterical laghter, cachinna-
истеричка psych: hysteriac (she).
истерия neur: hysteria.
истечение discharge, flow, issue, effusion, flux, effluve. [nal r.
истинное ребро anat: true rib, ster-
истиннокоренной зуб zool: molar tooth.
истинный запой = дипсомания.
истод bot: polygala, milkwort (Polygala). [ly (Polygalaceae).
истодовые (сем.) bot: milkwort fami-
истончение thinning.
история болезни case history, case
~ развития bio: life hystory. | record.
источающий слёзы lacrimous, lacrimose. [wormed.
источенный червями worm-eaten,
источник заражения source of infection. [enervate.
истощать exhaust, emaciate, waste,
истощающий exhausting, emaciating.
истощение exhaustion, emaciation, wasting, inanition, consumption.
истощимый exhaustible.
истощить p. a. of истощать.
истощиться become exhausted, see исхудать.
истребить p. a. of истреблять.
истребление extermination.
истреблять exterminate.
исхиоподит zool: ischiopodite.
исход exit, result, end, termination, outlet.
~ беременности pregnancy termination. [ture.
исходная культура bact: primary cul-
исхудавший emaciated, lean, thin.
исхудать grow lean, become thin, waste away, emaciate.
исцеление = излечение.
исцелить p. a. of исцелять.
исцелять = вылечивать.
исчезание сыпи derm: deflorescence.
исчерченность striation, lineolation.
исчерченный striated, lineolated.
итачек bot: anabasis.
итеригий ophth: web-eye.

итинерарий urol: lithotomy staff.
иудино дерево bot: Judas tree (Cercis siliquastrum).
ихневмонид = наездник.
ихорозногнойный saniopurulent.
ихорозный ichorous, ichoroid, sanious.
~ гной path: ichor, sanies.
~ распад ichorization.
ихтальбин pharm: ichthyol albuminate.
ихтарган = ихтиосульфокислое серебро.
ихтиоз derm: ichthyosis, scaly skin, fishskin disease.
ихтиозавры zool: ichthyosauri (Ichthyosauria), extinct reptiles.
ихтиозный ichthyotic.
ихтиолог ichthyologist.
ихтиология ichthyology.
ихтиоптеригиа (подкл.) zool: Ichthyopterigia (extinct reptiles).
ихтиостегалиа zool: Ichthyostegalia (extinct amphibians).
ихтиосульфокислое серебро pharm: silver ichthyolate.
ихтиофауна ichthyofauna, fish fauna.
ицерия entom: cotton-cushion scale (Iceria purchasi).
ишак = осёл домашний.
ишемический path: ischemic.
ишемия path: ischemia.
~ мозга cerebral ischemia.
~ слизистой носа shrinking of the nasal mucous membrane.
ишиас neur: ischialgia, sciatica.
ишиасный neur: ischialgic.
Ишихара Ishihara.
ишуретический urol: ischuretic.
ишурия urol: ischuria.
ищейка zool: sleuthhound (Canis familiaris irritans).
"ищущее опухоль" соединение rad: tumor-seeking compound.

К

к головному концу anat: cephalad.
~ дистальному концу distad.
~ задней стороне головы dorsocephalad.
~ ~ части тела posteriad, caudad.
~ заднему концу posteriad, caudad.
к концу terminad.
~ крестцу sacrad.
~ малоберцовой кости fibulad.
~ оси bot: introrse.
~ основанию basilad, basad.
~ передней части тела anteriad.
~ периферии peripherad.
~ проксимальному концу proximad.
~ рту orad.
~ спине dorsad.
~ средней линии mediad, mesad.
~ тылу dorsad.
~ центру bot: introrse.
кабан zool: 1. European wild boar, wild hog, aper (Sus scrofa); 2. collq: male hog, male pig.
кабаний boarish.
~ поросёнок = кабанчик.
кабаниха = дикая свинья.
*кабанчик zool: young wilboar.
кабарга = мускусный олень.
кабачок bot: marrow squash, marrow pumpkin, bush s., bush p. (Cucurbita pepo, L. var. ovifera).
каберне́ Cabernet (grape, wine).
кабина Линка av med: Link trainer.
~ с наддувом av med: supercharged cabin.
кабинет врача physician's office.
кабомба bot: water weed, fish grass (Cabomba).
~ каролинская fanwort (C. caroliniana, Gray).
Кабот Cabot.
Кавендиш Cavendish.
каверна cavern.
кавернозное дыхание path: cavernous breathing.
кавернома path: cavernous tumor.
кавказская саламандра zool: Caucasian salamander (Mertensiella caucasica).
~ черепаха zool: Caucasian turtle (Testudo graeca).
кавказский тур zool: Caucasian goat Capra caucasica.
кагу orn: kagu (Rhinocheti).
кагуар = кугуар.
кадмий cadmium, Cd.
кадочное растение tub plant.
кадык anat: laryngeal prominence, Adam's apple, pomum Adami.
казарка 1. orn: brant (Branta); 2. entom: beetle Rhynchites bacchus, fam. Attelabidae.
~ белощекая orn: barnacle (Branta leucopsis, Bernicla leucopsis).
казеоз caseation.

казеозный caseous, cheesy.
казимироя съедобная bot: cochil sapota (Casimiroa edulis, Llav. & Lex)
казуарина bot: beefwood, she-oak, coast oak, ironwood (Casuarina equisetifolia).
казуариновые (сем.)bot: beefwood family (Casuarinaceae).
казуары = австралийские страусы.
кайанус = горох голубиный.
кайман zool: cayman, alligator.
кайманова рыба = панцырная щука.
каймановы рыбы Lepidosteoidei.
кайра orn: murre, guillemot, willock.
~ длинноклювая = крачка.
кайры orn: murres, guillemots (Uria).
какаду orn: cockatoo (Cacatuinae, Kakatoё).
какамицли = кашачий хорёк.
какао cacao.
какаовелла bot: cocoa shells, cacao husks.
какаовое дерево bot: cacao (Theobroma cacao).
каки = хурма японская.
какодил chem: cacodyl, tetramethyldiarsenic.
какодилат chem: cacodylate.
какодиловая кислота chem: cacodylic acid, dimethylarsinic acid.
какодиловокислый натрий pharm: sodium cacodylate.
кактус bot: cactus, prickly pear, Indian fig (Opuntia, Mill.)
~ ежевидный округлый echinocactus (Echinocactus).
~ ~ удлинённый echinocereus (Echinocereus, Lem.)
~ лефофора narcotic peyyote (Echinocactus williansii, Lem.)
~ листовой со съедобными плодами Barbados gooseberry (Pereskia aculeata, Mill.)
кактусовые (сем.) bot: cactus family (Cactaceae).
кал feces, fecal matter, egesta, stercus.
~ животных dung, scats, droppings.
~ мух flyspeck.
калаазар path: kalaazar, visceral leishmaniasis, dumdum fever.
каламитовые (сем.) bot: Calamariaceae (extinct).
каламондин bot: calamondin (Citrus mitis, Blanco).
каламофиты (кл.) bot: Calamophytineae (extinct).
каламус bot: calamus palm-tree (Calamus of the tribe Lepidocarpae).
калан = морская выдра.
калган bot: galingale root.
~ дикий = лапчатка прямая.
калека cripple, maimed (person).
календула bot: marigold (Calendula).
калечение crippling, maiming.
калиевый chem: potassic.
калий potassium, kalium, K.
калийная соль chem: potassium salt.
калийное мыло potash soap.
калина bot: highbrush cranberry, pimbina, guelder rose, white hazel tree (Viburnum opulus).
~ -городовина mealy tree (V. lantana)
калифорнийский перепел orn: California quail (Lophortyx californica).
калкан ichth: brill (Rhombus).
калкановые (сем.) ichth: brills (Bothidae).
калла bot: calla (Arum palestinum, Boiss).
~ эфиопская lily of the Nile, see белокрыльник болотный.
каллифоры (сем.) entom: blow-flies (Calliphoridae).
каллихт catfish.
~ панцырной armored catfish.
каллус bot: callus.
каловая рвота stercoraceous vomiting.
каловидный fecaloid.
каловый fecal, stercoraceous.
~ камень path: coprolith, fecalith, stercolith, stercoroma.
каломель = хлористая ртуть.
калонг = летучая лисица.
калорийность calori(fi)c value, caloric content.
калорическая проба caloric test.
калорический опыт caloric test (Barani).
калория calorie, calory.
калуга ichth: Huso dauricus.
калужница болотная bot: cowslip, kingcup, May-blob, marsh marigold (Caltha palustris).
калутара kalutara (giant African snail)
калуфер bot: costmary, mint geranium (Chrysanthemum balsamita).
калькулёзный calculous.
кальмар zool: calamary, squid, sea arrow (Loligo).
кальцеолярия = кошельки.
кальциевый calcic.
~ баланс calcium balance.
~ обмен calcium metabolism.
кальций calcium, Ca.
кальциноз path: calcinosis.
кальциоз calciosis.
кальциферол calciferol.
кальцификация calcification.

камайла bot: kamila tree (Mallotus philippinensis, Muell. Arg.)
камала = камайла.
камбала ichth: flatfish, flounder, fluke, plaice.
~ белобрюхая Lepidopsetta bilineata.
~ двухлинейная Lepidopsetta bilineata.
~ -ёрш sand dab (Hippoglossoides).
~ лиманда Limanda.
~ малоротая Glyptocephalus.
~ морская Platessa.
~ остроголовая Cleisthenes.
~ речная Pleuronectes.
камбаловидная мышца anat: soleus (muscle).
камбаловые (сем.) ichth: flatfishes (Pleuronectidae).
~ (отр.) ichth: Pleuronectiformes.
камбиальный bot: cambiogenetic; attr: cambium.
камбий bot: cambium.
камеденосное дерево (австралийское) bot: tallowwood (Eucalyptus microcorys, F.et M.)
камеденосные (пор.) bot: Guttiferales.
камедетечение = гуммиоз.
камедистый gummy.
камедь pharm: gum.
камелия bot: camellia (Camellia).
каменистая клетка bot: stone cell.
~ пазуха anat: petrosal sinus.
~ часть anat: petrous part, pars petrosa (of the temporal bone).
~ ямочка anat: fossula petrosa.
каменистый канал zool: stone canal.
каменка orn: wheatear, see чеканчик луговой.
~ попутчик wheatear Saxicola oenanthe.
каменная болезнь calculous disease.
~ куница zool: beech marten (Martes foina).
каменный баран zool: wild goat (Capra ilex).
~ козёл Caucasian goat.
~ окунь rock bass (Serranus).
~ тур = каменный козёл.
камень path: calculus, concretion.
~ в виде тутовой ягоды urol: mulberry calculus.
камера chamber.
~ пестика bot: locule.
~ Седжвик-Рафтера для счёта планктона Sedgwick-Rafter plankton counting cell.
~ Тюрка hem: Türk's chamber.
~ увлажнения lab: dampening chamber.
камерная влага ophth: aqueous humor.
камертон tuning fork.

камка = морская трава.
камнеискатель urol: bladder sound, stone searcher.
камнеломка bot: saxifrage, stonebreak, rockfoil (Saxifraga).
~ болотная S. hirculus.
~ зернистая meadow saxigrage (S. granulata).
~ (корне) отпрысковая old-man's beard, Aaron's beard, strawberry geranium (S. sarmentosa).
~ теневая London pride (S. umbrosa).
камнеломковые (сем.) bot: saxifrage family (Saxifragaceae).
камнеобразующий path: lithogenetic.
камнесечение surg: lithotomy, pelviolithotomy.
камнеточец (моллюск) zool: rock-burrowing mollusk, rock borer, stone borer (Pholas).
камнещуп = камнеискатель.
камни path: calculus, concretion.
~ в бронхах bronchial calculus.
~ ~ мочевом пузыре vesical calculus.
~ ~ мочевом тракте urinary calculus.
~ ~ почечных лоханках staghorn c.
~ ~ почках renal calculus.
кампешевое дерево bot: campeachy wood (Haematoxylon campechianum).
кампилотропная семяпочка bot: campylotropous ovule.
камподеовидный entom: campodeform, campode-like.
камфора chem: camphor.
камфорная вода pharm: camphor water.
~ кислота camphoric acid.
камфорное дерево bot: camphor tree (Cinnamomum camphora, Nees et Eberm.)
~ масло pharm: 1. camphorated oil; 2. camphor oil.
камфорнокислый калий pharm: potassium camphorate.
~ хинин pharm: quinine camphorate.
камфорный camphoric, camphorated.
~ спирт pharm: spirit of camphor.
камчатский бобр zool: sea beaver (Enhydra lutris), see морская выдра.
~ краб zool: Japanese crab (Paralithodes camtschatica).
камыш bot: bulrush, club rush, sedge, ling (Scirpus).
~ песчаный гигантский melur (Elymus arenarius giganteus).
камышевидный bot: rushlike.

камышница orn: water hen, Florida gallinule (Gallinula chloropus). Cf. пастушки.
камышовка orn: reed warbler, water hen (Acrocephalus scirpaceus).
~ болотная marsh titmouse (A. palustris); see also камышница.
~ тростниковая reed bunting (A. arundinaceus).
канабин cannabin.
канаванин canavanine.
канадские плющи (сем.) bot: moonseed family (Menispermaceae).
канадский бальзам pharm: Canada balsam, balsam of fir.
~ бобр zool: beaver (Castor canadensis).
канал canal, canalis, duct; aqueduct.
~ приводящих мышц adductor canal.
~ сонной артерии anat: carotid canal. canalis caroticus.
~ улитки anat: cochlear duct.
~ шейки матки anat: uterocervical canal.
каналец anat: tubule, canaliculus.
канализационная труба sewer pipe.
канализация san: sewerage.
канальцевый anat: canalicular.
канап = канатник.
канареечник bot: canary grass, phalaris (Phalaris).
~ полосатый gardener's garter (P. picta).
~ тростниковый red canary grass (P. arundinaceae).
канареечн(иков)ые (подсем.) bot: canary-grass subfam. (Phalarideae, Link)
канарейка orn: canary.
канарейник = канареечник.
канатик anat: cord.
канатная пальма bot: coquilla (Attalea funifera, Mart.)
канатник bot: abutilon (Abutilon avicennae). See also грудника.
канегр = щавель клубненосный.
канель = аннона.
канифоль colophony, rosin.
канкрозное изъязвление oncol: carcineicosis.
канкрозный oncol: cancerous.
канна bot: canna (Canna).
~ красная Indian shot (C. coccinea).
~ съедобная Queensland arrowroot (C. esculenta).
каннибализм cannibalism.
каннибалистический cannibalistic.
каннибальное животное cannibal.
канновые (сем.) bot: Cannaceae.
канталупа bot: cantaloup(e) (Cucumis melo, var. cantalupensis, Naudin.)
кантаридин pharm: cantharidin.
канупер = калуфер.
канцер oncol: cancer.
канцероген oncol: carcinogen.
канцерогенез carcinogenesis.
канцеролог cancerologist.
канцерология cancerology.
канцерофобия psych: cancer(o)phobia.
канюк orn: hawk Buteo.
~ американский hen hawk (B. borealis).
канюльный surg: cannular, cannulate.
канюля surg: cannula.
~ для промывания perfusion cannula.
~ ~ промывания лобной пазухи frontal sinus tube.
~ Левина Levin tube.
кап bot: woodknob, burl, wart.
капание dripping, instillation.
капать drip, instil.
капелька droplet.
капельная воронка lab: dropping funnel.
~ инфекция droplet infection.
~ клизма rectal drip, protoclysis.
~ ~ по Мерфи Murphy drip.
капельница dropper, drop counter.
капельное вливание в нос nasal drip.
капельное сердце "drop" heart.
капельный метод (наркоза) surg: drop method (anesthetizing).
каперсник bot: caper (Capparis spinosa)
каперсовые (сем.) bot: caper family (Capparidaceae).
каперсы bot: capers.
каперцы = каперсы.
капилляр capillary.
капиллярное кровотечение path: capillary hemorrhage.
капиллярность capillarity.
капиллярный бронхит suffocative catarrh.
~ дренаж surg: capillary drainage.
~ пульс capillary pulse.
каплун orn: capon, castrated rooster.
каплунирование castration.
капля drop, gutta.
каплями drop by drop, guttatim.
капок bot: silk-cotton tree (Ceiba pentandra).
каприловая кислота caprylic acid.
каприфига bot: caprifig.
каприфоль = жимолость душистая.
капроновая кислота caproic acid.
капсицин capsicinum.
капский перипатус zool: Peripatopsis capensis.
капсула capsule (a membranous sac enclosing a part).
~ железы anat: glandilemma.
~ Шумлянского anat: Bowman's capsule.
капсулит path: capsulitis.
капсулотомия surg: capsulotomy.

капсульный capsular.

капсюля 1. capsule (a soluble shell for administering medicines); 2. rad: seed (implant).

каптол pharm: tannochloral.

капуста bot: cabbage, cole, see к. кочанная.

~ брюссельская Brussels sprouts.

~ древовидная = к. кормовая.

~ заячья 1. garden orpine, live-forever (Sedum telephium); 2. see осот огородный.

~ кочанная head cabbage (Brassica oleracea, var. capitata).

~ морская = ламинария.

~ ~ русская = катран.

~ савойская savoy cabbage.

~ собачья = пролеска.

~ спаржевая broccoli.

~ цветная cauliflower.

капустная кила phytp: clubroot.

~ пальма bot: cabbage palm (Euterpe oleracea, Mart.)

капустница entom: cabbage butterfly (Pieris).

~ большая cabbage white butterfly (P. brassicae).

~ малая turnip butterfly (P. rapae).

капустное дерево bot: cabbage tree (Andira inermis, HBK; Cordyline australis)

капуцин 1. zool: capuchin monkey (Cebus capucinus); 2. bot: see настурция садовая.

капуциновые (сем.) bot: nasturtium fam.(Tropaeolaceae).

капшак = крилл.

капюшонная крыса zool: hooded rat.

карагана = просо африканское.

карагач bot: smooth-leaved elm (Ulmus foliacea, Gilib.)

карадрина = совка малая.

каракалла = фасоль ароматная.

каракатица zool: cuttlefish, sepia, sound (Sepia).

каракульский баран zool: Karakul ram.

карамора = комар Tipula.

карандаш для стекла mcscop: glass pencil

карандашное дерево = можжевельник виргинский.

карантин san: quarantine.

карантинная служба san: quarantine service

карантинное свидетельство san: bill of health.

карапакс zool: carapace, head shield.

карапузик розовый entom: rose chafer (Macrodactylus subspinosus).

карапузики entom: histerid beetles (Histeridae), see жук-карапузик.

карась золотой = к. круглый.

~ круглый ichth: Carassius auratus.

~ продолговатый ichth: crucian carp (C. carassius).

~ серебряный = к. продолговатый.

карбаминовая кислота carbamic acid.

карбоангидраза pharm: carbonic anhydrase.

карбоксилаза carboxylase.

карболка = карболовая кислота.

карболовая кислота carbolic acid, phenic acid, phenol.

~ мазь pharm: carbolic acid ointment.

~ ртуть pharm: mercury carbolate.

карболовокислый хинин pharm: quinine carbolate, q. phenate.

карболовонатриевая соль pharm: sodium carbolate, s. phenate.

карболовый раствор carbolic acid solution.

карбонат chem: carbonate.

карбункул path: carbuncle, see сибирская язва.

кардамон bot: cardamon (Amomum cardamon.

кардиа anat: cardia.

кардиазол pharm: cardiazol.

кардиальная шейка anat: cardiac collum.

кардинальная вена anat: cardinal vein.

кардиолог med: cardiologist.

кардиосклероз path: cardiosclerosis.

кардиоспазм path: cardiospasm.

кардиоспектрограмма cardiospectrogram.

кардия anat: cardia(c orifice).

~ желудка = кардия.

кардо entom: cardo.

кардобенедикт bot: blessed thistle (Cnicus benedictus).

кардон = артишок испанский.

карета скорой помощи ambulance.

каретта = морская черепаха.

карибу zool: caribou (Rangifer caribu)

кариема orn: Cariamae.

кариес path: caries.

~ зубов dental caries.

~ позвонков vertebral caries, caries of the spine, tuberculosis of vertebra, Pott's disease.

кариозное состояние = кариозность

кариозность path: cariosity.

кариозный зуб carious tooth.

кариокинез hist: karyokinesis, mitosis.

кариокинетическое деление hist: karyokinetic division.

кариолиз hist: karyolysis.

кариолитический karyolytic.

кариоморфология bot: karyomorphology

кариоптерис bot: blue spiraea
(Caryopteris incana, Mig.)
кариосома hist: karyosome, karyosoma.
кариотип bot: karyotype. [(Carissa).
карисса bot: carissa, Christs's thorn
карканье (вороны) croaking (of raven)
каркас bot: hackberry (Celtis occiden-
каркать orn: croak. talis).
каркнуть p. a. of каркать.
Карлейль Carlisle.
карлик dwarf, homunculus, manikin, pygmy
карликовая колония mcbio: dwarf
colony, minute colony.
~ пальма bot: dwarf palm. cle.
карликовое дерево dwarf tree, arbus-
карликовость dwarfism, dwarfness,
nanism, nanosomia, microsomia.
карликовые куры = корольковые.
карликовый dwarfish, nanous, pumilus.
~ рост = карликовость.
~ сомик ichth: bullhead (Americus).
~ цепень helm: dwarf tapeworm
(Hymenolepis nana). [salt.
карлсбадская соль pharm: Carlsbad
карман pocket, pouch, ventricle, small
cavity.
~ мочевой пузырь-матка anat:
excavatio vesicouterina.
~ ~ пузырь-прямая кишка anat:
rectovesical pouch.
~ прямая кишка-матка anat: rectouterine excavation, r. pouch, cul-de-sac.
~ Ратке embr: Rathke's pouch.
карманная лупа pocket lens.
~ плевательница pocket sputum flask.
~ рецептурная книга pharm: prescription pocket-book.
карманный набор инструментов surg:
pocket instrument case.
"кармашки" на сливе = кармашковая
болезнь.
кармашковая болезнь phytp: plum
pocket (Taphrina pruni, Tul.)
кармашкообразный приёмник bot:
кармин carmine. bursicle.
карналлит chem: carnallite. [rifera, Mart
карнауба bot: carnauba (Copernicia ce-
карнаубская пальма = карнауба.
каротен carotene.
каротидный синус anat: carotid sinus.
каротин carotin.
каротиноид(а) carotenoid.
карп ichth: carp (Cyprinus carpio).
карпиоидес ichth: quillback (Carpioides)
карповая рыба cyprinid.
карповые (сем.) ichth: cyprinoid fam.
карпогон bot: carpogonium. |(Cyprinidae)
карпоеды (отр.) zool: Branchiura.
карпозубая рыба ichth: killifish,
top minnow (Fundulus); sailfinned k.
(Molliensia latipinna); etc.
карпозубые (сем.) ichth: killifish
family (Cyprinodontidae).
карпообразные рыбы carplike fishes
(Cypriniformes).
карпоспора bot: carpospore.
картавить pronounce r gutturally.
картамин carthamin.
картина крови hemogram, blood picture
картофелина bot: potato tuber.
картофель bot: potato (Solanum
~ китайский = ям. tuberosum).
~ сладкий = батат.
~ уругвайский aquatic potato
(S. commersonii, Dunal.)
картофельная ботва bot: potato
~ гниль phytp: late blight. haulm.
~ пробирка bact: potato tube.
~ среда bact: potato medium.
~ тина = картофельная ботва.
картофельный клин bact: potato
канцероген oncol: carcinogen. |wedge.
карциногенез oncol: carcinogenesis.
карциногенетический carcinogenetic.
карциногенный carcinogenic.
касалка bio: rod, tactile stimulation
касатик bot: iris, flag (Iris).|device.
~ американский blue flag, poison f.,
southern blue f. (I. versicolor,
I. virginica).
~ жёлтый yellow iris, water flag
(I. pseudacorus).
~ мечевидный кормовой krishum
(I. ensata, Thunb., or I. pabularia,
Naudin.) [rentina).
~ флорентинский white flag (I. flo-
касатиковые (сем.) bot: iris
family (Iridaceae).
касатка = 1. кит-убийца;
2. ласточка деревенская.
касаться touch, contact.
каскара bot: cascara sagrada (Phamnus
purshiana, DC); pharm: sacred bark.
каскарилла bot: cascarilla, sweetwood
(Croton eluteria, Benn.)
каспийская нерпа zool: Caspian seal
(Phoca caspica).
~ черепаха zool: Caspian-sea turtle
(Clemmys caspica).
каспийский тюлень zool: Caspian
seal (Phoca caspica).

каспиосома ichth: Caspiosoma.
кассаба = дыня-кассаба.
кассава = маниок.
кассия bot: senna (Cassia).
~ пучковая partridge pea, prairie senna, golden cassia (C. fasciculata).
кастелянша = бельевая сестра.
кастиллоя bot: castilloa (Castilloa elastica, Cerv.)
касторея = бобровая струя.
касторка collq: castor oil.
касторовое масло castor oil.
кастрат castrate.
кастрация surg: castration.
~ колосков bot: emasculation.
кастрирование = кастрация.
кастрированная самка spayed female, ovariectomized female.
кастрированный castrated.
~ хряк agr zool: barrow.
кастрировать castrate.
ката съедобная = хат.
катаболизм bio: catabolism.
катаболический catabolic.
катависса = лук многоэтажный.
катадромный ichth: catadromous.
каталаза bot: catalase.
каталепсия psych: catalepsy.
каталептический psych: cataleptic.
катализатор catalyst, catalyzer.
каталитический catalytic.
катальпа bot: catalpa, catawba (Catalpa, Scop.)
~ бигнониевая Indian bean (C. bignonicides, Walt.)
~ западная Western catalpa (C. speciosa
катаплексия psych: cataplexy.
катаплектический cataplectic.
катапультирование av med: catapult takeoff.
катаракта ophth: cataract.
~ стеклодувов glassblowers cataract.
катарактальная игла ophth: cataract needle.
~ ложечка ophth: cataract spoon.
катарактальный нож cataract knife.
катарактный ophth: cataractous.
катаробный katharobic.
катарр path: catarrh.
~ желудка catarrhal gastritis.
~ ~ и тонких кишок inflammation of the stomach and intestine, gastroenteritis.
катаральная желтуха int: simple jaundice.
катаральный конъюнктивит ophth: catarrhal conjunctivitis, blenophthalmia.
кататонический psych: catatonic.
кататония psych: catatonia.
катенация catenation.
катетеральная лихорадка urol: catheter fever.
катетеризация urol: catheterization.
катетеризировать urol: catheterize.
катехин catechol.
катеху catechu.
катод cathode.
катодный cathodal, cathodic.
катостомус ichth: hog sucker (Catostomus nigricans).
катран bot: Russian sea kale (Crambe tartarica, Jacq.)
катушка planorbis (Planorbis) mollusk.
~ роговая Planorbis corneus.

катык (помёт овцы или козы) zool: button, dropping(s).
катэлектротонус cathelectrotonus.
кауда zool: postabdomen.
каудальный caudal, caudate.
каузалгический neur: causalgic.
каузалгия causalgia, burning pain.
каузальный causal.
каулёлятилюс ichth: blanquillo (Caulolatilus princeps).
каулифлория bot: cauliflory.
каулофиллин caulophylline.
каури 1. zool: cowry (Cypraea moneta); 2. bot: see сосна каури.
каустика cautery, cauterization.
каучуковое дерево bot: caoutchouc tree (Castilloa elastica, Ficus elastica, Hevea brasiliensis).
"каучуковый" таз = остеомалятический таз.
каучуконос bot: rubber plant.
кафедра по медицине medical chair.
кафир = сорго каффрское.
кахексия path: cachexia.
кахектический cachectic.
качающаяся походка titubation, staggering gait.
качельная болезнь swing sickness.
качественное нарушение отправления dysfunction.
качественный qualitative.
качурка orn: petrel (Hydrobates, Oceanodroma).
каша mush, pap.
кашалот zool: cachalot, sperm whale (Physeter catodon, P. macrocephalus).
кашлевой path: tussal.
кашель path: cough.
кашемирская коза Cashmere goat (Capra hircus laniger).

кашица pulp, pap. [pultaceous.
кашицеобразный pulpy, pappy, mushy,
кашка 1. bot:see клевер красный;
2. pharm: electuary, lincture.
кашлевая пластинка bact: cough plate.
кашлять cough.
каштан bot: chestnut (Castanea, Mill.)
~ американский American chestnut (C. dentata).
~ благородный sweet chestnut, European c., French c., Italian c. (C. sativa).
~ земляной hognut (Conopodium majus, L. et B.)
~ конский horse chestnut, buckeye (Aesculus hippocastanum).
~ ~ розовый scarlet h. c.
~ съедобный = к. благородный.
каштаноцветные = сапиндоцветные.
каянус = горох голубиный.
квадратная доля (печени) anat: square lobe, lobus quadratus.
~ мышца верхней губы anat: quadratus labii superioris, levator labii superioris alaeque nasi.
~ ~ нижней губы anat: quadratus labii inferioris, depressor labii inferioris.
~ ~ поясницы anat: quadratus lumborum (muscle).
квадриплегия path: quadriplegia.
квадриплекс quadriplex.
кваканье (лягушки) croaking (of frog)
кваква orn: black-crowned night heron (Nycticorax nycticorax).
~ зелёная green h. (Butorides virescens)
квакша zool: tree frog (Hyla arborea).
квамаш съедобный bot: common camass (Camassia esculenta, Lindl.)
квассия ямайская bot: Jamaica quassia (Picrasma excelsa, Planch.)
квасцы chem: alum.
квебрахо(вое дерево) bot: quebracho (Loxapteryngium lorentzii).
кверулянт psych: quarreler, see сутяга.
кверцетин quercetin.
квискалюс orn: grackle (Quiscalus).
кевовое дерево = фисташка дикая.
кедр bot: cedar (Cedrus).
~ сибирский = сосна сибирская.
кедровка = ореховка.
кедровое дерево = сосна сибирская
~ масло cedar leaf oil, arbor vitae oil, thuja oil.
келоид derm: keloid.
келоидальный derm: keloidal.
кемквот = кумват.
кенаф bot: gambo hemp, ambari, Deccan hemp (Hibiscus cannabinus).
кенгуру zool: kangaroo (Petrogale xanthopus, Macropodidae).
~ -валлаби wallaby .
кендырь bot: Indian hemp, amyroot, apocynum, kendyr (Apocynum sibiricum, Pall. or Apocynum cannabinum, var. venetum, L.)
~ проломниколистный flytrap (A. androsaemifolium).
кенотоксин kenotoxin.
кентукское кофейное дерево = бундук.
керазин bio: kerasin, cerebroside (in brain tissue).
кератин keratin.
кератинизация keratinization.
кератиновый keratinous.
кератит ophth: keratitis, inflammation of the cornea.
кератоглобус ophth: keratoglobus.
кератома path: horny growth.
кератопластика ophth: keratoplasty.
кератопластический keratoplastic.
кервель bot: chervil (Anthriscus,Bern)
~ британский = к. одуряющий.
~ испанский myrrh (Myrrhis odorata, Scop.)
~ клубневой = к. корневой.
~ корневой tuberous chervil (Chaerophyllum bulbosum).
~ кудрявый curled chervil, salad c. (Anthriscus cerefolium, Hoffm.)
~ курчавый, листовой, настоящий, обыкновенный = к. кудрявый.
~ одуряющий Chaerophyllum temulentum.
~ репный = к. корневой.
~ садовый, салатный = к. кудрявый.
Кергуэлен Kerguelen; see also капуста.
кермек bot: sea lavender, marsh rosemary (Statice).
кермес bot: American grape (Phytolacca esculenta, Van Houtte).
керчак = рогатка северная.
кесарев гриб caesar's mushroom (Amanita caesarea, Fr.)
кесарево сечение surg: Cesarian section, Cesaretomy, partus caesareus.
кессонная болезнь caisson disease.
кета ichth: keta (salmon), chum, calico (Onchorhynchus keta).
кетгут surg: catgut.
кетмия = гибиск съедобный.

кетоглютаровая кислота ketoglutaric acid.
кетостероид ketosteroid.
кефалевидные (отр.) ichth: Mugiliformes. [(Mugilidae).
кефалевые (сем.) ichth: gray mullets
кефаль ichth: gray mullet, jumping m., blue-back m., big-eye m., josea (Mugil).
кефир kefir (European milk product).
кивательные судороги neur: nodding spasm.
киви(-киви) orn: kiwi, apterix (Apteryges), see бескрылые птицы.
кивсяк zool: millipede (Diplopoda, Chilognatha).
киданг ребролицый = олень-мунтьяк
кижуч ichth: silver salmon, coho s. (Oncorhynchus kisutsch).
кизельгур chem: kieselguhr, purified siliceous earth.
кизил bot: dogwood, cornel, evergreen thorn (Cornus); dogberry.
~ настоящий male dogwood, cornelian cherry (C. mas).
кизиловые (сем.) bot: dogwood family (Cornaceae).
кизильник bot: cotoneaster (Cotoneaster, Ehrh.); see also
~ японский = мушмула японская.
кизяк dung, manure, castings.
кикуи bot: kikuyu grass (Pennisetum clandestinum).
кила (капусты и т.п.) phytp: anbury clubroot, finger-and-toe.
килевые orn: carinates (Carinatae, Neognathae), see летающие.
килегрудный zool: carinate.
киленогий моллюск zool: heteropod Carinaria.
килец ichth: Onega-Lake whitefish (Coregonus albula infraspecies kiletz).
киль orn: carina.
килька ichth: sprat (Sprattus).
кимограф kymograph.
кингфиш ichth: kingfish (Menticirrhus, Scomberomorus cavalla).
киндаль = макадамия.
кинестезическое ощущение physl: kinesthetic sensation.
кинетонуклеус = парабазальное тельце.
кинкан = кумват.
киноа = лебеда киноа.
кинолента motion-picture film.
кииоринхи (кл.) zool: Kinorhyncha, Echinoderma.
кинурениназа kynureninase.

кипарис bot: cypress (Cypressus).
~ болотный bald c. (Taxodium distichum, Rich.)
~ пирамидальный true c., Italian c. (C. sempervirens).
кипарисовые (сем.) bot: cypress family (Cupressaceae).
кипповский аппарат bact: Kipp hydrogen generator.
кипрей = чай капорский.
кипячение boiling.
кипячёный boiled.
кирказон bot: birthwort (Aristolochia); pipevine, Dutchman's pipe (A. durior).
~ змеевидный Virginia shakeroot (A. serpentaria).
~ ломоносовидный birthwort (A. clematitis).
кирказоновые (сем.) bot: birthwort family (Aristolochiaceae).
кирпичник cf. малокровие к-ов.
кирпичный осадок mcscop: brick-dust deposit.
Кис Keith.
кисетный шов surg: purse-string suture, tobacco-bag suture.
кислая мочекислая магнезия chem: magnesium acid urate.
~ отрыжка path: sour eructation.
~ соль сернистой кислоты chem: bisulfite.
~ ~ серной кислоты chem: bisulfate.
кислица bot: 1. wood sorrel, lady's s. (Oxalis); 2. see яблоня дикая.
~ клубненосная oka (O. tuberosa).
~ обыкновенная wood sorrel, shamrock (O. acetosella).
~ ямайская = розелла.
кисличные (сем.) bot: wood-sorrel family (Oxalidaceae).
кисловатый acidulous.
кислород oxygen, O.
кислородная маска oxygen mask.
~ ~ летчика av med: pilot's oxygen mask.
~ недостаточность av med: oxygen want, hypoxidosis.
~ трубка av med: oxygen tube.
кислородно-азотная смесь av med: oxygen-nitrogen mixture.
кислородное голодание = кислородная недостаточность.
~ оборудование av med: oxygen equipment.
~ отравление oxygen poisoning.
~ резервное время av med: oxygen reserve time.

кислородный обмен oxygen exchange.
~ потолок летчика av med: pilot's oxygen ceiling. [acidity.
кислота 1. chem: acid; 2. sourness,
кислотное отравление acid poisoning.
кислотноосновное изменение chem: acid-base change. [librium.
~ равновесие metab: acid-base equi-
кислотность acidity.
кислотный acidic.
~ ожог surg: acid burn.
кислотостойкий acid-fast, acidproof.
кислотоустойчивость acid-fastness, acid resistance.
кислотоустойчивый acid-fast, acid-resistant, acidproof.
кислый мочекислый натр chem: sodium acid urate.
~ сок sour juice, verjuice.
киста cyst.
~ желёз языка path: ranula.
кистевик bot: Penicillium (fungus).
кистевой сустав anat: wrist joint.
кистеносный bot: racemiferous.
кистеобразный brush-like, tuft-like, penicillate. [(Crossopterygii).
кистепёрые ichth: crossopterygians
кистехвост entom: antique tussock moth (Orguia antiqua).
~ пятнистый O. gonostigma.
кистозная опухоль cystic tumor.
~ полость path: cyst cavity.
кистозный cystic.
кистоидное перерождение path: cystic degeneration.
кисточка racemule.
~ хвоста switch.
кисть bot: raceme, racemation; brush, penicil, tuft (of hairs); see гроздь.
~ винограда bunch of grapes.
~ руки anat: hand.
кит zool: whale.
~ -убийца killer whale (Grampus).
китайская корица pharm: Chinese cinnamon.
~ черепаха zool: Chinese turtle (Amida sinensis). [(domestic)
китайский гусь orn: Chinese goose
~ жёлтокорень = жень-шень.
~ окунь ichth: Chinese perch (Siniperca chua-tsi).
~ фонарик Chinese lantern plant, see физалис перуанский.
~ хинный кустарник = лихорадочник китайский.

китайское восковое дерево = к. сальное дерево.
~ масляное дерево = тунг.
~ сальное дерево bot: tallow tree (Sapium sebiferum, Roxb., or Croton sebiferus, L.)
~ свечное дерево = к. сальное дерево.
китовый zool: cetacean, of whales.
~ ус whalebone, baleen. [cea).
китообразные zool: cetaceans (Ceta-
кифоз path: kyphosis, humpback, hunch-
кифозус ichth: rudder fish |back. (Kyphosus sectatrix).[rachitic pelvis.
кифорахитический таз path: kypho-
кифосколиотический таз path: kyphoscoliotic pelvis. [pelvis.
кифотический таз obstet: kyphotic
кичим метельчатый = перекати-поле. [testinal worm.
кишечная глиста helm: mawworm, in-
~ игла surg: intestinal needle.
~ киста path: enterocyst.
~ микрофлора intestinal microflora.
~ оболочка anat: intestinal membrane.
~ палочка mcbio: coliform bacterium, Bacterium coli, Escherichia coli.
~ петля anat: intestinal loop.
~ стенка anat: intestinal wall.
~ флора intestinal flora.
кишечник anat: intestine.
кишечница = энтероморфа.
кишечного происхождения enterogenous.
кишечнодышащие zool: Enteropneusta (of the subphylum Hemichorda).
кишечное расстройство intestinal disorder. [enteric canal.
кишечномозговой канал embr: neur-
кишечнополостные zool: coelentrates (Coelentrata).
кишечный intestinal, enteral.
~ животный паразит enterozoon.
~ жом surg: intestinal clamp.
~ камень path: alvinolith, alvine concretion.
~ песок path: intestinal sand.
~ проток anat: trunkus intestinalis.
~ сок physl: intestinal juice.
~ ствол helm: cecum.
кишка anat: intestine, gut.
~ (у червей) cecum.
кишковидный intestiform.
кишнец = кориандр.
кл. = класс.

клавацин pharm: clavacin.
клавус entom: clavus.
кладенный = выложенный.
кладка ichth: egg mass, spawn.
~ (отложенные яйца) clutch.
~ яиц egg laying, oviposition.
кладодий bot: cladophyll.
кладониязbot: cladonia lichens (Cladonia)
кладофора bot: Cladophora (algae).
кладофоровые (сем.) bot: Cladophoraceae (algae).
кладоцера zool: cladoceran (Cladocera).
кладрастис bot: yellowwood (Cladrastis).
клапан valve, see also заслонка.
~ аорты anat: aortic valve.
~ лёгочной артерии anat: pulmonary valve.
клапанный порок valvular disease.
клапаноподобное действие av med: flapper-valve-like action.
кларкова колонна anat: Clarke's column.
класс bio: class (Classis).
классификатор classer.
классификационное испытание classification examination.
классификация bio: taxonomy.
~ болезней nosology, nosotaxy.
класть яйца bio: lay the eggs, oviposit.
клевер bot: clover, trefoil (Trifolium).
~ александрийский Egyptian c. (T. alexandrinum).
~ белый white c. (T. repens).
~ гибридный alsike c. (T. hybridum).
~ египетский = к. александрийский
~ заячий sand c., lady's fingers (Anthyllis vulneraria, L.)
~ инкарнатный crimson c., Italian c. (T. incarnatum).
~ корейский = леспедеца корейская.
~ красный red c. (T. pratense).
~ луговой meadow c., cow c., see к. красный.
~ мексиканский Mexican c. (Richardsonia scabra).
~ мясокрасный = к. инкарнатный.
~ нарядный = к. гибридный.
~ пашенный rabbit-foot c., old-field c., stone c. (T. arvense).
~ перевёрнутый reversed c. (T. resupinatum).
~ персидский Persian c., see к. перевёрнутый.
~ полевой hop clover (T. agrarium).
~ ползучий = к. белый.
~ прерийный parosela (Dalea, Parosela); prarie clover (Petalostemon).
~ пунцовый = к. инкарнатный.
~ средний zigzag clover (T. medium).
~ степной = к. прерийный.
~ шведский Swedish c., see к. гибр.
~ флоридский = нищенская трава.
~ японский = леспедеца корейская.
клевец tooth.
клей cement, mucilage, glue.
клейдающая ткань hist: gelatinous tissue.
клейкая клетка zool: adhesive cell.
клейкий mucilaginous, adhesive, glutinous.
клейковина bot: fibrin.
клейстогамия bot: cleistogamy.
клейстогамный bot: cleistogamous.
клейстоюкка bot: yucca-like plant (Clistoyucca arborescens, Trelease).
клематис = ломонос.
клементин = апельсин алжирский.
клемма = зажим.
клён bot: maple (Acer).
~ американский = неклен.
~ бумажный paperbark (A. griseum).
~ виргинский = неклен.
~ комнатный = грудника.
~ обыкновенный = к. остролистный.
~ остролистный Norway maple (A. platanoides).
~ сахарный sugar m., silver m., white m., soft m., river m. (A. saccharinum).
~ ясенелистный = неклен.
кленовые (сем.) bot: maple family (Aceraceae).
клепсина = улитковая пиявка.
клептомания psych: kleptomania.
клептофобия psych: kleptophobia.
клест orn: crossbill (Loxia).
~ американский yellow hammer (L. americana, L. mexicana).
~ мексиканский = к. американский.
клестогамия bot: cleistogamy.
клетка 1. hist: cell; 2. cage.
~ Дейтерса prop-cell.
~ для животных animal cage.
~ Лейдига Leydig cell.
~ мерцательного эпителия ciliated cell.
~ мостовидного эпителия pavement c.
~ невроглии glia cell, gliacyte.
~ плоского эпителия squamous cell.
~ почечного эпителия renal cell.
~ Сертоли Sertoli cell.
~ хлореллы chlorella cell.
клетки с ресничным пламенем = пламенные клетки.

клеткообразовательный hist: cytogenic, cell-forming.
клеткообразующий hist: cytogenerative
клеточка hist: cellule.
~ пыльцы bot: pollen grain.
клеточная оболочка hist: cellular membrane, cell wall.
~ патология cellular pathology.
~ стенка древесины bot: wood cell wall.
~ ткань hist: cellular tissue.
клеточное содержимое hist: cell contents.
~ ядро cell nucleus.
клеточный cellular, cell.
~ тяж embr: column of cells, cord.
~ центр = центросома.
~ цилиндр bot: cell cylinder.
клетчатка hist: cellular tissue.
~ водорослей algulose.
клешневидное соединение chem: chelate compound.
клешня claw, nipping claw, nipper, chela.
клещ entom: mite, tick, acarid (Acarus).
~ амбарный mite of the superfamily Tyroglyphoidea.
~ американский nigua, tigua, pique (Amblyomma americanum).
~ бычий cattle tick (Boöphilus calcaratus).
~ виноградный grape erineum mite (Eriophyes vitis).
~ водяной water m., hydrachnid (Oribathidae).
~ волосатый Glycyphagida.
~ галловый gall mite (Eriophydae).
~ грушевый pear mite (Eriophyes pyri); pear-leaf blister m. (Phyllocoptes pyri).
~ земляничный Tarsonemus fragariae.
~ зерновой grain mite (Tyroglyphus).
~ краснотелка zool: trombiculid mite, chigger.
~ кровососущий птичий chicken mite (Dermanyssus gallinoe).
~ луковый корневой Rhizoglyphus echinopus.
~ мучной flour mite, wheat m. (Tyroglyphus farinae); mill m. (Aleurobis farinae).
~ ~ американский mill mite (Tyroglyphys americanus).
~ очинный quill mite.
~ паутинный spider m. (Tetranychus urticae).
~ плодовый бурый Bryobia redikorzovi.
~ ~ красный red spider (Metatetranychus ulmi, Tetranychus bimaculatus).
~ пузатый Pediculoides ventricosus.
*~ сахарный sugar mite (Gliciphagus).
~ скотский cattle tick.
~ собачий dog tick, cattle tick, cattle tick (Jxodes ricinus).
~ сырный cheese mite (Tyroglyphus casei).
~ хищный Cheyletus eruditus.
~ черносмородинный галловый black mite (Eriophyes ribis nalepa).
~ чесоточный scab mite, itch m. (Sarcoptes hominis, S. scabiei).
~ южный скотский southern cattle tick (Boöphilus annulatus).
клеще- zool: acaro-.
клещевая лихорадка infect: tick fever.
клещевина = рицинник.
клещевинный bot: ricinic.
клещевой zool: acarian, acadid(i)an.
~ энцефалит path: acarid-bite encephalitis.
клёщи tongs.
клещи́ (отр.) zool: mites and ticks (Acarina).
клещик = клещ; see also уховёртка.
~ красный = клещ плодовый красный.
~ почковый bud mite.
клизма enema, enteroclysis.
~ сделанная самим больным autoclysis.
климактерий physl: climacteric, menopause.
климактерическая меланхолия psych: climacteric melancholy.
климактерический возраст physl: climacteric.
климатип bot: climatype.
климатотерапия climatic treatment.
клин wedge; anat: cuneus.
клиника clinic.
клинико-психологическая помощь clinical psychological service.
клиницист clinician.
клиническая картина clinical picture.
~ медицина clinical medicine.
~ проблема clinical problem.
клинические данные clinical evidence
клинический диагноз clinical diagnosis.
~ дозиметр rad: clinical dosimeter.
~ осмотр clinical examination.
клиническое наблюдение clinical observation.
~ преподавание clinical teaching.
~ применение clinical use.
клиновидная кость anat: sphenoid bone, os sphenoidale.
~ ~ стопы anat: cuneiform bone of tarsus, os cuneiformis.
~ ~ вторая second c. b. of t., middle c. b.
~ ~ первая first c. b. of t., inner cuneiform bone.
~ ~ третья third c. b. of t., outer c. b.

клиновидная пазуха anat: sphenoid
~ шейка path: conoid cervix. sinus.
клиновидное иссечение surg:
wedge-shaped excision.
клиновидно-обратнояйцевидный
bot: cuneate-obovoid.
клиновидный канатик = к. пучок.
~ лист bot: wedge-shaped leaf.
~ пучок anat: fasciculus cuneatus,
Burdach's column. [(phylum).
клинолистные (тип) bot: Sphenopsida
клиномания psych: clinomania, bedcase.
клинонёбное отверстие anat: sphenopalatine foramen.
клинтух orn: stockdove (Columba oenas).
клипеус entom: clypeus.
клистирная трубка clyster pipe.
клителлюм zool: clitellum.
клитор anat: clitoris.
клиторный anat: clitoridean, clitoridis
клоака zool: cloaca.
клоакальное отверстие zool: osculum
клоакальный cloacal. |in sponges).
~ сифон excurrent siphon, exhalant s.
(of a mollusk). [brane.
клоачная перепонка embr: cloacal mem-
клоачные звери zool: cloaca mammals
(Prototheria), see первозвери.
клобучок bot: calyptriform.
клокичковые (сем.) bot: bladdernut
family (Staphyleaceae).
клон bio: clone. [spasm, clonospasm.
клоническая судорога path: clonic
клоническое состояние clonicity.
клоновая культура bio: clone culture.
клонус neur: clonus.
~ стопы ankle clonus.
клонящееся дерево bot: nodding tree.
клоп entom: true bug; stainer; squash-b.
(Anasa); shore b. (Acanthiidae); elec-
tric-light b. (Belostomidae); etc.
~ австрийский = черепашка австр.
~ американский капустный harlequin
cabbage bug (Murgantia histrionica).
~ -арлекин = к. американский капустный.
~ водяной water bug (Hemiptera).
~ горный Dolycoris penicillatus.
~ грушевый Stephanitis pyri. [ta).
~ капустный cabbage bug (Eurydema orna-
~ луговой tarnished bug (Lygus
pratensis). [lineolatus).
~ люцерновый alfalfa bug (Adelphocoris
~ маврский = черепашка маврская.
~ огородный vegetable bug.

клоп-паразит шведской мушки
meadow plant bug (Miris dolobratus).
~ полевой = к. луговой.
~ полосатый Graphosoma italicum.[rius)
~ постельный bedbug (Cimex lectula-
~ разукрашенный = к. капустный.
~ рисовый rice bug (Leptocorisa acu-
~ травяной = к. луговой. ta).
~ трещинный capsid bug (Plesiocoris
rugicollis).
~ хлопковый cotton stainer.
~ ~ разукрашенный cotton lacebug
(Corythucha gossypii).
~ -черепашка = черепашка 2.
~ четырёхполосый травяной four-
striped plant bug (Poecilocapsus
lineatus). лые.
клопы = настоящие полужёскокры-
~ -щитники (сем.) entom: stink-bugs
(Pentatomidae).
клостериум bot: Closterium (algae).
клохтанье orn: cluck, chuck, cackling.
клохтать orn: cluck, chuck, cackle.
клочень = моль восковая.
клочковатый flocculent.
клубенёк tubercle, nodule.
клубень bot: tuber.
~ аконита pharm: aconite root.
~ картофеля potato tuber.
клубеньковая бактерия bot:
nodule(-forming) bacterium, Rhizobium,
Bacterium radicicola.
~ водоросль bulbous-rooted tangle
(Laminaria bulbosa).[ulose,nodulating.
клубеньковый tubercular, nodular, nod-
клубневидный гаметофит genet:
tuberiform gametophyte.
~ корень bot: tuberous root.[nodulating.
клубневой tuberous, tuberose, knobby,
клубнелуковица bot: bulbo-tuber corn.
клубненосное растение bot: tuberi-
ferous plant.
клубнеобразование bot: tuber formation, tuberization, nodulation.
клубнеплодное растение bot: tuberous
клубнеплоды bot: tuber crops. |plant.
клубника bot: garden strawberry
(Fragaria). [2. ball, clew, skein.
клубок 1. hist: prophase; spireme;
клубочек anat: glomerule, glomerulus.
~ артериальный anat: glomerulus.
~ Мальпигия hist: Malpighian tuft.
клубочковая железа anat: coiled
gland, convoluted gland.
клубочковый glomerular, glomerulose.

клуша orn: lesser black-headed gull (Larus fuscus graelsii).
*клык 1. anat: canine tooth, cuspid t.; 2. zool: tusk, lesser tusk (dog, wolf, boar).
клыковидный tusklike.
клыкообразная свёкла bot: fangy beet.
клюв orn: beak, bill, rostrum.
~ мозолистого тела anat: rostrum of corpus callosum.
~ основной кости anat: beak of the sphenoid.
клювач = клюворылый окунь.
клювик bot: antenna (in fruits).
клюво-акромиальная связка anat: coracoacromial ligament.
~ -плечевая мышца anat: coracobrachialis.
клювовидно-ключичная связка anat: coracoclavicular ligament.
~ -плечевая связка anat: coracohumeral ligament.
клювовидный ноготь path: parrot-beak nail.
~ отросток anat: coracoid (process); bio: rostrum.
~ таз path: rostrate pelvis, beaked p.
*клюворылый кит zool: ziphioid whale
~ окунь ichth: Sebastes mentella.
клюква bot: cranberry, mooseberry (Vaccinium oxycoccos).
~ крупноплодная large c., American c. (V.macrocarpon).
ключ-трава bot: moonwort (Botrychium lunaria, Sw.)
ключица anat: collarbone, clavicle.
ключичная вырезка anat: clavicular notch.
~ линия, средняя anat: midclavicular line.
ключичноакромиальная связка anat: acromioclavicular ligament.
ключичногрудинный anat: cleidosternal.
ключичное пространство anat: clavicular space.
ключичнолопаточный anat: cleidoscapular.
клядиум bot: twigrush (Cladium, P. Br.)
~ ямайский saw grass (C. jamaicensis).
кнаружи ectad, outward.
книга для записи назначений врача doctor's order book.
~ ~ отпускаемых ядовитых веществ pharm: poison register.
книдоциль zool: cnudocil (of a hydra).
книжка (третий желудок) zool: omasum, filter press, maniplies, psalterium.
книфофия bot: flame flower, torch lily (Kniphofia, Tritoma uvaria, Hook.)
кнур zool: male swine, boar.
коагулаза coagulase.
коагулировать(ся) coagulate.
коагуляционный coagulative.
коагуляция coagulation.
коала = сумчатый медведь.
коарктация coarctation.
коацервация bio: coacervation.
кобель zool: male dog. Cf. сука.
кобец orn: pern, honey buzzard (Pernis apivorus).
кобра zool: cobra (Naja).
кобыла zool: mare.
кобылка entom: small species of Acrididae; see also цикадка.
~ крестовая Paracyptera microptera.
~ рисовая rice grasshopper.
~ сибирская Gomphocerus sibiricus.
~ стройная Chorthippus albomarginatus
~ темнокрылая Stauroderus scalaris.
~ туркменская Ramburiella turcomana.
ковровая трава bot: carpet grass (Paspalum compressum, Nees).
ковыль bot: feathergrass, speargrass, matgrass (Stipa).
когорта cohort.
коготок small claw.
~ на лапке entom: tarsal claw.
коготь zool: claw.
~ хищной птицы talon.
когтеобразная кисть neur: claw hand
когтистая обезьяна = игрунок.
когтистый тритон = уссурийский к. т.
кодеин pharm: codeine.
коечное лечение bed rest.
коечный больной bed patient.
кожа 1. skin, cutis; 2. leather; 3. zool: see гренландский тюлень.
кожан обыкновенный zool: bat, rattlemouse (Vesperugo noctula).
Кожевников Kozhevnikov, Kojewnikoff.
кожеед entom: dermestid, mange.
~ ветчинный larder beetle (Dermestes lardarius).
~ зерновой Trogoderma granarium.
~ Фриша Dermestes frischi.
~ шиповатый Dermestes vulpinus.
кожееды (сем.) dermestids (Dermestidae)
кожистая оболочка bot: leathery jacket
кожистокрылые (отр.) entom: earwigs (Dermaptera).
кожистый leathery, coriaceous.
кожица pellicle, skin, see кожура.
кожная болезнь skin disease, cutaneous disease.
~ вена anat: cutaneous vein.
~ высыпь derm: cutaneous eruption, efflorescence.
~ доза rad: skin dose.
~ железа anat: cutaneous gland.
~ омозолелость derm: cutaneous callosity.
~ пластинка embr: cutis plate.

кожная проба = к. реакция.
~ реакция imm: skin test.
~ сыпь = к. высыпь.
~ туберкулиновая проба skin tuberculin test.
~ форма сапа infect: farcy.
~ чувствительность cutaneous sensibility.
~ язва derm: cutaneous ulcer.
кожное дыхание cutaneous respiration, transpiration.
~ кровообращение cutaneous circulation.
~ отделение (больницы) dermatologic department (ward).
~ чувство skin sense.
кожно-мускульный мешок dermomuscular tube.
~ -мышечный лоскут surg: musculocutaneous flap.
~ -слизистый mucocutaneous.
кожные оводы (сем.) = подкожные о.
~ сосуды anat: cutaneous vessels.
кожный cutaneous, dermal, skin.
~ лоскут surg: cutaneous flap, skin f.
~ ~ для пересадки surg: dermic graft.
~ нерв шеи anat: superficial cervical nerve, nervus cutaneus colli.
~ покров cutaneous covering, integument.
~ разрез surg: skin incision.
~ рог derm: cutaneous horn.
~ соскоб skin scraping.
~ сосуд anat: cutaneous vessel.
~ шов surg: cutaneous suture, dermal s.
~ эпителий hist: squamous epithelium.
кожура bot: skin, peal, outcovering, cortex, aril.
коза zool: goat, female goat.
~ ангорская Angora goat (Capra hircus var. angorensis).
козёл zool: goat (Capra); billy goat, male g. Cf. коза
козелец = скорцонер.
козелковый anat: tragal.
козелок anat: tragus.
козерог лилейный = коровка лилейная.
козлёнок zool: young goat.
~ косули = молодой олень.
козлиться zool: yean.
козлобородник bot: goatsbeard (Tragopogon).
~ луговой goatsbeard (T. pratensis).
~ -сальсифи salsify, oyster plant, vegetable oyster (T. porrifolius).
козлятник = астрагал.
~ лекарственный bot: goatsrue (Galega officinalis).
козодой orn: nighthawk; European nightjar (Carpimulgus).
~ жалобный whip poor-will (Caprimulgus vociferus).
~ обыкновенный goatsucker, European nightjar (C. europaeus).
козочка (рак) zool: ghost shrimp, caprellid (Caprella).

козья лихорадка = бруцеллёз.
козявка entom: small insect.
~ мавританская Tenebrioides mauritanicus.
коилия ichth: mao-hua-yii (Coilia).
коипу = бобр болотный.
койепут(овое дерево) bot: punk tree (Melaleuca leucadendron).
койот zool: coyote (Canis latrans).
кок-сагыз Russian blow-ball (Taraxacum kok-saghyz, Rodin).
кокаин pharm: cocaine.
кокаинизм cocainism, cocaine addiction.
кокаинист psych: cocainist, cocaine addict.
кокк mcbio: coccus.
кокки mcbio: cocci (pl.)
кокковая инфекция coccus infection.
кокковидное состояние mcbio: coccoid habit.
кокковый coccal.
коккоид mcbio: coccoid.
кокколит bot: coccolith.
кокконеис bot: Cocconeis (algae).
коккоподобный coccoid.
коккосфера bot: coccosphere.
коккофаги entom: Coccophagus.
коклюш infect: whooping cough, petrussis.
коклюшный petrussal.
~ кашель whoop(ing cough), hoop.
кокон entom: cocoon, case, chrysalis, kell.
коконопряд = совка хлопковая.
коконопряды (сем.) entom: lasiocampids, tent-caterpillars and lappet-caterpillars (Lasiocampidae).
кокорыш bot: fool's parsley, hedge parsley (Aethusa cynapium).
кокосовая пальма bot: coconut palm (Cocos nucifera).
кокосовое волокно bot: coir.
~ молоко coconut milk.
кокосовый краб zool: robber crab (Birgus latro).
Коксаки Coxsackie.
коксальный entom: coxal.
коксит path: coxitis.
коксоподит zool: coxopodite.
кокуиза = агава колючая.
кокушник = ятрышник.
кокцида entom: coccid, see щитовка, червец.
кокцидии (отр.) zool: Coccidia.
кокцидиоз = угрястость.
кокцинеллиды = божьи коровки.
кола bot: cola, kola, gorra (Cola, Buchea acuminata, Schott. et Endl.)
колба flask, bulb; shell, envelope.
~ из иенского стекла Jena flask.
~ с культурой mcbio: culture flask.
колбасное отравление botulism.
колбасный яд sausage poison.

колбочка cone.
~ сетчатки ophth: retinal cone.
колбочковая сетчатка anat: cone reti-
кол-во = количество. na.
колебание oscillation, vibration, fluctuation, swinging, variation.
~ кровяного давления variation of blood pressure.
колебательный нистагм ophth: oscillating nystagmus.
коленная чашка anat: kneecap, patella.
коленногрудное положение gyn: knee-chest position.
коленнолоктевое положение gyn: knee-elbow position, genucubital p.
коленно-пяточная проба knee-heel
коленный anat: genual. test.
~ рефлекс physl: patellar (tendon) reflex, knee jerk, knee kick.
~ сустав anat: knee joint.
колено 1. anat: knee, genu; stifle (of a horse); 2. bio: tribe; 3. bio: Phylum.
~ мозолистого тела anat: genu of corpus callosum.
коленчато-булавовидный усик entom: geniculate clavate antenna.
коленчатое тело anat: geniculum, geniculate body.
коленчатый стержень bot: articulated
~ усик entom: geniculate antenna. | rachis.
~ ~ (или побег) bot: jointed tendril.
колеокотиль bot: coleocotyle.
колеоптиль bot: coleoptile, coleoptilum.
колеориза bot: coleorhiza.
колибри orn: hummingbird, colibri (Trochilidae). [pain), gripe.
колика path: colic (paroxysmal abdominal
~ вследствие скопления газов flatulent colic, physospasmus.
~ вызванная глистами verminous colic
~ живописцев painter's colic.
~ при каменной болезни stone colic.
колики в животе abdominal colic; vet:
колит path: colitis. hoven.
колиформный mcbio: coliform.
количественная атрофия numerical atrophy.
количественный quantitative.
количество quantity, amount, number;
коллаген collagen. scale.
коллагеновый collagenic, collagenous.
коллапс collapse.
коллапсотерапия collapse treatment.
колларгол = коллоидальное серебро.
коллатеральная лучевая артерия anat: radial collateral artery.

коллатеральное кровообращение collateral circulation.
коллега colleague. [sonia).
коллинсония bot: horse balm (Collin-
~ канадская richweed, stoneroot (C. canadensis).
коллодий pharm: collodion. [дий.
~ шпанских мух = нарывной колло-
коллодийная повязка surg: cocoon dressing.
коллодийный мешочек bact: collodi-
коллоид colloid. on sac.
коллоидальное серебро pharm: colloid silver.
~ состояние colloidal state.
коллоидная химия colloid chemistry.
киллоидный зоб path: colloid goiter.
~ рак path: pultaceous cancer.
коловратка rotifer, wheel insect.
коловратки (кл.) zool: rotifers, wheel animalcules (Rotifera, Rotato-
коловраточный zool: rotiferal. | ria).
коловращательный аппарат zool: wheel organ, corona (of a rotifer).
колодка block; bottle stand.
колоказия съедобная bot: dasheen (Colocasia esculenta).
колоквинт bot: bitter apple (Cucumis colocynthis). [shaped.
колоколообразный campanulate, bell-
колокольчатый bot: campanulate.
колокольчик bot: bellflower (Campanula).
~ водосборный = водосбор обыкновенный.
~ крапиволистный nettle-leaved bellflower, throatwort (C. trachelium).
~ круглолистый harebell, bluebell (C. rotundifolia).
~ повиличный = повой заборный.
~ синий = горечавка синяя.
~ средний cup-and-saucer (C. medium, var. Calycanthema).
колокольчиковидный bell-shaped, belled, campanulate.
колокольчиковоцветные (пор.) bot: Campanulates (ord.)
колокольчиковые (сем.) bot: bellflower family, bluebell family (Campanulaceae). [al algae.
колониальные водоросли bot: coloni-
колониальный организм colonial organism.
колония colony; rookery (of birds).
~ для прокаженных leprosarium.
~ пеликанов pelican colony.

колос bot: ear, spike, head.
колоситься bot: come into ear, spire.
колосковая чешуя bot: (empty) glume, flower glume, cape.
~ ~ с килем bot: carinate glume.
колосняк = волоснец песчаный.
колосовидная головка bot: earhead.
~ повязка surg: spica bandage.
колосовидный bot: spiciform.
колосовые злаки bot: ear grasses, spikelet grasses.
колосок bot: spikelet, little ear.
~ хвоща cone.
колотая рана surg: stab wound, punctured w.
колотиф infect: colotyphoid.
колотье path: stitch.
колоцентез surg: colipuncture.
колоцинт = колоквинт.
колошение bot: earing.
колпак hood cap, dome, bowl, bonnet, bell jar.
колпачок bot: galea.
колтун Polish plait.
колумелла columella.
колхицин bot: colchicine.
колхицинирование bot: colchicine technique.
кóлы (передние зубы у лошади) gatherers.
колышащаяся зелень (трава) nodding verdure (grass).
кольраби bot: kohlrabi, kale turnip, Hungarian t. (Brassica caulorapa).
кольцевание ringing.
кольцевая гниль свеклы phytp: zonate deep scab of beets (Oospore cretacea, Krug.)
~ проба (на белок) chem: ring test.
~ пятнистость phytp: ring spottiness.
кольцевидная мышца отверстия anat: sphincter.
~ связка стопы annular ligament of the ankle.
кольцевидные волосы derm: ringed hair.
кольцевидный нож surg: ring knife.
~ хрящ anat: annular cartilage.
кольцешейный фазан ring-necked pheasant.
кольцо ring, annulus.
~ Кабота hem: ring body.
кольчатая нерпа zool: ringed seal (Phoca hispida).
кольчатое строение zool: annular structure, annelism.
~ цветорасположение bot: whorl.
кольчатые черви (тип) zool: segmented worms, annelid worms (Annelida).
кольчатый bot: see мутовчатый.
~ червь zool: segmented worm.
кольчатый червь строящий трубчатые домики tubeworm.
кольчец = кольчатый червь.
колюмеллярный zool: columellar.
колючая акула ichth: miller's dog (Acanthias).
~ семенная коробочка bot: prickly seedcase, hedgehog.
~ сердцевидка zool: spiny cockle.
колючеголовые черви helm: spiny-headed worms, thorny-headed worms, proboscis worms (Acanthocephales).
колючеголовый червь zool: spiny-headed worm, thorn-headed worm (Acanthocephales).
колючее растение muricated plant, hedgehog.
колючепёрые рыбы Cyprinidae.
колючие акулы (сем.) ichth: spined dogfishes (Squalidae).
колючий prickly, spiny, spiculate, spinescent, thorny, burred; see also остистый, шиповатый.
колючка bur, barb, thorn, acantha.
колючник бесстебельный bot: stemless carline.
колюшка ichth: stickleback (Gasterosteus); see also трехиглая колюшка.
~ большая = трехиглая к.
~ малая = девятииглая к.
колюшковые (сем.) ichth: stickleback family (Gasterosteidae).
колюшкообразные (отр.) ichth: Gasterosteiformes.
колющая боль stabbing pain.
колющие ротовые органы entom: piercing mouth parts.
кома psych: coma.
~ диабетическая = сахарный диабет.
комар entom: mosquito; Brit: gnat (Culicidae). See also комарик.
~ грибной fungus midge (Mycetophilidae, Fungivoridae).
~ -дергун = звонец.
~ -долгоножка crane fly (Tipula).
~ жёлтолихорадочный yellow-fever mosquito (Aedes aegypti).
~ кровососущий blood-sucking m.
~ малярийный malaria mosquito, anopheles (Anopheles).
~ обыкновенный northern house mosquito, Brit: gnat (Culex pipiens).
~ -ручейник long-legged fly (Tipula).
~ ~ огородный crane fly, daddy long-legs (Tipula oleracea).

комар туляремийный tularemia mosquito (Aedes vexans).
~ филариазный filariasis-transmitting mosquito (Anopheles hyrcanus).
комарик entom: gall midge (Cecidomyia).
~ галловый gallfly (Contarinia violicola).
~ грушевый pear midge (Diplosis pyrivora, Contarinia p.)
~ люцерновый галловый alfalfa gall midge (Aspondilia miki).
~ ~ почковый Perrisia ignorata.
~ ~ цветочный Contarinia medicaginis.
~ морковный carrot midge (Asphondylos umbellatarum).
~ просяной millet m. (Stenodiplosis parici).
~ пшеничный wheat midge (Contarinia tritici).
~ ржаной стеблевой Hybolasioptera cerealis.
~ розанный rose midge (Neocerate rhabdophaga).
комаровы носики = живокость посевная.
комароубивающее средство culicide.
комары (сем.) entom: mosquitoes (Culicidae). See also длинноусые мухи.
коматозное состояние psych: comatose condition.
комбинированный поворот obstet: combined version.
комбустия combustion, burn.
коменсал bio: commensal.
коменсализм bio: commensalism.
комиссура commissure.
комиссуральное волокно anat: commissural fiber.
комиссуротомия surg: commissurotomy.
комковатость (почвы) arg: crumbly condition.
комковатый lumpy.
коммелина bot: dayflower (Commelina).
коммелиновые (сем.) bot: spiderwort family (Commelinaceae).
коммоция commotio(n).
комната больных sick room.
~ для чистки рук перед операцией surg: scrub-up room.
комок клеток hist: cluster of cells.
комолое животное poll beast, pollard.
комолый zool: hornless, hummel.
компасная медуза zool: medura Chrysaora hyoscella.
компенсаторное кровообращение = коллатеральное к.
~ образование волокнистой ткани path: replacement fibrosis.
компенсация compensation.
комплекс малоценности psych: inferiority complex, feeling of i.
~ превосходства psych: superiority complex.
комплексное лечение complex treatment.
комплект хромосом genom.
комплемент complement.
~ -связывающее антитело complement-fixing antibody.
~ -связывающий complement-fixing.
компресс compress, pledget.
компрессионный перелом позвоночника av med: compression fracture of the spine.
~ стеноз евстахиевой трубы av med: compression-stenosis of the eustachian tube.
компрессия compression.
компрессорный surg: compressor.
компсотлипида orn: warbler of fam. Compsothlypidae.
комчужная трава = мать-и-мачеха.
конвергентное косоглазие ophth: cross-eye.
конвергенция ophth: convergence.
конвергировать(ся) ophth: converge.
конвертообразные кристаллы (оксалатов) envelope crystalls.
конвульсивный convulsionary, convulsivant, convulsive.
конвульсия convulsion.
~ эпилептического характера epileptiform convulsion.
конгелация congelation.
конгестия congestion.
конглютинация conglutination.
конгорот chem: congo red.
конденсаторная ионизационная камера rad bio: capacitor ionization chamber.
конденсаторный рентгенметр rad: capacitor r-meter.
конденсационная вода condensation water.
кондилома ven: condyloma.
кондилюра zool: star-nosed mole (Condylura cristata).
кондор orn: condor (Vultur gryphus).
"кондрашка" collq: cerebro-vascular accident, CVA.
кондуранго bot: condurango (Marsdenia cundurango, Reichb.)
конёк = валёк.
~ луговой orn: meadow pipet (Anthus pratensis).
конец 1. end, termination, terminal; point, tip; 2. death.

конечная артерия anat: end artery.

~ нить anat: terminal thread, filum terminale (of the spinal cord).

~ ость bot: tip awn.

~ почка bot: phyllophore.

~ стадия деления hist: final phase of fission, telophase.

~ фаланга anat: terminal phalanx.

конечномозговой embr anat: telencephalic.

конечноротые (подкл.) ichth: Teleostomi.

конечностный anat: extremital.

конечность anat: extremity, limb.

~ с клешнёй zool: chelate limb.

конечный мозг anat: endbrain, telencephalon.

~ продукт end product.

конидий bot: conidium.

конин conine.

конкремент(ы) path: concretion, calculus.

коннектива entom: connective.

коноплёвые (сем.) bot: hemp family (Connabinaceae).

конопля bot: hemp, marijuana, cannabis (Cannabis).

~ лесная = чай капорский.

~ маврициевая = фуркрея гигантская.

коноплянка обыкновенная orn: redpoll (Acanthis linaria), linnet (A. cannabina).

коноплянный bot: cannabic.

конофима entom: genus Conophyma (locusts).

конрингия восточная = горчица индийская.

консервант preservative.

консервативная хирургия conservative surgery.

консервативное лечение convervative treatment.

консервированная кровь banked blood.

консервированные фрукты canned fruits.

консервы canned food.

консилиум consultation.

консистенция consistency.

конская макрель zool: horse mackerel.

~ стопа horse foot, tip foot.

конские каштаны (сем.) bot: buckeye family (Hippocastanaceae).

конский = лошадиный.

~ навоз horse manure.

~ хвост 1. zool: horse's tail; 2. anat: cauda equina.

консонирующие хрипы consonating rales.

конституциональная медицина constitutional medicine.

~ психопатия constitutional psychopathy.

конституция constitution.

консультант consultant.

консультация advice; counsellor(s).

контагиозность contagiousness.

контакт contact.

контактная радиотерапия contact radiation therapy; see also аппликационный метод лечения.

контактное инфекционное заболевание prosodemic disease.

контии zool: snakes Contia.

контора больницы business office of a hospital.

контрактура contracture.

~ конечностей acrocontracture.

контракционное кольцо obstet: contraction ring.

контралатеральный anat: contralateral.

контрастная окраска mcscop: contrastive staining.

контрастное вещество x-ray: contrast medium.

~ средство x-ray: contrast medium.

контролёр checker.

контрольное животное control animal.

контрольный образец control sample.

~ опыт check experiment.

контузия surg: contusion.

контурирование outlining, contouring, silhouetting.

конус cone, taper, bevel.

~ нарастания bot: vegetative cone, apical c.

~ спинного мозга anat: conus medullaris.

конусовидная связка anat: conoid ligament.

конусообразный cone-shaped.

конуфер = калуфер.

конфабуляция psych: confabulation.

конфетное дерево bot: Japanese raisin tree (Hovenia dulcis, Thunb.)

конфлюирующие очаги confluent foci.

конхиолин zool: conchiolin.

конхологический conchological.

конхология conchology.

конхотом surg: turbinotome.

конхотомия otolar: turbinotomy.

концевая пластинка hist: end plate.

~ пятнистость phytp: tip blight.

~ часть тела zool: pygidium.

концевое разветвление terminal ramification.

~ тельце hist: terminal corpuscle.

концевой орган anat: end organ.

~ осязательный орган anat: tactor.

концентрация concentration.

~ ... в сыворотке serum concentration of...

концентрированный concentrated.

концентрическая пятнистость phytp: target spot (of potatoes).

концентрическое слабоумие psych: concentric dementia.
концептакуля bot: conceptacle.
концепция conception (abstract idea).
кон-ция = концентрация.
кончик tip, point.
~ верхней челюсти entom: lacinia.
~ корня bot: root tip, root base.
~ пальца ноги anat: toe tip.
кончики гребешка orn: points of comb.
конь 1. see лошадь; 2. ichth: Hemibarbus.
~ губарь ichth: Hemibarbus labeo.
конъюгант zool: conjugant.
конъюгата anat: conjugate.
конъюгаты (кл.) bot: Conjugatea class (algae).
конъюгация bio: conjugation.
~ хромосом bio: synapsis.
конъюгирующая особь zool: conjugant.
конъюнктива anat: conjunctiva.
~ глаза ocular conjunctiva.
~ склеры bulbar conjunctiva.
конъюнктивальная инъекция ophth: conjunctival injection.
конъюнктивальное кровоизлияние ophth: conjunctival hemorrhage.
конъюнктивальный мешок conjunctival sac.
конъюнктивиальный = конъюнктивальный.
конъюнктивит conjunctivitis.
конюшина = клевер красный.
координатор системы О'Рурка av med: O'Rourke's complex coordinator.
координация coordination.
координированные движения coordinated movements.
копайский бальзам pharm: balsam of copaiba.
копательная нога entom: burrowing leg.
копательный fossorial, burrowing.
копеечник съедобный bot: oyi (Hedysarum esculentum); see also ярутка полевая.
копепода zool: copepod (Copepoda).
копролит = каловый камень.
копулировать copulate.
копулировка bot: saddle grafting.
копулятивный zool: copulatory.
~ орган entom: petiole (of a mite, etc.)
копуляция zool: copulation.
копчёная пикша finnan haddie.
~ подсоленая сельдь kippered herring.
~ треска finnan cod, smoked cod.
копчик anat: coccyx, tail bone.
копчиковая железа 1. anat: coccygeal gland; 2. orn: preen g., uropygial g., oil gland.
копчиковые позвонки anat: coccygeal vertebrae, vertebrae coccygeae.

копытень bot: asarabacca, wild ginger (Asarum).
~ европейский hazelwort, wild nardus (A. europaeum).
копытка = саджа.
копытная болезнь = ногтоеда.
копытное hoofed animal, ungulate.
копытный зверь hoofed animal.
*~ лемминг zool: lemming (Decrostonyx, Cuniculus).
копыто zool: hoof.
копьевидный лист bot: spear-shaped leaf, halberd-shaped l., hastate-base l.
кора bark; cortex.
~ головного мозга anat: cerebral cortex.
~ гранатового дерева pomegranate bark.
~ надпочечника anat: adrenal cortex.
~ хинного дерева bot: calisaya bark.
~ цветоложа bot: cortex of the receptacle, columella.
корабельный врач ship surgeon.
~ червь zool: shipworm, teredo (Teredo).
кораблик zool: paper nautilus (Argonauta).
коралл zool: coral.
~ настоящий true coral (Madreporaria).
кораллина bot: coralline, nullipore (Corallinaceae).
коралловые полипы (кл.) zool: anthozoan polyps (Anthozoa).
корамин pharm: coramine, nikethamide.
кордаиты (пор.) bot: Cordaitales (extinct).
кордилина bot: dracaena, ti (Cordyline, Kunth.)
кордовник = ворсянка.
кордол = трибромсалол.
кордуль = испанский золотой корень.
коревой infect: morbillous.
коренной radical.
~ зуб molar tooth, masttooth, see also большой к. з., малый к. з.; vet: jawtooth.
~ обитатель aborigine, earliest known inhabitant, autochthon.
корень root.
~ валерианы pharm: valerian.
~ волоса anat: hair root.
~ горечавки bot: bitterroot (Gentiana).
~ зуба anat: tooth root, radix dentis.
~ лёгкого anat: root of the lung, radix pulmonis.
~ сенеги seneca snakeroot.
~ языка anat: radix linguae.
кореопсис bot: coreopsis, tickseed (Coreopsis).
~ красильный tickseed (C. tinctoria).
корешковая боль neur: radicular pain.
корешок bot: rootlet, radicle, see первичный корень.
~ водорослей holdfast.

корешок зародыша bot: embryo root.
~ нерва anat: nerve root.
~ чувствительного нерва anat: sensory root.
корзинка bot: anthodium, calathide.
корзиночное растение basket plant.
кориандр bot: coriander (Coriandrum sativum).
кориум entom: corium.
корифантовые bot: coryphanthanae.
корифена dolphin (Coryphaena hippurus).
корица cinnamon.
коричневая пятнистость шампиньонов phytp: verticillum disease.
коричное масло pharm: cinnamon oil.
коричнокислый натрий pharm: sodium cinnamate.
коричный cinnamic.
корка crust, cortex, bark.[of receptacle.
корковая часть плодоложа bot:cortex
корковое вещество hist: cortical substance, cortex.
корково-спинальный путь anat: corticospinal tract, pyramidal tract.
корковый cortical.
~ лишайник = накипной л.
~ слой anat: cortical layer, cortex.
корм zool: feed, fodder.
кормидий zool: cormidium (of a medusa).
кормилица ped: wet nurse.
кормить feed, nourish, nurse.
~ грудью ped: suckle, nurse at the breast.
кормление feeding, nourishing, nursing, alimentation.
~ грудью ped: breast-feeding, nursing.
~ через желудочный зонд gavage.
~ ~ нос nasal feeding.
кормовая трава arg: fodder grass.
корнеальный ophth: corneal.
корневая гниль phytp: root rot.
~ губка phytp: Fores annosus, Fries.
~ закомлеватость phytp: root swelling.
~ мочка bot: root fibril.
~ нематода = галловая н.
~ оболочка зуба peridontal membrane, pericementum.
~ плесень виноградной лозы phytp: vine root fungus.
~ поросль bot: stool shoots.
~ почка bot: radical bud.
~ система bot: roots (of a plant).
~ среда bot: root medium.
~ шейка bot: collum.
корневидный bot: root-shaped, rootlike, rhizomorphous.
корневище bot: rhizome, (subterranean) rootstock.
корневищные сорняки bot: couch grass.
корневищный bot: rhizomatous, rhizomatose, rhizophorous.
~ злак bot: quitch.
~ побег bot: creeper.
корнёвка латуковая entom: root-louse (Rhizobius lactucae).
корневое влагалище anat: root sheath.
~ питание bot: root nutrition.
корневой волосок bot: root hair.
~ гриб bot: root fungus.
~ канал anat: root canal.
~ клубенёк root nodule, r. gall, pip.
~ нарост phytp: root swelling.
~ отпрыск bot: root stalk, ratoon, rootstock, see побег от корня.
~ побег = к. отпрыск.
~ чехлик bot: rootcap, tip cap, calyptra, pileothiza.
корнеед entom: root borer (Anarsia, Tyrophorus canellus, Cylas formicarius)
корнеед(а) phytp: root rot, foot r.
~ свекловичная root rot of beets.
корнежгутиковые (отр.) zool: Rhyzomastigina, Pantostomatida.
корнеклубень = корневой клубенёк.
корненожка zool: rhizopod (Rhizopoda).
корненожки (подкл.) zool: Rhizopoda.
корненожковый zool: rhizopodous, rhizopodan.
корнеротые медузы (отр.) zool: Rhizostomeae.
корнесобственный bot: own-rooted, scion-rooted.
корнишон bot: cuke, (bur) gherkin (Cucumis anguria).
корноухий zool: crop-eared, earless.
корнцанг = хирургический пинцет.
коробочка small box; bot: capsule seedcase, fruitcase.
~ мака bot: poppyhead.
~ с крышечкой bot: pyxidium, pyxis.
коробочный звук int:bandbox sound.
~ червь хлопчатника = совка хлопковая.
корова cow (Cavicornia).
коровий bovine.
коровка бахчевая entom: squash lady-bug (Epilachna chrysomelina).
~ божья = божья коровка.
~ картофельная potato lady-bug (E. vigintioctomaculata).
~ красная = к. лилейная.
коровье молоко cow's milk.
коровья оспа vet: cowpox, vaccinia.
~ птица cowbird (Molothrus).
коровяк bot: mullein, torchweed, hag-taper (Verbascum); pharm: lungwort.

коровяк тараканный = к. тёмный.
~ тёмный moth mullein (V. blattaria).
короед entom: bark beetle, cambium b. (Ips, etc.)
~ большой еловый typographer bark b. (Tomicus typographus).
~ вершинный Ips acuminatus.
~ вязовый lesser elm-bark b. (Eccoptogaster multistriatus).
~ -гравёр engraver b. (Pityogenes chalcographus).
~ непарный Xileborus dispar.
~ персика peach-tree bark b. (Phlaeotribus liminaris).
~ пихты серебристой silver-fir bark b. (Tomicus curvidens).
~ сосновый engraver (Ips pini).
~ -типограф engraver b. (Bostrychus typographus, Ips typographus).
короеды (сем.) entom: bark beetles (Ipidae).
королёк orn: kinglet (Regulus).
~ желтоголовый goldcrest (Regulus regulus).
корольки = корольковые.
корольковые (сем.) orn: kinglets, dwarf fowls (Regulidae).
коромысло = стрекоза коромысло.
корональный coronal.
коронарное кровообращение coronary blood circulation.
коронарный синус coronary sinus.
~ склероз path: coronary sclerosis.
коронарорасширяющий coronary vasodilator.
коронаросклероз int: coronary sclerosis.
коронаротромбоз int: coronary thrombosis.
коронка odont: jacket crown.
~ зуба anat: tooth crown, corona dentis.
корончатая ржавчина phytp: crown rust.
короста mange, scabies, itch.
коростель orn: corn crake; Brit: landrail (Crex crex), water rail (C. pratensis).
коростовый vet: mangy.
короткая ножка наковальни anat: short crus of the incus.
короткий отросток молоточка anat: short process of the malleus.
~ отрывистый кашель tussiculation.
~ сгибатель anat: breviflexor.
~ стручок silicle.
~ хвост zool: scut.
коротковолновая терапия short-wave therapy.
коротковолокнистый short-stapled.
короткоголов африканский zool: Phrynomerus bifasciata.
короткоголовы zool: Brevicipitidae (batrachians).
короткоголовый zool: brachycephalic, brachycephalous.
короткое замыкание cf. реакция короткого замыкания.
~ ребро anat: short rib, false rib.
короткоклювая гагара orn: Brunnich's guillemot (Uria l. lomvia).
короткокрылый brachypterous.
коротконадкрылые жуки (сем.) entom: rove-beetles, staphylinids (Staphylinidae).
коротконогий entom: braphypodous.
короткоостистый bot: short-awned.
короткопалый path: brachydactylous, brachydactilic.
короткопестичный bot: thrum-eyed.
короткорогий скот zool: shorthorn cattle (Bos taurus).
короткостебельный bot: short-stalked, acaulescent.
короткостебельчатый цветок bot: short-caulicle flower, subcaulescent flower.
короткоусые мухи (подотр.) entom: short-antenna flies (Brachycera).
короткоусый entom: brachycerous.
короткохвостые раки zool: Brachyura.
короткохвостый поморник orn: Arctic skua (Stercorarius parasiticus).
короткошёрстый short-haired, short-woolled.
корпия surg: lint.
корпус corpus, body, trunk, torso.
коррегировать correct.
коррекция на бесконечность ophth: correction for infinity.
~ ~ расстояние ophth: correction for a distance.
~ очками correction by glasses.
корреляция correlation.
корсаковский психоз = полиневритический психоз.
~ синдром psych: Korsakoff's syndrome.
корсетная печень int: corset liver, tight-lace liver.
Корти Corti.
кортиев орган otolar: Corti's organ.
кортиева дуга anat: Corti's arch.
кортиевы клетки Corti's cells, floor cells.
~ столбики hist: acoustic rods.
кортизон cortisone.
кортикальный гормон cortical hormone.

кортико-адреналовая недостаточность cortico-adrenal insufficiency.
кортикостероид corticosterone.
кортикотропин conticotrop(h)in.
корточки cf. приседать на корточки
корь infect: measles.
коршун orn: kite (Milvus).
~ обыкновенный black kite (M. ater).
корюшка ichth: frostfish (Osmerus mordax); smelt (Osmeridae); surf s. (Mesopus pretiosus).
~ малоротая Hypomesus.
корюшковые (сем.) ichth: smelt family (Osmeridae).
косатка ichth: Liocassis.
~ -скрипун ichth: Pseudobagrus.
косатковые (сем.) ichth: Bagridae.
косач orn: black grouse (Tetrao tetrix, Lyrurus tetrix).
косая мышца живота (внутренняя, наружная) anat: obliquus abdominis (internus, externus) muscle.
~ среда bact: slant.
~ сывороточная среда serum slope, serum slant.
косица orn: sickle.
космариум bot: Cosmarium (algae).
косметика cosmetics.
косметический cosmetic.
косметическое средство cosmetic.
коснуться p. a. of касаться.
косоглазие path: strabismus, heterotopia, squint, cast.
косой агар bact: slant agar.
~ кровяной агар blood agar slant.
~ перелом surg: oblique fracture.
косолапость path: clubfoot, splay foot, stump foot.
косолапый orthop: talipedic.
косопосаженные зубы odont: snaggle teeth.
косорот обыкновенный ichth: plaice (Solea).
косорукость path: clubhand.
коста(льная жилка) entom: costa(l) vein).
костальный край крыла = передний край крыла.
костеизвлекатель surg: fish-bone catcher.
костеискатель rad chem: bone seeker.
костенеть ossify.
костенец bot: spleenwort (Asplenium).
~ постенный tentwort (A. rutamuraria).
костеобразование bone formation, osteogenesis.
костеобразовательная клетка hist: osteoblast, osteogenic cell.
костеобразующий osteogenic, ossiferous

костёр bot: bromegrass (Bromus).
~ безостый awnless b., Hungarian b., smooth b. (B. inermis).
~ кровельный cheat, chess (B. tectorum).
~ мягкий soft chess, soft b. (B. mollis).
~ полевой field b. (B. arvensis).
~ прямой upright b. (B. erectus).
~ ржаной rye b., cheat, chess (B. secalinus).
*~ униольный rescue grass (B. unioloides, НВК).
~ шершавый hairy b. (B. asper).
кости запястья anat: wrist bones, carpal bones.
костистая рыба teleost, bony fish.
костистые ichth: teleosts (Teleostei).
костлявый bony, ossiferous.
костная ампула anat: osseous ampulla.
~ зола bone ash.
~ киста osseous cyst.
~ мозоль path: callus.
~ опухоль path: osteoma, osseous growth.
~ перегородка anat: osteoseptum.
~ пила surg: bone saw.
~ полость anat: bone cavity.
~ проводимость physl: bone conduction, osteophony.
~ ткань hist: bony tissue, osseous t.
~ часть anat: bony portion.
костномозговая клетка hist: marrow cell.
~ полость anat: marrow cavity.
костномозговой канал anat: medullary canal.
костно-надкостный anat: osteoperisteal.
костнопузырные (отр.) ichth: Ostariophysi, see карпообразные.
костнохрящевые ichth: Chondrostei.
костнощитковые zool: Osteostraci (extinct).
костные ганоиды ichth: Holostei.
~ ножницы surg: bone scissors.
~ рыбы ichth: Osteichthyes.
~ щипцы surg: bone forceps, b. nippers.
костный osseous, osteal.
~ выступ anat: bony prominence.
~ клей bone gelatin.
~ лабиринт anat: bony labyrinth.
~ мозг anat: (bone) marrow, medulla ossium.
~ осколок surg: splinter of bone.
~ остов anat: bony frame, skeleton.
~ отросток anat: bony process.
~ рак oncol: bone carcinoma.
~ таз anat: bony pelvis, pelvis ossea.
~ шов surg: bone suture.

костоеда path: caries.
костоправ bonesetter.
косточка anat: ossicle, bonelet.
~ (плода) bot: stone, putamen, pyrene.
косточки Ворма = шовные косточки.
косточковый плод bot: stone fruit, pyrenocarp, drupe.
костра́ bot: 1. see костёр; 2. bullen, scutch, shive.
кострика = костра́.
костыль crutch. ["морская пенка".
кость 1. anat: bone, os; 2. zool see
~ запястья anat: carpal bone.
~ лица facial bone.
~ предплюсны tarsal bone.
~ таза pelvic bone.
~ черепа cranial bone.
костяк anat: skeleton.
костянка 1. zool: centipede Lithobius forficatus; 2. bot: see косточковый плод.
костяной bony, of bone, osseous.
костяночка bot: drupelet.
косуля zool: roe deer, fawn (Capreolus capreolus).
~ -самец roebuck.
косынка surg: triangular bandage cravat.
косяк ichth: shoal, swarm.
кот zool: male cat. Cf. кошка.
котёнок kitten.
котик zool: 1. small cat; 2. fur seal (Callorhynus ursinus).
~ морской = котик 2.
котики = клевер пашенный.
котиковый мех seal fur.
~ промысел seal fisheries.
котилозавры zool: Cotylosauria (Extinct reptiles).
котиться zool: to give birth (of a cat, ewe), lamb.
котная овца zool: pregnant sheep.
котность zool: pregnancy (of a cat, ewe).
коточки = кровохлёбка маленькая.
котята pl. of котёнок.
кофактор cofactor.
кофеин pharm: caffeine.
кофеинизм caffeinism.
кофейная ягода bot: coffee berry.
кофейное дерево bot: coffee tree (Coffea arabica).
кофермент coferment.
кохия bot: burning bush (Kochia, Roth).
~ веникоподобная summer cypress, belvedere (K. scoparia).
~ песчаная mock cypress (K. arenaria).
кохлеарная часть уха anat: cochlear portion of the ear.

коховский аппарат bact: steam sterilizer.
кочан капусты bot: cabbage head.
кочевая крыса zool: brown rat (Mus decumanus); see also крыса пасюк.
кочедыжник bot: lady fern (Aspidium filix femina).
~ чёрный black spleenwort (Asplenium adiantum-nigrum).
кочень entom: saddle.
кочерыга капусты bot: cabbage stump, heart of a cabbage head, cabbage stump, runt.
кочерыжка = кочерыга.
кочешок брюссельской капусты bot: bud of Brussels sprouts.
кошачий хорёк cat squirrel (Bassaria astuta).
кошачье мурлыканье int: cat's purr, purring, thrill.
кошачья двуустка zool: cat's distome (Opisthorchis felineus).
~ змея zool: snake Tarbophis.
~ лапка bot: pussy's toes, ladies' tobacco, everlasting (Antennaria).
~ ~ подорожниколистная rabbit tobacco (A. plantaginifolia).
кошельки bot: lady's slippers (Calceolaria).
~ русалок = яйца акул и скатов.
кошениль entom: cochineal, shield louse, wax scale (Coccus cacti).
кошка zool: cat (Felis); female cat.
~ домашняя domestic cat (Felis domesticus).
~ тигровая marguay (F. tigrina).
кошки (сем.) zool: cats (Felidae).
кошмар psych: nightmare, incubus.
коэнзим coenzyme.
коэффициент аппетита appetite quotient (rats, etc.)
~ давления pressure ratio.
краб zool: crab.
~ вскоре после линьки paper-shell crab.
~ каменный stone c. (Cancer pagurus).
~ камчатский Kamchatka c. (Paralithodes camtschatica).
~ перед линькой peeler.
~ -плавунец swimming crab, fiddler crab (Portunidae).
~ порцелляна porcellan crab (Porcellana).
*~ разбойник crab Birgus latro.
~ речной river crab (Telphus intermedia).
~ с икрой crab in berry.
~ ~ кожистым панцырем buckram.
~ ~ твёрдым панцырем hard crab.

краб северный Brit: stone crab (Lithodes).

~ японский гигантский Japanese giant c. (Macrocheira koempferi).

кравчик entom: beetle Lethrus.

краевая пластика surg: marginoplasty.

краевое положение marginal position.

~ стояние margination.

~ щупальце zool: marginal tentacle.

краевой marginal, limbic.

~ цветок bot: marginal flower, ray f.

край грудины anat: sternal margin, sternal border.

~ десен anat: gum margin.

~ печени anat: liver edge.

~ раны surg: lip.

крайняя плоть клитора anat: prepuce of the clitoris.

~ ~ члена anat: prepuce, foreskin of the penis.

крамерия bot: krameria (Krameria triandra, Ruiz. et Pav.)

кран faucet, stopcock, valve.

краниотабес path: craniotabes, soft occiput.

краниотомия surg: craniotomy.

крапива bot: nettle (Urtica).

~ водяная = роголистник.

~ глухая dead n. (Lamium), see яснотка

~ двудомная common n., stinging n. (U. dioica).

~ жгучая burning n., dog n. (U. urens).

~ китайская false n., ramie, green-leaved China grass (Boehmeria nivea).

крапивная лихорадка = крапивница.

крапивник orn: wren (Troglodytidae, etc)

крапивница hives, nettle rash, urticaria.

крапивные (сем.) bot: nettle family (Urticaceae).

крапивный bot: urticaceous.

~ лишай ped: red gum, gum rash, strophulus.

крапивоцветные (пор.) bot: Urticales.

краппи ichth: crappie (Pomoxis).

крапчатость bot: mottle, mottling.

~ листьев огурцов phytp: cucumber leaf blotch.

крапчатые семена bot: mottled seeds.

крапчатый speckled, blotched, mottled.

красавка see 1. bot белладонна; 2. orn: малый журавль.

краска stain, paint.

красная = нерка.

~ гниль phytp: red rot.

~ лакмусовая бумага chem: red litmus paper.

~ пелена av med: redout, "redding out".

~ сельдь (копчёная) red herring (smoked).

красная сердцевинная гниль phytp: firm red heart.

красноватый bot: reddish (rufus).

красноголовый redhead.

~ воробей orn: tree sparrow (Passer montanus).

красноднев bot: common orange, day lily (Hemerocallis fulva).

красное дерево = свиетения.

~ ядро anat: nucleus ruber.

краснозёрный bot: red-grained.

красноклювый гусь = русский г.

краснокрыл = фламинго.

краснопёр ichth: Pseudaspius.

~ монгольский Erythroculter mongolicus.

краснопёрка ichth: rudd (Scardinius erythrophthalmus).

~ дальневосточная Far-East rudd (Leuciscus brandti).

краснотел большой searcher, ground beetle (Calosoma sycophanta).

~ пахучий = к. большой.

краснотелка = клещ краснотелка.

краснохвост(ка) entom: tussock-moth (Dasychira, fam. Orgyidae).

~ буковая entom: pale tussock-moth (Dasychira pudibunda).

~ садовая = горихвостка с.

красношейная поганка orn: horned grebe (Colymbus auritus).

краснуха 1. infect: German measles, rubella, rötheln; 2. phytp: red rot.

красные водоросли bot: red algae (Rhodophyta).

красный гриб = подосиновик.

~ зверь red beast; deer.

~ коралл zool; red coral (Corallium rubrum).

~ кровяной шарик red blood cell.

красовласка bot: water starwort, w. chickweed (Callitriche).

~ весенняя water starwort (C. vernalis).

красовласковые (сем.) bot: water-starwort family (Callitrichaceae).

красоля = настурция садовая.

красотел = краснотел.

красотка = стрекоза-красотка.

красун = жук-красун.

красящее вещество крови hemochrome.

кратковременный short-time, short-duration, transitory, fleeting.

кратная проба раствора aliquot.

крахмал starch, amylum.

крахмал в моче path: amyluria.
~ из кассавы arrowroot.
крахмаловидный starchlike, amylaceous.
крахмалообразовательный starch-forming, amylogenic. [bandage.
крахмальная повязка surg: starch-
крахмальное зерно starch granule.
крахмальный starchy, amylaceous.
крачка orn: tern (Sterna, Chlidonias); Brit: terrick, tarrock, tirrock.
~ болотная sooty tern (Sterna fuscata).
~ обыкновенная common tern (Sterna h. hirundo).
крачки orn: terns (Sternidae).
креатин creatine.
креатинин creatinine.
креветка zool: 1. prawn, shrimplike animal (Crangon, Palaemon, Leander, Hyppolite, etc.); 2. Crevettina, Amphipoda.
~ обыкновенная zool: shrimp (Crangon crangon).
~ -огнемёт scarlet shrimp, flammenwerfer s. (Acanthephyra purpurea).
креветочный attr: prawn, shrimp.
крезол pharm: cresylic acid.
кремартартарный осадок beeswing, gauzy film (in old wine).
кремастер entom: cremaster.
крематорий san: crematory.
кремация san: cremation.
кремировать san: cremate. [spicule.
кремнеземовая игла zool: silicious
кремнероговые губки (отр.) zool: horny sponges (Cornacuspongida, Keratosa). сли
кремнеземки = диатомовые водоро-
кремний silicium, Si.
кремотартар pharm: cream of tartar.
креодонты zool: Creodontia (extinct).
креозол creosol.
креозотиновокислый натрий pharm: sodium cresylate.
крепитантный crepitant.
крепитация crepitatio, crepitation, crepitus (crackling, noise).
крепитирующий хрип crepitant rale, crackle.
крепкого телосложения strongly built.
кресло Барани av med: Barani chair.
~ для исследования examination chair.
~ ~ сердечных больных heart chair.
кресс = жеруха.
~ водяной = ж. аптечная.
~ -гулявник = ж. аптечная.

~ луговой = сердечник луговой.
крестец anat: sacrum; zool: rump-bone.
крестовичка вредная entom: locust Dociostaurus kraussi nigrogeniculatus.
~ малая D. brevicollis.
~ пегая Notostaurus albicornis.
крестовки zool: Pelodytes (frogs).
крестовник bot: groundsel, ragwort, squaw-weed (Senecio). [ronicum).
~ дороникoвый leopard's bane (S. do-
~ лесной mountain groundsel (S. sylvaticus). [latus, Schz.)
~ членистый candle plant (S. articu-
крестовница bot: crosswort (Crucianella).
крестоносец = жук-крестоносец.
крестообразная связка anat: crucial ligament. [cruris.
~ ~ голени anat: ligamentum cruciatum
крестообразное расположение частей bot: decussation of parts (of a flower). [incision.
крестообразный разрез surg: crucial
крестоцветное bot: cruciferous, crucifera, crucial.
крестоцветные (сем.) bot: mustard family (Cruciferae). [artery.
крестцовая артерия anat: sacral
~ впадина anat: hollow of the sacrum.
~ кость anat: sacral bone.
крестцовобугровая связка anat: great sacrosciatic ligament. sacrum.
крестцовое крыло anat: wing of the
~ отверстие anat: sacral foramen, hiatus sacralis. plexus.
~ сплетение anat: sacriplex, sacral
крестцовокопчиковая мышца anat: sacrococcygeus. [coccygeal.
крестцовокопчиковый anat: sacro-
крестцовоматочная связка anat: uterosacral ligament.
крестцовоостистая мышца anat: sacrospinalis muscle.
крестцовоподвздошное сочленение anat: sacroiliac articulation. [tic.
крестцовоседалищный anat: sacroscia-
крестцовые позвонки anat: sacral vertebrae, vertebrae sacrales.
крестцовый гребень anat: sacral promontory, crista sacralis.
~ канал anat: sacral canal, canalis sacralis.
~ рожок anat: sacral horn.
кретин psych: cretin (he).
кретинизм cretinism.

кретинический cretinous.
кретинка cretin (she).
кретиноидный cretinoid.
Креφорд Crawford.
кречет orn: merlin, pigeon hawk (Falco columbarius).
кривая выживания survival curve.
~ доза-эффект rad: dose-effect curve.
~ кровяного давления blood-pressure curve.
~ насыщения saturation curve.
~ пульса pulse curve.
кривоголовка двенадцатиперстная helm: hookworm Ancylostoma duodenale.
кривошея path: wryneck, torticollis.
кризис crisis.
~ (болезни) crisis, apostasis.
кризы crises.
крик shouting, scream.
крилл (эуфаусииды) krill.
криноида zool: crinoid.
криоглобулин cryoglobulin.
криоглобулинемия cryoglobulinaemia.
крипингдизиз derm: creeping eruption.
крипта anat: crypt.
~ миндалины anat: tonsillar crypt.
криптакантодес ghostfish (Cryptacanthodes).
криптолемус entom: predacious beetle Cryptolaemus montrouzieri.
криптомонады (отр.) zool: Cryptomonadina.
кристаллизационная вода chem: water of crystallization.
кристаллизовать(ся) crystallize.
кристаллоза pharm: sodium saccharinate.
кристаллы мочекислого аммония urol: hedgehog crystals.
критидиальная форма zool: Crithidia form.
критическая частота мельканий flicker critical frequency.
~ ~ слияния flicker critical frequency.
критический critical.
критическое состояние critical condition, emergency.
кровавая мокрота int: hemoptysis.
~ моча bloody urine, hematuria.
~ рвота vomiting of blood, hematemesis.
кровавое пятно petechia.
кровавый волдырь derm: blood blister.
~ индеец blood Indian.
~ понос path: bloody flux.
кровать (для вытяжения) при переломе surg: fracture bed.
крове- hemato-, blood-.
кровеносное кольцо zool: blood-vascular ring (in echinoderms).
кровеносный blood-carrying, sanguiferous.
~ путь blood channel.
~ сосуд anat: blood vessel.
~ ~ кожи cutaneous blood vessel.
кровеостанавливающий hemastatic, styptic.
~ коллодий pharm: styptic collodion.
кроверодный hematic, hematogenous.
кроветворение hematosis, hematogenesis, blood formation, sanguification.
кроветворная ткань hist: hematopoietic tissue.
кроветворное средство hematonic, blood tonic.
кроветворные органы physl: hematogenic organs, blood-forming organs.
кроветворный blood-forming, blood-producing, hematopoietic, hematogenic.
кровное родство consanguinity, blood relationship.
кровнородственный consanguineous.
кровозаменитель blood substitute.
кровоизвлечение = кровопускание.
кровоизлияние blood effusion, blood extravasation, hemorrhage, apoplexy.
~ в варолиев мост pontine hemorrhage.
~ ~ закрытую полость hematocele.
~ ~ мозг cerebral hemorrhage.
~ ~ полость плевры int: hemothorax.
~ ~ почку renal apoplexy.
~ ~ сетчатку ophth: retinal apoplexy.
~ ~ стекловидное тело ophth: vitreous haemorrhage.
кровообразование = кроветворение.
кровообращение blood circulation.
~ в печени hepatic circulation.
~ плода embr: fetal circulation.
кровоостанавливающая перевязка surg: perstriction.
кровоостанавливающее средство hemostatic, antihemorrhagic.
кровоостанавливающий пинцет surg: hemostatic forceps, hemostat.
кровоподтек path: bloodshot, suggillation, ecchymosis.
~ глаза suggillation, eye ecchymosis, eye suffusion.
кровопотеря loss of blood, bleeding.
кровопускание surg: bloodletting, phlebotomy, venesection, bleeding.
кровоснабжение blood supply.
кровососка = муха-кровососка.
~ овечья entom: sheep tick, ked (Melophagus ovinus).

кровососки (сем.) entom: louse-flies (Hippoboscidae).
кровососная банка wet cup, see банка 2.
кровососный blood-sucking, sanguivorous.
кровососущее животное blood-sucker.
кровососущий blood-sucking.
кровотечение bleeding, hemorrhage, passage of blood.
~ в родах obstet: intrapartum hemorrhage.
~ из влагалища gyn: vaginal h.
~ ~ носа nosebleed, epistaxis.
кровоток blood flow, bloodstream.
кровоточивость path: bleeding -sickness, hemophilia.
кровоточить bleed.
кровохаркание path: blood spitting, bloody expectoration, hemoptysis.
кровохлёбка bot: burnet (Sanguisorba).
~ лекарственная burnet - bloodwort (S. officinalis).
~ маленькая garden burnet (S. minor).
кровь blood.
кровяная двуустка zool: blood fluke.
~ клетка hist: blood cell.
~ плазма blood plasma.
~ пластинка blood platelet, thrombocyte.
~ сыворотка blood serum.
кровянисто-гнойный pyemic.
кровяное давление blood pressure.
~ депо blood depot.
~ молоко vet: bloody milk.
~ пятно blood stain.
~ тельце hist: blood corpuscle, b. cell.
~ русло physl: blood channel.
кровяной hematic, sanguineous.
~ агар bact: blood agar.
~ занос obstet: blood mole.
~ островок embr: blood island.
~ сгусток blood clot; thromb.
~ шарик blood cell.
кровянокапельный blood-drip.
кровяные споровики (отр.) zool: Haemosporidia.
крокодил zool: crocodile (Crocodilia).
крокодиловый crocodilian.
крокодилы zool: crocodiles (Crocodilia).
крокус bot: crocus (Crocus).
кролик zool: domestic rabbit (Lepus cuniculus).
~ пуховой ангорский Angora rabbit (Lepus cuniculus angorensis).
кролиководство rabbit breeding.
крольчата pl. of крольчёнок.
крольчёнок young rabbit.

крона zool: corona (of a rotifer).
~ дерева bot: limb of a tree, top.
кронистая верхушка bot: bushy top (of a tree).
кроншнеп orn: curlew, whaup, whimbrel (Phaeopus phaeopus).
кроссинговер genet: crossing over.
кроссовер genet: crossover.
крот zool: mole, molewarp (Talpa europea).
кроталин imm: crotaline.
кроталярия bot: rattlebox (Crotalaria).
~ стреловидная rattlewort (C. sagittalis).
кротовик bot: nepenthe (Nepenthes).
кротоновое дерево bot: purging croton (Croton tiglium).
кроты (сем.) zool: moles (Talpidae).
кроукер ichth: croaker.
крохаль orn: merganser, smew (Mergus, Lophodytes, etc.); see also нырковая утка.
~ хохлатый hooded merganser (Lophodytes cucullatus).
крошащийся friable.
крошка свекловичная entom: beetle Atomaria linearis.
кроющее перо orn: covert.
кроющие перья крыла = большие кроющие перья крыла.
~ ~ надхвостья orn: tail coverts.
~ ~ хвоста orn: tail coverts.
кроющий лист bot: scale leaf.
~ ~ почки bot: budscale, cataphyllary leaf.
круг Вилизия anat: circle of Willis.
~ кровообращения circulatory system.
~ тычинок bot: whorl of stamens.
круглая грудь path: round chest.
~ мышца (большая, малая) anat: teres (major, minor) muscle.
~ связка anat: round ligament.
~ ~ бедра anat: round ligament of hip.
~ ~ печени anat: ligamentum teres hepatis, round ligament of liver.
круглоголовки zool: Phrynocephalus (lizards).
круглоголовый кит zool: black whale, blackfish (Globiocephalus melas).
круглое окно anat: round window fenestra rotunda.
~ отверстие anat: foramen rotundum.
круглозадый zool: roundbacked.
круглозубчатый bot: crenate.
круглоклеточная инфильтрация path: round cell infiltration.

круглоклеточный hist: round-celled, globocellular.

круглолистый bot: round-leaved (rotundifolius).

круглопёрые (сем.) ichth: lumpfishes (Cyclopteridae).

круглоплодный bot: round-fruited, cyclocarpus.

круглоресничные (отр.) zool: Peritricha.

круглоротое zool: cyclostome (Cyclostomata).

круглоротые (кл.) cyclostomes (Cyclostomata).

круглоротый adj: cyclostomatous.

круглошовные мухи entom: circular-seamed flies (Cyclorrhapha).

~ ~ без лобного пузырька circular-seamed flies without a frontal suture (Aschiza).

~ ~ с лобным пузырьком circular-seamed flies with a frontal suture (Schizophora).

круглые глисты (кл.) zool: nematodes (Nematodes), see нематоды.

~ черви (кл.) zool: roundworms, nematodes (Nematoda).

~ ~ (тип) zool: Nemathelminthes.

круглый лист bot: orbicular leaf.

~ червь roundworm (Nemathelminthes); cabbage worm, c. snake (Mermithidae).

круговая мышца глаза anat: orbicularis oculi, o. palpebrarum muscle.

~ ~ зрачка sphincter pupillae.

~ ~ рта anat: orbicularis oris muscle.

круговорот ниацина niacin cycle.

кругожаберные zool: mollusks Patella, etc.

кругообразный circinate.

кругообращение circulation.

круп zool: croup.

крупка bot: whitlow grass (Draba).

крупная рыба coarse fish.

~ саламандра zool: large salamander, mud puppy.

~ форель bull trout (Salmo).

~ чукучановая рыба buffalo fish (Catostomidae).

крупногрудая mastous.

крупнозубый megadont, macrodont.

*крупнолистый bot: large-leaved (macrofolius).

крупноплодный bot: large-fruited (macrocarpon).

крупнопузырчатые хрипы large-bubbling rales.

крупносемянный bot: large-grain(ed).

крупностебельная трава bot: reed.

крупноцветный bot: large-blossom, large-flowered (grandiflorus).

крупноягодный bot: large-berried.

крупноячейный large-meshed.

крупный морской окунь ichth: giant black sea bass, jewfish, warsaw (Epinephelus, Stereolepis); green head, squid hound (Roccus lineatus).

~ рогатый скот bovine animals, black cattle.

крупозное воспаление лёгких croupous pneumonia, lobar p., fibrinous p.

крутик = индиго ложное.

кручёны панычи = ипомея.

кручёный шёлк surg: twisted silk.

крушень-древоточец entom: goat moth (Cossus ligniperda).

крушина bot: buckthorn (Rhamnus).

~ вечнозелёная lauristine (Viburnum tinus).

~ зазубренная arrowwood (V. dentatum).

~ каролинская Carolina buckthorn, Indian cherry (Rhamnus caroliniana).

~ ломкая alder buckthorn (Rhamnus frangula).

~ слабительная common buckthorn, purging b. (R. cathartica).

крушинник = крушина.

крушинные = крушиновые.

крушиновые (сем.) bot: buckthorn family (Rhamnaceae).

крушиноцветные (пор.) bot: Rhamnales.

крыжовник bot: gooseberry (Grossularia)

крыжовниковые (сем.) bot: gooseberry family (Grossulariaceae).

крыланы = плодоядные летучие мыши.

крылатка 1. bot: samara, key fruit, winged f. 2. zool: see полосатый тюлень.

крылатые насекомые (подкл.) entom: winged insects (Pterygota).

крылатый winged; bot: pinnate, pennate, penned.

крыло zool: wing; ala (of a roundworm).

крыловая пластинка entom: wing membrane.

~ чешуйка entom: squama.

крыловидная кость zool: pterygoid.

~ мышца (внутренняя, наружная) anat: pterygoideus (internus, externus)

~ связка anat: alar odontoid ligament.

крыловидный канал anat: pterygoid canal.

~ отросток anat: pterygoid process.

крыловой четырёхугольник entom: wing quadrangle.

крылонёбная ямка anat: fossa pterygopalatina.

крылоногий моллюск zool: pteropod, flying snail.

крылышко entom orn: alula, bastard wing.

крылья носа anat: alae nasi.
крыса zool: rat (Rattus).
~ пасюк Norway rat (R. norvegicus).[lis)
крыска entom: rat-tailed maggot (Erista-
крыша черепа anat: skull cap, calvaria,
крышечка = крышка. calvarium.
крышка lid, opercle, operculum.
крэб bot: crab apple (Pyrus malus).
крючковатая кость запястья anat: hamate bone, unciform b. ceps.
крючковатые щипцы surg: volsella for-
крючковатый adunc(ate), uncinate, hooked, hamated, hamular, grappling.
~ пинцет surg: hook forceps.[unciform b
крючковидная кость anat: hamate bone,
крючковидный hamiform, hamate, uncinate.
крючок hook; surg: tenaculum, retractor.
~ для косоглазия ophth: squint hook.
~ крючковатой кости anat: hooklike process, hamulus.
~ сводчатой извилины мозга anat: uncinate gyrus, uncus.
кряж дерева bot: wood trunk.
кряканье утки quack of a duck.
кряква orn: mallard, wild duck (Anas platyrhynchos).
ксантеллы xantellae.
ксантин pharm: xanthine.
ксантопсия ophth: xanthopsia, yellow
ксантофилл xanthophyll. vision.
~ ракообразных astaxantin.
ксантофильный xanthophyllic.
ксантофор xanthophore.
ксантохромия derm: xanthochromia.
ксения genet: xenia.
ксеногамия bio: xenogamy.
ксеродерма xeroderm(i)a.
ксероз path: xerosis, asteatosis.
~ конъюнктивы ophth: xerosis conjunctivae, xerophthalmia.
ксеротермический xerothermic.
ксерофит bot: xerophyte, xerophilous
ксерофитный bot: xerophytic. plant.
ксилема bot: core, xylem.
ксиридациевые (сем.) bot: yellow-eyed grass family (Xyridaceae).
ксирис bot: yellow-eyed grass (Xyris).
ксистереурис ichth: long-finned flounder (Xystereurys liolepis).
ксифидиоцеркарий helm: xiphidiocerca-
ктенидий entom: ctenidium. ria.
ктеногобиус ichth: scallop-fish (Ctenogobius stigmaticus).
ктеноидный ichth: ctenoid.

ктеноплана zool: crawling ctenophore Ctenoplana kowalewskii.
ктенофора = гребневики.
ктыри (сем.) entom: robber-flies (Asilidae).
кубаревидный turbinate.
кубатура space, cubic meters.
кубитальная жилка entom: cubital vein, cubitus.
кубитус entom: cubitus. [epithelium.
кубический эпителий hist: cuboidal
кубовидная кость anat: cuboid bone, os cuboideum.
кубок Нептуна zool: Neptune's goblet (Poterion neptuni).
кубышка 1. entom: locust clutch, egg-sac; 2. bot: yellow pond-lily, cow-lily, spatter-dock, (Nuphar, Sm.)
~ жёлтая yellow p.-l. (N. luteum, Sm.)
кувшинка bot: water-lily, water-nymph (Nymphaea).
~ ароматная fragrant water-lily, pond-lily, sweet white water-lily; Brit: sweet-scented w.-l. (N. odorata, Ait.)
~ белая white water lily (N. alba).
~ голубая = лотос голубой.
~ душистая = к. ароматная.
~ чистобелая water-lily (N. candida).
кувшинковое растение bot: nymphaeaceous plant.
кувшинковые (сем.) bot: water-lily family (Nymphaeaceae).
"кувшинчатое растение" = крото-
кувшинчатый bot: urceolate. вик.
кугуар zool: cougar, puma, mountain lion, silver lion (Felis concolor).
кудахтанье = клохтанье.
кудахтать = клохтать.[canus crispus.
кудрявый пеликан orn: pelican Pele-
кузнечик entom: long-horned grasshopper (Tettigonia). [T. caudata).
~ зелёный green g. (T. viridissima,
~ рисовый rice leaf hopper (Nephotettix bipunctatus).
~ серый gray g. (Decticus verrucivorus)
кузнечики (сем.) entom: long-horned grasshoppers (Tettigonidae).
кузнечиковые (надсем., подотр.) l.-h. grasshoppers (Tettigonioidea).
кузовок 1. ichth: trunkfish, horn t., spotted t., shellfish, boxfish, cuckold (Ostracion); 2. bot: cyathium.
кузька = жук-кузька.
кузьмичёва трава = эфедра.
кукельван = рыболовная ягода.

куклородный entom: pupiparous. caseworm
куколка entom: pupa, chrysalis, nymph,
~ шелковичного червя silkworm chrysalis.
куколкообразный entom: pupiform.
куколочный entom: pupal.
куколь bot: corn cockle (Agrostemma).
~ обыкновенный purple cockle (A. githago).
~ посевной lychnis (Lychnis githago).
кукурбитин cucurbitin.
кукуруза bot: Indian corn, maize (Zea mays).
~ лопающаяся = к. разрывная.
~ разрывная popcorn (Z. m. everta).
~ сахарная sweet corn.
кукурузный зерноед entom: seed-corn maggot (Calandra granaria, Pegomyia fusciceps)
~ червь entom: corn borer, see мотылёк кукурузный.
кукушечная трава = дриада восьмилепестковая.
кукушка orn: cuckoo.
~ обыкновенная common cuckoo (Cuculus canorus).
кукушки (сем.) orn: cuckoos (Cuculidae)
кукушкин лён bot: common hair-cup moss, goldilocks (Polytrichum commune).
~ цвет = дрёма.
кукушкины слёзки = ятрышник.
кукушонок orn: young cuchoo, cuckoo chick.
кулан = джигетай.
Кули Cooley.
кулига (птиц) bevy (of birds), flock.
кулик orn: sandpiper (Limosa, Actitis).
~ болотный ringneck (L. melanura).
~ -сорока oyster catcher (Haematopus).
кулики orn: sandpipers, limicolines (Limicolae).
кулия ichth: band-tailed sea-perch (Kuhlia taeniura).
кульбаба bot: hawkbit, milk gowan (Leontodon).
~ осенняя fall dandelion, "arnica", August flower (L. autumnalis).
культивирование cultivation.
культивировать cultivate.
культура culture.
~ из одной клетки bact: single cell culture.
~ под открытым небом outdoor culture.
~ ткани tissue culture.
культурная среда mcbio: cultural medium.
культя surg: stump.
~ бедра thigh stump.
~ пуповины obstet: stump of cord.
~ шейки матки gyn: cervical stump.
куманика bot: berry Rubus fruticosus.
кумват bot: kumquat (Citrus fortunella, Swingle).
кумжа ichth: salmon trout (Salmo trutta trutta).
кумулятивная доза rad: cumulative dose.
кумулятивное действие cumulative action, c. effect.
кумуляция cumulation.
кунджа ichth: trout Salvenius leucomaenis.
кунеус entom: cuneus.
кунжут = сезам.
кунжутное масло pharm: sesame oil, benne o.
куница zool: marten, sable.
~ благородная pine m. (Mustela martes).
~ древесная = к. благородная.
~ лесная = к. благородная.
~ настоящая = куница.
куницы (сем.) zool: musteline family (Mustelidae).
кунция плодовая bot: kunzia (Kunzea pomifera, F. Muell.)
куньи (сем.) = куницы (сем.)
кунья акула ichth: smooth dogfish, tope (Mustelus mustelus).
купа деревьев bunch of trees.
купава bot: globeflower, trollius (Trollius).
~ азиатская T. asiaticus, Meyers.
~ европейская T. europaeus.
купавка = купава.
купальница = купава.
купальный костюм bathing suit.
купальня bathing establishment.
купанье bathing; swimming.
купать bathe.
купаться bathe (oneself).
купировать stop, cup off, cut short.
купырь bot: chervil (Anthriscus, Bernh.)
курай = солянка.
кураре pharm: curare.
куратор med: intern observing the patient.
курация observation, care.
курганчик mound (anthill, etc.)
курение smoking.
курильщик smoker.
куриная грудь path: chicken breast, pigeon b.
~ слепота path: night blindness, nocturnal b., nyctalopia, nyctotyphlosis.
~ чума fowl plague.
куриные orn: gallinaceans (Galli, Galliformes)
куриный adj orn: gallinaceous.
~ зародыш chick embryo.
курица hen (Gallus domesticus).
куркума = имбирь жёлтый.
куроводческое хозяйство agr: chicken farm, poultry farm.
куропатка orn: partridge (Perdix perdix).
~ белая willow ptarmigan (Lagopus albus).

куропатка красная orn: red-legged partridge (Alectoris, Caccabis rufa).
~ тундровая common ptarmigan (Lagopus mutus).
~ шотландская red grouse (L. scoticus).
курорт health resort. [cian.
курортный врач health-resort physi-
курослеп = калужница болотная.
курочка orn: young hen, pullet.
~ водяная = камышница.
~ горная Caccabis.
курс course.
~ лечения course of treatment.
курсант mil: cadet. [school.
курсы медсестёр nurses' training
~ усовершенствования врачей post-graduate medical courses (or school).
курчавить(ся) curl. [feature.
курчавость верхушки phytp: curly top
~ листьев phytp: leaf curl.
~ ~ персика phytp: peach leaf curl (Exoascus deformans).
курчавый bot: curled (crispus). [gy.
кусание ногтей nail biting, anychopha
кускус zool: marsupial of Phalangerinae
кускута = повилика. group.
*кусочки льда crackled ice.
куст bot: bush, shrub.
~ земляники strawberry plant.
кустарник bot: brush, shrubs, shrubbery, frutex, underbrush.
кустарниковая собака zool: bush dog (Icticyon venaticus). tescent.
кустарниковидный bot: shrub-like, fru-
кустарниковый bot: bushy, brushy, shrubby, frutescent, fruticose (frutex).
кустистость bot: bushiness, shrubbiness frutescence.
кустистый лишайник bot: bushy lichen.
куститься bot: form a shrub, tiller.
кустящееся растение tillered plant.
кутикула cuticle, cuticula.
кутикулярная транспирация cuticular transpiration.
кутинизировать cutinize.
кутора = землеройка водяная.
кутра bot: dogbane, apocynum.
кутровые (сем.) bot: dogbane family
кутум ichth: roach Rutilus frisii kutum.
кухня для питательных сред bact: media kitchen. [(Apocynaceae).
куцый bobtailed.
кучелява = чилибуха.
кучка small heap, mound; zool: cast (of excretions of a worm).

Кушинг Cushing.
кущение tillering (of grasses, etc.);
кюретка gyn: curet. top growth.

Л

лабазник bot: Filipendula, Mill.
~ вязолистный queen-of-the-meadow (F. ulmaria, Max.)
~ обнажённый meadowsweet (F.denudata).
~ шестилепестный dropwort (F. hexapetala, Gilib.)
лабильность lability.
лабильный labile. [abile.
~ при низкой температуре frigol-
лабиринт labyrinth.
лабиринтный labyrinthine. [toiformes.
*лабиринтовые (отр.) ichth: Anabon-
лабиринтодонтиа zool: Labyrinthodontia (extinct amphibians).
лаблаб = боб индийский.
лаборант laboratory technician.
лаборатория laboratory.
лабораторный диагноз laboratory
~ отчёт laboratory report. |diagnosis.
~ служитель laboratory attendant.
лаванда bot: lavender (Lavandula spica
~ аптечная spike (L. vera). |vera, DC.)
~ морская = статица. [vender.
лавандовое масло pharm: oil of la-
лаватера = хатьма. [nobilis).
лавр bot: laurel, bay-tree (Laurus
~ американский sassafras (Sassafras).
~ благородный = лавр.
~ горный = л. калифорнийский.
~ калифорнийский California laurel (Umbellularia californica).
лаврак ichth: Morone.
лавровая ягода bot: bayberry. [water.
лавровишнёвая вода pharm: laurel
лавровишня bot: laurel cherry, bay c. (Prunus laurocerasus).
лавровое дерево = лавр. [(Lauraceae)
лавровые (сем.) bot: laurel family
лавролистный bot: laurel-leaved, lauri-
лаврушка = волчеягодник. |folius.
Лавуазье Lavoisier.
лагенария = тыква бутылочная.
лагерный тиф camp fever, typhus.
лагофтальм ophth: lagophthalmos, hare
лагофтальмический lagophthlmic. | eye.

ладанник bot: labdanum (Cistus creticus, C. ladaniferus).
ладанниковые (сем.) bot: rockrose fam. (Cistaceae).
ладо́нная артерия пальцев, общая anat: common volar digital artery.
~ дуга anat: palmar arch.
~ мышца (длинная, короткая) anat: palmaris (longus, brevis).
ладо́нный апоневроз anat: palmar aponeurosis.
ладонь anat: palm, vola.
ладьевидная кость запястья anat: navicular bone of hand, scaphoid b. of hand.
~ кость стопы anat: navicular bone of foot, scaphoid of f., os naviculare pedis.
~ чешуйка bot: keeled lemma.
ладьевидный boatshaped, navicular, scaphoid, cymbiform, keeled.
ладьеобразная ямка anat: fossa navicularis.
ладьеобразный = ладьевидный.
~ живот path: boatshaped abdomen, boatbelly.
лазарет = госпиталь.
лазающее растение bot: climbing plant.
лазающий bio: climbing, scansorial.
лайка = упряжная собака.
лайм bot: lime (Cytrus aurantifolia).
лакедра ichth: jackfish (Seriola); rudder fish, amber f., shark's pilot, kahala.
лакмус litmus.
~ красильный Croton tinctorium.
лакмусовая бумага litmus paper.
лакмусовое молоко bact: litmus milk.
лаковая кровь laky blood.
лаковое дерево bot: 1. Japanese varnish tree, lacquer tree (Rhus vernicifera, DC.); 2. Belgium walnut (Aleurites mollucana, Willd, A. triloba, Forst.)
лаковый hem: lake-colored.
лаконоска bot: pokeweed (Phytolacca).
~ американская poke, scoke, garget, pigeonberry (P. americana).
лаконосные (сем.) bot: pokeweed family (Phytolaccaceae).
лакрица pharm: licorice.
лакричник обыкновенный bot: licorice, liquorice (Glycyrrhiza glabra).
лакричный порошок parm: licorice powder.
лактальбумин milk albumin.
лактариус bot: Lactarius mushrooms.
лактационный lactational.
лактация lactation.
лактобацилла lactobacillus.
лактоза = молочный сахар.
лактол pharm: betanaphtol lactate.
лактометр lab: lactometer, milk tester.
лакуна anat: lacuna.
лакунарное расстройство памяти psych: lacunar derangement of memory, "islets of memory".
~ слабоумие psych: lacunar dementia.
лакунарный anat: lacunal, lacunar(y).
лакунный = лакунарный.
лакфиоль = желтофиоль.
лалофобия neur: stutter spasm.
лама zool: llama (Lama).
ламантин zool: manate, sea cow (Trichechus, manatus).
ламаркизм Lamarkism.
ламбдовидный шов anat: lambdoid suture.
ламинариевые (пор.) bot: tangles (Laminariales) algae.
ламинариевый laminarian.
ламинарин chem: laminarin.
ламинария bot: tangle, kelp (Laminaria).
~ луковичная sea furbelow, furbelowed hangers (L. bulbosa).
~ пальчатая fan kelp, sea girdles, tangle, sea staff, sea wand (L.digitata).
~ сахарная sweet tangle, sea belt (L. saccharina).
Ланганс Langhans.
лангансов слой anat: layer of Langhans.
Ланге Lange.
Лангерганс Langerhans.
лангуст zool: sea crawfish (Palinurus); langouste, spiny lobster, thorny l.
ландкартовидные пятна на коже neur: meningitic streakes.
ландкартообразный язык path: geographical tongue, mappy t.
ландыш bot: lily of the valley (Convallaria majalis).
ланолин lanolin, wool fat, wool grease.
лантар-пальмира = сахарная пальма.
ланцет surg: lancet.
~ для кровопускания surg: lancet for phlebotomy.
~ ~ прививок vaccinostyle.
ланцетник zool: lancelet, amphioxus (Amphioxus lanceolatus).
ланцетный лист bot: lanceolate leaf.
ланцетовидная двуустка helm: lancet fluke (Dicrocoelium lanceatum).
ланцетовидный lanceolate.
лань zool: fallow deer (Dama dama).
лапа zool: paw.
лапаротомия surg: laparotomy.
лапка entom: leg, chela, tarsus.
лапчатка bot: five-finger, cinquefoil (Potentilla).
~ болотная march five-finger (P. palustris).
~ гусиная bot: silverweed (P. anserina).

лапчатка прямая bot: erect cinquefoil (P. erecta).
~ серебристая silvery cinquefoil (P. argentea).
~ стелющаяся P. supina.
~ -узик tormentil (P. tormentilla, Neck) see л. прямая.
лапчатоноги (отр.) orn: pinnatipeds (Heliornithes).
лапчатоногий zool: web-footed.
лапчатый = пальчатый, дланевидный.
лапша-рыба = саланкс.
ларвицид entom: larvicide.
ларга zool: common seal.
ларгин pharm: silver protalbin.
ларингоспазм path: laryngospasm.
ларингоцеле path: laryngocele.
лариофагус entom: Lariophagus distenguendus (Pteromalidae).
ласка zool: weasel (Mustela nivalis).
ласкавец = володушка круглолистная.
ласт zool: flipper, fin.
ластовень острый bot: mosquito plant (Cynanchum acutum).
ластовнёвые (сем.) bot: milkweed family (Asclepiadaceae).
ластоногие zool: pinnipeds (Pinnipedia)
ластоногое zool: pinniped(ian).
ласточка 1. orn: swallow; 2. ichth: fish of the Pomacentridae family.
~ городская orn: house martin, European m. (Chelidon urbica).
~ деревенская common swallow (Hirundo rustica).
~ краснобрюхая barn swallow (Chelidon erythrogaster, Hirundo rufula).
ласточки (сем.) orn: swallows (Hirundinidae).
ласточкино гнездо orn: martin house.
ласточниковые = ластовнёвые.
латекс bot: latex, milky sap.
латентный latent.
латерализация звука otolar: lateralization of the Weber test.
латеральная лодыжка anat: lateral malleolus.
латеральный зуб zool: lateral tooth.
~ пучок anat: lateral funiculus.
латимерия ichth: Latimeria.
латромерис entom: Latromeris senex (Trichogrammatidae).
латук = салат-латук.
~ ядовитый strong-scented lettuce (Lactuca virosa).
лауреров канал zool: Laurer's canal.
~ проток = л. канал.
лахсфорель = озерная форель.
лахтак = морской заяц 1.

лающий кашель barking cough, dog c.
лебеда bot: goosefoot, pigweed (Chenopodium); see марь.
~ белая pigweed, lamb's quarters (C. album).
~ душистая = л. мексиканская.
~ киноа kenwa, quinoa (C. quinoa).
~ мексиканская Mexican tea (C. ambrosioides).
~ морская sea purslane (Atriplex halimus).
~ садовая garden orach, mountain spinach (A. hortensis).
~ серобеловатая shad scale (A. canescens).
~ татарская frosted orach (A. Laciniata).
~ хеноа = л. киноа.
~ шпинатная = л. саловая, "гусиные лапки".
лебедовые (сем.) bot: goosefoot fam. (Chenopodiaceae).
лебедь orn: swan (Cygnus).
~ австралийский = л. чёрный.
~ -кликун whooper, wild s. (C. musicus)
~ новоголландский = л. чёрный.
~ чёрный black s. (Chenopsis atrata, Cygnus atratus).
лёботес ichth: triple-tail, flasher black perch (Lobotes surinamensis).
лев zool: lion (Felis leo).
левая ориентация left-handedness.
левейллула крымская phytp: fungus Leveillula taurica, Arnaut.)
левкадендрон bot: silver tree (Leucadendron argenteum, R. Br.)
левкой bot: stock, gilliflower (Matthiola, R. Br.)
~ двурогий gilliflower (M. bicornis).
~ душистый night-scented stock (M. odoratissima, R. Br.)
~ махровый true stock, common s. (M. incana).
~ простой = л. двурогий.
левкопис entom: Leucopis bona (Ochthiphilidae).
левое предсердие anat: atrium cordis sinistrum.
левозавёрнутый sinistral.
левозакрученность sinistrotorsion.
левозакрученный left-hand coiled.
леворукость sinistrality.
левый left, sinistral.
~ желудочек сердца anat: left venrticle of the heart.
левша sinistral, left-handed individual.
лёгкая лихорадка path: febricula.
~ пальпация light touch palpation.
~ травма minor injury.
лёгкий озноб path: perfrigeration.
легко переваривающий easily digesting, eupeptic.

легко переваримый easily digestible, eupeptic.
легковесное семя bot: lightweight [seed.
лёгкое 1. anat: lung; 2. light, easy.
~ конвульсивное движение neur: crispation.
~ слабительное pharm: aperient, laxative, mild purgative.
лёгочная альвеола anat: lung alveola, air cell, air sac, air vesicle.
~ артерия anat: pulmonary artery.
~ вена anat: pulmonary vein.
~ вентиляция ventilation of the lungs.
~ гипертония pulmonary hypertension.
~ двуустка helm: lung fluke, bronchial fluke (Distomum pulmonale).
~ доля anat: lung lobe.
~ каверна path: lung cavern.
~ трава = медунка.
~ трубка (или дудка) orn: lung tube.
~ улитка zool: lunged snail.
~ чахотка path: pulmonary consumption.
~ чума infect: pneumonic plague.
лёгочница bot: Lobaria lichens.
лёгочное кровотечение = кровохаркание.
~ поле x-ray: lung field.
~ сердце int: pulmonary heart.
лёгочные моллюски (подкл.) zool: fresh-water and land snails (Pulmonata).
лёгочный pulmonary; lunged, pulmonife- [rous.
~ камень path: pulmonary calculus.
~ объем lung volume.
~ эпителий pulmonary epithelium.
ледник ice cellar.
ледовитоморская минога zool: Arctic Ocean lamprey.
ледовитоморский of Arctic seas.
ледяной компресс ice poultice.
~ шкаф icebox.
лежать распростёртым lie flat.
лежачее положение lying attitude.
лежащий близко к основанию anat: subbasal.
~ ~ к середине admedial, admedian, [paramesial.
~ ~ от края submarginal, ectomarginal.
~ вне оси abaxial.
~ ~ скелета episkeletal.
~ внутри internal.
~ вокруг кисты pericystic.
~ ~ матки perihysteric.
~ ~ предсердия periatrial.
~ впереди варолиева моста prepon- tile.
~ ~ пузыря prevesical.
лежащий впереди ушной раковины preauricular.
~ выше колена supergenual.
~ кпереди от аорты preaortic.
~ ~ от верхней челюсти premaxilla- ry.
~ ~ от локтя antecubital.
~ ~ от прямой кишки prerectal.
~ ~ от ската мозжечка preclival.
~ ~ от спинной струны prochordal.
~ ~ от уха prootic.
~ лицом вниз prone, procumbent.
~ между мочеточниками interureteric.
~ над глазным яблоком epibulbar.
~ ~ мозолистым телом supercallo- sal.
~ ~ ребром epicostal.
~ на спине dorsicumbent.
~ ниже вертлужной впадины subacetabular.
~ ~ порога раздражения subliminal.
~ ничком = л. лицом вниз.
~ около середины submedial.
~ перед яичником preovarian.
~ под клювовидным отростком subcoracoid.
~ ~ мозолистым телом subcallosal.
~ ~ мягкой мозговой оболочкой subpial.
~ ~ первым шейным позвонком sub- [atloidean.
~ ~ печенью subhepatic.
~ ~ подъязычной костью infrahyoid.
~ ~ сводом головного мозга subfornical.
~ ~ сильвиевой бороздой subsylvian.
~ ~ скуловой костью subjugal.
~ позади варолиева моста postpontile.
~ ~ вертлужной впадины postaceta- bular.
~ ~ глаза postocular.
~ ~ глазного яблока retrobulbar.
~ ~ матки postuterine.
~ ~ островка (Рейля) retroinsular.
~ ~ радужки retroiridian.
~ ~ рта postoral.
лёжбище котиков zool: sealing grou nd.
лёжкий agr bot: long-keeping.
Лейдиг Leydig.
лейкемический leukemic.
лейкемия hem: leukemia.
лейкодерма leukoderma, white skin.
лейкодермический leukodermic.
лейкоз = лейкемия.
лейкозин leucosin.
лейкома ophth: leukoma, wall eye.
лейкоматозный leukomatous.

лейкомицин leucomycin.
лейконоидный тип zool: leuconoid type
лейкопенический leukopenic.
лейкопения hem: leukopenia.
лейкоплакия path: leukoplakia, milky stain.
лейкопласт bio: leukoplast.
лейкоцит hem: leukocyte.
лейкоцитарный leukocytic.
лейкоцитин leukocitin.
лейкоцитоз hem: leukocytosis.
лейкоцитозный leukocytotic.
лейомиома leiomyoma.
лейостомус ichth: masooka (Leiostomus xanthurus), chopa blanca, roach, goody.
лейотропный = левозакрученный.
лейцин chem: leucine, aminoisocaproic acid.
лейциновый chem: leucic.
лейшманиальная форма Leishmania form.
лейшмания zool: Leishmania.
лекарский помощник = фельдшер.
лекарственная ванна phys-ther: medicated bath.
~ смесь pharm: mixture.
~ сыпь derm: drug rash.
~ трава pharm: medicinal herb.
лекарственное вещество pharm: medicinal substance.
*~ лечение drug treatment.
~ растение medicinal plant, herb, simple.
~ средство = лекарство.
лекарство pharm: drug, medicament, medicine, medicinal preparation, pharmacon.
лекарствоведение pharmacology.
лекпом = фельдшер.
лектотип bot: lectotype.
лемминг zool: lemming (Lemmus, Myodes).
лемниск (скребней) lemniscus.
лемуры zool: lemurs (Prosimiae).
лён bot: flax (Linum); common flax (L. usitatissimum).
~ кукушкин = кукушкин лён.
~ слабительный fairy flax, purging flax (L. catharticum).
ленивец zool: sloth (Bradypus, Choloepus)
ленивцы (сем.) zool: sloth family (Bradypodidae).
лёновые (сем.) bot: flax fam. (Linaceae).
ленок 1. ichth: Brachymystax lenok; 2. bot: see кореопсис.
лента band, ribbon, tape.
~ -рыба ichth: ribbon-fish (Regalecus).
лентец helm: tapeworm.
~ человеческий = л. широкий.
~ широкий broad tapeworm (Diphyllobothrium latum).
лентообразный ribbonlike, streaked.
ленточка спор хвоща bot: elater.
ленточные черви (кл.) helm: cestodes, tapeworms (Cestoda).
ленточный глист helm: tapeworm, taenia, cestode.
~ червь tapeworm.
леопард zool: leopard (Felis pardus).
лепестковидный bot: petaloid, petaliform.
лепестковый = лепестный.
лепестный bot: petalled, petalline.
лепесток bot: 1. leaflet, foliole; 2. petal.
лепешка lozenge, troche, pastil(le).
лепидодендроны (кл.) bot: Lepidodendrineae (cl., extinct).
лепидодендроновые (сем.) bot: Lepidodendraceae (fam., extinct).
лепидозавры zool: Lepidosauria (reptiles).
лепидосирен ichth: Lepidosiren.
лепоспондили zool: Lepospondyli (extinct amphibians).
лепрозный leprous, leprotic, lepric.
лепрозорий leprosarium.
лептомонадная форма zool: Leptomonas form.
лептоспироз vet: leptospirosis.
лептотрикс Leptothrix ochracea (iron bacterium).
лептоцефалида ichth: leptocephalid.
лепчица = подмаренник цепкий.
лесбианка path: Lesbian woman.
лесбийская любовь Lesbianism.
*лесная куница zool: forest marter (Martes martes).
~ мышь zool: forest mouse, sylvan m., woodmouse (Apodemus sylvaticus).
~ собака = кустарниковая с.
лесное растение forest plant.
лесной bot: sylvan (sylvaticus).
~ кулик = вальдшнеп.
~ слизень zool: slug Arion bourguignati.
леспедеца bot: bush clover (Lespedeza, Michx.)
~ корейская Korean lespedeza, Japanese clover (L. striata).
лессония bot: Lessonia (algae).
лестница преддверия anat: scala vestibuli.
лестничная мышца (передняя, средняя, задняя) anat: (anterior, medius, posterior) scalene muscle, scalenus.
леталь(ный) lethal.
летаргический path: lethargic.
~ энцефалит path: lethargic encephalitis, sleeping sickness, Economo's disease.
летаргия lethargy.

летария bot: letaria (Letaria).
летающие orn: volants, flying birds (Volantes), see килевые
лётная авария av med: flying accident aviation accident.
~ болезнь av med: flying sickness, airmen's psychoneurosis.
~ глухота aviation deafness.
~ неврастения = лётная болезнь.
~ усталость av med: flying fatigue.
летний понос ped: cholera infantum (obs
лётное напряжение av med: flying stress, airmen's psychoneurosis.
~ обмундирование av med:flying clothing.
~ утомление = лётная усталость.
лётный год swarm year (of locust, etc.)
~ шлем av med: flight helmet.
летняя пища summer diet.
летучая белка = летяга.
~ змея zool: flying snake (Chrysopelea).
~ лисица fox bat (Pteropus edulis).
~ мазь pharm: volatile liniment.
~ мышь zool: bat (Chiroptera).
~ ~ обыкновенная common bat, insect-eating b. (Vespertilio murinus).
~ рыба flying fish (Exocoetus).
~ собака = летучая лисица.
летучее масло pharm: volatile oil.
летучие мыши (отр.) zool: bats (Chiroptera).
летучий дракон zool: flying dragon (Drago volans), an Indian lizard.
летучка bot: pappus.
летучки европейские (сем.) ichth: European flying fishes (Exocoetidae).
лётчик flyer, airman.
~ -бомбардировщик bomber pilot.
~ -истребитель fighter pilot.
~ -курсант flying cadet.
летяга zool: flying squirrel.
~ обыкновенная Sciuropterus volans.
~ -тагуан Pteromys volans petaurista.
леурестес ichth: grumion (Leuresthes tenius).
лецитальный embr:lecithal.
лечащий врач attending physician.
лечебная гимнастика = лечение движениями.
~ доза rad: therapeutic dose.
лечебница = больница.
лечебное заведение clinic, hospital, infirmary, dispensary, etc.
~ средство remedy, curative means.
лечебный curative, sanative, therapeutic
лечение treatment, cure, therapy.
~ антибиотиками antibiotic therapy.
лечение белковыми препаратами protein therapy.
~ ваннами = лечение купаниями.
~ виноградом botryotherapy, grape cure.
~ внушением psych: suggestion therapy.
~ водами = л. минеральными водами.
~ водой (снаружи) hydrotherapy, hydrotherapeutics.
~ воздухом aerotherapeutics, aerotherapy.
~ втираниями inunction treatment.
~ гипнозом hypnotic treatment, hypnotherapy.
~ голоданием limotherapy, hunger cure
~ грязевыми ваннами illutation.
~ движениями movement cure, kinesitherapy, kinesiatrics.
~ дигиталисом digitalization.
~ диэтой = диэтотерапия.
~ жаропонижающими antipyretic treatment.
~ железом iron medication.
~ зубов dental treatment.
~ инсулином insulinization.
~ кислотами acid treatment.
~ купаниями balneotherapy, balneation.
~ массажем massotherapy.
~ минеральными водами 1. balneatherapy, crenotherapy; 2. mineral-water drinking treatment.
~ молоком milk cure.
~ морскими купаниями sea-bathing treatment, thalassotherapy.
~ мышьяком arsenic treatment.
~ на дому home treatment.
~ обильной диетой phagotherapy.
~ облучением rad: (ir)radiation treatment.
~ опухоли tumor treatment.
~ отвлекающими средствами derivation.
~ пастеровскими прививками Pasteur treatment.
~ перекармливанием suralimentation, overalimentation, forced feeding.
~ песочными ванными ammotherapy.
~ покоем rest cure.
~ препаратами мышьяка arsenization.
~ ~ сурьмы stibiation.
~ ~ щитовидной железы thyroidization.
~ психическим воздействием psychotherapy.
~ слабительными treatment with laxatives, purgation, catharsis.
~ собственной кровью autohemotherapy.

лечение солнечными лучами heliotherapy.
~ сухоядением dipsotherapy, thirst cure
~ сыворотками serotherapy.
~ теплом thermotherapy.
~ туберкулином tuberculinization.
~ физическими методами physical therapy, physical medicine.
~ холодом frigotherapy, cryotherapy.
~ цветными лучами chromotherapeutics.
лечить treat, cure.
~ паллиативными средствами palliate.
лещ ichth: golden shiner (Abramis).
~ амурский белый Parabramis.
~ ~ чёрный Megalobrama.
лещина bot: hazel, hazelnut, filbert (Corylus).
~ обыкновенная C. avellana.
лжеапельсин = маклюра.
лжекипарис нутканский bot: yellow cedar (Chamaecyparis nootkatensis).
либеркюнова железа anat: Lieberkühn's gland
лигамент hinge (of a bivalve mollusk).
~ раковины zool: hinge ligament.
лигатура surg: ligature.
лигатурная игла surg: aneurism needle.
лигнин lignin, cellulose wadding.
лигула bot: ligule.
лиено-портальный lieno-portal.
лизимахия bot: loosestrife (Lysimachia).
лизин lysine.
лизинообразовательный lysogenic.
лизис lysis, defervescence.
лизогения lysogenesis.
ликантропический psych: lycanthropic.
ликантропия psych: lycanthropy.
ликвидамбар bot: sweet gum (Liquidambar); bilsted (L. styraciflua), see стиракс.
ликмофора bot: Lycmophore (algae).
ликогала Lycogala (algae).
ликодес ichth: Lycodes.
ликопод bot: lycopod.
ликоподий = плаун.
ликофора helm: lycophore, decacanth larva.
лилейник bot: daylily (Hemerocallis).
~ жёлтый yellow d. (H. flava).
~ оранжевый common orange d. (H. fulva)
лилейные (сем.) bot: lily fam. (Liliaceae)
лилея bot: flowering quillwort (Lilaea).
лилиецветные (пор.) bot: Lilieflorae, Liliales.
лилия bot: lily (Lilium).
~ американская swamp lily (Crinum americanum).
~ жёлтая yellow daylily, lemon d. (Hemerocallis flava).
лилия золотистая queen of lilies (Lilium auratum, Lindl.)
~ красная orange lily (L. bulbiferum).
~ кудреватая = сарана большая.
лима = фасоль лимская.
лиманда = ершоватка.
лимквот bot: limequat (hybrid of Citrus aurantifolia and Fortunella japonica).
лимниграф limnograph.
лимнолог limnologist.
лимнологический limnological.
лимнология limnology.
лимнопланктон bio: limnoplankton.
лимон bot: lemon (Citrus limonia).
~ бадранки rough lemon (C. medica).
~ дикий = л. бадранки.
~ полудикий = л. бадранки.
лимониида entom: crane fly (Limoniidae).
лимонная трава bot: lemon grass, see сорго лимонное.
лимонновиннокаменнокислый натрий pharm: sodium citrotartrate.
лимонное дерево citron tree (Citrus medica, C. limon).
~ масло lemon oil.
лимоннокислая окись железа с лимоннокислым аммонием pharm: iron and ammonium citrate.
лимоннокислый висмут pharm: bismuth citrate.
~ кокаин pharm: cocaine citrate.
~ кофеин pharm: citrated caffeine.
~ литий lithium citrate.
~ натрий sodium citrate.
~ магний magnesium citrate.
~ парафенетидин paraphenetidin c.
~ хинин quinine citrate.
лимоннорастворимый фосфат citric soluble phosphate.
лимоннофосфорнокислый натрий sodium citrophosphate.
лимонный сок lemon juice.
лиму bot: limu (edible alga).
лимфаденит path: lymphadenitis.
лимфаденоидная ткань lymphoid tissue.
лимфангит vet: weed.
лимфатическая железа anat: lymphatic gland.
~ клетка hist: lymph cell.
~ ткань hist: lymphatic tissue.
~ цистерна anat: cisterna chyli.
лимфатические бляшки anat: noduli lymphatici aggregati Peyeri.
лимфатический сосуд lymphatic, lymph vessel.
~ узел(ок) lymph node, lymphoglandula.
лимфатическое пространство anat: lymph space.
лимфогрануломатоз path: lymphogranulomatosis, Hodgkin's disease.

лимфоидная ткань hist: lymphoid
лимфопения lymphopenia. tissue.
лимфосаркома lymphosarcoma.
лимфоцит lymphocyte.
лингбия bot: Lyngbia (algae).
линдан pharm: lindane, grammexane.
линдерния bot: false pimpernel
(Lindernia). [(Coccinellidae).
линдорус entom: Lindorus lophanthae
линейка Пренса ophth: Prince rule.
линейная ржавчина phytp: (late) stem
rust (Puccinia graminis).
~ ~ пшеницы wheat rust.
линейное возвышение ridge. [linear.
линейно-ланцетовидный bot: lance-
линейный лист bot: linear leaf.
линза lens.
линимент liniment.
линия line; mcbio: strain.[dry fruit).
~ растрескивания bot: suture (of a
~ перелома surg: fracture line.
~ шва мошонки anat: raphe of the
линнеевский Linnaean. scrotum.
Линней Linné, Linnaeus.
линь ichth: Tinca.
линька zool: molt(ing), shedding,
mewing, changing (feathers),ecdysis,
excaviation (of a snake), deplumation
линяние = линька. (of a bird).
линять zool: molt, etc. [shedder.
линяющее животное molting animal,
линяющий краб zool: shell-casting crab,
buster.
лиофилизация lyophilization.
лиофилиз(ир)ованный lyophilized.
липа bot: linden, lime tree, teil
(Tilia).
~ американская basswood, whitewood
(T. americana).
~ мелколистная small-leaved lime tree
(T. parvifolia, Ehrh.)
липаза lipase.
липид lipid.
липкая кожа clammy skin.
~ подушечка сложной пыльцы bot:
caudicle. Cf. поллиний.
липкий sticky, adhesive, tenacious,
viscid, glutinous.
~ пластырь adhesive plaster, sticking p.
липкопластырная повязка adhesive-
plaster bandage.
липкопластырное вытяжение surg:
adhesive extension. [(Tiliaceae).
липовые (сем.) bot: linden family
липовый орешек bot: lime capsule.

липовый цвет bot: lime-tree blossom.
липогенез lipogenesis.
липоид lipoid.
липоидная гранула lipoid granule.
липоидный обмен lipoid metabolism.
липоидоз path: lipoidosis, lipoid
histiocytosis. щий.
липолитический = жирорасщепляю-
липома lipoma, fatty tumor.
липотропный lipotropic.
липофусцин lipofuscin.
липохром lipochrome. [lappula, Lehm.)
липучка bot: blue bur (Echinospermum
липушник = подмаренник цепкий.
лира Давида = псалтырь.
лириопида entom: crane fly (Liriopi-
dae, Ptychopteridae).
лиса = лисица.
лисица zool: fox (Vulpes vulpes).
~ -самец dog fox.
лисичка bot: chanterelle (mushroom).
~ ложная false c. (Cantharellus
aurantiacus, Fr.)
~ настоящая chanterelle (C. cibarius).
лисохвост bot: foxtail (Alopecurus).
~ коленчатый marsh f., water f. (A.
geniculatus).
~ луговой meadow f. (A. pratensis).
~ полевой slender f., black grass,
black bent (A. agrestis).
~ равный short-awn foxtail (A. aequa-
lis).
лист bot: leaf.
~ пальмы или папортника frond.
листва foliage, leafage.
лиственница bot: larch (Larix).
~ американская American l., black l.,
tamarack, hackmatack (L. laricina).
~ тонкочешуйчатая Japanese l. (L.
leptolepis, Murr.)
~ японская = л. тонкочешуйчатая.
лиственничная губка = трутовый
гриб.
лиственный bot: foliar, foliate, leaf.
~ лес leaf wood, broad-leaved forest.
листвяк bot: thallus.
листоблошка entom: leafhopper, psylla
see also медяница.
~ грушевая pear psylla.
~ капустная = л. луковая.[sicae).
~ луковая onion psylla (Trioza bras-
~ морковная carrot rust-fly (Trioza
viridula).
листоблошки (сем.) entom: leafhoppers (Psyllidae).

листоватый лишайник bot: leaf-like lichen, sheet-like lichen.
листовая конечность bot: leaf tip, leaf apex.
~ обвёртка bot: husk (in maize).
~ пила surg: blade saw.
~ пластинка bot: leaf blade.
~ подушечка bot: pulvinus.
~ почка bot: leaf bud.
~ ржавчина phytp: leaf rust.
листовёртка entom: leafroller, tortricid moth, tortris; see also плодожорка.
~ апельсиновая = л. цитрусовая.
~ виноградная grape berry moth, grape codling moth (Polychrosis viteana, P. batrana, Clysia ambiguella).
~ вишнёвая cherry fruit worm (Grapholitha paccardi).
~ всеядная "omnivorous" leafroller (Cacoecia podana).
~ гороховая = плодожорка гороховая.
~ гроздевая = л. виноградная.
~ двулётная Clysia ambiguella.
~ дубовая oak moth, oak-leaf roller (Tortrix viridana).
~ заморозковая Exapate congelatella.
~ ивовая кривоусая Pandemis heparana.
~ клеверная clover-head caterpillar (Grapholitha interstinata).
~ лубяная pine-shoot moth (Laspeyresia coniferana).
~ льняная = плодожорка льняная.
~ можжевеловая juniper webworm (Phalonia rutilana).
~ плодовая fruit-tree leafroller, fruit tortrix moth.
~ почкоедная = почкоед.
~ разноцветная плодовая Argyroploce variegana.
~ розанная Cacoecia rosana.
~ сливовая lesser apple-worm (Grapholitha, Enarmonia prunivora).
~ смородинная Pandemis ribeana.
~ фруктовая = л. плодовая.
~ цитрусовая orange tortrix (Tortrix citrina).
листовёртки (сем.) entom: leafrollers (Tortricidae).
листовидная ткань hist: leaf-like tissue.
листовидный = листообразный.
~ скат ichth: Raja fyllae.
~ сосочек anat: foliate papilla.
листовка bot: follicle.
листовое влагалище bot: sheath.
~ расширение лишайников bot: thallus.
листовой bot: (of) leaf, foliar, foliated.
~ орган bot: foliage organ.
~ пучок foliar bundle.
листовой хлопковый червь = совка малая.
~ червь хлопчатника = совка малая.
~ черешок bot: leaf peliole.
~ ~ огородных bot: chard.
листогрыз entom: leaf miner (Lina).
~ земляничный "козявка" = листоед земляничный.
листоед entom: leaf beetle, leaf-eating bug (Chrysomelidae).
~ азиатский Chrysochares asiatica.
~ баклажанный eggplant tortoise beetle (Cassida pallidula).
~ бобовый bean beetle (Luperodes menetriezi).
~ горчичный mustard leaf-beetle (Colaphellus).
~ земляничный strawberry beetle (Galerucella tenella).
~ ивовый Phyllodecta vittelina.
~ мальвовый Podagrica malvae.
~ осиновый Melasoma tremulae.
~ рапсовый Entomoscelis adonidis.
~ сосновый black pine leaf beetle (Galeruca pinicola).
~ спаржевый asparagus beetle (Crioceris asparagi).
~ ~ 12-точечный twelve-spotted asparagus beetle (C. a. 12-punctatus).
~ тополевый poplar-leaf beetle (Melasoma populi).
~ хреновый horse-radish leaf beetle (Phaedon cochleariae).
~ щавелевый Gastroidea viridula.
~ южноамериканский striped cucumber beetle (Diabrotica vittata).
листоеды (сем.) entom: chrysomelids, leaf-beetles (Chrysomelidae).
листожаберный zool: follobranchiate.
листок обёртки соцветия bot: involucral bract.
~ принятия больного admission slip.
~ сложного листа bot: pinna.
листоногий рак zool: phyllopod (Phyllopoda).
листоноговидные zool: Phyllostraca (subclass of Crustacea).
листонос zool: leaf-nosed bat (Hipposideros).
листоносые (сем.) zool: leaf-nosed bats (Phyllostomidae).
листообразный bot: foliaceous, leafy.
листопад bot: leaf fall, exfoliation.
листоподобный стебель bot: leaf-like stem, cladophyll.
листорасположение bot: arrangement of leaves, phyllotaxy.
листосложение bot: vernation.

листостебельное растение bot: cormophyte. [mosses (Cormophyta).
листостебельные мхи bot: frondiferous
листочек bot: very small leaf; bract.
~ сложного листа bot: pinnule.
листья кока pharm: coca leaves.
литический lytic.
литотамнион bot: Lithothamnion (algae).
литторина zool: periwinkle (Littorina rudis). [drain drop by drop.
лить по каплям drip, dribble, trickle,
лихенологический bot: lichenological.
лихенология bot: lichenology.
лихенофлора bot: lichenoflora.
лихорадка path: fever.
~ денге infect: dengue, breakbone fever.
~ при прорезывании зубов ped: dentition fever. [ted fever.
~ Скалистых гор Rocky Mountain spot-
лихорадочная трава = авран.
лихорадочник = авран.
~ китайский bot: Chinese fever plant (Paederia foetida).
лихорадочное состояние path: febrile state, feverishness, febrility, pyrexia.
лихорадочный febrile, feverish, pyrexial, pyretic.
~ жар path: fever heat.
~ озноб path: febrile chill.
лицевая вена anat: facial vein.
лицевое предлежание face presentation
лицевой нерв anat: facial nerve, 7th
~ скелет facial skeleton. cranial n.
~ угол anat: facial angle.
~ череп anat: bony skull.
лиций = дереза.
лицо face.
личинка zool: larva, maggot, grub.
~ амблистомы zool: axolotl.
~ асцидии zool: tadpole larva.
~ беззубки zool: glochidium.
~ вислокрылки entom: hellgrammite (Co-
~ древоточца entom: woodworm. |rydalus).
~ желудочного овода entom: bot.
~ жука entom: grub.
~ иглокожего zool: echinopluteus.
~ капустной мухи entom: root maggot.
~ комара entom: gnatworm, wiggler.
~ ленточного червя = цистицерк.
~ миноги zool: ammocoete larva.
~ мухи Eristalis = крыска.
~ мясной мухи entom: screw worm.
~ насекомого insect larva, nymph.
~ ~ с неполным превращением crawler.

личинка (овода и т.п.) под кожей животного entom: wormil.
~ пяденицы entom: looper.
~ ручейника entom: caddis worm.
~ рыбы larval fish.
~ сельди herring larva.
~ хирономиды entom: chironomid larva.
личинковый венчик bot: personate co-
личинник bot: caterpillars, |rolla. snails (Scorpiurus vermiculata).
личиночная стадия entom: larval stage.
~ ~ ленточного червя plerocercoid.
личинохордовые zool: urochords (Urochorda), see оболочники.
личиночный zool: larval.
личные качества personality traits.
личный анамнез personal history.
лишай vet: lichen, see парша.
лишайник bot: lichen. [usneoides).
~ тилландзия long moss (Tillandsia
лишайники (тип) bot: lichens (phylum
лишать почек bot: disbud. | Lichenes).
~ токсических свойств detoxicate.
~ чувствительности anesthetize.
лишение девственности defloration.
лишённый аппетита anorectic,
~ век ablepharous. anorectous.
~ волос hairless.
~ дендритов hist: adendritic.
~ жгутиков nonflagellate.
~ желёз eglandular.
~ жизни devitalized.
~ запаха inodorous.
~ зооспор azoosporic.
~ зубов edentulous.
~ клапанов avalvular, evalvate.
~ комплемента uncomplemented.
~ конечностей zool: limbless.
~ крышечки inoperculate (mollusk).
~ крышки nonoperculate.
~ лёгких apulmonic.
~ лица aprosopous.
~ мускулатуры emusculate.
~ нервов denervated.
~ околоцветника bot: gymnanthous.
~ пальцев path: adactyl(ous).
~ перегородки nonseptate, eseptate.
~ прилистников bot: estipulate.
~ прицветников bot: ebracteate.
~ протоплазмы aplasmic.
~ пыльника bot: inantherate.
~ рёбер decostate.
~ сердца path: acardiac.
~ смолистых веществ pharm: deresi-
~ сосочков zool: epapillate. nate.

лишённый сосудистой системы zool: anangian.
~ спинного мозга path: amyelic, amyelous.
~ спор bot: sporeless.
~ стебелька bot: unstalked.
~ хлорофилла bot: etiolated.
~ черепа path: acranius.
~ щитовидной железы dethyroidized.
~ щупиков entom: epalpate.
~ явственных суставов anarthrous.
~ ядра hist: denucleated.
~ яичек path: anorchous. [some.
лишняя хромосома supernumerary chromo-
лоб 1. anat: forehead; 2. entom: frons.
лобан ichth: striped mullet (Mugil cephalus).
лобарная пневмония lobar pneumonia.
лобелиевые (сем.) bot: lobelia family (Lobeliaceae). [asthma weed.
лобелия bot: lobelia (Lobelia);pharm:
~ кардинальская cardinal flower (L. cardinalis).
~ надутая Indian tobacco, asthma weed
~ одутлая = л. надутая. | (L. inflata)
лобия bot: dolichos, hyacinth bean (Dolichos biflorus, D. lablab).
лобковая дуга anat: pubic arch.
~ кость anat: pubic bone, os pubis.
лобковое возвышение anat: mons pubis.
~ ~ у женщины mons veneris.
лобная доля anat: frontal lobe.
~ извилина мозга (верхняя, нижняя) anat: (superior, inferior) frontal gyrus. [os frontale.
~ кость anat: forehead bone, frontal b.,
~ мышца anat: frontalis muscle,epicrani-
~ пазуха anat:frontal sinus. |us m.
~ полоса entom: vitta frontalis.
лобно-височный anat: frontal-and-temporal. [presentation; vet:brow p.
лобное предлежание obstet: frontal
лобно-затылочный anat:fronto-occipital.
~ -носовой anat: frontonasal.
~ -скуловой anat: frontomalar.
~ -челюстной anat: frontomaxillary.
лобный бугор anat: frontal protuberance f. eminence.
~ гребень anat: frontal ridge, f. crest.
~ отросток anat: frontal process.
~ ~ скулы frontosphenoidal process.
~ рефлектор otolar: head mirror, frontal m.
~ шов anat: frontal suture, metopic s.
лоботодий mcbio: lobopodium.
лоботодия zool: lobopod, lobose pseudopod.

лобулярная пневмония path: lobar
лобэктомия surg:lobectomy.| pneumonia.
лов zool: catch.
~ венуса quahauging.
~ крабов crabbing.
~ омаров lobstering.
~ пищи zool: food-getting activities.
ловец венуса quahauger.
~ жемчуга pearl fisher.
~ крабов crabber.
~ омаров lobsterman.[finger dexterity.
ловкость (движений) пальцев av med:
ловля налету hawking (of insects).
логанова ягода bot: loganberry (Rubus vitifolius).
логарифмическая фаза bio: log phase.
логомания psych: logomania.
логопед logopedist.
логопедия logopedics, logopedia.
лодикула bot: lodicule.
лодочка bot: keel, cover slip (of the papilionaceous flower).
лодочкообразный = ладьевидный.
лодыжечный anat: malleolar.
лодыжка anat: ankle, malleolus.
лодыжковый anat: malleolar.
ложбинка bot: suture (plume, apricot).
ложе anat: matrix.
~ цветка = цветоложе.
ложечка surg: scoop.
~ для хрусталика ophth:lens spoon.
ложечная трава = ложечница.
ложечница bot: scurvygrass, spoonwort (Cochlearia).
ложка spoon.
~ для удаления жёлчных камней surg: gall-stone scoop. [form.
ложкообразный spoon-shaped, cochleari-
ложная беременность obstet: pseydopregnancy, afetal pregnancy, phantom pregnancy, pseudocyesis.
~ болезнь false disease, pseudomalady.
~ голосовая связка anat: ventricular fold, false vocal cord, plica ventri-
~ киста path: cystoid. cularis.
~ луковичка bot: pseudobulb.
~ мутовка bot: false whorl. [downy m.
~ мучнистая роса phytp:false mildew,
~ ~ винограда phytp: downy mildew of grape, brown rot, gray rot (Plasmopora viticola).
~ ~ роса лука phytp:onion mildew,
~ ножка entom: proleg. | white rot.
~ перепонка path: pseudomembrane.
~ шелуха bot: arillode.

ложная ягода bot: spurious berry.
ложногусеница entom: caterpillar-like larva (of Tenthredinoidea).
ложное воспоминание psych: pseudo-reminiscence.
~ ощущение false sensation, paresthesia.
~ ~ ампутированной конечности neur: stump hallucination.
~ перечное дерево = схинус.
~ ребро anat: false rib.
~ слоевище bot: pseudothallus.
~ цветочное кольцо bot: false whorl.
ложнокардинальный pseudocardinal.
ложнококон entom: puparium.
ложноконская пиявка zool: horse-leech (Haemopis).
~ ~ малая small horse-leech.
ложнокоренной зуб zool: premolar tooth
ложномучнистая роса = ложная мучнистая роса.
ложноножка zool: pseudopod(ium).
ложноножковые zool: Pseudopodiata, see саркодовые.
ложнопевчие orn: suboscines, pseudo-songbirds (Suboscines).
ложноскорпион pseudo-scorpion.
ложнослоник какаовый entom: Araecerus fasciculatus.
ложнослоники (сем.) entom: Anthribidae.
ложность ощущений falsity of sensations.
ложнощитовка акациевая entom: soft scale Eulecanium corni.
~ сливовая E. prunastri.
ложнощитовки (сем.) entom: soft scales Lecaniidae.
ложные жабры zool: pseudo branchia.
~ роды obstet: false labor.
~ скорпионы (отр.) zool: false scorpions (Pseudoscorpionida, Chelonethida).
~ схватки obstet: false pains.
ложный занос obstet: false mole.
~ зонтик bot: false umbel.
~ плод bot: false fruit, spurious f.
~ ствол bot: long shoot.
~ сустав path: false articulation, f. joint.
~ туберкулёз pseudotuberculosis.
~ ход path: false passage.
~ цилиндр mcbio: pseudocast, false cast, spurious c.
~ шампиньон = поганка бледная.
~ шов bot: pseudoraphe.
лоза bot: osier shoot. Cf. трубная лоза.
лозофан pharm: cresol iodide.
лойник bot: heal-all, carpenter weed (Prunella vulgaris).
локализация localization; location, site, seat.
локализованная боль local pain, topoalgia.
локальная доза rad: local dose.
локва = мушмула.
локомоторная атаксия locomotor ataxia, tabes dorsalis, ripples.
локомоторный anat: locomotive, locomotor.
локоть anat: elbow.
локтевая артерия anat: ulnar artery.
~ железа anat: epitrochlear gland.
~ кость anat: elbow bone, ulna.
~ ямка anat: olecranon fossa.
локтевой anat: ulnar, cubital, anconal.
~ нерв anat: ulnar nerve.
~ отросток anat: olecranon (process).
~ разгибатель кисти anat: extensor carpi ulnaris.
~ рефлекс elbow jerk.
~ сгиб anat: elbow bend.
~ сгибатель кисти anat: flexor carpi ulnaris.
~ сустав anat: elbow joint.
локус locus.
ломкий brittle, frangible.
ломкость ногтей brittleness of nails
ломонос bot: clematis, virgin's bower (Clematis).
ломота rheumatic pain.
лонгана = нефелиум.
Лонгейкр Longacre.
лонная дуга anat: pubic arch.
~ кость anat: pubis, lapbone, s. pubis.
лонное сращение anat: pubic symphysis,
лонный бугорок anat: pubic tubercle, tuberculum pubicum.
лоно = лонное сращение.
лопасть ноги zool: flabellum.
~ хвоста zool: fluke (of a whale).
лопатка anat: scapula, shoulder blade.
~ гороха bot: pea pod.
лопаткообразный spatulate.
лопатовидный spatulate.
лопатоногая жаба zool: spadefoot toad.
лопатоногие zool: scaphopods (Scaphopoda, Solenoconcha).
~ моллюски zool: toothshells, tusk shells (Scaphopoda).
лопатонос ichth: Pseudoscaphirhynchus.
лопаточная артерия, поперечная anat: transverse scapular artery, suprascapular a.
~ вырезка scapular notch.
~ линия anat: scapular line.
~ ость anat: spine of the scapula.
лопаточно-подъязычная мышца anat: omohyoid (muscle).
лопатчатый лист bot: spatulate leaf.
лопающийся на части bot: dissilient, dehiscent.
лопнуть burst (open), crack.

лопух = лопушник.
лопушник bot: burdock, clotbur (Arctium)
~ большой great burdock, common b. (A. lappa).
лордоз path: lordosis, spinal incurvation, saddle back.
лори = стройный л., толстый л.; zool: loris.
лоскут flap.
~ взятый от другого вида животного surg: heterograft, helerotransplant.
~ ~ от другого лица isograft homograft.
~ ~ от животного zoograft.
~ слизистой оболочки mucosal graft.
~ (ткани) для пересадки surg: graft.
лоскутная ампутация surg: flap amputation.
~ экстракция ophth: flap extraction.
лоскутный разрез surg: flap section.
лососевые (сем.) ichth: salmon family (Salmonidae).
лосось ichth: salmon (Salmo salar).
~ молодой salmon parr, brandling.
~ -таймень = кумжа.
~ тихоокеанский Pacific salmon (Oncorhynchus).
*лось zool: moose (Alce).
~ американский American moose (Alce americana).
~ обыкновенный moose (A. machlis).
~ сохатый = л. обыкновенный.
~ самец bull moose.
лотос bot: lotus, lotos, sacred bean (Nelumbo, Adans); sacred lotus (N. nucifera, Gaertn.)
~ американский = л. жёлтый.
~ белый magnolia lotus (Nelumbo lotus, var. alba, Hort.)
~ голубой blue lotus (Nymphaca caerulea)
~ жёлтый yellow nelumbo, water-chinquapin, pond-nuts, wonkapin (N. lutea).
~ индийский East Indian lotus, sacred (N. nucifera, Gaertn.)
лофотрих mcbio: lophotrichate.
лофофор (мшанки) lophophore.
лох bot: oleaster (Elaeagnus).
~ серебристый silverberry (E. commutata, Bernh.)
~ узколистный oleaster, Russian olive (E. angustifolia).
лоховые (сем.) bot: oleaster family (Elaeagnaceae).
лохии obstet vet: cleansings.
лоцман = рыба-лоцман.
лошади (сем.) zool: horse family (Equidae).
лошадиная аскарида horse's ascarid (Parascaris equorum).

лошадиный equine, of a horse; jumentous (odor).
лошадь horse (Equus caballus).
~ Пржевальского zool: wild horse Equus przewalskii.
лошак hinny (Equus hinnus).
луб bot: phloem.
лубоед entom: timber beetle, ambiosia b.; see also короед.
~ большой сосновый pine beetle (Myelophiles piniperda, Blastophagus p.)
~ кавказский Caucasian timber beetle (Phloetribus caucasicus).
~ малый сосновый small pine beetle (Blastophagus minor).
~ ясеневый пёстрый Hylesinus fraxini.
лубоеды entom: Hylesinae.
лубок surg: splint.
лубяная ткань bot: phloem tissue.
лубянистая мякоть bot: phloem parenchyma.
лубяное волокно bot: bast fiber, pericycle.
луговик = аира.
~ извилистый common hairgrass, wavy h. (Deschampsia flexuosa).
~ коленчатый = л. извилистый.
~ северный = аира дернистая.
луговой meadowy.
луговой тетерев orn: prairie chicken (Tympanuchus cupido).
лужанка zool: mollusk Viviparus contectus.
~ обыкновенная V. viviparus.
лужница bot: mudwort (Limosella).
лузга bot: peelings, husk.
луизианский мох Louisiana moss, see лишайник тилланзия.
лук bot: onion (Allium).
~ виноградный field garlic, wild onion (A. vineale).
~ дудчатый spring onion, Welsh o. (A. fistulosum).
~ египетский Egyptian onion, tree o. (A. cepa bulbellifera).
~ зелёный scallion.
~ картофельный potato o., see лук-шалот.
~ медвежий ramson broad-leaved garlic (A. ursinum, A. victorial).
~ многодетковый multiplier (A. cepa).
~ многоэтажный catawissa (A. fistulosum, var. catawissa).
~ обыкновенный common onion (A. cepa).
~ -перо green onion, scallion.
~ песчаный = л. дудчатый.
~ -поррей leek (A. porrum).
~ -резанец chives (A. schoenoprasum).

лук репчатый bulb onion, common o. (A. cepa).
~ -севок set o.
~ -сеянец blackseed onion.
~ -скорода = л. резанец.
~ -татарка = л. дудчатый.
~ -шалот shallot, eschalot, underground o. (A. ascalonicum).
луковица bot: bulb.
~ аорты anat: aortic bulb.
~ лука bot: onion bulb.
~ мочеиспускательного канала anat: bulb of the urethra, b. of the penis.
~ преддверия anat: vestibular bulb.
луковиценосный bot: bulbiferous.
луковицеобразный bulblike, bulbous.
луковицеподобный = луковицеобразный
луковичка bulbil, bulblet, clove.
луковично-пещеристая мышца anat: bulbocavernosus muscle.
луковичный bulbaceous, bulbous, bulbar.
луковый oniony.
лукума bot: lucuma, mammee sapota, mammee colorado, mamey (Lucuma mammosa, Gaertn.)
~ сетчатая egg-fruit (L. nervosa, DC.)
лумпенусовые (сем.) ichth: Lumpenidae.
луна-рыба moonfish, headfish, ocean sunfish (Mola mola).
лунатизм = снохождение.
лунатик somnambulist, sleepwalker.
лунка серебристая entom: prominent Phalera bucephala.
лунная слепота vet: moon blindness.
лунник bot: honesty, satin flower (Lunaria).
~ оживающий lunary (L. rediviva).
луноцвет bot: moon flower (Calonyction aculeatum, House, or Ipomoea bonanox).
луночковая пиоррея path: pyorrhea alveolaris.
луночковый отросток (челюсти) anat: alveolus, bony socket of a tooth.
*лунь orn: harrier, marsh hawk (Circus cyaneus, etc.); Montagu's harrier (Cirens pygargus).
~ болотный = л. камышовый.
~ камышовый marsh harrier (Circus aeruginosus).
лупа loupe, magnifying lens.
лупин = люпин.
лупиться peel off; cf. шелушение.
лупулин lupulin (in hops).
луфаревые (сем.) ichth: Pomatomidae.
луфарь ichth: greenfish, bluefish, snapper, skipjack, tailor (Pomotomus saltatrix).

луч ray, radius; zool: arm.
~ (морских звёзд) zool: finger.
лучевая артерия anat: radial artery.
~ болезнь radiation sickness.
~ катаракта radiation cataract.
~ кость anat: radius.
~ пастеризация radiopasteurization.
~ терапия radiation therapy.
лучевидный отросток zool: arm.
лучевики (отр.) zool: radiolarians (Radiolaria).
лучевое поражение radiation injury.
лучевой инсульт radiation insult.
~ коралл zool: actinozoan.
~ нерв anat: radial nerve, musculospiral nerve.
~ ожог radiation burn.
~ разгибатель кисти (длинный, короткий) anat: extensor carpi radialis (longus, brevis).
~ сгибатель кисти anat: flexor carpi radialis.
~ синдром radiation syndrome.
лучезапястный сустав anat: radiocarpal joint.
лучеиспускание radiation.
лучеиспускающий radiating.
луче-ладонный anat: radiopalmar.
~ -локтевой сустав anat: radioulnar joint.
~ -пальцевый radiodigital.
лучепёрые ichth: Actinopterygii.
лучистые zool: actinozoa (Radiata).
лучистый венец embr: radiating crown, corona radiata.
~ грибок bact: ray fungus (Actinomyces)
~ скат ichth: Raja radiata.
лучица = хара.
лучицы = харовые.
лыска = лысуха.
лысость = облысение.
лысун hard seal (Phoca groenlandica).
лысуха orn: coot, dabchick (Fulica).
лысый bald.
~ бычок ichth: Mesogobius.
львиная лапка = сушеница альпийская.
львинка soldier fly (Stratiomyiidae).
львиный зёв bot: snapdragon (Antirrhinum).
львица zool: lioness.
льдянковые = аизоевые.
льнянка bot: toad-flax, butter-and-eggs (Linaria vulgaris, Mill., Antirrhinum linaria).
льняное масло linseed oil.
~ семя linseed.
льюизия оживающая bot: bitterroot (Lewisia rediviva, Pursh.)

любастик bot: lovage (Levisticum officinale, Koch.)
любисток = любастик.
любитель кошек cat fancier.
любка двулистная butterfly orchid, blunt-leaf orchid, one-leaf rein orchis (Platanthera bifolia, Habenaria obtusata, Rich.)
любовь love, amor.
люголевский раствор pharm: compound solution of iodine.
людвигия bot: false loosestrife (Ludwigia)
~ болотная water purslane (Ludwigia palustris).
~ разнолистная seedbox (L. alternifolia)
люди (сем.) zool: men (Hominidae).
люксилюс ichth: common shiner, spawn eater (Luxilus cornutus).
люмбаго int: lumbago.
люмбальная пункция surg: lumbar puncture.
люминал pharm: luminal, phenobarbital.
люминесцентный микроскоп luminescence microscope.
люпин bot: lupine (Lupinus).
~ белый white lupine (L. albus).
~ древовидный tree lupine (L. arboreus).
~ жёлтый yellow lupine (L. luteus).
~ шершавоволосый blue lupine (L. hirsutus).
люпус = волчанка.
лютианус ichth: mangrove snapper, gray s., lawyer (Lutianus griseus).
лютик bot: crowfoot, buttercup (Ranunculus)
~ водяной water c. (R. aquatis).
~ волосолистный white water c. (R. trichophyllus).
~ едкий tall buttercup, common b., bitter b. (R. acris).
~ жестколистный bot: white water crowfoot (R. subrigidus).
~ золотистый goldilocks (R. auricomus).
~ полевой corn crowfoot (R. arvensis).
~ ползучий creeping buttercup (R. repens).
~ -прыщинец spearwort (R. flammula).
~ ядовитый cursed c. (R. sceleratus).
лютиковые (сем.) bot: crowfoot family (Ranunculaceae).
лютка = стрекоза лютка.
люфа bot: luffa (Luffa cylindrica).
люцерна bot: medick (Medicago); alfalfa, lucerne (M. sativa).
~ арабская spotted medick (M. arabica).
~ древовидная moon trefoil (M. arborea).
~ жёлтая = л. хмелевидная.
~ жестковатая southern bur clover (M. rigidula).
~ зубчатая bur clover (M. denticulata).
~ кустовая tree medick (M. arborea).
~ малая bur clover (M. minima).
люцерна песчаная = л. средняя.
~ пятнистая bur clover (M. maculata).
~ серповидная yellow medick, true moon trefoil (M. falcata).
~ спиралеплодная snail clover (M. turbinata).
~ средняя variegated alfalfa, intermediate lucerne (M. varia, M. sativa).
~ хмелевая = л. хмелевидная.
~ хмелевидная black medick, nonesuch, hop clover (M. lupulina).
~ щитовидная snails, snail trefoil (M. scutellata).
люцернарии (отр.) zool: Lucernariida, Stauromedusae.
люцифераза luciferase.
люциферин luciferin.
Лябори Laborit.
лягва = лягушка.
лягодон ichth: robin, pinfish, saltwater bream, chopa spina (Lagodon rhomboides).
лягушатник = водокрас лягушечный.
лягушатниковые = водокрасовые.
лягушачий живот path: frog belly.
лягушачья икра zool: frog spawn, f. eggs
~ многоустка zool: frog fluke (Polystomum integerrinum).
~ опухоль path: ranine tumor, ranula.
~ походка path: frog gait.
лягушечник = водокрас лягушечный.
лягушка zool: frog, batrachian (Rana).
лягушки (сем.) zool: frogs (Ranidae).
лягушкозуб zool: Ranodon.
лядвенец bot: birdsfoot trefoil, bastard indigo (Lotus).
~ рогатый birdsfoot trefoil, yellow t., Greek lotus (L. corniculatus).
~ топяной marsh birdsfoot trefoil (L. uliginosus, Schk.)
~ четырёхлопастный square-pod pea (L. tetragonolobus).
лядник пахучий = зубровка душистая.
ляжка zool: haunch, gaskin (of a cow), hock joint (of a cock); entom: coxa.
лямблии lamblia (unicellular parasites).
лямблиоз int: lambliosis (cholecystitis, chronic enteritis).
ляпис pharm: lunar caustic, silver nitrate.
ляписная палочка pharm: silver nitrate stick.
ларингит path: laryngitis.

М

магелланова корица bot: Magellan cinamon (Drimys winteri, Forst.)
магистр master.
магний magnesium, Mg.
магнолиевые (сем.) bot: magnolia family (Magnoliaceae).
магнолия bot: magnolia (Magnolia).
~ виргинская сизозелёная small m., laurel m., sweet bay, swamp bay, beaver tree, laurel (M. virginiana, Morong.)
~ крупноцветная large-blossom magnolia (M. grandiflora).
магуей = агава колючая.
мадия bot: tarweed (Madia sativa, Mol.)
мадрепоровая пластинка zool: madreporic plate (in asterids).
мадрепоровые кораллы (пор.) zool: stony coralls (Madreporaria).
мадрепоровый коралл zool: madreporarian coral.
мадурская стопа madura foot, mycotoma, maduromycosis.
мажется gyn: spotting.
мазама = олень мазама.
мазевый карандаш pharm: salve pencil.
мазок lab: smear, film.
~ крови blood smear.
~ окрашенный по Граму mcscop: gram-stained smear.
мазохизм path: masochism.
мазохист masochist.
мазь pharm: ointment, salve, unguent(um).
~ для носа nasal salve.
~ против ожога burn ointment.
маис = кукуруза.
маисовые (подсем.) bot: maize subfamily (Maydeae, Mathieu).
майка entom: Mayfly (Meloë).
майло-джугара bot: milo.
майник bot: Mayflower.
*майоран садовый bot: annual majoran (Origanum majorana, Majorana hortensis, Much.)
майская болезнь = весенний паралич.
майский жук = хрущ майский.
майяка bot: pool moss (Mayaca).
мак bot: poppy (Papaver).
мак водяной bot: water poppy (Hydrocleis nymphoides).
~ дикий corn p. (Papaver rhoeas).
~ колючий prickly p., rough p. (Argemone mexicana).
~ мексиканский = м. колючий.
~ опийный common p., opium p. (P. somniferum). Cf. семена опийного мака.
~ -самосейка = м. дикий.
~ -снотворный = м. опийный.
~ целандинный celandine p. (P. stylophorum, Hart.)
Мак-Дугал MacDougal.
Мак-Лейк McLake
Мак-Фарленд McFarland.
макадамия bot: popple nut, Queensland nut (Macadamia ternifolia, Mull.)
макайра ichth: marlin (Makaira).
макак zool: macaco (Macacus).
~ резус rhesus monkey.
маквиллямия bot: water hyssop (Macuillamia, Raf., or Bacopa rotundifolia, Michx.)
макет mockup, breadboard, model, prototype, simulator.
~ ткани rad bio: phantom.
маклюра bot: osage orange, bow wood (Maclura pomifera, Schneid.)
мако bot: maco (Gossypium barbadense, var. gallini).
маковые (сем.) bot: poppy family (Paparaceae).
маковый papaveraceous.
макоцветные (пор.) bot: Rhoeadales, Papaverales.
макрелещука ichth: skipper, skipjack (Scomberesox saurus).
макрелещуковые (сем.) ichth: skippers (Scomberesocidae).
макрель ichth: mackerel, bluefish (Scomber).
макрогамета macrogamete.
макроглия hist: macroglia.
макродактилия path: macrodactylia, giant fingers or toes.
макрозооспора macrozoospore.
макронуклеус bio: macronucleus.
макропланктон bio: macroplankton.
макропод paradise fish (Macropodus).
макросклера (губок) zool: macrosclere.
макроскопическая картина gross appearance.
макроскопический macroscopic, gross.
макросома macrosome.
макроспора bot: megaspore.
макроспорангий bot: megasporangium.
макрофаг hist: macrophage.

макрофит bot: macrophyte.
макрофлора bot: macrophytic plants.
макроцистис bot: macrocyte (Macrocystis) brown algae.
~ грушеобразный giant kelp, vine kelp (M. pyrifera).
макроцитоз path: macrocytosis.
макрурус ichth: rat-tail (Macrurus).
макрурусовые (сем.) ichth:Macruridae.
максилла anat: maxilla.
максиллопеда zool: maxilloped.
максиллярная нога zool: maxilliped.
максиллярный anat: maxillary.
максимальный maximal.
малаколог malacologist.
малакология zool: malacology.
малая ампутация surg: minor amputation.
~ берцовая кость anat: fibula.
~ грудная мышца anat: coracopectoralis, entopectoralis.
~ губа anat: nympha; cf. срамная губа.
~ качурка orn: storm petrel (Hydrobates pelagicus).
~ крачка orn: little tern (Sterna a. albifrons).
~ кривизна (желудка) anat: lesser curvature.
~ многоугольная кость запястья anat: lesser multangular (or multangulum) minus, trapezoid.
~ полярная чайка orn: Iceland gull (Larus glaucoides).
~ седалищная вырезка anat: lesser ischiadic notch.
~ хирургия minor surgery.
~ чайка orn: little gull (Larus minutus).
~ ягодичная мышца anat: entogluteus.
малёк baby fish, young fish, small fry; see also молодь.
маленькая пилюля pharm: pillet.
маленький высохший прицветник bot: chaff.
~ гребешок zool: queen scallop (Pecten opercularis).
~ угорь (входящий в реку) ichth: elver.
маленькими дозами in small doses.
маленькое животное small animal, animalcule.
малигнитет malignancy.
малина bot: raspberry (Rubus idaeus).
~ степная = эфедра.
малиновка orn: robin.
~ лесная = м.-пересмешка.
~ -пересмешка icterine warbler (Hipolais icterine).
малиновый язык infect: strawberry tongue.

малио zool: malio Gecarcinus.
маллеатный жевательный аппарат zool: malleate jaws (of rotifers).
маллеораматный жевательный аппарат (коловраток) zool: malleo-ramate jaws (of rotifers).
малоберцовая кость anat: fibula, splint bone, perone.
~ мышца (длинная, короткая) anat: peroneus (longus, brevis) muscle.
малоберцовый fibular.
маловетвящийся subramose, sparingly branched.
малое выделение мочи path:oliguria.
~ крыло клиновидной кости anat: lesser wing of sphenoid bone.
~ слюноотделение path: oligoptyalism.
малокровие path: anemia.
~ с серповидными клетками hem: sickle-cell anemia.
малокровный anemic.
маломерная рыба undersized fish.
малоресничные (отр.) zool: Oligotricha.
малорослое животное runt.
малорослый кустарник bot: stunted brushwood.
~ подвой agr: small stature stock.
малоротый чёрный окунь ichth: small-mouth black bass, yellow perch (Micropterus dolomieu), southern small-mouth bass (M. pseudaplites).
малосемянный bot: few-seeded.
малотус "обезьянья морда" bot: kamila tree (Mallotus philippinensis, Muell. Arg.)
малоумие psych: oligophrenia.
малохромосомное растение chromosome-deficient plant.
малощетинковые кольчецы (кл.) zool: oligochaetous worms, tubificid worms (Oligochaeta).
малые акулы (сем.) ichth: small sharks (Scilliorhinidae).
~ косицы orn: lesser sickles.
~ крылья клиновидной кости anat: small wings of the sphenoid bone, ala parva.
малый буревестник orn: Manx shearwater (Puffinus p. puffinus).
~ вертел anat: entotrochanter.
~ журавль orn: small crane (Grus virgo).
~ коренной зуб anat: premolar tooth, bicuspid tooth.

малый круг кровообращения anat: pulmonary circulatory system, lesser circulatory system.
~ прудовик zool: Limnaea truncatula.
~ сальник anat: lesser omentum.
~ таз anat: lesser pelvis.
~ функциональный невроз minor functional neurosis.
~ эпилептический припадок neur: petit mal epilepsy.
мальва bot: mallow (Malva), see просвирняк.
мальвовые (сем.) bot: mallow family [(Malvaceae).
мальвоцветные (пор.) bot: Malvales order.
*мальма ichth: trout Salvenius malma.
мальпигиев сосуд hist: Malpighian vessel (or tubule).
мальпигиево тельце hist: Malpighian body, Malpighian corpuscle.
мальтийская лихорадка = бруцеллёз.
малярийная селезенка path: ague cake, ague spleen.
малярийный malarial, malarious, aguish.
~ комар see under комар.
малярийный психоз malaria psychosis.
малярия malaria, ague.
мамка ped: wet nurse.
маммит = грудница.
мамонт zool: mammoth (Elephas primigenius).
мамонтово дерево = веллингтония.
мамонцилла = медовая ягода.
мангль = мангровое дерево.
манго bot: mango (Mangifera indica).
мангольд bot: mangold, see свёкла листовая.
мангостан bot: mangosteen (Garcinia mangostana, G. pedunculata).
мангр = мангровое дерево.
мангро поблёскивающее bot: saltbush (Avicennia nitida, Jacq.)
мангровое дерево bot: mangrove (Rhizophora mangle).
мангровые (сем.) bot: mangrove family (Rhizophoraceae).
мангуст zool: mongoose (Herpestes).
мандарин bot: mandarin (Citrus nobilis, var. deliciosa, Swingle).
мандибулярная дуга embr: mandibular arch.
мандрагор = подофил.
мандрагора лекарственная bot: mandrake, love apple (Mandragora officinalis, Mill.)
мандрил zool: mandrill, large African baboon (Mandrillus, Papio mormon).
манежные движения neur: circus movements.
манжет(к)а cuff.
~ для определения кровяного давления blood-pressure cuff.
~ обыкновенная bot: lady's mantle (Alchemilla vulgaris).
маниак psych: maniac.
маниакальная речевая спутанность psych: manic speech confusion.
маниакально-депрессивный психоз manic-depressive psychosis, affective-reaction psychosis.
маниакальное помешательство raving madness.
маниок(а) bot: manioc, cassava (Manihot utilissima, Pohl., or Jatropa manihot). Cf. ятропа.
~ сладкий sweet manioc, sweet-potato tree, aipi (M. dulcis, Pax.)
манипуляция manipulation.
~ обоими руками conjoined manipulation.
манифестный manifest.
мания psych: mania.
~ бродяжничества dromomania.
~ красоты callomania.
~ мудрости sophomania.
~ обжорства phagomania.
~ покупок oniomania.
~ размышлений brooding mania.
~ сутяжничества processomania.
~ хирургических операций psychopathis chirurgicalis.
манная трава = манник.
манник bot: manna grass (Glyceria, R.Br.)
~ пловучий floating manna grass, floatgrass (G. fluitans).
мантийная линия zool: pallial line.
~ лопасть zool: mantle lobe (in mollusks).
~ полость zool: mantle cavity, pallial chamber.
мантия mantle.
~ мозга = плащ мозга.
маньчжурский заяц zool: Manchurian hare (Lepus mandschuricus).
маразм path: marasmus.
маразмический marasmic.
марал zool: Siberian deer, S. stag (Cervus canadensis asiaticus).
маранта bot: arrowroot (Maranta).
марантовые (сем.) bot: arrowroot family (Marantaceae).
мараттиевые (пор.) bot: Marattiales.
~ (сем.) bot: Marattiaceae (fam.)
марганец manganese, Mn.
марганцовка collq: see марганцевокислый калий.

марганцевокислый калий potassium permanganate.
маргаритка bot: daisy (Bellis).
~ обыкновенная marguerite, common garden daisy, English d. (B. perennis).
маргинальная клетка hist:border cell.
маргинальный шум marginal sound.
маргоза margosa (oil).
маргуай = кошка тигровая.
маревые = лебедовые.
марена = усач днепровский.
~ красильная bot: madder (Rubia tinctorum).
~ сердцелистная munjeet (R. cordifolia).
мареннин marennin (pigment).
мареновые (сем.) bot: madder family (Rubiaceae).
мареноцветные (пор.) bot: Rubiales.
маринка ichth: Schizothorax.
маркгравиевые (сем.) bot: Marcgraviaceae.
марлевая маска surg: gauze face mask.
~ повязка surg: gauze dressing.
марлевый бинт surg: gauze bandage.
~ тампон gauze pack, gauze plug.
~ шарик surg: gauze sponge.
марлерезка surg: gauze cutter.
марля gauze.
мармеладный плод bot: marmalade fruit, see лукума.
марсилейные (сем.) bot: marsilea family (Marsileaceae).
марсилея bot: marsilea, water clover (Marsilea).
мартиниевые (сем.) bot: martynia family (Martyniaceae).
мартиния bot: unicorn plant (Proboscidea, Schm.)
~ луизианская proboscis flower, ram's horn (P. louisianica).
мартышка zool: marmoset tamarin (Cercopithecus).
мартышкообразные (сем.) zool: monkey family Cercopithecidae.
марь = лебеда.
~ амброзиевидная = лебеда мексиканская.
~ вонючая stinking goosefoot (Chenopodium vulvaria).
~ головчатая strawberry blite, Indian paint (C. capitatum).
~ Доброго Генриха = "гусиные лапки"
~ цельнолистная = "гусиные лапки"
марьян-корень = пион.
маршанциевые (пор.) bot: thallose liverworts (Marchantiales).
маршанция bot: marchantia (Marchantia polimorpha).

маска entom: labium.
маскированное заболевание masked disease.
маскирующийся краб zool: masked crab (Corystes).
маскулинизирующий virilizing.
маслёнок bot: butter mushroom (Boletus luteus).
маслина bot: olive (Olea europaea).
~ американская wild olive (Osmanthus americanus, Gray).
~ дикая = лох.
маслинные (сем.) bot: olive family (Oleaceae).
масличная пальма bot: oil palm (Elaeis guineënsis, Jacq.)
масли̇чные = маслинные.
масло 1. butter; 2. oil; attar (volatile).
~ горьких миндалей pharm: oil of bitter almond.
~ какао pharm: cacao butter, theobroma oil.
~ померанцевой корки pharm: orange oil.
~ померанцевых цветов pharm: orange flower oil, neroli oil.
маслюк butterfish (Centronotus; Stromateidae; Poronotus triacanthus),

масляная кислота chem: butyric acid, butanoic acid.
~ пальма bot: palm Elaeis guineensis.
~ проба butter test.
маслянистый butyraceous, butyrous, buttery, butyroid; oily, unctuous.
масляное дерево bot: wood-oil tree (Aleurites fordii, Hemsl., or A. cordata, R. Br.)
массаж massage.
массажист masseur.
массажистка masseuse.
массивная ложноножка mcbio: lobopodium.
массирование masseuring.
массовая терапия mass treatment.
массовое заражение растений epiphytoxics.
массовый напад entom: bad attack.
мастакс zool: mastax (of rotifers).
мастиковое дерево bot: mastic tree, lentiscus (Pistacia lentiscus).
мастит path: mastitis.
мастодонт zool: Mastodon (extinct).
мастоидная кость anat: mastoid bone.
мастоидэктомия surg: mastoidectomy.
мастурбация psych: masturbation.
матамата zool: matamata (turtle).
матѐ bot: Paraguay tea, yerba (matѐ) (Ilex paraguariensis, St. Hil.)

материал для прививки inoculum.
материнка = нут.
материнская звезда hist: mother star, mother aster, monaster.
~ клетка hist: mother cell, brood c.
материнские семена genet: maternal
материнский maternal. seeds.
материнское растение bot: pistillate parent.
материя 1. bio see гной; 2. matter, substance; 3. fabric, cloth. [ли.
матерка = женское растение конопматико bot: matico (Piper angustifolium).
матка 1. anat: uterus, womb; 2. agr zool:
маточка anat: utricle, utriculus. | mare.
~ мужская anat: male utricle, utriculus masculinus.
маточковый anat: utricular. [ment.
маточная связка anat: uterine liga-
~ труба anat: uterine tube, oviduct.
маточник = змееголовник молдавский.
маточнобрюшная беременность obstet: uteroabdominal pregnancy.
маточное зеркало gyn: uterine mirror.
~ кровотечение uterine bleeding.
~ отверстие трубы anat: uterine opening of the oviduct, ostium internum.
~ стадо zool: brood stock.
маточно-трубный anat: uterotubal.
маточно-яичниковая беременность obstet: uteroovarian pregnancy.
маточные рожки = спорынья. [seeds.
~ семена genet: maternal seeds, mother
маточный зев anat: mouth of the uterus.
~ зонд gyn: uterine sound.
~ колпачок uterine veil, cervical pessary (contraceptive).
~ шум obstet: uterine souffle.
матрёнка bot: feathered columbine (Thalictrum aquilegifolium).
маттиола = левкой. [farfara).
мать-мачеха bot: coltsfoot (Tussilago
маун аптечный = валериана аптечная. [(Valerianaceae).
мауновые (сем.) bot: valerian family
мауреровская зернистость hem: Maurer's dots.
махаон entom: swallow-tail butterfly (Papilio machaon).
махать крыльями orn: flutter.
маховое крыло orn: oar feather.
~ ~ второго порядка orn: secondary.
~ ~ первого порядка orn: primary.

маховое перо orn: oar feather, remige.
маховые перья второго порядка orn: secondaries.
~ ~ первого порядка orn: primaries, flight feathers.
махония bot: mahonia (Mahonia).
махорка bot: wild tobacco, rustic t. (Nicotiana rustica).
махровый bot: double-flowering.
мацерация maceration.
мацерировать macerate.
мацони Caucasian soured milk.
мачёк bot: yellow-horned poppy (Glaucium luteum).
мачиленца entom: machilenza.
маш = фасоль азиатская.
~ -салат = валерианница овощная.
машинка для скатывания бинтов surg: bandage roller.
~ ~ стрижки волос hair clipper.
маяка bot: bog moss (Mayaca).
мбалоло = палоло. [смерть.
мгновенная смерть = внезапная
мегакариоцит hist: megakaryocyte.
мегалобластическая анемия megaloblastic anemia.
мегалоколон path: giant colon, Hirschsprung's disease.
мегалопа zool: megalops.
мегалоцит hem: gigantocyte.
мегантроп meganthropus.
мегаспора bot: megaspore.
мегаспорангий bot: megasporangium.
мегастоматобус ichth: bigmouth buffalo (Megastomatobus cyprinella).
мегатерий zool: Megatherium (a species of Gracigrada, cf. тихоходы).
мегафен megaphen.
мегацин megacine.
мед- medical.
медведи (сем.) zool: bears (Ursidae).
медведка entom: mole cricket, fen c. (Gryllotalpa). [africana).
~ восточная Eastern mole cricket (G.
~ обыкновенная common m.c.(G.gryllo-
~ одношипная G. unispina. |talpa).
медведь zool: bear (Ursus).
"медвежье ухо" = коровяк.
"медвежья лапа" = акант.
~ ягода bot: 1. buckberry (Gaylussacia ursina); 2. see водяника чёрная;
Меддокс Maddox. | 3. see толокнянка.
медеола bot: Indian cucumber (Medeola virginiana).
медиа(льная жилка) = срединная ж.

медиальная лодыжка anat: medial malleolus.
медиально-кубитальная жилка entom: vena medio-cubitalis.
медиальный пучок anat: medial funiculus.
медик medical man (physician, student).
медикамент medicament, drug.
медикаментозное лечение drug therapy, treatment by medicines, medication.
медикаментозный medicamental.
медицина medicine.
медицинская биография больного case history, anamnesis.
~ камера rad: health chamber.
~ норма physical standard.
~ пиявка zool: medicinal leech (Hirudo medicinalis).
~ помощь medical care.
~ радиология radiological medicine.
~ сестра nurse.
медицинский осмотр physical examination, medical examination.
~ персонал medical personnel, m. staff.
~ пункт medical station.
~ струнец = ришта.
~ факультет medical school (of a university).
~ эксперт medical examiner.
медицинское исследование medical investigation; physical check(up).
~ образование medical education.
~ обслуживание medical care, medical attendance.
~ освидетельствование physical examination.
медичка medical woman (physician, student, etc.)
медлительный sluggish.
медляк кукурузный entom: Pedinus femoralis (Tenebrionidae).
~ песчаный Opatrum sabulosum.
~ степной Blaps halophila.
~ широкогрудый = м. степной.
медобслуживание = медицинское обслуживание.
медовая ягода bot: honeyberry (Melicocca bijuga).
медовик мангровый = мангро поблёскивающее.
медовка = медяница яблонная.
медовник = жабрей.
медовые соты honeycomb.
медовый сахар honey sugar.
медонос = медоносное растение.
медоносная флора honey flora.
медоносное растение bot: honey plant, nectariferous plant, bee plant.
медоносный bot: nectarous.
медосборная площадь bee pasture.
медоуказчик orn: Indicatorus.

медперсонал = медицинский персонал.
медпомощь = медицинская помощь.
медпункт = медицинский пункт.
медсестра nurse.
~ здравохранения public health nurse.
медсостав medical staff.
медуалина ichth: half-moon (Medualina californiensis).
медуза zool: jellyfish, medusa.
медузка zool: young medusa, small m.
медузовидный zool: medusiform.
медузоид zool: medusoid.
медуллярная борозда embr: medullary groove.
~ пластинка embr: medullary plate.
медуллярный рак oncol: soft cancer.
медуница see 1. люцерна хмелевидная; 2. жабрей; 3. клевер красный.
медунка bot: 1. lungwort (Pulmonaria); 2. = люцерна хмелевидная; 3. = жабрей.
медяница see 1. веретеница; 2. листоблошка.
~ грушевая entom: pear psylla (Psylla pyri).
~ яблонная apple-tree psylla, apple sucker (P. mali), apple capsid (Plesiocoris rugicollis).
медянка = гладкий уж.
межбугорковая борозда anat: intertubercular sulcus.
межвертельная линия anat: intertrochanteric line.
межвидовое скрещивание interspecies cross.
межвидовой bio:interspecific.
межволокнистый interfibrous.
межволокновый = межволокнистый.
межворсинчатый hist: intervillous.
междольчатый interlobular.
междоузлие bot: internode, culm, ha(u)lm, neck.
между ветвями interramal.
~ двумя мозговыми извилинами anat: intergyral.
междугубный вырост interlabium (of roundworms).
межжаберный промежуток isthmus.
межжелудочковая перегородка anat: interventricular septum.
межжелудочковое отверстие anat: foramen interventriculare.
межзапястный сустав anat: intercarpal joint.
межзубной odont: interproximal.
межклеточная пластинка hist : interstitial lamella.
межклеточное вещество hist: intercellular substance.

межключичная связка anat: inter-
clavicular ligament.
межкомиссионный период mil: period
between physical examinations.
межкостная мышца (ладонная, тыльная) anat: interossei (volar, dorsal).
~ перепонка anat: interosseous membrane.
межкостный гребень anat: interosse-
~ нож surg: catling. ous crest.
межкрестцовые отверстия anat:
foramina intersacralia.
межлопаточное пространство anat:
interscapulum.
межлопаточный anat: interscapular.
межменструальные боли intermenstrual
pain. [muscular septum.
межмышечная перегородка anat: inter-
межмыщелковое возвышение anat:
intercondylar eminence. [duncularis.
межножковая ямка anat: fossa interpe-
межостистый anat: interspinous.
межпластинчатый interlamellar.
межплевральная спайка anat: interple-
межплодник bot:mesocarp.|ural adhesion.
межпозвоночная вырезка anat: intervertebral notch.
межпозвоночное отверстие anat:
intervertebral foramen.
межпородная помесь hybrid between
межпочечный anat:interrenal. races.
межпредсердная перегородка anat:
interatrial septum.
межрёберная аортальная артерия
anat: aortic intercostal artery.
~ мышца anat: intercostal muscle.[costales
межрёберные нервы anat: nervi inter-
межреберье anat: intercostal space.
межродовой intergeneric.
межседалищный anat: intersciatic.
межсосочковый anat: interpapillary.
межсуставной anat: interarticular.
межтеменная борозда anat: inter-
parietal fissure.
межтрапповый intertrappean.
межуточная беременность obstet:
parietal pregnancy.
межуточный intermediate, interstitial.
~ обмен intermediate metabolism.
межфаланговый сустав anat: interpha-
langeal joint; knuckle. |interchondral.
межхрящевой anat: intercartilaginous,
межчелюстная железа intermaxillary
gland (in amphibians).
~ кость anat: intermaxillary bone, inter-
мезга alburnum. maxilla.
мезентериальная нить zool: mesenterial
filament.

мезенхима hist:mesenchyme,mesenchyma.
мезенхимная опухоль mesenchymoma.
мезенхимный mesenchymal.
мезогиппус zool: Masohippus (extinct).
мезоглея zool: mesogloea.
мезоглия hist: mesoglia.
мезодерма anat: mesoderm. [blastic.
мезодермальный mesodermal; embr:meso-
мезозавры zool: Mesosauria (extinct
мезозойский mesozoic. |reptiles).
мезокарпий bot: mesocarp.
мезокотиле bot: mesocotyle.
мезолимнион mesolimnion.
мезопланктон bio: mesoplankton.
мезотелий hist: mesothelium.
мезотелиома mesothelioma.
мезофитный bio: mesophytic.
мезофрагма entom: mesophragm.
мейбомиева железа ophth: Meibomian
gland, tarsal gland.
Мейо Mayo.
мейоз genet: meiosis.
Мейснер Meissner. [tilage.
меккелев хрящ zool: Meckellian car-
мелакопия = горбыль светлый.
меланжер hem: blood-count pipette.
меланизм path: melanism.
меланин melanin.
меланобласт hist: melanoblast.
меланодермия path: melanoderm(i)a.
меланоз path: melanosis.
меланокарцинома melanocarcinoma.
меланома melanoma.
меланофор hist: melanophore.
меланурический path: melanuric.
меланурия melanuria.
меланхолик psych: melancholiac.
меланхолический melancholic.
меланхолия melancholy, melancholia.
меласса molasses. [coated feed.
мелассированный корм agr:sugar-
мелегетта = перец арабский.
мелена melena.
мелеспиза orn: song sparrow (Melos-
мелисса bot: balm (Melissa). |piza).
~ аптечная common balm, lemon b.,
balm mint (M. officinalis).
мелия bot: pride-of-India, China-tree,
margosa (Melia azedarach).
мелкая акула ichth: small shark, mor-
gay, dogfish (Squalidae, Carchariidae)
~ американская устрица neck clam
~ мышца small muscle, fine m.|(Ostrea).
~ нематода eelworm.
~ рыбёшка fry.
~ скумбрия ichth: spike.

мелкая спора bot: sporidium.
~ треска ichth: scrod.
~ чешуйка squamella.
~ щука ichth: pickerel (Esox niger, E. americanus, E. vermiculatus).
мелкие кровоизлияния petechia,
~ семена bot: fine seeds. |purpura.
~ хрипы fine rales.
мелкий тремор path: fine tremor.
мелкобахромчатый bot: fimbrillate.
мелковолокнистый bot: fine-fibrous, close-grained (of xylem).
мелкого размера ichth: minnow-sized.
мелко зазубренный = мелкозубчатый
мелкозернистый fine-grained, close-g.
мелкозубчатый finely serrate, serrulate, crenulate, denticulate.
мелкоклеточный hist: small-celled.
мелколепестник = богатинка.
мелколесье bot: undergrowth. [ease.
мелколистность phytp:little-leaf dis-
мелкоореховатый finely nutty.
мелкоосколочная рана mil: spatter
мелкоочаговый acinous. wound.
мелкопильчатый bot: finely sawtoothed,
мелкоплодный small-fruiting.|serrulatus.
мелкопузырчатые хрипы small babbling rales.
мелкоразмолотый finely ground.
мелкосеменные (пор.) bot: Microspermae (ord.) [xylem).
мелкослойный bot: fine-grained (of
мелкоточечный punctulate.
мелкочешуйчатый finely squamosed, squamulose, squamulate, scurfy.
мелкоячеистый fine-meshed, finely honeycombed; cf. ячеистый.
мелкоячейный = мелкоячеистый.
мелозира bot: Melosira (alga).
мелькания pl: flicker.
мельничный газ silk bolting cloth.
меляноцетус ichth: black whalelet (Melanocetus).
мембрана membrane, diaphragm.
~ с избирательной проницаемостью bio: permselective membrane. [tozoa).
мембранелла zool: membranella (in pro-
мембранный фильтр membrane filter.
менадион menadione.
менделеевская таблица chem: Mendele-
менделизм Mendelism.|eff chart,periodic c
мендес-антилопа zool: addax (Addax nasomaculatus).
менёк ichth: cusk (Brosmius).
мензурка measuring glass, graduated g., medicine g., beaker.

менингеальный meningeal.
менингит path: meningitis. [tis.
~ основания мозга basilar meningi-
менингококковая инфекция meningococcus infection.
менингококковый meningococcal.
мениск meniscus.
менопауза menopause. [norrhea.
менорагия gyn: menorrhagia, hyperme-
меностазия gyn: menostasia, suppressed menstruation.
менструальное жёлтое тело = жёлтое тело менструации.
менструальный menstrual, catamenial.
~ цикл menstrual cycle.
менструация menstruation, catamenia.
~ без овуляции anovular menstruation.
менструировать menstruate.
менструирующая женщина menstruant.
ментальность mentality.
ментициррус ichth: ground mullet (Menticirrhus), sea m., barb, bull-
ментол pharm:menthol. |head whiting.
менхаден ichth: menhaden,
Brevoortia tyrannus,

мера measure.
~ предосторожности precaution.
мерикарпий bot: mericarp.
мерин gelded horse.[sheep (Ovis aries).
меринос(овая овца) agr zool:merino
мерисмопедия bot: Merismopedia (colo-
меристема bio: meristem. |nial algae).
меристематический meristematic.
меристемный bio: meristemetic.
меристический meristic.
меритерий zool: Moeritherium (extinct)
меркаптоэтиламин mercaptoethylamine.
меркурол pharm: mercury nucleid.
мерланг ichth: whiting (Odontogadus).
~ черноморский Black-Sea w. (O. mer-
мерланка = мерланг. langus).
мермисы worms Mermitidae.
мерабластическое яйцо embr:mero-
мерозоит zool: merozoite.|blastic egg.
меромиза entom: fly Meromyza saltatrix.
мерон entom: meron.
мероприятие measure, step, procedure.
меростомовые zool: Merostomata (of phylum Arthropoda), see ракоскорпио-
мерпурат pharm: merpurate. ны.
мёртвая голова entom: sphinx Acheron-
~ спелость dead ripeness.|tia atropos.
мертвенность (шелкопряда) = фляшерия.
мертвецкая mortuary, morgue.

мёртвое пространство dead air spaces (in lungs).
~ тело dead body. [beetle Aclypea opaca.
мертвоед гладкий entom: carrion-
~ голый c.-b. Aclypea undata.
~ тёмный c.-b. Silpha obscura.
мертвоеды (сем.) entom: carrion-beetles (Silphidae). [lity.
мертворождаемость obstet: mortinata-
мертворождённый obstet: stillborn.
мёртвый dead.
мертензия bot: lungwort (Mertensia).
~ морская sea l., oysterleaf (M. mari-
мертиолат pharm: merthiolate. |tima)
мерулиус bot: Merulius (fungi).
~ домовый = м. плачущий.
~ плачущий M. lacrimans, Fr.
Мерфи Murphy. [fibrillation.
мерцание желудочков ventricular
мерцательная аритмия int: ciliary arrythmia.
~ клетка hist: ciliated cell; flame c.
мерцательное движение ciliary mo-
~ пламя ciliary flame. tion.
мерцательный эпителий hist: ciliated epithelium. [scotoma.
мерцающая скотома ophth: flimmer
мескито bot: algaroba, carob (Prosopis).
мескитовое дерево bot: mesquit(e) (Prosopis juliflora, DC.)
месмеризм mesmerism, psycheism.
местная анестезия local anesthesia.
~ эпилепсия = джексоновская э.
местное заболевание local(ized) dis-
~ лечение topical treatment. ease.
~ малокровие path: ischemia.
~ полнокровие path: hyperemia.
~ поражение path: focal lesion.
местный наркоз local anesthesia, toponarcosis.
место воздействия point of action.
~ отхождения anat: origin.
~ распространения bio: habitat.
местообитание bio: habitat, occurrence
месячные (крови) physl: menses.
метаболизм metabolism.
метаболический metabolic.
метаболия bio: metaboly (in protozoa).
метакортандрацин metacortandracin.
метаксения genet: metaxenia, metaxeny.
метаксилема bot: metaxylem.
металимнион metalimnion.
металлический звон bell sound, coil s., bell tympany, tinkling.
метамер zool: metamere.
метамерия metamerism.
метамерность metamerism.
метамерный metameric.
метамиэлоцит hist: metamyelocyte.
метаморфоза metamorphosis.
~ пола sex reversal.
метанауплиус zool: metanauplius.
метанефрос zool: metanephros.
метастаз path: metastasis.
метастазирование metastatic spread.
метастатическая опухоль oncol: metastatic tumor.
~ подагра transferred gout. [cancer.
метастатический рак metastatic
метать детёнышей zool: litter, cub.
~ икру ichth: lay, shed the eggs, oviposit, cast forth; spat (oysters).
метафаза hist: metaphase.
метахромазия hist: metachromasia.
метахроматическое включение hist: metachromatic granule.
метахроматичность metachromatism.
метацеркария metacercaria.
метёлка bot: panicle, head (of grass).
~ с различными типами ветвления bot: thyrse.
метельник прутьевидный bot: Spartium junceum.
метельчато-колосовые злаки = султанные з.[grasses, paniculate g.
метельчатые злаки bot: panicle(d)
метельчатый bot: panicle(d).
метеоризм path: meteorism, tympanites; see also вздутие. [gical.
метеоробиологический meteorobiolo-
метизировать agr zool: mongrelize.
метилацетониланилин methyl-acetonyl-aniline.
метилен chem: methylene.
метиленгиппуровая кислота pharm: methylene hippuric acid.
метилендигалуссовокислый висмут pharm: bismuth methylenedigallate.
метилмышьяковокислый натрий pharm: sodium methylarsenate.
метилоранж methyl orange.
метилфенилгликоколл methyl-phenyl-
метионин methionine. glycocoll.
метионинтионил methionine sulfoxide.
метка mark, tag.
~ для рыб fish tag.
метла обыкновенная = метлица.
метлица 1. bot: silky bentgrass, corn grass (Apera spika-venti); 2. entom: caddis fly (Phryganeodea).

метлица подсолнечная entom: sunflower moth (Homolosoma nebulella, Hb.)
метоксихлор chem: methoxychlor.
метоптерин methopterin.
метральгия gyn: uterine pain.
"метрика" collq: birth certificate.
метрит gyn: metritis.
мефенезин pharm: mephenesin.
меха furs, furriery. [nical stimulus.
механический раздражитель mecha-
механически форсированный выдох av med: mechanically forced expiration.
механотерапия manipulative treatment.
меч-рыба swordfish (Xiphias gladius).
~ -трава bot: twig rush (Cladium).[ate.
мечевидный sword-shaped, ensiform, gladi-
~ отросток (грудины) anat: xiphoid process, ensisternum.
~ хрящ anat: ensiform cartilage.
мечение marking; rad: labeling, tagging
меченый C_{14} каротин rad: C_{14} labeled carotene.
мечехвост zool: king crab, horseshoe c. horsefoot (Limulus polyphemus).
мечехвосты (отр.) zool: king crabs
мечтание psych: reverie. (Xiphosura).
Мешберн Mashburn.
мешковидный sacciform.
мешкожаберные zool: Marsipobranchii, see круглоротые.
мешок anat: sac, bag(like covering),
~ амниона embr: amniotic sac. |pouch.
~ любовных стрел zool: dart sac (in
мешотчатый sacculate(d). |mollusks).
мешочек saccule, sacculus, utricle.
миалгический path: myalgic.
миалгия path: myalgia.
миастения path: myasthenia.
мигание ophth: blinking, nictitating.
мигательная перепонка ophth zool: nictitating membrane, haw.
мигательночелюстной рефлекс neur: jaw-winking reflex.
мигать blink, wink.
мигрант migrant.
миграционная стадия личинок helm: metacercarial stage.
миграция migration, wandering.
мигреневый path: migrainous.
мигрень path: migraine.
мигрирующее микроядро zool: wandering (male) micronucleus.
мигрирующие рыбы catadromous fishes.
мигрирующий migrating, migratory.
мидиевая банка zool: mussel ground.
мидия zool: sea mussel with byssus (Mytilus). [lis).
~ обыкновенная common mussel (M.edu-
~ съедобная = м. обыкновенная.
мие- = миэ-. [(Mysidacea).
мизида zool: mysid, opossum-shrimp
~ реликтовая crustacean Mysis relicta.
мизидные = расщеплённоногие.
мизинец anat: little finger.
мизолин mysoline.
мизофобия psych: mysophobia, filth
микобактерия mycobacterium. |dread.
микобактин mycobactin.
микоз path: mycosis.
~ ротовой полости orn: thrush.
микоза bot: mycose.
микозный path: mycotic.
микоин micoin.
миколог bot: mycologist.
микология mycology.
миколютеин mycolutein.
микомицеты bot: mycomycetes (fungi).
микориза bot: mycorrhiza.
микотоксикоз mycotoxicose [plants.
микотрофия растений mycotrophy in
микрастериас bot: Micrasterias (algae)
микроаэрофильный microaerophilic.
*микроб mircobe, germ.
микробиолог microbiologist.
микробиологический microbiologic.
микробиология microbiology.
микробная инфекция microbiosis.
микробный microbic, microbal, microbian, germinal.
микробоноситель germ carrier.
микробоубивающее средство microbicide, germicide.
микробоубивающий microbicidal, germi-
микрогамета microgamete. cidal.
микроглия hist: microglia.
микрогорелка lab: microburner.
микроживотное animalcule.
микрозаурия zool: Microsauria (extinct)
микрозооспора microzoospore. [line.
микрокристаллический microcrystal-
микромания psych: delusion of littleness, micromania. [screw.
микрометрический винт micrometer
микронуклеус bio: micronucleus.
микроопределение microdetermination.
микроорганизм microorganism.
микропиле bot: micropyle.
микропипетка lab: micropipette.
микропланктон microplankton.
микропогон ichth: crocus, ronco (Micropogon undulatus).

микропрепарат lab: microslide, slide mount.
микропреципитин microprecipitin.
микрорастение microphyte.
микрореспирометр microrespirometer.
микросжигание microincineration.
микросклера microsclere (of sponges).
микроскоп microscope.
микроскопистmicroscopist.
микроскопическая анатомия microscopic anatomy, histology.
микроскопическое животное microscopic animal, microzoon.
микроскопия microscopy.
микросома microsome.
микроспора bot: microspore.
микроспорангий bot: microsporangium.
микроспоридии (отр.) zool: Microsporidia.
микроспорогенез bot: microsporogenesis.
микросреда microenvironment.
микросфера bot: fungi Microsphaera.
микротом microtome, histotome.
микрофанурус исчерченый entom: Microphanurus semistriatus.
микрофауна microfauna.
микрофиляриоз microfilariasis.
микрофлора microflora.
~ и микрофауна microbiota.
микрофотография photomicrograph.
микрохимический microchemical.
микрохимия microchemistry.
микроцефалическая идиотия psych: microcephalic idiocy.
микроцефалический path: microcephalic, microcephalous.
микроцефалия path: microcephaly.
микроцистис bot: Microcystis (colonial algae).
микроэлемент microelement.
микседема path: myxedema, Gull's disease.
микседематозный myxedematous.
миксина hagfish.
миксины ichth: hagfishes (Myxini).
миксобактерия myxobacteria.
миксома path: myxoma.
миксоматоз myxomatosis.
миксоматозный myxomatous.
миксомицет bot: myxomycete (fungus).
миксоптеригий clasper.
микстура pharm: mixture.
миктерия orn: wood ibis (Mycteria americana, Tantalus loculator).
миктероперка ichth: scamp (Mycteroperca falcata).
милиарный miliary, millet-seed size.
милиарный туберкулёз int: miliary tuberculosis.
миллефоль = стотысячник обыкновенный.
мильдью phytp: mildew, see ложная мучнистая роса.
мимариды (сем.) entom: Mymaridae.
мимикрическая окраска bio: assimilative coloration.
мимикрия mimicry, living camouflage.
мимический паралич лица neur: histrionic palsy.
мимоза bot: mimosa; see also акация австралийская.
~ стыдливая humble plant, sensitive plant (Mimosa pudica).
мимозовые (подсем.) Mimosoideae subfamily.
~(сем.) Mimosaceae family.
миндалевидное ядро amygdalus.
миндалина 1. anat: tonsil(la); 2. bot: almond (seed).
~ Герлаха anat: Gerlach's tonsil.
миндаль bot: almond (Amygdalus).
~ горький bitter a. (A. communis).
~ земляной ground a., yeloow nut grass (Cyperus esculentus).
индийский = миробалан.
~ сладкий sweet almond.
~ тропический = миробалан.
миндальная эмульсия pharm: almond milk.
миндальное масло pharm:almond oil.
миндальнокислый антипирин pharm: antipyrine mandelate.
минёр entom: miner.
~ гороховый pea-leaf miner.
~ клюквенный fruit worm (Mineola vaccinii).
~ нутовый fly Liriomyza cicerina.
~ спаржевый asparagus miner (Argomyza simplex).
минёры cf. моли.
минералокортикоидный mineralocorticoid.
минеральная вода mineral water.
минеральные воды 1. mineral waters; 2. watering place.
минеральный источник mineral spring.
~ обмен mineral metabolism.
минимальный minimal.
минирующие мушки (сем.) entom: Agromyzidae.
Министерство здравоохранения Public Health Ministry (USSR).
министрема ichth: spotted sucker (Mynystrema melanops).
минночехликовые cf. моли.

минога zool: lamprey, See also морская м., речная м.
миноги zool: Lampreys (Petromyzones).
минтай ichth: pollack, pollock (Theragra chalcogramma).
минутный объем дыхания respiratory minute volume.
~ ~ сердца cardiac output.
миобластома myoblastoma.
миогипсина miogypsina.
миозит path: myositis.
миозитический myositic.
милкард anat: myocardium.
миокардиодистрофия int: myocardid dystrophy. [myocardosis.
миокардиопатия int: myocardiopathy,
миокардит path: myocarditis.
миоклонический myoclonic.
миоклонус myoclonus.
миометрий anat: myometrium.
мионема zool: myoneme.
миопический ophth: myopic.
миопиэзин miopiesin.
миопия ophth: myopia.
миотом embr: myotome.
миофриски zool: myofrisks.
миоценовый miocene.
мирабель bot: mirabelle, see вишне-слива.
миражирование agr: candling (of eggs).
мирацидий zool: miracidium.
мирингопластика otolar: myringoplasty.
мирихтис ichth: snake eel (Myrichthys colubrinus).
мирмекофил entom: myrmecophile, ant-loving.
миробалан bot: myrobalan, almendra (Phyllanthus emblica, Terminalia catappa).
мирон 1. ichth: see усач; 2. entom: see бражник виноградный.
*мирофис ichth: worm ell (Myrophis).
мирт болотный bot: leatherleaf, cassandra (Chamaedaphne calyculate, Moench.)
~ восконосный = восковник 1.
~ обыкновенный bot: myrtle (Myrtus communis).
мирта болотная = восковник 1.
миртовые (сем.) bot: Myrtaceae.
миртоцветные (пор.) bot: Myrtales, Myrtiflorae.
митилизм path: mytilism.
митоз hist: mitosis.
митотическая активность mitotic activity.
митохондрия bio: mitochondria.
митральный клапан anat: mitral valve.
митральный стеноз path: mitral stenosis.
~ шум mitral murmur.
мицелевидный mycelium-like.
мицелий bot: mycelium.
мицелла micella.
мицеллярный micellar.
мицетом entom: micetomos.
Мичерлих Mitscherlich.
миэлин neur: myelin.
миэлиновый myelinous.
миэлит path: myelitis.
~ вследствие прижатия pressure myelitis.
миэлитик myelitic.
миэлобласт hist: myeloblast.
миэлограмма x-ray: myelogram.
миэлоидная ткань hist: myeloid tissue.
миэлома oncol: myeloma.
миэлоцит hist: myelocyte.
младенец baby, infant.
младенческий опыт infantile experience.
младший хирург assistant surgeon.
млекообразующий lactific.
млекопитающее zool: mammal (Mammalia)
млекопитающие zool: mammals (Mammalia), see звери.
млекопитающий adj: mammalian.
млечная трубка bot: lactiferous vessel.
млечник bot: 1. lactarius (Lactarius); 2. sea milkwort (Glaux);3.milk vessel.
млечносоковый bot: lactescent.
млечный lactic, lacteal; chylous, chyliferous.
~ проток anat: lactiferous duct, milk duct.
~ синус anat: lactiferous sinus.
~ сок physl: chyle; bot: milky sap, latex.
~ сосуд anat: chyliferous vessel; bot; milk vessel, latex v.
мнемоника psych: mnemonics.
мнимая беременность obstet: false pregnancy.
~ смерть apparent death, mors putativa.
мнимое восприятие psych: hallucination.
многоатомный спирт chem: polyol.
многобороздчатый multisulcate.
многобугорчатые млекопитающие zool: Multituberculata (extinct).
многоветвистые турбеллярии (отр.) zool: polyclads (Polyclada, Polycladida).
многовитковый multispiral.
многоглазая планария zool: many-eyed planarian (Polycelis nigra).
многогнёздный multilocular, plurilocular, polycystic, see also многокамерный.

многодольчатый multilobate.
многожгутиковые (отр.) zool: Polymastigina.
многожгутиковый bio: multiflagellate.
многозачатковый genet: polyembryonic.
многозубчатый multicuspid.
многокамерный many-chambered, polythalamous, multilocular, see also многогнёздный.
многоклеточные животные multicell animals, metazoans (Metazoa, Polycytozoa).
многоклеточный multicellular.
многокоренник bot: water flaxseed, great duckweed (Spirodela).
многокоренной multirooted.
многокорзиночное растение bot: multiple-headed plant.
многократное деление multiple fission.
многократно-складчатый bot: plicate.
многолепестные bot: polypetalae.
многолепестный bot: polypetalous.
многолетний bot: perennial.
многолетник bot: perennial.
многометамерные черви zool: Vermes polymera, see кольчатые черви.
многомлечник = истод.
многоножка milleped, diplopod, wireworm (Blanjulus, Spirobolus, etc.)
~ обыкновенная bot: polypody, wall fern (Polypodium vulgare).
многоножки (кл.) zool: myriapods (Myriapoda).
многообразие variety, diversity, polymorphism.
многоосный сустав anat: multiaxial joint.
многопёр ichth: Polypterus.
многопёрые ichth: Polyteri.
многоплодная беременность obstet: multiple pregnancy.
многоплодниковые bot: polycarpicae.
многоплодный bot: polycarpous.
многопоровые грибы (сем.) bot: pore fungi (Polyporaceae).
многорезцовые zool: Polyprotodontia.
многоресничатый multiciliate.
многоречивость = болтливость.
многорожавшая multipara.
многорядный multirow, polystichous.
многосегментный zool: polysomitic.
многосемянный bot: manyseeded.
многослойный эпителий hist: tesselated epithelium, stratified e.
многостебельчатое растение bot: multiple-headed plant.
многоугольная кость = большая, малая м. к.

многоцветковый bot: multiflorous, multiflowered, polyanthous, many-flowered (multiflorus).
многоцветница entom: multicolor angle-wing (Vanessa polychloros).
многоцветный 1. polychromatic; 2. see многоцветковый.
многочленистые цестоды helm: polyzoic cestodes.
многочленистый multiarticulate, many-segmented.
многощетинковые кольчецы (кл.) zool: polychaetous worms, sandworms, tube worms, etc. (Polychaeta).
многощетинковые (черви) = м. кольчецы.
многоядерный multinuclear.
многоядность zool: polyphagia.
множественная беременность multifelation.
~ инфекция multiinfection.
множественное воспаление нервов path: multiple neuritis, polyneuritis.
~ ~ суставов polyarthritis.
~ образование зародышей bio: polyembryony.
множественные родимые пятна multiple naevi.
множественный келоид multiple keloid.
~ перелом surg: multiple fracture.
~ склероз path: multiple sclerosis.
мобильный mobile.
могар bot: mohar, see просо итальянское.
могущий загнивать putrescible.
модиола zool: modiola (Modiola).
моёвка молодая = крачка.
~ обыкновенная orn: kittiwake (Rissa t. tridactyla).
можжевеловая ягода bot: juniper berry.
можжевельник bot: juniper (Juniperus).
~ виргинский red cedar, savin, pencil cedar (J. virginiana).
~ казацкий (казачий) savin (J. sabina).
~ красный red juniper (J. oxycedrus).
мозазавры zool: Mosasauria (extinct).
мозаика сахарного тростника phytp: sugar cane mosaic.
мозаичность phytp: mosaic disease.
мозг anat: brain, encephalon. See also головной м., костный м., спинной м. и т.п.
"~ разрывается" av med: skull feels as if about to burst.
мозговая вена anat: cerebral vein.
~ волна brain wave.
~ грыжа path: cerebral hernia.
~ доля anat: cerebral lobe.
~ извилина anat: gyrus, brain convolution.

мозговая кость marrowbone.
~ оболочка anat: meninx.
~ пластинка embr: neural plate.
мозговидное вещество hist: medullary substance.
мозговик = овечий м.
мозговое вещество anat: medulla.
~ ~ почки hist: renal medulla.
~ кровообращение cerebral (blood) circulation.
мозговой anat: cerebral, encephalic.
~ водопровод anat: cerebral aqueduct, aqueduct of Silvius.
~ желудочек anat: ventricle of the brain.
~ кровоток cerebral blood stream.
~ мост anat: pons.
~ песок path: brain sand, corpora arenacea.
~ плащ anat: brain mantle, pallium.
~ придаток anat: pituitary body or gland, hypophysis cerebri.
~ пузырь embr: (primary) brain vesicle; cerebral v.
~ ствол anat: brain stem.
мозжечковый anat: cerebellar.
мозжечок anat: cerebellum.
мозоленогие (подотр.) zool: camels (Tylopoda).
мозолистое тело anat: corpus callosum.
мозолистый callous.
мозоль callus, callositas, tyloma, tylosis, keratoma; clavus, corn.
мозольный пластырь pharm: corn plaster.
мойва ichth: capelin (Mallotus villosus).
мокнущая экзема derm: weeping eczema.
мокрец 1. entom: culicoide, sandfly, punkie, "no-see-um" (Culicoides); 2. vet: malanders.
мокрица 1. entom: woodlouse (Oniscus); 2. see звездчатка средн.
~ обыкновенная zool: sowbug (Oniscus asellus).
~ свёртывающаяся Armadillum cinereum.
~ сухопутная = м. обыкновенная.
мокричник bot: alsine, chickweed (Alsine).
мокричный bot: alsinaceous.
мокрота sputum.
~ с жилками крови path: blood-streaked sputum.
молелистовёртка яблонная entom: Simaethis pariana.
молелистовёртки (сем.) entom: Glyphipterygidae.
моли выемчатокрылые (сем.) entom: moths Gelechiidae.
~ горностаевые (сем.) ermine-moths (Hyponomeutidae).
~ -минёры узкокрылые (сем.) narrow-winged leaf-miners (Lyonetidae).
~ минночехликовые (сем.) leaf-miner case-bearer moths (Incurvariidae).
~ настоящие (сем.) entom: tineids moths (Tineidae). See моль.

моли-пестрянки (сем.) Lithocolletidae.
молибден molybdenum, Mo.
молиния bot: moorgrass (Molinia).
~ голубая purple m. (M. caerulea).
моллиенизия ichth: sailfin Mollie (Mollienisia latipinna)
моллюск mollusk.
~ с сифоном siphon-feeder mollusk.
моллюски (тип) zool: mollusks (Mollusca).
моллюсковый zool: molluscan.
молодая возрастная группа ichth: recruit stock.
~ жирная сельдь matty.
~ личинка zool: larvule.
~ особь zool: juvenile, young.
~ свинья zool: gilt, immature sow.
~ сельдь ichth: sperling (Clupea harengus).
~ треска dorse.
~ устрица zool: young oyster, germling.
молодило bot: houseleek (Sempervium).
молодняк youngsters; young stock (cattle).
молодой гаметофит young gametophyte,
~ заяц zool: young hare, leveret.
~ луфарь ichth: skip meckerel (Pomotomus saltatrix), snapping m., blue snapper.
~ олень zool: young deer, roe fawn.
~ погониас ichth: striped drum (Pogonias cromis)
~ спорофит = м. гаметофит.
молодь zool: young(sters); spat (mollusks); ichth: brood, fry, baby fish, fingerling, advanced fry; see also малёк.
~ лосося salmon fry.
~ сельди brit (Clupea harengus).
молозивное тельце colostrum corpuscle.
молозивный colostric.
молозиво physl: colostrum, foremilk, beestings.
молозийный = молозивный.
молокан синий bot: little bluestem (Mulgedium tataricum, DC.)
*молóки ichth: milt roe, soft r., testicular fluid.
молокó milk.
~ кормилицы ped: wet nurse's milk.
молокогонное средство (ga)lactogogue.
молокоотсос breast pump.
молоткообразное искривление пальца ноги path: hammer toe.
молоткообразные движения кистей рук neur: maleation.
~ пальцы ног path: hammer toes.
молоточек anat: hammer, malleus.
молоточковый anat: mallear.
молот-рыба hammer-head shark (Sphyrna zygaena).
молочаецветные (пор.) bot: Euphorbiales.
молочай bot: spurge, milkwort, wolf's milk (Euphorbia).

молочай гигантский giant milkweed (Asclepias gigantea, Willd.) [spurge.
~ чиновидный bot: mole plant, caper
~ японский Japasese spurge (Pachysandra terminalis, Sieb.& Fuss.)
молочайник = млечник. [ous plant.
молочайное растение bot:euphorbiace-
молочайные (сем.) bot: spurge fam.(Eu-
молочная вена milk vein.|phorbiaceae).
~ железа anat: mamma(ry gland), milk-
~ кислота lactic acid. |secreting g.
~ планария zool: planarian Dendrocoelum
~ смесь milk mixture. lacteum
~ сыворотка whey. [полевой.
молочник = 1. млечник; 2. осот
молочница ped: thrush, mycotic stomatitis; vet: aphtha, ulcer in the mouth; milk fever.
молочное брожение lactic fermentation.
~ дерево bot: milk tree (Brosimum galactodendron).
~ тельце milk corpuscle.
молочнокислое брожение = молочное
~ серебро pharm: silver lactate. |б.
молочнокислые бактерии lactobacilli.
молочнокислый висмут bismuth lactate.
~ кокаин pharm: cocaine lactate.
~ магний pharm: magnesium lactate.
~ натрий pharm: sodium lactate. [te.
~ эфир бетанафтола betanaphthol lacta-
молочномагниевая соль = молочнокислый магний. [pyretic.
молочнолихорадочный path: galacto-
молочный зуб anat: milk tooth,temporary
~ камень vet: milkstone.|t.,deciduous t.
~ сахар milk sugar.
~ свищ surg: milk fistula.
~ скот agr: dairy cattle.
~ струп milk scab.
~ шарик mcscop: milk globule.
молукская трава bot: balm (Molucella laevis). [phaga, etc.)See моли.
моль entom: tineid, moth (Tinea, Tricho-
~ амбарная wheat-flour moth (Tinea granella). [lus.
~ бересклетовая Hyponomeuta cognatel-
~ вишнёвая побеговая Argyresthia ephipella.
~ восковая wax moth, bee m., miller (Tinea mellonella, Galleria m., etc.)
~ гороховая pea moth (Laspeyresia, semasia nigricana).
~ зерновая grain moth, wolf m. (Tinea granella); Angoumois grain moth (Sitotroga cerealella), flyweevil (S. arearella).

моль зонтичная entom:umbelliferous-plant moth (Depressaria depressella).
~ капустная diamond-back moth (Plutella maculipennis, P.cruciferarum).
~ картофельная potato moth (Phthorimaea operculella). [taperiella).
~ ковровая tapestry moth (Trichophaga
~ комнатная = м. малая платяная.
~ крошка small miner Lyonetia.
~ лиственничная larch miner (Coleophora laricella). [assectella).
~ луковая onion moth (Acrolepia
~ малая платяная lesser clothes moth, webbing m. (Tineola bisselliella)
~ малинная moth (Lampronia rubiella, Incurvaria rubiella).
~ мальвовая mallow moth (Gelechia malvella). [oleellus).
~ маслинная olive-tree moth (Prays
~ мебельная = м. малая платяная.
~ мелкая восковая lesser wax moth (Ancherioia grisella).
~ ~ медовая = м. мелкая восковая
~ мучная flour m. (Ephestis kuehniella)
*~ пестрянка сиреневая moltey lilac moth (Caloptila syringella).
~ ~ тополевая motley poplar moth (Lithocolletis populifoliella).
~ платяная = м. малая платяная.
~ плодовая fruit-tree ermine moth (Hyponomeuta padellus); see also м. яблонная.
~ подсолнечниковая = огнёвка п.
~ пчелиная = м. восковая.
~ рябиновая apple-fruit miner (Argyresthia conjugella).[schema ocel.)
~ свекловичная beet miner (Gnorimo-
~ смородинная currant moth (Incurvaria capitella). [glicinivarella).
~ соевая soybean moth (Laspayresia
~ стеблевая Ochsencheimeria taurella.
~ тминная caraway-plant moth (Depressaria nervosa).
~ фруктовая полосатая peach twig-borer (Anarsia linealata).
~ хищная pyralid (Pyralidae).
~ хлебная = м. зерновая.
~ хлопковая pink bollworm (Pectinophora gossypiella).
~ ~ чеканщица Platyedra vitella.
~ черёмуховая горностаевая Hyponomeuta evonymellus. [polyphemus).
~ шелковичная polyphemus moth (Telea
~ яблонная apple-tree ermine-moth (Hyponomeuta malinellus); see also моль плодовая.

моляр molar. [pregnancy.
молярная беременность obstet: molar
момордика bot: momordica (Momordica).
~ бальзамическая balsam pear (M. balsamina). [charantia).
~ харантская art pumpkin, la-kwa (M.
монада bio: monad. [tract.
монаковский пучок anat: rubrospinal
монантохлёэ bot: salt-flat grass (Monanthochloë littoralis, Engelm.)
монарда bot: monarda, horsemint, balm
~ дидима oswego tea, bee [(Monarda). balm, fragrant balm (M. didyma).
~ трубчатая wild bergamot (M.fistulosa)
монастер = материнская звезда.
монашенка = шелкопряд-монах.
монгольская идиотия psych: Mongolian idiocy, Mongolism.
монера bio: monera.
монетный звон path: bell sound.
~ столбик hem: coin roll, rouleau. Cf. образование монетных столбиков.
монетоизвлекатель coin catcher.
монетообразный nummiform, nummular.
монитор zool: monitor (Varanidae).
моногенез bio: monogenesis.
моногенетические сосальщики (подкл.) zool: monogenetic trematodes (Monogenea, Heterocotylea).
монозиготный genet: monozygotic.
монокальций calcium.
монокарпический bot: monocarpic.
монокотиль bot: monocotyl(edon).
монокулярная диплопия ophth: monocular diplopia.
монокулярное зрение ophth: monocular
мономорфизм monomorphism. [vision.
мононуклеар hem: mononuclear leukocyte.
мононуклеоз path: mononucleosis.
моноплегия path: monoplegia.
моноспермия bio: monospermy.
монотаксис ichth: mamamu (Monotaxis).
монотипный род bot: monotypic genus.
монотрих mcbio: monotrichate.
монотычиночный bot: monandrous.
моноуксуснокислый пирогаллол pharm: pyrogallol monoacetate.
монофагия zool: monophagia.
монофилетический monophyletic.
моноциклический monocyclic.
моноцит hem: monocyte.
моноцитный hem: monocytic.
моноцитоз path: monocytosis.
мор = чума.
моральная идиотия psych: moral idiocy.
моральная распущенность moral
морг morgue. delinquency.
моргание = мигание. [рыло.
морда zool: face, snout; see also
мордовник bot: globe thistle (Echi-
морель bot: marilla, amarella, |nops). morello, pale sour cherry (Prunus cerasus acida, Ehrh.)
морж zool: walrus, morse, sea horse (Odobenus, O. rosmarus). [baenidae).
моржи (сем.) zool: walrus family (Odo-
морилка bio: killing tube, k. jar.
мория psych: moria.
морковь bot: carrot (Daucus).
моровая язва = чума.
морозник bot: bear's-foot (Helleborus).
~ восточный lenten rose (H. orienta-
морозобоина frost crack, f.hole[lis).
морозобой winterkilling.
морозостойкость frost resistance, f. hardiness.
морошка bot: molka, baked-apple (berry), cloudberry (Rubus chamaemorus).
морская бабочка zool: sea butterfly (Pteropoda) mollusk.
~ болезнь seasickness.
~ вода sea water.
~ водоросль seaweed, varec. [rina).
~ выдра zool: sea otter (Enhydris ma-
~ звезда zool: asterid, starfish.
~ ~ обыкновенная common starfish (Asterias rubens).
~ змея zool: sea snake (Hydrophiidae).
~ камбала ichth: true plaice (Pleuronectes platessa).
~ капуста bot: kombu (Laminariaceae).
*~ корова zool: 1. extinct sea cow (Rhytina stelleri); 2. manatee, sea cow (Trichechus latirostris); 3. ichth: stargazer (Astroscopus).
~ кубышка = голотурия.
~ лилия zool: crinoid, sea lily (Crinoidea); feather star (Antedon).
~ лисица ichth: 1. thrasher shark (Alopias vulpes); 2. Raja clavata.
~ минога zool: sea lamprey (Petromyzon
~ мшанка zool:ross, sea mat. [marinus).
~ мышь ichth: dragonet (Callionimus lyra); frogfish (Antennarius).
~ ~ (червь) zool: sea mouse (Aphrodite).
~ пенка (головоногих) cuttle bone.
~ птица seabird.
~ свинка zool: guinea pig, cavy (Cavia porcellus, c. cobaja).
~ свинья zool: porpoise, puffer, herring hog (Phocaena).

морская собачка zool: smooth blenny (Blennius folis).
~ трава bot: sea grass, eelgrass, wrack alva marina (Zostera marina, Z. nana, Ruppia maritima, Salicornia).
~ улитка zool: periwinkle, winkle (Littorina, Thais).
~ ~ обыкновенная common winkle (L. littorea).
~ уточка zool: goose barnacle (Lepadidae)
~ форель = кумжа.
~ чайка orn: seagull, great black-headed gull (Larus marinus).
*~ черепаха hawksbill turtle
~ щука ichth: barracuda (Sphyraena); merluccio, hake (Merluccius productus); tea-snipe, bill-fish, needle fish, silver gar (Tylosurus marinus); ling (Molva).
морские ежи zool: sea urchins (Echinoidea).
~ звёзды (кл.) zool: sea stars, starfished (Asteroidea).
~ иглы (сем.) ichth: Syngnathidae.
~ лилии (кл.) zool: crinoids (Crinoidea)
~ лисички (сем.) ichth: Agonidae.
~ перья zool: pennatulida (Pennatulidae).
~ свинки (сем.) zool: guinea pigs (Caviidae).
~ слизняки (сем.) ichth: Liparidae.
~ черепахи (подотр.) zool: sea turtles (Chelonidea).
~ языки (сем.) ichth: soles (Soleidae)
морское блюдечко zool: limpet Patella.
~ блюдце zool: medusa Aurelia aurita.
~ купанье sea bathing, sea swimming.
~ перо zool: sea pen (Pennatula, Funiculina).
~ ухо = м. ушко.
~ ушко (моллюск) zool: sea-ear, ormer, ear shell, abalone, awabi (Haliotis).
~ хозяйство mariculture.
морской ангел ichth: monkfish (Squatina).
~ бекас ichth: bellows fish (Macrorhamphosus).
~ бобр = камчатский б.
~ веер zool: sea fan (coral).
~ воробей = пинагор.
~ врач marine physician.
~ дракон ichth: sea dragon, weever (Trachinus).
~ дьявол great devilfish (Manta).
~ ёж zool: sea urchin, echinid (Echinoidea).
~ ёрш scorpion fish, rock cod, brown rockfish, flyfish (Scorpaenidae); green rockfish (Sebastichthys flavidus); black rockfish, priest fish (Sebastosomus mystinus), etc.
~ ~ черноморский Scorpaena porcus.
~ жёлудь zool: acorn barnacle (Balanus).

морской заяц zool: 1. bearded seal (Erignatus barbatus); 2. sea hare (Aplysia) mollusk.
~ змий = морская змея.
~ карантин maritime quarantine.
~ кольчатый карась ichth: Diplodus annularis.
~ конёк 1. ichth: sea horse (Hippocampus); see also тряпичник; 2. anat: hippocampus.
~ кот zool: see м. котик; ichth: see хвостокол.
~ котик zool: fur seal (Callorhinus ursinus).
~ ~ из Аляски Alaska fur seal (C. alaskanus).
~ лев seal lion, circus seal (Zalophus)
~ лимон zool: sea lemon (Doris) mollusk.
~ лов котиков pelagic sealing.
~ лук bot: sea onion, squill (Urginea scilla, Steinh., U. maritima, Baker).
*~ налим ichth: rockling (Gaidropsarus)
~ огурец = голотурия.
~ окунь ichth: sea bass (Spicara smaris; Centropristes striatus; Cynoscion nobilis; Sciaenops ocellatus); striped bass (Roccus saxatilis); rosefish hemdurgan (Sebastes marinus); etc.
~ ~ тихоокеанский Sebastodes.
~ паук sea spide (Pycnogonida).
~ пёс = собачья акула.
~ петух ichth: gurnard, gurnet, sea bat, sea robin (Trigla; Prionotus).
~ салат bot: algae: sea lettuce (Ulva lactuca); green laver, oyster green (U. latissima); limu pahapaha.
~ слизень zool: sea slug (Aeolis, Doris, Lamellidoris).
~ слон zool: elephant seal, sea elephant (Macrorhinus leoninus, Miraunga angustirostris).
~ угорь ichth: sea eel (Conger vulgaris); conger eel (C. conger).
~ финик zool: date-mussel (Lithophagus lithophagus).
~ чорт ichth: angler, monkfish, allmouth, wide-gape, goosefish, molligut, kettleman (Lophius piscatorius).
*~ язык ichth: common sole (Parophys vetulus); slippery s., Chinese s. (Microstomus pacificus); American s. hogchoker (Achirus fasciatus).
морула hist: mulberry body.
морфий pharm: morphine.
морфин pharm: morphine.
морфинизм morphinism, morphine addiction.
морфинист morphine addict.
морфогенез morphogenesis.

морфогенетический morphogenetic.
морфолог morphologist.
морфологический morphologic(al).
морфология morphology.
морфометрия morphometry.
морщина wrinkle, crease, pucker, furrow.
морщинистость wrinkling, etc., cf. морщинистый.
морщинистый wrinkled, creasy, shrunken, rugose, ridged, crumpled, puckery, puckered, corrugated, shriveled.
москит entom: mosquito, punkie, see комар.
мослак fetlock joint (of horse).
мост 1. bridge; 2. anat: pons.
мостик odont: bridge, bridgework.
мостовидный эпителий hist: pavement epithelium, scaly e.
мостовой bridge-type; anat: pontal, pontic, pontile, pontine.
моторика motor system; motility.
моторная амузия motor amusia.
~ афазия motor aphasia, aphemia.
~ бляшка anat: motor end-plate, myoneural junction.
~ деятельность желудка peristaltic activity of the stomach. [bance.
моторное нарушение path: motor distur-
мотт аконитолистная = фасоль аконитолистная.
мотылёк entom: moth, pyralid, butterfly; see also огнёвка. [lalis).
~ кукурузный corn borer (Pyrausta nubi-
~ луговой beet webworm (Loxostege sticticalis).
~ подсолничниковый = огнёвка подсолничниковая.
~ стеблевой = м. кукурузный.
мотылица = моль восковая.
мотыль (личинка хирономид) entom: bloodworm.
мотыльковые (подсем.) bot: papilionaceous subfam. (Papilionoideae), see бо-
~ (сем.) Papilionaceae. бовые.
мох bot: moss (Muscus).
~ листовой true moss (M. frondosus).
~ ползучий = плаун булавовидный.
мохнатый pilous, villous, vilose, pubescent, long-hairy (villosus); see
мохноногий orn: plumiped. |пушистый.
мохнорыл = свайник-великан.
мохообразные (тип) bot: bryophytes (phylum Bryophyta, Briopsida).
*мохообразный bot: bryophylic.
моча urine; zool: lant, stale.
моча беременных pregnancy urine, p.u.
~ из почки kidney urine.
мочевая кислота uric acid.
мочевина urea.
мочевинный ureal.
мочевой urinary, urinose, urinous.
~ камень path: urinary calculus.
~ каналец anat: uriniferous tubule.
~ мешок embr: allantois.
~ осадок urinary sediment.
~ пузырь anat: urinary bladder.
~ сахар urine sugar.
~ свищ path: urinary fistula.
~ сосочек zool: urinary papilla.
~ тракт anat: urinary tract.
~ цилиндр mcscop: urinary cast.
мочегонное средство diuretic, emictory, uragogue, urinative.
мочегонный препарат diuretic.
мочеизнурение = диабет.
мочеиспускание physl: urination, emiction, mic(turi)tion.
мочеиспускательный anat: urethral.
~ канал anat: urethra, urinary canal.
мочекислый артрит int: uratic arthritis. [diathesis.
~ диатез path: lithic diathesis, uratic
~ инфаркт uratic inspissation.
мочекровие path: uremia.
мочеотделение 1. excretion of urine; 2. output of urine.
~ ночью nycturia.
мочеполовая диафрагма anat: urogenital diaphragm. [ry.
мочеполовой urogenital, genitourina-
~ треугольник anat: urogenital tri-
мочеприемник san: urinal. angle.
мочеразделитель segregator.
мочеточник anat: ureter.
мочеточниковая складка anat: bar of the bladder, interureteric b.
мочеточниковый ureteric.
мочеточнико-лоханочный anat: ureteropelvic. [pass urine.
мочиться physl: urinate, micturate,
мочка 1. anat: see ушная мочка; 2. retting, soaking, dampening.[beard.
мочки bot: filaments, root fibrils,
мочковатый корень bot: branching filamentous root, bearded r., fibrous r.
мошка entom: small dipteran, midge, moth, mosquito.
~ грибная fungus-gnat (Mycetophilidae).
~ грушевая = медяница г.
~ яблонная = медяница я.

мошкара entom: midges, mosquitoes.
мошки (сем.) entom: black-flies (Simuliidae).
мошонка anat: scrotum.
мошоночная грыжа = паховая г.
мошоночный scrotal.
моющее средство detergent, abluent.
мраморная антеннария ichth: Pterophryna timida.
мудрствование cf. болезненное мудрствование.
мужебоязнь psych: androphobia.
мужеподобность virilism, masculinity.
мужеподобный android, andromorphous.
~ таз obstet: android pelvis.
мужоция bot: Mougeotia (algae).
мужская клетка male cell.
мужские половые органы anat: male genitalia.
мужское отделение male department (of a hospital).
~ половое бессилие path: invirility, impotence.
~ растение bot: staminate plant.
мужской мочеприемник san: male urinal.
мужчина man, male.
музыкальная глухота sensory amusia.
мукоед entom: cucujid, grain-eater.
~ короткоусый рыжий Laemophloeus ferrugineus.
~ рыжий L. testaceus.
~ суринамский corn silvanus, saw-toothed grain beetle (Oryzaephilus surinamensis).
мукоеды (сем.) entom: cucujids, grain-eaters (Cucujidae).
мукоид mucoid.
мукор bot: Mucor (fungus).
муксин ichth: whitefish Coregonus muksun.
мул zool: mule (Equus mulus).
мультицепс helm: Multiceps.
мульча agr: mulche.
муляж waxed model, cast.
мунджак = олень-мунтьяк.
мундштук mouthpiece.
мунтьяк = олень-мунтьяк.
муравей entom: ant (Formica).
~ аргентинский Argentine a. (Iridomyrmex humilis).
~ белый = термит.
~ домовый house ant (Monomorium pharaonis).
~ -древоточец destructive carpenter ant, wood a. (Camponotus herculeanus).
~ -земледелец agricultural ant, harvesting a. (Pogonomyrmes barbatus).
~ кроваво-красный blood-red slave-maker a. (Formica sanguinea).
~ рабочий worker ant.
муравей рабочий с зачаточными крыльями pteregate.
~ -разрушитель = м.-древоточец.
~ рыжий лесной forest ant, red a. (Formica rufa).
~ садовый corn-field a. (Lasius niger).
~ тёмнобурый common black a. (Formica fusca).
~ чёрный = м. садовый.
муравейник entom: ant hill, formicary.
муравьед zool: anteater, ant bear (Myrmecophaga, Tamandua, Cyclopes).
~ австралийский Australian anteater (Myrmecolius fasciatus).
муравьеды (сем.) zool: anteaters (Myrmecophagidae).
муравьежук entom: Thanasimus formicarius (Cleridae).
муравьелюбы bot: myrmecophilous (plants).
муравьиная кислота formic acid.
муравьиное яйцо entom: ant egg; collq: ant cocoon.
муравьинонуклеиновокислое серебро pharm: silver methylene-nucleinate.
муравьиные львы (сем.) entom: ant lions (Myrmeleonidae).
муравьиные (надсем.) entom: ants (Formicoidea).
муравьиный эфир pharm: formic ether.
"мурашки" = ползание мурашек.
мурена ichth: moray (Muraenidae); hamlet (Gymnothorax moringa).
мускатная печень path: nutmeg liver.
мускатниковые (сем.) bot: moschatel family (Adoxaceae).
мускатное дерево bot: moschatel (Adoxa).
мускатный moschatous.
~ "цвет" bot: mace, nutmeg outer covering.
мускул muscle, see мышца.
~ заднего прохода anat: anal sphincter.
~ -замыкатель adductor (in mollusks).
мускулатура zool: musculature, muscles.
мускулистый sinewy, having (many or powerful) muscles.
мускульная пластинка embr: muscle plate, myotome.
мускульные присоски helm: acetabula, true suckers.
мускульный muscular.
~ желудок orn: gizzard.
мускус pharm: musk.
мускусная крыса = ондатра.
~ настойка pharm: tincture of musk.
мускусное дерево bot: musk tree (Marlea vitensis, Olearia, Orgophylla)
мускусный musk (moschatus).
~ бык zool: musk ox (Ovibos moschatus).

мускусный олень zool: musk deer
(Moschus moschiferus).
~ осминог zool: lesser octopus (Eledone)
мусор garbage, trash.
мусорщик zool: scavenger.
мутабильность genet: mutability.
мутагенное действие mutagenic activi-
мутант mutant. ty.
мутантная линия mutant strain.
мутационное действие mutagenic acti-
мутация mutation. vity.
мутизм psych: mutism.
мутиляция mutilation.
мутирующий ген genet: mutant gene.
мутное набухание path:cloudy swelling.
мутность turbidity.
мутный turbid.
мутовка bot: whorl, verticil.
~ прицветников involucre.
мутовчатые (пор.) bot: Verticillatae.
мутовчатый bot: verticillate.
муть slime, dredge, silt.
муфлон zool: moufflon (Ovis orientalis,
O. musimon).
муха entom: fly, musca, muscid (Muscidae)
~ вишнёвая cherry fly (Rhagoletis
cerasi).
~ -галлица = мухи-галлицы (сем.)
~ гессенская Hessian fly (Mayetiola
destructor).
~ дынная melon fly (Myiopardalis par-
dalina, Carpomija caucasica). [trans).
~ жигалка stable fly (Stomoxys calci-
~ житняковая Dicraeus pallidiventris.
~ жужжалка grasshopper bee fly (Sys-
toechus vulgaris). [sericata)
~ зелёная green-bottle fly (Lucilia
~ ~ мясная green flesh fly (Lucilia
caesar).
~ зелёноглазая ribbon-footed cornfly
(Chlorops teniopus, C. pumilionis).
~ капустная весенняя cabbage maggot
(Pegomya, Hylemyia brassicae, Chortophila brassicae).
~ ~ корневая cabbage-root maggot
(Erioschia brassicae, Hylemyia b.)
~ ~ летняя cabbage maggot (Chortophila
floralis). [armillata.
~ колосковая Amaurosoma flavipes; A.
~ комнатная housefly (Musca domestica)
~ ~ малая latrine fly (Fannia scalaris)
~ -кровососка lousefly (Hippoboscidae).
~ круглошовная = круглошовные
мухи.
~ крыжовниковая gooseberry maggot.

муха луковая onion fly (Phorbia ce-
petorum, Hylemyia antiqua, Chortophi-
~ майская = метлица. [la natiqua).
~ маленькая little fly (Sciara bicolor, S. solani, Phora minuta).
~ малинная = м. стеблевая
малинная. [oleae).
~ маслинная olive-tree fly (Dacus
~ минирующая miner fly (Agromyzidae,
etc.) [griseola).
~ ~ ячменная barley miner (Hydrellia
~ морковная carrot rust-fly, negro
fly (Psila rosae).
~ мясная flesh fly, blowfly (Sarco-
phaga); meat fly (Musca vomitoria).
~ навозная dung fly (Cordyluridae).
~ настоящая muscid fly (Muscoidea).
~ -однодневка Mayfly (Meloë).
~ озимая wheat bulb fly (Hylemyia co-
~ осенняя = м. жигалка. [arctata).
~ плодовая fruit fly (Trypetidae).
~ ~ средиземноморская Mediterranean fruit fly (Ceratitis capitata).
~ рисовая rice-stem fly (Atherigona);
paddy f. (Lepteorisa varicornis).
~ розовая галловая rose gallfly
(Aramigus fulleri).
~ ростковая Chortophila florilega.
~ сафлорная safflower fly (Acanthio-
philus helianthi).
~ свекловичная spinach-leaf miner,
mangold fly (Pegomyia hyosciami,
P. betae).
~ скорпионова mecopteron (Mecoptera).
~ скотская horn fly (Haematobia ser-
rata, H. irritans).
~ спаржевая = листоед спаржевый.
~ средиземноморская = м. плодовая средиземноморская.
~ стеблевая малинная raspberry-stem
fly (Chortophila dentiens). [casei).
~ сырная cheese maggot (Piophila
~ -танцовщица dance-fly (Empidae).
~ томатная tomato fly (Acritochaeta
excisa).
~ трюфельная truffle fly (Zelomiza).
~ -убийца robber-fly, death tick
(Asilidae).
~ хальцис chalcid-fly (Chalcidoidea).
~ хищная = м.-убийца.
~ це-це tsetse-fly (Glossina morsitans,
G. paplalis).
*~ шведская frit-fly (Ocsinosoma frit).
~ шпанская = шпанка ясеневая.
~ яровая Phorbia genitalis.

муха ячменная = м. минирующая ячменная.
мухи-галлицы (сем.) entom: gall-flies (Cecidomyidae, Itonididae).
~ це-це (сем.) entom: tsetse-flies (Glossinidae).
мухоловка1. orn: flycatcher (Myiarchus, Empidonas, Nuttaloornis, etc.); 2. bot: see рыжей; 3. san: flytrap (device).
мухоловковые (сем.) orn: flycatcher family (Muscicapidae, Tyrannidae).
мухомор bot: fly amanita, fly agaric.
~ белый = поганка бледная.[muscaris)
~ красный crimson fly amanita (Amanita
мучительный excruciating, tormenting, racking.
мучнистая роса phyth: powdery mildew.
~ ~ крыжовника gooseberry mildew.
~ ~ сирени powdery mildew of lilac (Microsphaera alni).
~ ~ лука onion mildew.
~ ~ яблонь apple mildew.
мучнисторосные = периспориевые.
мучнистость mealiness.
мучнистый farinaceous, mealy.
мушечный пластырь pharm: cantharidal blister plaster, fly blister.
мушка entom: (small) fly.
~ плодовая fruit fly, drosophila.
~ шпанская = шпанка ясеневая.
мушмула bot: medlar (Mespilus).
~ японская loquat (Eriobotrya japonica, Lindl.)
мхи (кл.) bot: mosses (Musci).
мшанка zool: bryozoan, moss animalcule.
мшанки zool: bryozoans (Bryozoa). Cf. внутрипорошицевые мшанки.
мыло soap.
мыльная клизма soapsuds enema.
мыльные испражнения path: soap stools.
мыльный спирт tincture of green soap.
мыльнянка bot: fuller's herb (Sapona-
~ аптечная = м. лекарственная.|ria).
~ лекарственная soapwort, bouncing bet (S. officinalis). [vaccaria).
~ -тысячеголов cowherb, cow cockle (S.
мыльный корень bot: soap root, see мыльнянка.
мыс anat: promontory.
~ крестца anat: sacropromontory.
мыт vet: strangles, diarrhea.
мытник американский bot: wood betony
мыть wash. |(Pedicularis canadensis).
мычание zool: lowing, mooing, bellowing.
~ телёнка bleat(ing).
мышатник = термопсис.
мышей bot: green foxtail, bottle grass (Setaria viridis).
мышехвостник маленький bot: mouse-tail (Myosurus minimus). [asthenopia.
мышечная астенопия ophth: muscular
~ атаксия neur: muscular ataxia, amyota-
~ атрофия path: muscular atrophy. | ria.
~ боль muscle pain, myalgia.
~ возбудимость physl: muscular irrit-
~ грыжа path: myocele. ability.
~ дистрофия path: muscular dystrophy.
~ лакуна anat: lacuna musculorum.
~ лента кишки anat: taenia.
~ перегородка zool: mesentery.
~ ригидность path: muscular stiffness.
~ сила muscle strength.
~ слабость muscular debility.
*~ сократимость myotility.
~ ткань hist: muscular tissue.
мышечного происхождения myogenic.
мышечное брюшко = брюшко мышцы.
~ волокно hist: muscle fiber.
~ чувство muscular sense.
мышечно-железистый musculoglandular.
мышечнокожный нерв anat: musculocutaneous nerve. [musculotubarius.
мышечнотрубный канал anat: canalis
мышечные подёргивания path: tic, twitching of muscles.
мышечный muscular, sarcous.
~ баланс muscle balance.
~ пучок muscle bundle.
~ тяж anat: muscular band.
мышиная опухоль mouse tumor.
мышиные (сем.) zool: mouse family Old-World rats & mice (Muridae).
мышца anat: muscle.
~ волоса anat: arrectores pilorum.
~ поднимающая веко eyelid levator, levator palpebrae superioris.
~ ~ задний проход anal levator.
~ ~ лопатку levator (anguli) scapulae.
~ ~ яичко anat: cremasteric muscle.
~ сжимающая глотку constrictor of pharynx.
~ ~ задний проход anal sphincter.
~ сморщивающая брови corrugator.
~ стремечка stapedius muscle.
~ сустава joint muscle.
~ черпаловидного хряща arytenoid m.
~ широкой фасции бедра tensor fasciae latae, tensor vaginae femoris.
мышцы-близнецы anat: gemelli muscles.
~ речевого аппарата muscles of
мышь zool: mouse (Mus). speech.

мышь домашняя meadow mouse (Mus humilis).
~ лесная wood mouse (Mus silvaticus).
~ песчаная = землеройка.
мышьяк arsenic, As.
мышьяковая кислота arsenic acid.
~ соль chem: arsenate.
мышьяковистая кислота arsenous acid.
мыщелковый anat: condylar.
мы́щелок anat: condyle, condylus.
Мэн Maine. [timothy (Muhlenbergia).
мюленбергия bot: muhlenbergia, wild
мюллеров канал embr: duct of Müller.
мюллеровская личинка zool:Müller's
мягкая вода soft water. larva.
~ гниль phytp: soft rotting [leptomeninx.
~ мозговая оболочка anat: pia (mater)
~ ракушка zool: soft clam (May arenaria)
squirt clam, sandgaper. [(Aspidonectes).
~ черепаха zool: soft-shelled turtle
мягкие зубы malacotic teeth.
мягкий soft, mollis.
~ вазелин pharm: soft petrolatum.
~ шанкр ven: soft chancre, chancroid,
~ шпадель padded tongue blade. [sus molle.
мягкое вещество soft substance, semi-
~ нёбо anat: soft palate. solid s.
мягкокожистые черепахи (подотр.)
zool: turtles Trionychoidea. [gii.
мягкопёрые (отр.) ichth: Malaxoptery-
мягкотелое животное zool:malacozoan.
~ насекомое soft-bodied insect.
мягкотелые zool: malacozoans, see
моллюски. [Anomura.
мягкохвостые раки (подотр.) zool:
мягкошанкерный ven: chancroidal.
мягчительное средство malactic,
emolient, demulcent.
мягчительный soothing, demulcent, mol-
мязга bot: pulp, squash. lient.
мякина agr bot: chaff.
мякинная оболочка bot: husk.
мякинный chaffy, paleaceous.
мякотное нервное волокно hist:
medullated nerve fiber. [ous.
мякотный pulpal, pulpar, pulpy, pultace-
мякоть bot: pith, parenchyma, pap, pulp;
mush (of a fungus).
мясистая оболочка 1. anat: tunica
dartos; 2. bot:sarcoderm (of a seed).
~ часть (плода) bot: sarcocarp.
~ чешуя (лука) bot: succulent layers
(of onion).
мясистое растение bot: succulent
~ соцветие bot: spadix. | plant, fleshy p.

мясистое цветоложе bot: fleshy
receptacle. [succulence.
мясистость meatiness, fleshiness,
мясистый meaty, fleshy, succulent.
~ занос obstet: fleshy mole, carneous
~ нарост orn: fill (of a cock). |mole.
мясная вода lab: meat infusion.
мясное отравление meat poisoning.
мясной бульон mcbio: beef broth.
~ скот beef cattle.
мясные консервы canned meat.
~ споровики (отр.) zool: Sarcospo-
мясо flesh; beef, meat. ridia.
мясомолочная кислота sarcolactic
acid, paralactic acid.
мясопептонный агар bact: meat-
мясорубка meatgrinder. |infusion agar.
мясцо anat: caruncle.
мята bot: mint (Mentha). [gium).
~ болотная Brit: pennyroyal (M. pula-
~ водяная water m., brook m. (M.
aquatica).
~ горная basil (Pycnanthemum).
~ дикая horse m. (M. longifolia).
~ зелёная spearmint (M. spicata).
~ кошачья ground ivy (Nepeta hederacea). [difolia).
~ круглолистная apple m. (M. rotun-
~ кудрявая curled m. (M. crispa).
~ лимонная 1. bergamot mint (M. cit-
rata, Ehrh.); 2. see мелисса.
~ перечная peppermint (M. piperita).
~ полевая Japanese m. (M. arvensis).
~ ползучая creeping m. (M. requieni).
~ стелящаяся = м. ползучая. [ная.
~ -холодка white m., see м. переч-
мятлик bot: meadow grass, speargrass,
bluegrass (Poa).
~ боровой wood-meadow grass (P. nemo-
~ лесной = м. боровой. ralis).
~ луговой Junegrass, speargrass,
Kentucky bluegrass, smooth meadowgrass (P. pratensis). [grass (P.trivialis)
~ обыкновенный rough-stalked meadow-
~ однолетний low speargrass, annual
bluegrass, six-weeks grass (P.annua).
~ поздний fowl meadowgrass (P.triflora).
~ сплюснутый Canada bluegrass, wiregrass (P. compressa).
~ трехцветковый = м. поздний.
мятная эссенция pharm: pepermint.
мятное масло pharm: mint oil.

Н

на всех четырёх = на четырёх ногах
~ глаз sized up by the naked eye; in the gross, macroscopically. Cf. глазомер.
~ месте in situ.
~ передней части спины anat: dorsoanteriorly.
~ середине спины anat: middorsal.
~ четырех ногах zool: on all fours, pronograde.
набивка impaction.
наблюдатель observer.
набор для инъекций hypodermic injection kit, hypo unit.
~ ~ исследования крови lab: blood testing set.
~ ~ исследования мочи lab: urine testing set.
~ ~ клинических анализов clinitest kit.
~ инструментов set of instruments.
~ стёкол ophth: spectacle case.
набрюшник abdominal bandage, a. binder, a. belt.
набухание swelling, distension, tumefaction, intumescing, dilation.
набухать swell (up), etc. cf. набухание.
набухнуть p. a. of набухать.
навага ichth: navaga (Eleginus navaga).
"Навель" = апельсин типа "Навель".
навзнич (lie) on one's back, dorsicumbent.
навикула bot: Navicula (algae).
навозник bot: coprinus (Coprinus).
~ запятаевидный shaggy-mane mushroom, horsetail (C. comatus).
~ кукурузный entom: beetle Pentodon idiota.
~ серый inky-cap mushroom, ink-cap (Coprinus atramentarius).
~ слюдовидный glistering coprinus (C. micaceus).
навозный жук entom: dung-beetle, see жук-навозник.
навылет through; cf. сквозное огнестрельное ранение.
навязчивая идея psych: fixed idea.
навязчивое действие psych: compulsive action.
~ состояние psych: obsessive state.
нагана vet: nagana fever (due to Tripanosoma brucei).
нагнаиваться path: suppurate.
нагнёт vet: gall.
нагноение suppuration, abscess, purulence, pyosis; vet: festering.
~ в шве surg: stitch abscess.
~ кожи cutaneous suppuration.
~ придатков gyn: adnexa suppuration.
~ сустава pyarthrosis.
нагноиться p. a. of нагнаиваться.
нагноительная лихорадка path: suppurative fever.
надавливание на козелок pressure over the tragus.
надблоковый нерв anat: supratrochlear nerve.
надбровая дуга anat: superciliary arch.
надводная растительность bot: emergent vegetation.
надводное растение emergent plant.
надводный emergent, emersed.
надглазничный рефлекс physl: ophthalmic reflex.
надглоточник entom: epipharynx.
надглоточный узел entom: brain.
надгортанник anat: epiglottis.
надгортанный anat: epiglottic.
надгрудинная ямка anat: suprasternal notch.
надевать на нос зажим clip the nose.
надзор за пищевыми продуктами food supervision.
надкл. = надкласс.
надкласс bio: superclass.
надклеточные формы zool: Giardia, Hypermastigina.
надклювье (верхняя половина клюва) orn: maxilla.
надключичная ямка anat: hollow above the clavicle.
надключичный нерв anat: supraclavicular nerve.
надкожица anat: epidermis.
надколенник = коленная чашка.
надкостница anat: periosteum.
надкостничный anat: periosteal.
надкрылье entom: elytrum, sheath, first wing, shard.
надлобковое камнесечение urol: epicystotomy.
надлом surg: infraction, greenstick fracture.
надлопаточный нерв anat: suprascapular nerve.
надминдалевидная ямка anat: supratonsillar fossa.
надмыщелковый anat: epicondylic.
надмыщелок anat: epicondyle.

надостная мышца anat: supraspinatus.
~ ямка anat: supraspinous fossa.
надотр. = надотряд.
надотряд bio: superorder.
надпазушный supra-axillary.
надпереносье anat: glabella, nasal eminence.
надпестичный bot: epigynous.
надпор. = надпорядок.
надпорядок bio: superorder.
надпочечная железа anat: suprarenal gland.
надпочечник = надпочечная железа.
надпочечный anat: epinephral.
надрез superficial incision, s. cut.
~ влагалища gyn: colpotomy.
надрезной лист bot: incised leaf.
надрыв vet: swaying.
надсада = надрыв.
надсегментарный отдел мозга anat: hemispheres of the cerebrum.
надсем. = надсемейство.
надсемейство bio: superfamily.
надсечённый bot: bifid, incised.
надтреснувший chapped (skin, etc.)
надувание inflation, bloating, distension.
надувать inflate, puff up, distend.
надувающийся мешок av med: inflated bag.
надувной матрац air mattress.
надуть p. a. of надувать.
надхвостная железа = копчиковая железа.
надхрящница hist: perichondrium.
надчревная артерия (верхняя, глубокая, нижняя, поверхностная) anat: (superior, deep, inferior, superficial) epigastric artery.
~ аура neur: epigastric aura.
~ область anat: epigastrium.
наездник entom: ichneumon fly (Megarhyssa, Ophion, etc.)
наездники (сем.) entom: ichneumon flies (Ichneumonidae).
назальный nasal.
наземное растение land plant.
назион anat: nasion.
назначение лекарства prescribing of a medicine.
назофарингеальный nasopharyngeal.
найдёныш ped: foundling.
*накипной лишайник bot: scab-like lichen.
накипь scale, incrustation, fur; scum.
накладка для сосков ped: nipple shield.
накладывание application.
~ лигатуры = наложение л.
накладывать бандаж bandage.
~ лигатуру surg: tie with ligature, ligate.
накладывать тампон = тампонировать.
~ шинную повязку surg: dress in splints.
наклёвывать orn: chip.
наклевать p.a. of наклёвывать.
наклон кпереди anat: anteversion.
~ матки кпереди anat: anteversion of the uterus.
наклон(ение) вперед anteversion.
~ в сторону gyn: lateroversion.
наклонность к истерии neur: hystericism.
наковальня anat: anvil, incus.
наконечник nozzle; cannule.
~ ирригатора irrigating tip.
накопление amassing, storing, accumulation; see also скопление.
накрывать (колпачком) clap on.
накрыть p. a. of накрывать.
налево sinistrad.
належать пролежни develop bedsore.
налёт deposit, film, thin coating; bloom.
~ на языке path: fur(red tongue).
~ часов av med: flying time.
наливное яблоко bot: transparent apple.
налим ichth: burbot, eelpout (Lota).
налитые глаза path: suffused eyes.
налить p. a. of лить, наливать.
наличие бактерий в крови bacteremia.
~ варикозных вен path: varicosity.
~ двойной матки path: dimetria.
~ зубовидных отростков anat: dentelation.
~ лакун lacunosity.
~ мышечного аппарата musculation.
~ растительных функций vegetality.
~ хвоста caudation.
~ шести пальцев на руке или ноге path: hexadactylism.
наличник entom: clypeus.
наличниковый entom: clypeal.
наложение application; imposition, laying upon.
~ лигатуры surg: ligation.
~ повязки surg: application of dressing.
~ почечного свища (для отведения мочи) = нефростомия.
~ шва surg: suturation.
~ шин(ы) surg: splintage, splinting.
~ щипцов obstet: application of forceps.
наложить p. a. of накладывать.
намазать p. a. of намазывать.
намазывать anoint, smear ointment on.
наминка vet: corn, capellet, thrush (horses).
намокание steeping, soaking.
намыливать soap.
намылить p. a. of намыливать.
нанду = rea.

нанизм nanism.
наннопланктический nannotype.
наннопланктон nannoplankton.
наннопланктонное растение nannoplankton plant.
напад entom: attack, invasion, depredation, infestation.
напальчник finger stall.
наперстянка = дигиталис.
наплыв bot: woodknob, see кап.
наполнение сердца filling of the heart.
направительное веретено hist: direction spindle.
~ тельце hist: directing corpuscle.
направление взгляда ophth: visual axis.
направо dextrad.
напрыск = черва.
напрягаемость physl: erectility.
напрягать(ся) exert (oneself), strain, erect.
напряжение tension, stress, strain.
~ соков bot: turgor.
~ тканей turgescence, turgor.
напрячься p. a. of напрягаться.
нарастание growing, growth, building up, rise, accretion.
~(симптомов) path: aggravation (of symptoms), augment(ation).
нарастающая ткань bot: meristem.
нарастающий верхушкой bot: acrogenous.
нарвал zool: narwhal, see единорог 1.
нард = сорго лимонное.
~ дикий = копытень европейский.
наркоз narcosis.
нарколепсия neur: narcolepsy.
нарколептик narcoleptic.
нарколептический narcoleptic.
нарколог narcologist.
наркоман narcomaniac, narcotic (person), drug addict, dope addict.
наркомания psych: narcomania, narcotic addiction.
наркотизатор surg: anesthesist.
наркотизированная собака barbitalized dog.
наркотизированный surg: anesthetized.
наркотизировать surg: anesthetize.
наркотик narcotic (drug).
наркотикораздражающий narcotico-acrid, narcotico-irritant.
наркотический narcotic.
наркотическое состояние narcotic state, narcotism.
~ средство narcotic.

народная медицина folk medicine.
народное название popular name, common n., colloquial n., vernacular n.
нарост growth, outgrowth, excrescence, accretion; callus.
~ копытного рога vet: convexity of sole.
~ на веке vet: haw (in horse).
~ (на дереве) woodknob.
нартеций европейский bot: Lancashire asphodel (Narthecium ossifragum).
наружная жевательная лопасть entom: outer lobe, galea.
~ лодыжка anat: lateral malleolus, malleolus lateralis.
~ прямая мышца (глаза) anat: external recti, rectus oculi lateralis.
~ температура external temparature.
~ цветковая чешуя bot: lemma, floral glume.
~ челюстная артерия anat: external maxillary artery, facial artery.
~ шишка (геморроидальная) surg: external pile.
наружное косоглазие ophth: divergent strabismus, exotropia.
~ кровотечение external bleeding.
~ облучение rad: surface irradiation, external irradiation.
~ основание черепа anat: basis cranii externa.
~ паховое кольцо anat: external abdominal ring.
~ слуховое отверстие anat: auricular foramen.
~ употребление external use.
~ ухо anat: external ear.
наружномыщелковый anat: ectocondylar.
наружность appearance, look.
наружночерепной anat: ectocranial.
наружные половые органы anat: genitals.
наружный геморрой path: external hemorrhoids.
~ зернистый слой (мозга) anat: external granular layer.
~ кожный нерв бедра anat: lateral cutaneous nerve of thigh.
~ маточный зев anat: external orifice of the uterus.
~ мыщелок anat: ectocondyle.
~ отит external otitis.
~ паразит ectoparasite.
~ поворот obstet: external version, abdominal version.
~ скелет zool: exoskeleton.
~ слой external layer.

наружный слуховой проход anat: external auditory canal, meatus acusticus externus.
нарушение зрения impairment of vision.
~ (мышечной) координации path: ataxia, dystaxia.
~ окраски color break.
~ отправления dysfunction.
~ питания imbalance in nutrition.
~ пищеварения digestion disturbance, dyspepsia.
~ психики psychic disorder.
~ равномерной деятельности arrhythmia. [phrenosis.
~ сна psych: sleep disturbance, hypno-
~ тонуса disorder of tonicity, dystonia.
~ целости (ткани) solution of continuity.
нарцисс bot: narcissus (Narcissus).
~ белый = н. поэтический.
~ жёлтый daffodil, trumpet d. (N. pseudonarcissus).
~ поэтический poet's n., pheasant's eye (N. poeticus).
нарциссовые = амариллисовые.
нарыв abcsess, pus blister.
нарывники (сем.) entom: blister bettles (Meloidae).
нарывное средство pharm: vesicant.
нарывной коллодий pharm: cantharidal collodion, blistering collodion.
~ пластырь pharm: blistering plaster.
наряд orn: plumage.
насасывать suck up, draw up; pump into.
наседка sitter, sitting hen, broodhen.
наседное пятно orn: brood spot.
насекание scarification.
насекомое entom: insect (Insecta).
насекомоопыляемый bot: insect-borne.
насекомоядное insect eater; adj: insectivorous.
насекомоядные zool: insectivores, insect-eating mammals (Insectivora).
~ летучие мыши (подотр.) zool: insectivorous bats (Microchiroptera).
насекомоядный insect-eating, insectivorous, entomophagous. [xapoda).
насекомые entom: insects (Insecta, He-
~ с неполным превращением (подотдел) incomplete-metamorphosis insects (Paraneoptera).
~ с полным превращением (подотдел) complete-metamorphosis insects (Oligoneoptera).
население bio: population, stock.
население ила mud population.
населяющий почву soil-inhabiting.
насечка 1. notch(es), cut(s); 2. scarification.
~ (на дереве) bot: streak (of a tree).
насиживание = высиживание.
насиживать = высиживать.
насильственное действие compulsive action, violation.
~ кормление forcible feeding.
~ разделение тканей surg: divulsion.
наследование inheritance, succession.
наследственная модификация heritable modification.
~ передача genet: hereditary trans-
~ черта hereditary feature. |mission.
наследственно hereditarily.
~ отягощенный hereditary tainted.
~ сифилитический ven: congenital syphilitic, heredosyphilitic.
наследственное предрасположение hereditary predisposition.
наследственность heredity.
наследственный heritable, inherited.
~ сифилис = врожденный с.
наследуемость heritability.
наследуемый heritable. [rhinitis.
насморк nasal cold, common c., coryza,
насосать p. a. of насасывать.
настаивание pharm: infusion (process).
настаивать infuse.
настой(ка) pharm: infusion, tincture.
~ валерианы valerian tincture.
~ горечавки tincture of gentian.
~ индийской конопли tincture of Indian hemp.
~ корицы tincture of cinnamon.
~ росного ладана tincture of benzoin.
~ стручкового перца tincture of capsicum. [gull (Larus).
настоящая чайка orn: scavenging
настоящее гуттаперчевое дерево India-rubber tree (Isonandra gutta).
~ ядрышко клетки genet: plasmosome.
настоящие комары (сем.) entom: mosquitoes (Culicidae).
~ ленточные черви (подкл.) cestodes, tapeworms (Eucestoda).
~ летучие мыши (подотр.) = насекомоядные летучие мыши.
~ мухи (сем.) entom: typical muscids (Muscidae).
~ мхи = зелёные мхи.
~ певчие orn: oscines, songbirds (Oscines).

настоящие полужесткокрылые (отр.) entom: true bugs (Hemiptera, Heteroptera).
~ саранчовые (сем.) entom: real locusts (Acrididae).
~ филины orn: true owls (Bubonidae).
~ ящерицы zool: lizards (Lacertidae).
настоящий ленточный червь zool: polyzootic cestode (Cestoda).
~ пелагический eulimnetic.
~ планктон euplankton.
настроение psych: mood, mental disposition, humor.
настурциевые (сем.) bot: tropaeolum family (Tropaeolaceae).
настурция bot: nasturtium, tropaeolum (Tropaeolum). [peregrinum).
~ канарская canary-bird flower (T.
насытить p. a. of насыщать.
насыщать saturate.
~ кислородом oxygenate.
насыщение saturation; satiety.
~ артериальной крови кислородом av med: oxygen saturation of arterial blood.
насыщенность крови кислородом av med: oxygen saturation of the blood.
насыщенный saturated; turgid.
натальская трава Natal grass (Tricholaena rosea, Nees).
натальский прыщ Natal sore, see пендинка.
натёчный абсцесс path: wandering abscess, hypostatic a., abscessus per decubitum.
~ ~ в суставе path: arthrifluent
натика zool: gastropod Natica. [abscess.
натирать спиртом rub with alcohol.
натощак fasting.
натриевокалийная соль винной кислоты pharm: potassium and sodium
натрий sodium, Na. tartrate.
натужиться exert oneself, strain.
натурализовавшийся naturalized, denizen. [шийся.
натурализованный = натурализовав-
натуралист naturalist.
натуральная величина life size.
натуральный natural. [muscle.
натягивающая мышца anat: tensor
натяжение 1. tension; 2. surg: see
наука science. затяжение.
~ о болезнях pathology.
~ ~ болезнях растений phytopathology.
~ ~ водорослях bot: phycology.
наука о глазе ophthalmology.
~ ~ лечении оперативным путём surgery.
~ ~ питании dietetics.
~ ~ причинах болезней etiology.
~ ~ функциях организма physiology.
науплиус zool: nauplius (larva of a crustacean). [tiloidae).
наутилиды (отр.) zool: nautili (Nau-
наутилус жемчужный zool: pearly nautilus (Nautilus pompilius).
наутопедиум ichth: midshipman (Nautopaedium porosissimum).
научный scientific.
~ институт по удобрениям и инсектофунгицидам Scientific Institute for Fertilizers and Insectofungicides. [worker, research w.
~ работник scientist, scientific
нафталин pharm: naphthalene.
нафтилуксусная кислота naphthylacetic acid.
нафтол chem: naphthol.
нахлебник bio: commensal.
нахлебничество zool: hanging-on, leaning-on, commensalism.
находиться в спячке hibernate.
~ на излечении be under treatment.
находка occurrence.
находящийся вне организма extraorganismal.
~ в нормальном положении normally posed.
~ ~ спячке zool: hibernating, torpid.
~ внутри стекловидного тела anat: intravitreous.
начало inception, primordium.
~ (болезни) outbreak (of disease).
начальная доза initial dose. [tion.
~ концентрация initial concentra-
~ стадия initial stage, initial phase.
начальный initial, incipient, inceptive.
~ диагноз primary diagnosis. [bloom.
начинать цвести bot: come into
начинающий разлагаться putrescent.
нашатырный спирт chem: ammonia water.
нашатырь chem: ammonium chloride.
наяда bot: naiad, water weed, fish grass (Najas).
наядовые (сем.) bot: naiad family, naiadaceous plants (Najadaceae).
неадэкватная реакция psych: inadequate reaction, inappropriate r.
неактивный туберкулёз inactive tuberculosis.

небалии zool: Nebaliacea, see тонкопанцырные раки.
небелковый азот nonprotein nitrogen.
небеременная nonpregnant.
нёбная дужка anat: palatine arch.
~ занавеска anat: velum palatinum.
~ кость anat: palatine bone, os palatinum.
~ миндалина anat: palatine tonsil.
нёбный palatine, palatal.
~ отросток anat: palatine process.
~ свод anat: palatine vault.
*нёбо anat: palate, root of the mouth.
небобовое растение nonleguminous plant.
неболезненный unpainful.
неболезнетворный nonpathogenic, avirulent. Cf. болезнетворный.
небольшое углубление = ямочка.
небродильный azymic, unfermented.
неветвящийся nonbranching.
невизирующий глаз nonsighting eye.
невменяемый unimputable. Cf. вменяемый.
невнятность indistinctness, slurring.
невозможность глотать path: aglutition.
невооружённый глаз unaided eye, unassisted eye, naked eye.
~ цепень hist: hookless tapeworm, see бычий цепень.
невоспалённый uninflamed.
невоспалительный noninflammatory.
невосприимчивость insusceptibility.
~ к заражению immunity.
невосприимчивый insusceptible; immune.
~ к яду гремучей змеи imm: antibotropic.
невоспринимаемое движение av med: unperceived motion.
невоспринимаемый вираж av med: unperceived bank.
невправимая грыжа surg: irreducible hernia.
невралгическая боль neuralgic pain.
~ ~ в надчревье gastralgia.
невралгия neuralgia.
~ седалищного нерва = ишиас.
~ тройничного нерва facial neuralgia trigeminal neuralgia.
невральный neural.
неврастеник neurastheniac.
неврастения neurasthenia.
невредимый uninjured, intact.
невризм "neurism" (neurogenic theory of medicine).
невринома neurinoma, schwannoma.

невро- neuro-, see also нейро-.
неврогенная теория медицины neurism (Botkin-Pavlov theory).
невроглия = нейроглия.
невроз neurosis.
~ мочевого пузыря irritable bladder.
~ навязчивости obsession, compulsion neurosis.
~ страха anxiety neurosis.
неврозный neurosal.
невролиз neurolysis.
невролитический neurolytic.
невролог neurologist.
неврологическое обследование neurologic examination.
неврология neurology.
невропатический neuropathic.
невропатолог neuropathologist.
невропатология neuropathology.
невропластика surg: neuroplasty, nerve grafting.
невросифилис neurosyphilis, neurolues.
неврососудистый neurovascular.
невротик neurotic.
невротическая конституция neurotic constitution.
невротоксин neurotoxin.
невротоксический neurotoxic.
невротомия neurotomy.
невротонический neurotonic.
невротрофическое расстройство neurotrophic disorder.
невроцель zool: neuroc(o)ele.
невскрывшийся untripped (flower).
невскрытый zool: round (of a fish); bot: see невскрывшийся.
невсхожесть nongermination, nonemergence.
невыговаривание буквы л path: paralambdacism,
невыделение молока path: agalactia.
невыдерживающий высыхания siccolabile.
невыносливый nonhardy.
невыполненное зерно bot: imperfect grain.
негалофильный nonhalophilic.
негативизм (активный, пассивный) psych: (active, passive) negativism.
негативная окраска bact: negative staining.
негелевский таз obstet: Naegele pelvis.
негигроскопическая вата nonabsorbent cotton.
негнездовый nonbreeding.
негниючка = тисс, туя.
негной-дерево = тисс.
негнойный nonpurulent, apy(et)ous.

негоден mil: unfit.
негодность mil: unfitness.
Негундо = неклен.
недавно вылупившийся zool: newly-emerged.
недержание path: incontinence, involuntary urination or evacuation.
~ кала rectal incontinence.
~ мочи urinary incontinence, enuresis.
недоброкачественная пища poor-quality food, spoiled f., putrescent f.
недозрелый bot: unripe.
недокармливание underfeeding.
недомогание indisposition, malaise, discomfort; collq: misery.
недоносок premature infant; zool: slink
недоношенный obstet: prematurely born, abortive.
недоразвитая матка path: pubescent uterus.
недоразвитие underdevelopment, infantilism.
~ половой системы path: hypogenitalism.
~ пыльцы bot: pollen abortion.
~ семяпочки bot: ovule abortion.
недоразвитый underdeveloped, partially developed, rudimentary, infantile.
недостаток deficiency, lack, want, shortage, shortcoming, drawback, scarcity.
~ аппетита want of appetite.
~ воли psych: abulia.
~ питания = недостаточное питание
~ полового побуждения want of sexual impulse.
~ рефракции ophth: refractive error.
~ слюны path: aptialism.
недостаточная координация hyposynergy.
~ окраска mcscop: understaining.
~ освещенность underillumination.
недостаточное действие (мышцы) underaction (of a muscle).
~ питание undernourishment, malnutrition; oligotrophy.
~ развитие underdevelopment.
~ ~ венозной системы path: hypovenosity.
~ ~ кожи path: adermogenesis.
~ ~ сегментов bio: lipomerism.
~ ~ тканей и органов path: aplasia.
~ снабжение кислородом av med: lack of oxigen supply.
~ сокращение глазных мышц ophth: underaction of the external ocular muscles.
недостаточность insufficiency, inadequacy, incompetence; see also недостаток.
недостаточность аортального клапана path: aortic incompetence.
~ аорты path: aortic insufficiency.
~ дыхания path: respiratory insufficiency.
~ зрения defective vision.
~ клапанов path: valvular incompetence.
~ митрального клапана path: mitral incompetence.
~ надпочечных желёз path: suprarenal failure.
~ печени path: liver deficiency.
~ питальных веществ nutritional deficiency.
~ (работы) сердца = порок сердца
~ роговой ткани path: aceratosis.
~ трехстворчатого клапана path: tricuspid regurgitation.
недостаточный вес underweight.
~ тонус вазомоторов poor vasomotor tonus.
недотрога bot: balsam, jewelweed, snapweed, touch-me-not (Impatiens).
~ бледная pale touch-me-not (I. pallida).
~ двуцветная jewelweed (I. biflora).
недотроговые (сем.) bot: touch-me-not family (Balsaminaceae).
недоящаяся agr zool: barren, idle.
недуг disease, affliction, infirmity, see болезнь.
нежвачные (подотр.) zool: nonruminants (Nonruminantia).
нежелание работать path: indisposition to work.
неживой nonliving.
нежизнеспособность nonviability.
нежизнеспособный nonviable, unvital, abiotic.
нежная мышца anat: gracilis (muscle)
нежное растение delicate plant.
нежный плод bot: delicate fruit.
~ паучок (или канатик) anat: fasciculus gracilis, Goll's column.
незабудка bot: forget-me-not, scorpion grass (Myosotis).
незагрязнённый uncontaminated.
незаиливающийся nonsilting.
незаквашенный unleavened.
незакрывание рта path: antitrismus.
незамкнутый zool: lacunar (blood system).
незаражённые семена bot: noninoculated seeds.
незаражённый uninfected. Cf. заражённый.
незаразный noninfectious, noncommunicable, noncontagious.
незаращение переднего родничка path: persistence of the anterior fontanel.

незасоряющийся nonclоggable.
незатихающий insubsiding, unabating, quenchless (pain, etc.)
незаторможённый uninhibited.
нездоровый unhealthy, unwell, unsound, insalubrious.
незернистое кровяное тельце hist: agranulocyte.
незлокачественный nonmalignant.
незначительная идея psych: inconsequential idea. [greenness.
незрелость unripeness, immaturity,
незрелый unripe, immature, green,
незубчатый bot: edentate.
неизлечимый incurable. [cate.
неимеющий коркового слоя noncorti-
~ полного превращения bio: heterometabolic.
~ рёбер = безрёберный.
~ сосочков nonpapillated.
неинфицированный uninfected.
неионизированный unionized.
неистовство psych: fury, rage, frenzy.
неистовствовать psych: rage.
нейрилемма anat: neurilemma.
нейрит neurite, axon.
нейро- neuro-, see also невро-.
нейроглия hist: neuroglia.
нейрогуморальный neurohumoral.
нейродерматит path: neurodermatitis.
нейрон anat: neuron.
нейронный neuronal.
нейропсихиатрия neuropsychiatry.
нейрорецидив neurorelapse.
нейрососудистая астения neurocirculatory asthenia.
~ регуляция neurocirculatory control.
нейроспора neurospora (mold).
нейрофан zool: neurophane.
нейрофизиология neurophysiology.
нейроциркуляторная устойчивость neurocirculatory stability.
нейроэлектричество neuroelectricity.
нейстон neuston.
нейтрализатор кислоты antacid.
нейтрализующий змеиный яд antivenomous.
нейтралрот neutral red.
нейтронная терапия neutron therapy.
нейтронотерапия neutron therapy.
нейтрофил neutrophil.
нейтрофильные зёрнышки neutrophil granules.
некатор helm: hookworm (Nector america-
некатороз helm: necatoriasis. nus).

неклен bot: ash-leaved maple, box elder (Acer negundo, Negundo aceroides).
неклеточная структура hist: noncellular structure.
неклеточный noncellular.
неклубеньковый bot: nonnodulating. Cf. клубеньковый.
некоагулируемый incoagulable.
неколючий bot: unarmed.
неконгруентность incongruity.
неконгруентный incongruous.
неконтагиозный noncontagious, see незаразный.
неконтагиозный постит noncontagious posthitis, sheath-rot.
неконтролируемый рост uncontrolled growth.
некоординированность asynergy, acynergia.
некорневая подкормка arg bot: nonroot nutrition.
некосой агар bact: unslanted agar.
некочанная капуста bot: nonheading cabbage, loose-leaved cabbage.
некрапчатый nonmotted.
некризисный acritical, noncritical.
некробиоз path: necrobiosis.
некровоточащая шишка (геморроидальная) surg:blind pile. [ker.
некроз 1. path: necrosis; 2. bot: can-
~ челюсти при хроническом отравлении фосфором path: phosphorus necrosis, Lucifer-match disease.
некронефроз int: necronephrosis.
некротический necrotic.
некрофил psych: necrophile.
некрофилия psych: necrophilism.
некрофильный necrophilous.
некрофобия psych: necrophobia.
нектар bot: nectar.
нектарин bot: nectarine, smooth-skinned peach (Prunus nucipersica).
нектарник bot: nectary, floral gland, honeycup.
~ в шпорце bot: nectar spur.
нектарниковая чешуйка bot: nectar
нектарный bot: nectarous. [scale.
нектарообразующий bot: nectariferous.
нектон necton, nekton.
нектофор = плавательный колокол.
нектридиа zool: Nectridia (extinct amphibians).
нектрия картофеля phytp: winter rot.
~ лиственных пород phytp: wood canker (Nectria galligena, Bress.)

нелепая идея psych: absurd idea.
нелетающий птенец orn: flapper.
нелетучее масло nonvolatile oil.
нелеченный untreated.
нелиняющий nonmoulting.
нелипкий nonsticky.
нелогичная идея illogical idea.
нельма ichth: Stenodus leucichthys nelma.
нелюмбо = лотос.
нематеций bot: nemathecium.
нематода zool: nematode, eelworm.
~ зевоты кур zool: gapeworm (Syngamus trachealis).
~ земляничная strawberry nematode (Aphelenchoides fragariae).
~ причиняющая узловатость корней растений zool: gallworm (Heterodera marioni).
~ пшеничная zool: wheat-gall nematode, wheat worm (Anguina tritici, Tylenchus tritici).
~ свекловичная zool: sugar-beet eelworm (Heterodera schachtii).
нематодоподобные zool: Nematomorpha, see волосатиковые.
нематоды (кл.) zool: nematodes (Nematoda).
нематоциста zool: nematocyst.
немертина zool:nemertean, acoelomate Bilateria worm.
немертины (подтип) zool: nemerteans, nemerti(ne)ans (Nemertine).
неметавший икру ichth: unspawned.
неметамерный nonmetameric.
немеченый untagged.
немигрирующий nonmigratory.
немой mute.
неморской nonmarine.
немота mutism.
немотивированный противоимпульс psych: negativism.
немощный infirm.
немощь infirmity.
немужественный subvirile, nonmanly.
ненависть к новому psych: misoneism.
ненаркотизированный unanesthetized, conscious.
ненаследственный nonheritable.
ненастоящая сардина ichth: Sardinella.
ненасытный insatiable.
ненасыщенный unsaturated.
ненормальная волосатость pilosis, hirsutism.
~ секреция parasecretion.
~ сонливость excessive sleepiness, hypnolepsy, narcolepsy.
ненормально большие груди macromastia.
~ ~ ноги или руки macromelia.
~ длинная толстая кишка macrocoly.
~ острое чувство обоняния hyperosmia.
~ частое мигание ophth: nictitation.
ненормальное опорожнение abevacuation.
~ питание кожи heterodermotrophy.
~ положение сердца ectocardia.
~ расположение органов heterotaxis.
~ состояние abnormal state, abnormal condition, abnormality.
~ увеличение почек nephromegaly.
~ уплощение applanation.
ненормальность abnormality.
ненормальный abnormal ; psych:insane.
необработанный untreated.
необразующий спор asporogenic, nonsporing.
необрастающий состав antifouling composition.
необратимый irreversible.
необызвествленный calcium-free.
необычная сеть = чудесная сеть.
неогермитрин pharm: neogermitrine.
неогобиус ichth: Neogobius.
неодинаковость зрения в обоих глазах ophth: heteropsia.
неоднозначная выраженность изменений diversified manifestation of changes.
неодревесневший побег bot: turion.
неоживимый irrevivable, irresuscitable
неокрашенный препарат unstained preparation.
неокрашивающийся nonstaining, chromophobic.
неомыляемый nonsaponifiable.
неомыляющийся nonsaponifiable.
"неопалимая купина" = ясенец "неопалимая купина".
неоперившийся orn: unfledged.
~ птенец orn: squab.
неопиритиамин neopyrithiamin.
неоплазма neoplasm, new growth.
неопластический neoplastic.
неоплодотворение nonfertilization.
неоплодотворенный unfertilized.
неоплятицефалюс ichth: tiger flathead (Neoplatycephalus macrodon).
неопровержимое доказательство incontrovertible evidence.
неопушённый стебель bot: bald stem.
неорганизованный unorganized.
неорганическая химия inorganic chemistry.

неосальварсан pharm: neosalvarsan, neoarsphenamine.
неосинефрин pharm: neosynephrin (nose drops).
неоспоридии (подкл.) zool: Neosporidia, Cnidosporidia.
неосыпающаяся культура agr: nonshattering crop.
неотения zool: neotenia.
неотетразолий chem: neotetrazolium.
неотложная операция surg: emergency operation.
~ хирургия emergency surgery, urgent s.
неотропический neotropical.
неочищенный crude, unrefined.
неощутимое потение insensible perspiration.
неощутимость пульса acrotism.
непарная вена anat: azygos vein.
~ кишечная трубка zool: rhabdocoele intestine (of a redia).
непарнокопытные zool: odd-toed, perissodactyls (Perissodactyla), see однокопытное.
непарнопалые zool: Mesaxonia (extinct).
непарно-перистосложный лист bot: odd-pinnate leaf.
непарный unpaired, azygos.
непатогенный nonpathogenic.
непереваренный undigested.
неперевариимый indigestible.
непереносимый unbearable, intolarable.
непигментированный pigmentless.
непитающийся nonfeeding.
непищевые отношения zool: nonpredatory relations.
неплодная корова = яловая к.
неплодоносное дерево bot: nonbearing tree.
неплодородность infertility.
неплодородный infertile.
неповреждённый uninjured, intact.
неподвижное сочленение anat: gomphosis.
неподвижность immobility, nonmotility, fixity, stiffness.
~ сустава ankylosis.
неподвижный immobile, stationary, motionless, fixed, stiff.
~ зрачок ophth: fixed pupil.
~ столик mcscop: fixed stage.
неподлежащий операции surg: inoperable.
непоказательный результат inconclusive result.
непокрытая корова = яловая к.
неполегающий bot: erect.
неполная летаргия hemilethargy.
~ обеспложенность semisterility.
неполная сердечная блокада path: incomplete heart block.
неполное насыщение subsaturation.
~ окостенение imperfect ossification.
~ превращение entom: incomplete metamorphosis, hemimetaboly.
неполнозубые zool: edentates (Edentata, Xenarthra).
неполнозубый zool: edentate.
неполноценность imperfect quality; psych: inferiority.
~ клапана path: valvular incompetence.
~ сердца incompetance of the heart.
неполноценный imperfect-quality; psych: inferior.
~ белок imperfect albumin, incomplete protein.
неполный incomplete, short, partial, subtotal.
~ антиген incomplete antigen, hapten, partial antigen.
~ перелом surg: incomplete fracture.
~ прикус odont: malocclusion.
неполовозрелый preadolescent.
непоражённый unaffected.
непортящийся nonperishable.
непосредственная аускультация immediate auscultation.
~ причина immediate cause, proximate c.
непосредственно окружающий circumadjacent.
непосредственное заражение immediate contagion.
непосредственный посев на среды bact: direct culture.
непоступление жёлчи в кишечник acholia.
неправильная диета faulty diet.
~ менструация gyn: menoxenia.
~ перистальтика dysperistalsis.
~ работа сердца cardiac irregularity.
неправильно зазубренный лист bot: laciniated leaf.
~ расположенные зубы odont: misplaced teeth.
~ сидящий зуб odont: malturned tooth.
неправильное образование malformation.
~ окостенение pathological ossification.
~ питание faulty nutrition, denutrition.
~ пищеварение maldigestion.
~ положение malposition, allotopia, dystopy.
~ ~ зуба trusion, odontoloxy.
~ ~ зубной коронки odont: coronal trusion.

неправильное предлежание obstet: malpresentation.
~ произношение буквы с sigmatism.
~ ~ гортанных (г, к) gammacism.
~ прорезывание зубов ped:maleruption.
~ развитие maldevelopment. [mation.
~ ~ половых органов genital malfor-
~ соединение malunion.
~ сочленение malarticulation.
~ сращение vicious union.
неправильность incorrectness, abnormality, irregularity.
неправильный incorrect, abnormal,irre-
~ зрачок ophth: irregular pupil. |gular.
~ морской ёж spatangid.
~ прикус odont: malocclusion, abocclusion, abnormal occlusion. [occlusion.
~ ~ мешающий жеванию afunctional
непрерывность сознания psych: continuity of consciosness.
непрерывный регистратор планктона continuous plankton recorder.
~ шов surg: continuous suture.
неприживающееся растение solute
неприлипающий nonadherent. plant.
неприрастающий solute.
непристающий nonadhering.
неприятное ощущение unpleasant sensation, discomfort.
~ самочувствие discomfort.
непрободённые фораминиферы (подотр.)zool: imperforate foraminifers (Imperforata).
непроглатывание path: aphagia.
непроизвольный involuntary, unintentional. [impenetrability.
непроницаемость impermeability,
непроницаемый impermeable, impenetrable
~ для пыли dusttight. |opaque, tight.
непропорциональный disproportionate.
непропускающий газа gastight.
~ лучей radiopaque. [seeds).
непротравленный agr: nontreated (of
непроходимость impassability, imperviousness,obstruction.
непроходимый impassable, impervious.
непрощупываемый impalpable.
непрощупывающийся = непрощупывае-
непроявляющийся nonmanifest. мый.
непрямое деление = сложное д.
~ дыхание indirect respiration. [flex.
непрямой рефлекс physl: indirect re-
неравенство зрачков = неравномерность з.
неравномерность зрачков ophth: anisocoria.

неравностворчатый zool: inequivalve.
неравносторонний bot: inequilateral; oblique.
неразборчивость в еде indiscretion
неразведенный undiluted. |in diet.
неразвернувшийся лист bot: rudimentary leaf, bud scale. [ched tentacle.
неразветвлённое щупальце zool:unbran-
неразвитость underdevelopment, failure of development. [drop.
неразгибание пальцев ноги neur:toe
неразрастающийся птеригий ophth: inactive pterygium. [conduct.
неразумное поведение psych:irrational
нераспознанный unidentified, undiscri-
~ случай path: missed case. |minated.
нерасположение indisposition, distaste.
нерастворимость insolubility.
нерастворимый insoluble.
нерастрескивающийся bot: indehis-
нерасчленённый nonsegmented. |cent.
нерв anat: nerve.
~ половых органов и бедра anat: genitofemoral nerve.
нерватура листа = нервация л.
нервация (листа) bot: venation (of a leaf).
нервная болезнь nervous disease.
~ ветвь anat: nerve branch.
~ возбудимость nervous irritability.
~ диспепсия path: nervous indiges-
~ единица hist: nerve unit. [tion.
~ клетка hist: nerve cell, neurocyte.
~ неустойчивость nervous instability. [ectoderm, neuroblast.
~ пластинка embr: neural plate, n.
~ проводимость nervous conductivity.
~ проказа neural leprosy.
~ система anat: nervous system.
~ ткань hist: nervous tissue.
~ трубка embr: neural tube.
нервно- neuro-, neural.
~ -мышечная регуляция neuromuscular control. [system.
~ -мышечная система neuromuscular
~ -рецепторный аппарат anat: neuroreceptor apparatus.[lar regulation.
~ -сосудистая регуляция neurovascu-
~ -трофический neurotrophical.
нервного происхождения neurogenic, neurogeneous.
нервное влагалище anat: nerve
~ волокно hist: nerve fibre.|sheath.
~ напряжение nervous strain.
~ нарушение nervous disturbance.

нервное окончание anat: nerve termination.
~ отделение (больницы) neurologic department.
~ раздражение nervous irritation.
~ сердцебиение nervous palpitation.
~ сплетение anat: neuroplex.
~ явление nervous manifestation, nervous phenomenon.
нервный валик embr: neural column.
~ путь anat: nerve track.
~ ствол anat: nerve trunk.
~ тяж hist: nerve cord; zool: retinaculum, cf. скребень.
нервозность nervousness.
нереагирование nonresponsiveness.
нереида = нереис.
нереис zool: clamworm (Nereis, Neanthes).
*нереоцистис bot: nereocyte (Nereocystis); ribbon kelp (N. lutkeana) brown algae.
нерестилище ichth: spawning ground, egg-laying area.
нереститься ichth: shed the eggs, spawn.
нерестовать = нереститься.
нерестовая миграция ichth: spawning migration.
нерестовик ichth: spawning pond, hatching pond.
нерестовый инстинкт spawning instinct.
~ период spawning season.
~ пруд = нерестовик.
нерестующая особь spawner.
нерестующий spawning.
нерестящаяся группа breeding congress.
нерешительность indecision.
неритический neritic.
нерка ichth: red salmon, Alaska red, quinault, sockeye, suk-kegh (Oncorhynchus nerka).
неровность травостоя (стеблестоя) bot: unevenness of stand.
неровный uneven, rough, ragged, erratic.
неродственное разведение outbreeding.
нерожавшая (женщина) nullipara.
нерпа обыкновенная zool: hair seal (Phoca hispida).
несамопроизвольный nonspontaneous.
несахарный диабет path: diabetes insipidus.
несварение желудка path: indigestion.
несвертываемый incoagulable.
несвязность речи (мышления) incoherence, divagation, rambling speech (thought).
несгибаемость inflexibility.
несгораемый incombustible.
несегментированный unsegmented.
несегментный bio: ameristic.
несекреторный asecretory.
несерьезное заболевание minor disease.
несессильный nonsessile.
нескрещиваемость nonhybridization.
неслия метельчатая круглая bot: ball mustard (Neslia paniculata).
несовершенные грибы bot: imperfect fungi (Fungi imperfecti).
несовершенный цветок bot: imperfect flower, diclinous flower.
несовместимость incompatibility; nondisjunction.
несовместимый incompatible.
~ с железом pharm: antisideric.
несогласованность discordance, incoordination, maladjustment, mismatch.
несодержащий альбумозы albumose-free.
~ мышьяка arcenic-free.
~ сахара sugar-free.
несоответственный incongruent, incongruous, noncorresponding, incompatible.
несоответствие incongruity, incompatibility; nondisjunction.
несочленованные nonarticulated.
несочленовный anat: inarticulate.
несостоятельность дыхательного центра failure of the respiratory center.
неспастический aspastic.
неспаянный path: nonadherent.
неспелый bot: unripe, immature.
неспособность inability, incapability, incompetency.
~ к спорообразованию bio: apospory.
~ к труду invalidism, incapacitation.
~ писать neur: loss of ability to write, agraphia.
~ различать цвета color blindness.
~ свертываться incoagulability.
~ считать acalculia.
неспособный свертываться incoagulable.
несращение nonunion.
несросшиеся asymphytous.
несросшийся перелом surg: ununited fracture.
нестебельчатый bot: stemless, stalkless, unstalked, exscape, acaulescent.
нестерильный unsterile.
нестеснение psych: no restraint.
нестор orn: New-Zealand parrot Nestor.
нестрекающие zool: nonstinging animals (Acnidaria, subphylus of Coelenterata).
нестрекающие (подтип) zool: Acnidaria.

несушка agr: laying fowl, layer (hen).
несущая клешню конечность zool: cheliped.
несущий вилообразный отросток zool: furciferous.
~ волоски piliferous.
~ жабры gill-bearing.
~ кисть bot: racemose.
~ на спине zool: dorsiferous.
~ семяпочку bot: ovuliferous.
~ сосочки zool: mammilate.
~ спорангий sporangiferous.
~ усики entom: cirriferous.
~ флаг bot: vexillary.
~ щетинки stylate.
несформировавшееся семя ovule.
несчастный случай 1. accident; 2. fatality.
несъедобный inedible.
~ гриб bot: toadstool.
несыпнотифозный больной nontyphus-fever patient.
нетель = тёлка.
нетипируемый штамм mcbio: untypable strain.
нетипичный atypical, nontypical, off-type.
нетоксичность nontoxicity.
нетоксичный nontoxic.
нетопырь = кожан.
неточный термин inexact term.
"не тронь меня" bot: see 1. мимоза стыдливая; 2. недотрога.
нетрудоспособный incapacitated; psych: incompetent; see also инвалид.
нетуземный ecdemic.
неувядающий bot: nonwilting, everblooming.
неуклюжесть awkwardness.
~ движений clumsiness of movements.
неукоренившийся bot: nonrooted.
неукореняющийся bot: nonrooted.
неумеренность intemperance.
~ в еде overindulgence in eating.
неусвояемый inassimilable.
неусидчивость restlessness.
неустойчивость instability.
неутолимый quenchless (thirst, etc.)
нефелида small horse-leech.
нефелиум bot: longan (Nephelium longana); rambutan (N. lappaceum); see also лопушник.
неформалинный unformalinized.
нефорощь веничная = кохия веникоподобная.
нефотосинтезирующий nonphotosynthetic.
нефридиальный nephridial.
нефридий zool: nephridium.
нефрит path: nephritis.
нефритический nephritic.
нефрогенный nephrogenic.
нефроз path: nephrosis.
нефролитиаз pat : nephrolithiasis.
нефрон anat: nephron.
нефросклероз path: nephrosclerosis.
нефростомия urol: nephrostomy.
нефротиф nephrotyphoid.
нефтевание san: petrolization.
нефтевать san: petrolize.
нехворощ = полынь горькая.
нехирургический nonsurgical.
нехрущ = хрущ июньский.
нецветковый bot: nonflowering.
нечеткое зрение indistinct vision.
нечеткость зрения blurring of vision.
нечленистые ленточные черви monozoic cestodes (Cestodaria).
нечленораздельность речи anathria.
нечленораздельный inarticulate.
нечувствительность insensibility.
~ к запахам anosmia.
~ к раздражителям absence of reaction, anergy.
нечувствительный insensitive.
~ к боли analgic, analgetic.
неявственно исчерченный substriate.
неядовитость nontoxicity.
неядовитый nontoxic, nonpoisonous.
неясно очерченный ill-defined.
ниацин niacin.
нивяник bot: oxeye daisy, white oxeye (Chrysanthemum leucanthemum).
нигелла = чернушка.
нигер bot: niger (Guizotia oleifera).
нидаментальная железа zool: nidamental gland (in cephalopods).
нидулярия bot: Nidularia fungi.
нижневисочное поле зрения ophth: lower temporal field of vision.
нижнеглазничная борозда anat: infraorbital sulcus, s. infraorbitalis.
нижнеглазничное отверстие anat: infraorbital foramen.
нижнегубные щупальца entom: labid palpi, palpi labiales.
нижненосовое поле зрения ophth: lower nasal field of vision.
нижнечелюстное отверстие anat: mandibular foramen.
нижнечелюстной нерв anat: mandibular nerve.
~ сустав anat: (temporo)mandibular joint.
нижние листья bot: basal leaves.

нижние рожки щитовидного хряща anat: inferior cornua of the thyroid cartilage.
~ участки тела underparts.
~ челюсти entom: lower jaws, maxillae.
нижний lower; under; anat: inferior.
~ задний inferoposteal.
~ клык anat: stomach tooth.
~ крыловой четырёхугольник entom: subquadrangle.
~ отрезок пищевода anat: epicardia.
~ рог anat: underhorn.
~ рост bot: undergrowth.
~ слой lower layer, sublayer.
~ щит zool: plastron.
нижняя гортань = певчая г.
~ губа anat: underlip; zool: labium.
~ завязь bot: inferior ovary.
~ конечность anat: lower extremity.
~ косая глазная мышца anat: obliquus oculi inferior.
~ (наружная) колосковая чешуя bot: lower empty glume.
~ носовая раковина anat: inferior nasal concha, inferior turbinate bone, concha nasalis inferior.
~ прямая глазная мышца anat: rectus oculi inferior, infrarectus.
~ часть lower part; entom: ventral side.
~ ~ живота anat: lower abdomen.
~ ~ микроскопа substage.
~ ~ подклювья orn: gonys.
~ ~ растения bot: foot end.
~ челюсть anat: lower jaw, mandible, inferior maxilla, mandibula.
низведение верхушки apicolusis (of a lung).
низкоопущенное сердце path: abdominal heart, pendulous heart.
низкорослость bot: dwarfness.
низкоствольный bot: short-stemmed, low-stemmed, low-pole.
низкотравный shortgrass.
низшее животное lower animal.
низшие звери zool: lower mammals (Metatheria), see сумчатые звери.
~ насекомые apterygota.
~ ракообразные (подкл.) zool: lower crustaceans (Entomostraca).
~ хордовые zool: lower chordates (Hemichorda and Urochorda).
низший гриб bot: lower fungus.
никандра = физалис перуанский.
никотинамид nicotinamide.
никтагиновое растение bot: nyctaginaceous plant.
никтагиновые (сем.) bot: nyctanthous plant family, four-o'clock f. (Nyctaginaceae).
никталопия ophth: moonblindness, nyctalopia.
никтинастия bot: nyctinastism, nyctinasty; nyctitropism.
никтурия path: nycturia.
нильский крокодил zool: Nile crocodile (Crocodilus niloticus).
нимфа entom: nymph (of a mite).
нимфальный период entom: nymphal stage.
нимфейные = кувшинковые.
нимфоидес bot: floating heart (Nymphoides).
нимфоманиачка psych: nymphomaniac.
нимфомания psych: nymphomania.
нинюрский Niniyur.
нипа = пальма нипа.
нисса bot: tupelo, pepperidge, sour gum (Nyssa).
~ водяная cotton gum (N. aquatica).
~ лесная black gum (N. sylvatica).
ниссовые (сем.) bot: sour gum family (Nyssaceae).
нистагм ophth: nystagmus.
нистагмический nystagmic.
нистагмоидное движение nystagmoid movement.
нисходящая аорта anat: descending aorta.
~ ободочная кишка anat: descending colon.
нисходящий descending, decurrent.
~ неврит path: descending neuritis.
нитевая реакция lab: thread reaction.
нитевидный threadlike, filamentory, filiform, filariform.
~ гаметофит bot: filiform gametophyte.
~ пульс path: thready pulse.
~ рост mcbio: filiform growth.
~ сосочек anat: filiform papilla.
~ усик entom: filiform antenna, thread-like antenna.
нитежаберные моллюски (отр.) zool: Filibranchia, Anisomyaria, Prionodesmacea.
нителла bot: nitella (Nitella flexilis).
нитратредуктаза nitrate reductase.
нитра(т)редуцирующая система nitrate reductase system.
нитрификация nitrification.
нитрифицировать nitrify.
нитрифицирующие бактерии nitrifying bacteria.
нитрифицирующий nitrifying, nitrate-producing.
нитробактерия nitrobacterium.

нитроглицерин pharm: clyceryl trinitrate.
нитрофуран chem: nitrofuran.
нитчатая водоросль bot: filamentous alga, conferva.
нитчатка = нитчатая водоросль.
нитчатый filarial, filaceous.
~ грибок bot: thread fungus.
~ червь zool: filarial worm, threadworm.
нить thread, filament; anat: filum.
~ грибницы = гифа.
~ лучистого грибка bact: actinomyces thread.
НИУИФ = Научный институт по удобрениям и инсектофунгицидам.
ничком = лежащий лицом вниз.
нищенская трава bot: beggarweed (Desmodium tortuosum, DC.)
новое заселение zool: restocking.
новокаин pharm: novocain, procaine hydrochloride.
новокрылые насекомые Neoptera.
новообразование neoplasm, (aberrant) new growth.
~ в виде цветной капусты path: cauliflower growth.
~ груди path: breast growth.
~ лёгкого path: pulmonary neoplasm.
~ матки gyn: uterine growth.
~ прямой кишки path: rectal growth.
новорожденный newborn, neonatal, baby.
нога leg, foot; arm (of a cephalopod); haunch, gaskin (of a cow).
~ брюхоногого zool: conch foot.
ногодержатель gyn: leg holder.
ногопёрые (отр.) ichth: Pediculati, Lophiiformes.
ноготки bot: marigold (Calendula).
ноготок аптечный = ноготки.
ноготь anat: nail, unguis.
~ пальца ноги toenail.
~ ~ руки fingernail.
ногохвост ильмовый entom: prominent Exaereta ulmi.
ногохвостка жёлтая entom: springtail Bourletiella lutea.
~ зелёная green flea Sminthurus viridis.
ногохвостки (сем.) entom: springtails (Collembola), see also вилохвостка.
ногохвостые = ногохвостки.
ногочелюсть zool: maxilliped (of a crustacean); entom: mouth-foot, jawfoot, gnathopodite.
ногощупальцы zool: pedipalpi.
ногтевая пилка nail file.
~ фаланга anat: nail bone.
~ щетка nail brush.

ногтевое ложе anat: matrix of a nail, nailbed, matrix unguis.
ногтевой anat: ungual.
~ валик anat: nail wall, nailfold.
~ желобок anat: nail groove.
ногтеобразовательный onychogenic.
ногтечистка nail cleaner.
ногтоеда path: whitlow (felon, paronychia); vet: panaritium.
ноди orn: noddy (Anous; Micranous).
нож surg: knife.
~ для отделения слизистой оболочки mucosa knife.
ножевая рана surg: knife wound.
ножеобразный cultrate, cultriform.
ножка stalk, pedicle, pedicel, peduncle, stipe, stem (of mushroom); anat: crus; entom: pedicellum (of an antenna).
~ аллантоиса embr: allantois stem, allantois stalk.
~ глазного пузыря embr: optic pedicle.
~ жёлчного мешка embr: pedicle of yolk sac.
~ мозга anat: brain stem, cerebral peduncle.
~ пестика bot: stipe.
ножки клитора anat: crura clitoridis.
ножная ванна pediluvium.
~ икра = икра ноги.
ножницеобразная походка path: crosslegged gait.
ножницы для бинтов surg: bandage scissors.
~ ~ марли gauze scissors.
~ ~ перерезки пуповины obstet: umbilical scissors.
~ ~ швов stitch scissors.
ножное предлежание obstet: foot presentation.
ножной pedal.
ноздреватый cancellous, honeycombed, spongy, porous.
ноздревой anat: narial.
ноздря anat: nostril, naris.
нозематоз nosematosis, see пебрина.
нозография nosography.
нозологическая единица disease entity.
нозология nosology.
Нойонс Noyons.
нома path: noma, cancrum oris, gangrenous stomatitis.
номадизм psych: nomadism.
номенклатура органов organonymy.
нора́ zool: burrow, hole, tunnel.
норадреналин norepinephrine, noradrenaline.
норвежский омар zool: Norway lobster (Nephrops norvegicus).
норичник bot: figwort (Scrophularia).
норичниковые (сем.) bot: figwort family (Scrophulariaceae).

норка zool: mink (Pitorius).
~ американская American mink (P. vison)
~ европейская European mink (P. lutreola, Lutreola lutreola).
нормальное зрение ophth: normal vision, emmetropia.
~ состояние normality, normalcy.
нормальные дневные хищники (подотр.) orn: normal day birds of pray (Aquila, Buteo, Milvus, Accipiter, Falco, etc.)
нормальный normal; psych: sane.
~ глаз normal eye.
нормы медицинского освидетельствования mil: regulations for physical examinations.
норник zool: burrowing animal.
норэпинефрин norepinephrine.
нос anat: nose.
носарь = бирючок.
носилки stretcher, litter.
~ на колесах wheel stretcher.
носилочный больной litter patient.
носитель carrier.
~ брюшнотифозной палочки infect: typhoid carrier.
~ вибриона bact: vibriocarrier.
~ ленточного глиста helm: host of tapeworm.
носовая кость anat: nasal bone, os nasale.
~ перегородка anat: nasal septum.
~ полость anat: nasal cavity.
~ раковина anat: scroll bone, turbinate [bone.
носовое зеркало otolar: nasal speculum.
~ кровотечение path: nose bleeding, epistaxis.
~ крыло anat: nasal ala.
~ отверстие = ноздря.
носовой nasal, rhinic.
~ гребень anat: nasal crest.
~ зонд otolar: nasal probe.
~ оттенок голоса = гнусавость.
~ ход anat: nasal passage.
носоглотка anat: nasopharynx, epipharynx.
носоглоточные оводы (сем.) entom: bot-flies and warble flies (Oestridae).
носолобный шов anat: nasofrontal suture.
носорешётчатый anat: nasethmoid.
носорог 1. zool: rhinoceros (Rhinoceros bicornis); 2. entom: see жук-носорог.
носороги (сем.) zool: rhinoceros family (Rhinocerotidae, Rhinoceridae).
носоротовой anat: oronasal.

нососкуловой anat: nasomalar.
носослёзный канал anat: nasolacrimal duct, canalis nasolacrimalis.
ностальгический nostalgic.
ностальгия nostalgia, homesickness.
носток bot: Nostoc (algae).
носуха zool: coati.
носящий яйца ovigerous.
нотропис ichth: cayuga minnow (Notropis cayuga); redfin, common shiner (N. cornutus).
ночесветки bio: flagellates Noctiluca miliaris, N. scintillans.
ночецветные = никтагиновые.
ночная красавица = любка двулистная.
~ потливость path: night sweat.
*ночница entom: noctuid, night moth, owlet-mouth (Noctuidae), night butterfly (Agrotis).
ночное животное nocturnal-habit animal.
~ зрение night vision.
~ недержание мочи path: nocturnal enuresis, bed wetting.
ночной горшок night pan.
~ испуг ped: night terrors.
~ образ жизни nocturnalism.
~ паралич neur: night palsy.
~ пот path: night sweat.
ночные страхи ped: pavor nocturnus, night terrors.
ноющая боль aching pain.
нравственное помешательство psych: moral insanity.
нуг = гвизоция.
нудизм psych: nudism.
нуклеиновая кислота nucleic acid.
~ ртуть pharm: mercury nucleid.
нуклеиновокислый натрий sodium nucleinate.
нуклеиновый обмен nuclein metabolism.
нуллипора zool: nullipore.
нуммулиты zool: Nummulites, Camerina (extinct).
нут bot: gram, Bengal grain, mother pea, coffee pea (Cicer arietinum).
нутревики bot: gastromyces (Gastromycetes).
нутрец vet: cryptorchid.
нутрия zool: nutria, see бобр болотный.
нухальный nuchal, see затылочный.
нуцеллус bot: nucellus.
нуцеллярная эмбриония genet: nucellar embryony.
нырковая утка orn: European diving duck, canvasback (Nyroca valisineria).

нырок 1. entom: see моль рябиновая; 2. orn: diver (Fuligulinae); see нырковая утка.
~ красноголовый pochard (Nyroca ferina).
ныряющий зоб = загрудинный зоб.
нью-гемпшир New Hampshire (chickens).
ньюфаундлендская собака zool: Newfoundland dog (Canis familiaris extrarius Terrae Novae).
ньям = ям.
нюнька = манник.
нюхательная соль pharm: smelling salt.
нянина сказка ped: nursery tale.

O

обваренное место scald.
обваривать scald, parboil.
~ и снимать шелуху pharm: blanch (almonds, etc).
обварить p. a. of обваривать.
обвёртка envelope.
~ цветка или початка bot: spathe.
обвиваться bot: clasp.
обвивной шов surg: harelip suture, transfixion suture.
обвислое лицо path: flabby face, flaccid face.
обвитие пуповины obstet: coiling of the cord.
обвиться p. a. of обвиваться.
обволакивать корни bot: incase the roots.
обдавать кипятком scald, parboil.
обдать p. a. of обдавать.
обеднение крови кислородом av med: lack of oxygen in blood, anoxemia.
обезболивание analgizing, anesthetization.
обезболивать analgize, anesthetize.
обезболивающее средство anodyne, analgesic, analg(et)ic.
обезболить p. a. of обезболивать.
обезводить p. a. of обезвоживать.
обезвоженный dehydrated.
обезвоживание dewatering, dehydration.
обезвоживать dewater, dehydrate.
обезвреживание rendering harmless; rad: decontamination.
~ яда detoxication, evenomation.
обезглавленный decapitated.
обезглавливание decapitation.
обездвиженность = ступор.
обезжиренный degreased, nonfat, defatted, fat-free.
обезжиривание defatting, degreasing.
обезжиривать defat, degrease.
обезжирить p. a. of обезжиривать.
обеззараженный aseptic; disinfected.
обеззараживание asepsis, antisepsis; disinfection.
обеззараживающее (средство) antiinfective, antiseptic; disinfectant.
обезлесить bot: deforest.
обезлес(н)ение bot: deforestation, disafforestation.
обезображивание mutilation, deforming, disfiguring.
обезображивающий полиартрит int: deforming polyarthritis.
~ рубец path: disfiguring scar.
обезьяна zool: monkey, ape.
обезьяны (отр.) zool: simians, apes, monkeys (Simiae).
обезьянья кисть path: monkey hand, ape hand.
~ морда = малотус.
обёртка bot: involucre (of a flower cluster).
обескровить p. a. of обескровливать.
обескровленный exsanguinated, blanched, bloodless, dehematized.
обескровливание exsanguination, blanching, dehematizing.
обескровливать exsanguinate, blanch, dehematize.
обесплодить p. a. of обеспложивать
обеспложенный sterilized; see also бесплодный.
обеспложивание sterilization.
обеспложивать sterilize.
обесцветить p. a. of обесцвечивать
обесцвечение decolor(iz)ation, blanching, destaining; etiolation; bleaching.
обесцвечивание = обесцвечение.
обесцвечивать decolorize, blanch, destrain; etiolate; bleach.
обесцвечивающее средство decolorant, bleach.
обжечься p. a. of обжигаться.
обжигание крапивой urtication.
обжигаться burn (oneself).
обжорство gluttony.
обильное выделение overflow, profuse discharge, defluxion.
обильный пот profuse sweating.
~ рост mcbio: plentiful growth, heavy g.
обитатель илистых луж zool: mud-puddler.

обитатель прибрежий zool: coastal dweller.
~ холодных вод bio: cool-water dweller.
обитающий в крови sanguicolous.
~ ~ организме рыб piscicolous.
~ ~ стоячей воде stagnicolous.
обкалывание иглой surg: acupressure.
обкладочная клетка anat: parietal acid cell, oxyntin cell.
облавливание catching.
область аккомодации глаза ophth: range of accommodation.
~ аорты anat: aortic area.
~ глаза ophthalmic region.
~ нереста = нерестилище.
~ притупления path: dull area.
~ распространения range.
облатка pharm: wafer, cachet.
облегчать allay, relieve, ease.
облегчающий одышку anapnoic.
облегчение alleviation, relief.
облегчить p. a. of облегчать.
облепиха bot: sea buck thorn (Hippophae rhamnoides).
облёт flight.
обливание (водой) phys-ther: affusion, suffusion (pouring of water upon a patient).
~ холодной водой cold affusion.
облигатный obligatory.
облиствение bot: foliation, leafing; frondescence.
облиственный bot: foliated, foliaceous, leafy, leaved.
облитерация obliteration.
облитерированный obliterated.
облитерирующий тромбангиит path: thrombangiitis obliterans.
облов catching.
обложенный язык path: furred tongue.
обломочный материал detritus.
облучаемость radiation exposure.
облучение rad: irradiation, exposure.
~ всего тела whole body irradiation.
~ изнутри internal irradiation.
~ пациента irradiation of a patient.
~ рентгеном x-ray irradiation.
~ снаружи surface irradiation, external i.
облысение acomia, alopecia, baldness, calvities, defluvium capillorum.
обман памяти psych: perversion of memory, paramnesia.
~ чувств false sense perception, hallucination.
обмен exchange, interchange.
~ в капиллярах capillary exchange.
~ веществ bio: metabolism.
обмен веществ в коже cutaneous metabolism.
~ ~ связанный с ростом организма metabolism partaining to growth.
~ газов exchange of gases.
обменная кислотность chem: exchange acidity.
~ нейтральность chem: exchange neutrality.
обменные ионы chem: exchangeable ions.
обмер грудной клетки chest measurements.
обморожение frost bite; chilblain, (erythema) pernio; kibe.
обморок syncope, fainting, collaps, swoon(ing).
обморочное состояние syncopal state, syncopic state, faintness.
обморочный приступ syncopal attack, fainting spell.
обмывание washing (off).
обнажать denude, expose.
обнажение denudation, exposure.
обнажённое дерево bot: bald tree.
обнажённый naked, bare, achlamydate.
обнаружение detection, locating, finding.
обнаруживать detect, locate, find; uncover, exhibit.
обнаружить p. a. of обнаруживать.
обновитель revitalizer.
~ дернины rejuvenator.
обобщать psych: generalize.
обобщение generalization.
обобщённый generalized.
обобщить p. a. of обобщать.
обогатительная культура mcbio: enrichment culture.
обогащениеenrichment.
ободочная артерия anat: colic artery.
~ кишка anat: colon.
ободочн(окишечн)ый anat: colic, colonic.
обоеполый bot: monoecious.
~ цветок bot: monoclinous flower.
оболонь = заболонь.
оболочечно-корковый anat: meningocortical.
оболочечный tunicary.
оболочка membrane , coat(ing), tunic(a), envelope, sheath(ing), cover(ing), cuticula, blanket; shell, case, casing.
~ глаза anat: eye tunic.
~ желтка zool: vitelline membrane.
~ клетки cell membrane, cell wall.
~ материнской клетки mother membrane.
~ Насмита = эмалевая кожица.

*оболочка семени bot: hud.
~ яйца egg shell.
оболочники zool: tunicates (Tunicata), see личиночнохордовые.
обоняние olfaction.
обонятельная аура neur: olfactory aura.
~ доля (мозга) anat: olfactory lobe.
~ луковица anat: olfactory bulb.
~ ямка embr: olfactory pit.
обонятельномозговой anat: rhinencephalic.
обонятельные измерения olfactometry.
обонятельный волосок hist: olfactory hair.
~ мозг anat: rhinencephalon.
~ нерв anat: olfactory nerve, first cranial nerve.
оборвать p. a. of обрывать.
оборонительная способность imm: defense ability.
оборонительные мероприятия defense means.
оборонительный bio: defensive, aposematic.
оборот улитки anat: turn of the cochlea.
обострение (болезни и т.п.) aggravation, exacerbation, intensification (of a disease, etc.)
~ памяти psych: hypermnesia.
обоюдная несовместимость genet: cross incompatibility.
обоюдоострый biacuminate.
обрабатывать гирудином hem: hirudinize.
~ глицерином glycerize.
~ осмиевой кислотой osmicate.
~ спиртом alcoholize.
обработать p. a. of обрабатывать.
обработка образцов lab: processing of samples, handling of samples.
образ жизни mode of life, habits.
образец 1. sample, specimen, test-piece; 2. model, pattern.
образование 1. formation, production, generation, creation; 2. education.
~ анастомоза между ободочной и прямой кишкой surg: colorectostomy.
~ ~ со слепой кишкой cecostomy.
~ антител imm: formation of antibodies, production of antibodies.
~ бластулы embr: blastulation.
~ вакуолей hist: vacuolation.
~ видов bio: speciation.
~ волдыря blistering, epispastic activity.
~ волокнистой ткани fibrosis.
~ волокон fibrillation.
~ геммул zool: gemmulation.
~ гноя path: pus formation.
образование грыжи path: herniation.
~ дентина dentinification.
~ дивертикула path: diverticulization.
~ жгутиков bio: enflagellation.
~ жёлчи bilification.
~ зубного цемента embr: cementification.
~ зубной эмали amelification.
~ инфаркта path: infarction.
~ искусственного сфинктера surg: sphincteroplasty.
~ ~ сустава surg: arthroplasty.
~ каверн cavitation.
~ камня path: lithogenesis, lithogeny.
~ карманов pocketing.
~ канальцев canaliculization.
~ кожи cutification.
~ костной ткани osteogeny.
~ крапивных волдырей derm: urtication.
~ куколки entom: pupation, nymphosis.
~ кутикулы bio: cuticularization.
~ лейкоцитов hist: leucopoiesis.
~ лимфы physl: lymphization.
~ маточной кисты gyn: metrocystosis.
~ млечного сока chylifaction, chylosis.
~ монетных столбиков hem: nummulation, rouleaux formation.
~ нитей filamentation.
~ новых клеток из протоплазмы старых rejuvenescence.
~ папул path: papulation.
~ петель looping.
~ плаценты embr: placentation.
~ плода obstet: fetation.
~ пузырей vesication.
~ пузырьков vesiculation.
~ пустул path: pustulation.
~ пятен maculation, spotting.
~ разных сегментов bio: dysmerogenesis.
~ сахара bio: glycogeny.
~ свищей path: fistulization.
~ секвестра path: sequestration.
~ складок plication.
~ соли salification.
~ струпа surg: escharosis.
~ трабекул hist: trabeculation.
~ трех зародышевых листков embr: tridermogenesis.
~ трупного жировоска adipoceration.
~ туберкулов path: tuberculization.
~ узелков nodulation.
~ узлов knotting.
~ уксуса acetification.
~ холестерина cholesterogenesis.
~ хрящевой ткани chondrosis.

образование цист cyst formation.
~ эпидермиса epidermization.
~ яйца egg formation, oögenesis.
образовательная клетка embr: formative cell.
~ ткань hist: morphotic tissue.
образовательный formative, morphotic.
~ желток embr: formative yolk.
образовать p. a. of образовывать.
образовывать почки bot: gemmate.
~ пучки fasciculate.
образующий антитела imm: forming antibodies, producing antibodies.
~ белок albuminiparous.
~ вакцину vaccigenous.
~ ветви ramiparous.
~ влагалище sheathing.
~ две складки biplicate.
~ жировую ткань adipogenous.
~ здоровую ткань euplastic.
~ карпогений bot: carpogenous.
~ кровеносные сосуды embr: vasifactive.
~ лейкоциты hem: leucopoietic.
~ лепестки bot: petaliferous.
~ лецитин lecithigenous.
~ млечный сок chylifactive, chylific, chylopoietic.
~ мышечную ткань sacrogenic, producing muscle.
~ пару zool: mated.
~ пигмент chromogenic.
~ пиоцианин bact: pyocyanogenic.
~ эмульсию emulsive.
~ эндоспоры endospore-forming.
~ ядрышко nucleolar-organizing.
~ яйцо oogenous.
~ ~ или семяпочку bio: ovulogenous.
обрамленный волосками ciliated.
обрастание epibiose.
~ диатомеями bot: diatom fouling.
~ судов ship fouling.
обрастающие (подводные сооружения) организмы fouling organisms, fouling community.
обратимость reversibility, convertibility.
обратимый reversible, convertible.
обратная волна (крови) regurgitation.
~ перистальтика path: reversed peristalsis, retrostalsis.
обратное действие retroaction.
~ развитие involution.
~ скрещивание genet: reciprocal crossing, recrossing.
обратноизогнутое колено (у лошади) broken knee.
обратноконический bot: obconical.
обратноланцетный bot: oblanceolate.
обратноланцетовидный bot: oblanceolate.
обратносердцевидный bot: obcordate.
обратнояйцевидный bot: obovate.
обратный прилив крови path: regurgitation of blood.
~ ток back flow, reflux.
обращённая семяпочка bot: anatropous ovule.
обращённый наружу extrorse.
обрезание surg: circumcision, posthetomy.
обрезанный circumcised, apellous.
обросший (ракушками) barnacled.
обрубленный truncated.
обрыв abruption; break, discontinuity.
~ плаценты obstet: ablatio placentae, abruptio placentae.
обрывание abrupting; breaking.
обрывать болезнь abort.
обрывающее лечение abortive treatment.
обрывающий течение болезни checking a disease, abortive.
обрывистая речь neur: clipped speech.
обрызгать p. a. of обрызгивать.
обрызгивание sprinkling, spraying.
обрызгивать sprinkle, spray.
обсеменение insemination, seeding.
обследуемый examinee.
обследующий examiner.
обстетрический obstetric.
обстипация obstipation.
обструкция obstruction.
обтекаемый streamlined.
обтекание circumfluence.
обтереть p. a. of обтирать.
обтирание wiping, drying (oneself); rubbing down.
~ губкой sponging.
~ полотенцем toweling.
обтирать wipe, dry (oneself); rub down.
обугливание carbonization, charring.
обугливать(ся) char, carbonize.
обуглить(ся) p. a. of обугливать(ся).
обход round.
обширный таз obstet: generally enlarged pelvis.
общая анестезия general anesthesia.
~ атрофия general atrophy.
~ инфекция systemic infection.
~ обёртка bot: general involucre.
~ подвздошная артерия anat: common iliac artery.
~ слабость general weakness, general debility, asthenia.

общая смерть организма somatic death.
~ сонная артерия anat: common carotid, cephalic artery.
~ терапия general treatment.
~ хирургия general surgery.
общее заболевание general disease, systemic disease.
~ заражение general infection.
~ истощение организма cachexia.
~ кровообращение general circulation.
~ настроение psych: general mood.
~ недомогание general malaise, "sick all over."
~ облучение whole body irradiation.
~ расстройство организма systemic disturbance.
~ состояние general condition, systemic condition.
~ ~ здоровья general health.
~ физическое состояние general physical condition.
~ явление general phenomenon.
общество врачей medical society.
общесуженный таз obstet: generally contracted pelvis.
общие отёки подкожной клетчатки anasarca, generalized edema.
общий general, common, communis, overall.
~ жёлчный проток anat: common bile-duct.
~ малоберцовый нерв anat: common peroneal nerve, lateral popliteal n.
~ массаж phys-ther: general massage.
~ наркоз surg: general anesthesia.
~ паралич path: general paralysis.
~ разгибатель пальцев anat: extensor digitorum communis.
объедание overeating.
объеденные листья bot: ragged leaves.
объединение врачей union of physicians.
объектив mcscop: objective, object glass.
объективация psych: objectivating, exteriorization.
объективные данные objective evidence
объективный симптом objective symptom.
объем дыхания volume of breathing.
объемлющий bot: clasping (leaf, etc.)
объятие самцом (лягушки) самки amplexus.
объячеивать ichth: enmesh.
обызвествление аортальных клапанов path: aortic valve calcification.
~ артерии path: calcification of an artery, arteriostosis.

обыкновенная вода ordinary water, plain water.
обыкновенный bot: common (vulgaris, trivialis).
обычная лабораторная работа laboratory routine.
обычный распорядок работы routine.
~ стол ordinary diet.
обязательная заявка mandatory notice.
~ прививка imm: compulsory vaccination.
обязательное оспопрививание compulsory vaccination.
овальная ямка anat: fossa ovalis.
овальное отверстие foramen ovale.
овально-ланцетовидный bot: ovate-lanceolate.
~ -округлый bot: ovate - orbicular.
овальный oval; bot: ovate.
~ лист bot: ovate leaf.
овариальный ovarian.
овёс bot: oat (Avena sativa).
~ африканский = о. византийский.
~ византийский African oat (A. byzantina, C. Koch.)
~ восточный черногривый black Tartarian oat (A. sativa orientalis).
~ голый sweet oat (A. nuda).
~ желтеющий yellow oat-grass, trisetum (A. flavescens).
~ золотистый = о. желтеющий.
~ ложный дикий = овсец.
~ одногривый = о. восточный черногривый.
~ татарский = о. восточный черногривый.
~ черногривый blackhull oat (A. sativa, var. montana).
~ щетинистый meagre oat (A. strigosa).
овечий zool: ovine.
~ мозговик helm: tapeworm Multiceps multiceps, brainworm.
овечья шерсть (губка) zool: sheep's wool sponge (Hippospongia gossipina).
овикапт zool: oocapt.
овицид chem entom: ovicide.
овогенез embr: ovogenesis.
овод entom: gadfly, horsefly, deerfly (Oestridae); botfly (Larvivoridae).
~ большой желудочный = о. конский.
~ бычий bomb-fly, ox warble, cattle grub (Hypoderma bovis).
~ ~ полосатый heel-fly (Hypoderma lineatum).
~ желудочный = о. конский.
~ кожный warble fly (Hypodermatinae).

овод конский common botfly, stomach bot, horse botfly (Gastrophilus intestinalis).
~ краснохвостый red-tailed botfly, nosefly (Gastrophilus haemorrhoidalis).
~ носовой олений throat botfly (Gastrophilus nasalis)
~ овечий полостной sheep botfly (Oestrus ovis).
овощи bot: vegetables.
овражек = суслик.
овсец bot: fatuoid (Avenastrum, Jessen).
~ луговой meadow oatgrass (A. pratensis)
~ опушённый meadow oatgrass (A. pubescens, Jess, or Avena pubescens).
овсовые (подсем.) bot: oat subfamily (Aveneae, Nees.)
овсюг bot: bearded oat, poor o., wild o. (Avena fatua).
овсяница 1. orn: see овсянка 1; 2. bot: fescue grass (Festuca).
~ высокая bot: tall fescue (F.elatior).
~ красная chewing fescue (F. rubra).
~ луговая meadow fescue (F. pratensis).
~ овечья sheep's fescue (F. ovina).
овсяницевые (подсем.) bot: fescue subfamily (Festuceae, Ness.)
овсянка 1. orn: small European finch: yellowhammer, yellow bunting, clotbird (Emberiza citrinella); 2. ichth: small fish Leucaspius delineatus; 3. oatmeal (mush, porridge).
~ жёлтая = овсянка.
~ камышовая reed bunting (Emberiza schoeniclus).
~ обыкновенная = овсянка.
~ садовая ortolan (E. hortulana).
овсянковые (сем.) orn: yellowhammer family (Emberizidae).
овсяное масло avenol.
овсяный bot: avenaceous.
~ корень = козлобородник-сальсифи.
овуляция ovulation.
овца ewe, female sheep (Ovis).
овцебык = мускусный бык.
овчарка sheep dog (Canis familiaris domesticus pecuarius).
овшивение pediculation, infestation by lice.
оглушение stupefaction; stunning, deafening.
огнёвка entom: pyralid.
~ акациевая = о. бобовая
~ бобовая lima-bean pod borer (Etiella zinckenella).
~ восковая = моль восковая.
~ грушевая pear-tree pyralid (Numonia pyrivorella).
~ зерновая = о. табачная.
огнёвка зонтичная carrot pyralid (Loxostege palealis).
~ какаовая = о. табачная.
~ капустная cabbage pyralid (Mesographe forficalis).
~ клюквенная black-headed cranberry worm, fireworm, cranberry girdler (Crambus hortuellus, Eudemus vaccinia-na).
~ крыжовниковая gooseberry pyralid (Zophodia convolutella).
~ кукурузная European corn borer (Pyrausta nubilalis, P. silacealis).
~ мельничная Mediterranean flour moth (Ephestia kühniella); wheat-flour moth (Tinea granella).
~ мучная meal snout moth (Pyralis farinalis).
~ -плодожорка Eusophera bigella.
~ подсолнечниковая sunflower moth (Homoeosoma nebulella).
~ просяная = о. кукурузная.
~ сафлорная safflower moth (Myelois cinctipalpella).
~ стручковая Evergestis extimalis.
~ табачная tabacco moth (Ephestia elutella).
~ шишковая coniferous moth (Dioryctia abietella).
~ шоколадная = о. табачная.
~ южная амбарная Indian meal moth (Plodidia interpunctella).
огнёвки (сем.) entom: pyralids (Pyralididae).
огнестрельная рана surg: gunshot wound.
~ ~ живота abdominal gunshot wound.
~ ~ кости bone gunshot wound.
оголение denudation.
оголённый denude.
огонёк bot: see купава.
огонори bot: ogo-nori (Gracilaria),see грацилярия.
огородная зелень agr: greens, green-stuff.
огородник agr: vegetable grower.
огородничество agr: vegetable growing, gardening.
огородный слизень zool: garden slug (Limax).
ограда anat: claustrum.
ограничение (приема) жидкости fluid restriction.
ограниченно трудоспособный partially incapacitated.
огудина (огурцов, тыквы) bot: top (of cucumbers, squash).
огузок anat: buttocks.
огурец bot: cucumber (Cucumis sativus).
~ бешеный = деряба.
~ вестиндийский = о. колючий.

огурец дикий echinocystis, wild balsam apple (Echinocystis, T. & G.)
~ змеиный serpent gourd (Trichosantes anguina). [anguria).
~ колючий bur cucumber, gherkin (C.
~ мексиканский chayote (Sechium edule, Schw., Chayota edulis, Jacq.)
~ многолетний = тыква вонючая.
огуречная трава = бораго.
огурчик bot: cuke, small cucumber.
одеревянелый = одревеснелый.
одержимость psych: obsession.
~ навязчивыми идеями psych:rumination
~ ~ состояниями psych: obsessive ruminative state.
одернованный sodded.
одерновать p. a. of одерновывать.
одерновывать sod.
одинаковая острота зрения в обоих глазах isopia. [generic.
одинакового происхождения bio: con-
одинаковое владение обеими руками ambidexterity, ambidextrism, ambidex-
одинаковой форма isomorphic. |trality.
одиночная асцидия zool: sea squirt.
однобратный bot: monadelphous. [ous.
одноветвистый bot: uniramose, uniram-
одногнёздный unilocular, monothalamous.
одноголосые (подотр.) orn: suborder Anisomyodi.
одногорбый верблюд zool: Arabian camel, dromedary (Camelus dromedarius).
обнодневка = подёнка. [(edon).
однодольное растение bot:monocotyl-
однодольные (кл.) bot: monocotyledons, Monocotyledoneae (class).
однодольный unilobar; bot: monocotyledonous. [plant.
однодомное растение bot: mon(o)ecious
однодомный bot: monoecious, andromonoecious.
одножгутиковый bio: monociliated.
однозачатковый genet: monoembryonis.
однозернянка bot: lesser spelt, einkorn (Triticum monococcum).
одноименная диплопия ophth: homonymous diplopia.
однокамерный one-chambered, monothalamous, unilocular.
одноклеточные животные zool: one-celled animals (Monocytozoa), see протоморфные животные.
одноклеточный one-celled, single-celled, unicellular.
~ организм bio: single-cell organism, monad, unicell.

однокопытное zool: one-hoofed, soliped (Perissodactyla, Equidae),see непарнокопытные.
однокоренной monoradicular.
однократное облучение rad: single exposure. [mones.
однолёгочные (отр.) ichth: Monopneu-
однолепестковое растение bot: monopetalous plant.
однолетнее дерево yearling.
однолетник bot: 1. yearling;2. annual.
однолистный bot: monophyllous.
однолопастный bot: unifoliate.
одноосный сустав anat: monaxial joint. [gynous.
однопестичный bot: one-pistil, mono-
одноплодолистиковый bot: monocarpellary.
однопокровные bot: Monochlamydeae.
однополый monosexual.
~ цветок bot: diclinous flower.
однопредсердные моллюски (отр.) zool: Monotocardia (mollusks).
однопроходные zool: monotremes (Monotremata).
однопроходный adj: monotrematous.
одноразное облучение rad: single exposure. [nis.
однорогая матка path: uterus unicor-
однородный рабдит zool: rhabdoid.
однорядный bot: monostichous.
односемядольное и т. п. = однодольное и т.п. [spermous.
односемянный bot: single-seeded,mono-
однослойная культура ткани mcbio: monolayer tissue culture.
однослойный one-layer, single-layer, monolayer, monostratal, unilaminate.
~ пузырёк = бластула. [mollusk.
одностворчатый моллюск univalve
одностебельный bot: single-stemmed.
односторонний unilateral, one-sided.
~ паралич мышц hemiplegia.
односторонняя невралгия hemialgy.
односуставный anat: monarthric.
однотипно-лиственное растение bot: homophyllous plant.
однотычиночный bot: one-stemen, monostaminal, haplocaulous.
одноукосный (клевер и т.п.)bot: single-cut, late-flowering (clover, |etc.)
одноцветковый bot:uniflorous.
одночленистый one-segmented, uniarticulate, monozoic.
одноядерная клетка mononuclear cell.

одноядерный uninucleate, uninuclear.
одноядность zool: monophagia.
однoядный zool: monophagous.
однояйцовая двойня monozygous twins.
однояйцовый adj: one-egg.
одноярусный bot: fastigiate.
одомашнение domestication, taming.
одомашненный domesticated, tamed.
одонтолог odontologist.
одонтологический институт dental institute, odontological institute.
одонтология odontology.
одревесневший = одревеснелый.
одревеснелая ткань bot: ligneous tissue.
одревеснелый bot: lignified, woody, hardened.
одревеснение lignification.
одревеснеть p. a. of древеснеть.
одряхление = дряхлость.
одуванчик bot: dandelion, blowball (Taraxacum, Zinn.)
одурманивающее средство stupefacient, narcotic.
одурь = белладонна.
одутловатость puffiness, bloat.
одутловатый puffy, puffed up, bloated; see also вздутый.
одутлый bot: inflated (inflatus).
одушевлённость animation.
одушевлённый animate.
одышка difficult breathing, dyspnea, pant(ing), breathlessness, shortness of breath; vet: chest foundering.
оживать revive.
оживающий в сумерки bio: crepuscular.
оживитель revitalizer.
оживление 1. resuscitation; 2. animation (vivacity).
оживлять 1. resuscitate; 2. animate.
ожига bot: woodrush (Luzula, DC).
ожиговые = ситниковые.
ожидальня waiting room.
ожика = ожига.
ожиревшая почка path: fatty kidney.
ожиревший fatty.
ожирелость fatness.
ожирение obesity, adiposis, adiposity.
ожиреть p. a. of жиреть.
ожить p. a. of оживать.
ожог 1. burn, ambustion; 2. bot: blight.
~ второй степени second degree burn.
~ кислотой acid burn.
~ листьев phytp: wildfire (of tobacco leaves).
~ медузы zool: sting of medusa.
~ от вспышки flash burn.
ожог первой степени first degree burn.
~ третьей степени third degree burn.
оздоравливать render sanitary.
оздоровить p. a. of оздоравливать.
оздоровление sanitation, assanation.
оздоровляющий salutary.
озеленённый verdant.
озёрная палия ichth: lake salmon (Cristovomer namaycush).
~ форель ichth: lake trout, see also форель.
озёрный планктон lake plankton, limnoplankton.
озеро anat: lake, lacus.
озимый червь = гусеница совки озимой.
озноб shiver(ing), chill, cold fit, algor, rigor, algidity.
ознобление = озноб.
ока bot: oka (Oxalis tuberosa).
окаймлённая пóра bot: bordered pit.
окаймлённый манграми mangrove-bordered.
окаменелая кость petrified bone, osteolith.
окаменение petrifaction.
окапи zool: okapi (Ocapia johnstoni).
океаническая сельдь ichth: sea herring (Clupea harengus), Atlantic herring, common herring.
океанограф oceanographer.
океанографический oceanographic(al).
океанография oceanography.
океанология oceanology.
окисление oxidation.
окислитель oxidizer, oxidant, oxidizing agent.
окислять oxidize.
окись oxide.
~ бария chem: baryta, barytes, barium oxydatum.
~ углерода chem: carbon monoxide.
окихинолинсульфоновокислый калий pharm: oxyquinoline potassium sulphate.
окозлиться p. a. of козлиться.
окологрудинная линия anat: linea parasternalis.
оkoложаберная полость zool: atrial cavity.
окoложаберный zool: peribranchial.
околоlепестный цветок bot: perigynous flower.
околоматочная клетчатка anat: parametrium.
околоплодная оболочка placenta.
околоплодник bot: pericarp.
околоплодные воды obstet: amniotic fluid, waters.
околопозвоночная линия anat: linea paravertebralis.

околопочечный anat: perinephric.
околоротовой anat: circumoral, adoral circumbuccal.
околосердечная сумка anat: pericardium, pericardial sac.
околососковый кружок anat: mammary areola, areola mammae.
околосуставный anat: periarthric.
околоток = медпункт.
околоушная железа anat: parotid gland
околоцветник bot: perianth, floral envelope.
околощитовидная железа anat: parathyroid gland.
околоядерный hist: paranuclear, paranucleate.
окольная локтевая артерия (верхняя, нижняя) anat: (superior, inferior) ulnar collateral artery.
~ лучевая артерия anat: radial collateral artery.
окончание ending, finishing, termination, expiration.
~ двигательного нерва hist: motor ending.
~ чувствительного нерва hist: sensory ending.
окончательный диагноз final diagnosis.
~ хозяин bio: final host, definitive h.
окончатый fenestrated.
окопная лихорадка = волынская л.
окопник bot: comfrey, tailhead (Symphytum).
~ острый prickly comfrey (S. asperum).
~ русский Russian c. (S. peregrinum).
~ шерстистый = о. острый.
окоривание decortication, stripping of the bark.
окостеневающий ossifying.
окостенение ossification.
окотилло bot: ocotillo (Fouquieria splendens, Engelm.)
окотиться p. a. of котиться.
окоченелый stiff, numb, stark.
окоченение stiffness, numbness, obdormition, rigidity, rigiditas.
окра = гибиск съедобный.
окраек листа bot: leaf edge, leaf welt, leaf margin.
окрайковый bot: marginal.
окрапивление urtication.
окраска stain(ing), tinction, pigmentation; painting.
~ жгутиков bact: flagellum staining.
~ по Граму mcscop: Gram staining.
~ срезов hist: section staining.
окрашенный препарат stained preparation.
окрашивание staining; coloring, coloration; painting.
~ мазков bact: smear staining.
~ срезов lab: section staining.
окрашивать дополнительно mcscop: counter stain.
окрашивающийся суданом lab: sudanophile.
округлая мелкая спора bot: globose sporidium.
округлое расширение в гифах грибков bot: bromatium.
округлый orbicular.
~ в разрезе terete.
окружать оболочкой ensheath.
окружающая лопатку артерия anat: circumflex scapular artery.
~ плечевую кость артерия (задняя, передняя) anat: (posterior, anterior) humeral circumflex.
~ среда environment, surroundings.
окружающие условия environment.
окружающий кишечник peri-intestinal.
~ миндалину anat: periamygdalar.
~ мышцу perimuscular.
~ ноготь anat: periungual.
~ островок Рейля anat:circuminsular.
~ пищевод circumesophageal.
~ позвонок anat: perispondylic.
~ роговицу anat: perikeratic.
~ рот anat: perioral.
~ слепую кишку anat: pericecal.
~ сосочек anat: peripapillary.
~ хрусталик anat: perilenticular.
~ ядро circumnuclear.
окружность circumference.
оксалатный камень urol: calcium oxalate stone.
оксигемоглобин oxyhemoglobin.
оксигенотерапия oxygenotherapy.
оксикислота oxyacid.
оксилюциферин bio: oxyluciferin.
оксим oxime.
окситиамин oxythiamin.
окситотический oxytotic.
окситоцин oxytocin.
оксихроматин hist lab: oxychromatin.
октоплоид genet: octoploid.
окукление entom: nymphosis, pupation.
окукливаться entom: pupate.
окуклиться p. a. of окукливаться.
окулировать agr: bud, inoculate.
окулировка agr: budding, inoculation.
окулист ophthalmologist, oculist.
окуляр mcscop: ocular, eye-piece.
окунёвые (сем.) ichth: perches (Percidae).

окунеобразные (отр.) ichth: Perciformes.
окунещуковые (отр.) ichth:Percesoces.
окунь ichth: perch (Perca); bass (P. fluviatilis); see also американский окунь.
окуривание fumigation.
окуривать fumigate.
~ серой sulfurize.
окурить p. a. of окуривать.
олеандр bot: oleander, rosebay (Nerium oleander).
оледенение glaciation.
олеинокислая ртуть pharm: oleate of mercury.
олеинокислый натрий pharm: sodium oleate.
оленеводство agr: stag breeding.
олени (сем.) zool: deer family (Cervidae).
олений лишайник = о. мох.
~ мох bot: reindeer lichen (Cladonia rangiferina, Hoffm.)
олёнка entom: rose chafer (Epicomites hirta).
олень zool: deer.
~ благородный red deer (Cervus elaphus)
~ болотный swamp deer (Rucervus duvaucelli).
~ мазама American deer (Cariacus).
~ -мунтьяк muntjac (Cervulus muntjac).
~ пампасский Blastoceras campestris.
оленья собака = шотландская борзая.
~ трава bot: deer grass (Scirpus cespitosus).
олива anat: olive, olivary nucleus.
оливка = маслина.
оливковое масло olive oil.
оливкообразный bot: olivary.
олигонитрофильный bot: oligonitrophilic.
олигоплитес ichth: leatherjacket (Oligoplites saurus).
олигосахарид oligosaccharide.
олиготрофия oligotrophy.
олиготрофный oligotrophic.
олигофаг zool: oligophagus.
олигофреническое слабоумие psych: oligophrenic dementia.
олигофрения psych: oligophrenia.
олигохета zool: oligochaete.
олигоцитемия hem: oligocythemia.
олигурия oliguria.
*олуша orn: solan (Sula).
~ -глупыш gannet (Sula bassana).
*~ красноногая red-footed booby (Sula piscator).
олфактометрия (методом вдувания) (blast) olfactometry.
ольпидиум bot: Olpidium (fungus).
ольпидиум капустный O. brassicae.
ольха bot: alder (Alnus).
~ американская speckled alder, tag alder (A. rugosa).
~ белая white alder, summer sweet. Cf. белые ольхи (сем.)
~ мелкопильчатая common alder (A. serrulata).
~ морщинистая = о. американская.
~ орегонская red alder (A. oregona).
~ серая green alder (A. viridis, DC, or A. incana, Willd.)
~ чёрная black alder (A. glutinosa).
омар lobster (Homarus).
~ европейский European l. (H. gammarus).
~ обыкновенный common lobster (H. vulgaris).
~ с икрой berried lobster.
омег пятнистый = болиголов крапчатый.
омежник bot: water celery (Oenanthe).
~ трубчатый water dropwort (Oenanthe fistulosa).
~ шафраноподобный O. crocata.
омела bot: mistletoe (Viscum).
~ белая common m. (V. album).
~ европейская = о. белая.
омеление calcification.
омеловые (сем.) bot: mistletoe family (Loranthaceae).
омертвевать mortify, necrose, necrotize, die.
омертвевший mortified, necrotic.
омертвение mortification, necrosis.
омертветь p. a. of омертвевать.
омматидий entom: ommatidium.
омозолелость path: callosity.
омолаживание тканей bio: rejuvenescence in tissues.
омолаживающий rejuvenating, rejuvenescent.
омолодить rejuvenate.
омоложение rejuvenation, rejuvenescence.
омуль ichth: Arctic-Sea whitefish (Coregonus autumnalis).
омфалодес bot: navelwort (Omphalodes).
омшанник beehouse.
омыление saponification.
онагр onager (Equus onager).
онагриковые = онагровые.
онагровое растение onagraceous plant.
онагровые (сем.) bot: evening-primrose family (Onagraceae).
онанизм onanism.
онанировать masturbate.
онанист onanist.
ондатра muskrat (Ondatra zibethica,

онейроидный psych: oneiroid.
онемевший numb.
онемение numbness.
онкология oncology.
онкосфера helm: onchosphere.
онопордум = татарник.
онтогенез bio: ontogenesis, ontogeny.
онтогенетический ontogenetic, biontic.
онтогения ontogeny.
онхоцеркоз onchocerciasis.
оогамия oogamy.
оогамный bio: oogamous.
оогенез bio: oogenesis.
оогоний bio: oogonium.
оокинет ookinete.
оокинетический ookinetic.
оолит oölite.
оомицеты bot: oomycetes (Oomycetales) fungi.
ооспора bot: oospore.
оотека entom: ootheca.
оотип zool: ootype (in flukes, etc.)
ооциста zool: oöcyst.
ооцит bio: oocyte.
опавшая листва bot: shed leaves.
опадать fall (off), shed, shack.
опадающий shedding, deciduous.
опадение листьев bot: 1. leaf fall, shedding of leaves; 2. phytp: leaf blight.
~ плодов agr: (preharvest) fruit drop.
~ хвои bot: needle fall.
опаливать singe (off).
опалины = протоцилиаты.
опалить p. a. of опаливать.
опаршивевший vet: mangy.
опасность для матери obstet: maternal danger.
~ для плода obstet: fetal danger.
~ заражения infection hazard, contagiousness.
опахало (пера) orn: web, vane (of a feather).
опенаук bot: openauk (Apios tuberosa).
опёнок bot: honey fungus, armillaria (Armillaria, Fr.)
~ настоящий honey-colored armillaria, honey fungus, shoestring f., collar crack (A. mellea).
~ олений fawn-colored pluteus (Pluteus cervinus).
~ уховидный mock oyster, oyster mushroom (Pleurotus ostreatus).
оперативная хирургия operative surgery.
оперативные роды obstet: instrumental labor.
операционная (комната) surg: operating room.
~ сестра surg: scrub nurse.
операция operation.
~ исправления косоглазия ophth: strabotomy.
~ наложения высоких щипцов obstet: high operation.
~ ~ щипцов obstet: forceps operation.
~ образования искусственного зрачка ophth: coreoplasty.
~ сделанная в два приёма surg: two-stage operation.
~ ~ в несколько приёмов multistage operation.
~ ~ в один приём one-stage operation.
оперение 1. bot: bushing, staking; 2. orn: plumage.
оперённый orn: fledged, feathered, plumigerous, plumose.
оперившийся = оперённый.
~ птенец orn: fledgling.
оперируемость surg: operability.
оперкулярный ichth: opercular.
опеченевать hepatize.
опеченелый path: hepatized.
опеченение path: hepatization.
опеченеть p. a. of опеченевать.
опиекурильщик psych: opium smoker, opiophile.
опий pharm: opium; opiate.
опиоман psych: opiomaniac.
опиомания psych: opiomania.
опиофагия psych: opiophagia, opium-eating.
описательная анатомия descriptive anatomy.
опистонема ichth: thread herring (Opisthonema oglinum).
оплодотворение bio: fertilization, impregnation, ingravidation, insemination, fecundation, fructification.
оплодотворённое яйцо embr: fertilized ovum.
оплодотворённый bio: fertilized, etc.
оплодотворить p. a. of оплодотворять
оплодотворитель bio: fertilizer.
оплодотворять fertilize, etc. Cf. оплодотворение.
оплодотворяющая способность fertility.
оподельдок pharm: soap liniment.
опознавание identification.
ополаскивание rinsing.
опомиза entom: fly Opomyza florum.
опора support, sustentaculum; bot: foothold.
опоражнивать empty, void; evacuate, excrete, purge.
опорная клетка hist: sustentacular cell.
~ пластинка zool: mesogloea (of coelentrates).
~ система anat: structural system.
опорно-трофическая ткань anat: connective tissue.
опорный support(ing), sustentacular.
~ корень bot: prop root, brace r.

опорожнение emptying (out); excretion, evacuation.
~ желудка (или кишечника) evacuation of the bowels, gastric emptying, passage.
опорожнить p. a. of опоражнивать.
опорос farrow.
опоссум zool: opossum (Didelphis).
~ обыкновенный opossum, possum (D. marsupialis).
опоссумы (сем.) zool: opossums (Didelphiidae).
опохмелиться p. a. of опохмеляться.
опохмеляться drink alcohol during the hangover from a previous drinking.
опоясанный bot: banded.
опоясывание girdling, cincture; cf. ощущение опоясывания.
опоясывающая анестезия neur: girdle anesthesia.
~ боль girdle pain.
опоясывающий girdle, zonate.
~ лишай derm: herpes zoster, shingles.
~ слой мозга = поверхностный о.с.м.
оппозиция вивисекции antivivisection
определение 1. determination, determining, location, locating, finding; testing; chem: assay; identification; 2. definition (of a term, etc.)
~ беременности pregnancy test.
~ возраста age determination.
~ гемоглобина hemoglobin estimation.
~ группы крови blood typing.
~ количества белка albuminimetry.
~ ~ сахара saccharimetry.
~ кровяных групп = о. группы крови
~ обмена веществ metabolimetry.
~ остроты слуха acoumetry.
~ отцовства legl: paternity test.
~ родословной agr zool: pedigreeing.
~ степени косоглазия ophth: strabometry.
~ тонуса tonometry.
~ удельного веса мочи urinometry.
~ цветного индекса hem: chromocytometry.
определитель (ная таблица) bio: classification key.
определяющая причина determining cause.
опрелость derm: chafing, intertrigo.
опробкование bot: corking over, suberization.
опрыскивание spraying, nebulization.
опрыскивать spray, atomize, nebulize.
опсанус ichth: toadfish, sea robin (Opsanus tau).
опсонизирующее антитело opsoning antibody.
оптик optician.
оптика optics.
оптимальный optimal, optimum.
оптический optic.
оптогиральная иллюзия optogyral illusion.
опунция bot: opuntia (Opuntia).
опускание lowering, dipping; depression (of the eye).
опухание path: swelling, tumefaction, tumescence, see also вздутие, набухание.
~ сустава joint swelling.
опухать swell, tumefy.
опухлость swelling, the state of being swollen, tumidity, tumescence, see also вздутие.
опухлый swollen, tumid, tumefacient.
опухнуть p. a. of опухать.
опухолевая болезнь tumor disease.
опухолевидный tumorlike.
опухолеподобное скопление излившейся крови hematoma, focalized extravasation of blood.
опухоль swelling, tumor.
~ из костной ткани osteoma.
~ кровеносных сосудов hemangioma.
~ лимфатических сосудов lymphangioma.
~ мозга brain tumor.
~ подмышечной впадины axillary tumor.
~ семенной железы seminoma, embryonal carcinoma.
опушённая ость bot: feathery awn.
опушённое влагалище (листа) bot: hairy sheath.
опушённость = волосистость; cf. пушок.
опушённые листья bot: pubescent leaves.
~ чешуйки bot: ciliolate glumes.
опушённый downy, pappose, nappy, woolly, villous, flossy, sericeous, see пушистый.
~ спутанными волосками tomentose.
~ стерженёк bot: villous rachilla.
опущение descent, descending; path: ptosis, prolapse, abnormal depression, falling down.
~ верхнего века ophth: dropped lid.
~ внутренних органов path: splanchnoptosis.
~ диафрагмы path: phrenoptosis.
~ желудка prolapse or downward displacement of the stomach.
~ кишечника path: enteroptosis.
~ матки gyn: hysteroptosis, uterine descent.
~ почки int: prolapse of a kidney, nephroptosis.
опущенный lowered, descended, fallen, ptosed.
опыление bot: pollination.
~ ветром wind pollination, anemophily.

опыливание agr: dusting.
опылитель bot: pollinizer.
~ (-насекомое)(insect) pollinator.
опылить(ся) p. a. of опылять(ся)
опыляемое насекомыми растение entomophilous plant.
~ птицами растение ornitophilous p.
опылять(ся) bot: pollinate.
опыт Барани с указательным пальцем Barany's pointing test, finger-nose test.
опытный участок experimental plot.
опьянение inebriation, intoxication, drunkenness.
оральный полюс zool: oral end.
орангутанг zool: orangutan (Simia satyrus).
оранжерея greenhouse, hothouse.
орач = лебеда садовая.
орбита orbit.
орбитальный orbital.
оргазм physl: orgasm.
орган organ.
~ выделения anat: excretory organ; zool: nephridium.
~ выпускающий шелковичную нить entom: filator (of a silkworm).
~ для захватывания пищи bio: organ of food capture.
~ обоняния anat: olfactory organ.
~ размножения reproductive organ.
~ свечения bio: luminous organ.
~ чувств(а) anat: sense organ.
органелла zool: organelle.
организм organism.
~ питающийся голозойно phagotroph.
органическая химия organic chemistry.
органические остатки organic remains.
органический подбор bio: organic selection.
~ психоз organic psychosis.
органическое поражение path: organic lesion.
~ соединение chem: organic compound.
органогель chem: organogel.
органогенез embr: organogenesis.
органоид hist: organoid.
органолептический organoleptic.
органология organology.
органотерапия organotherapy.
органчик zool: coral Tubipora.
органы дыхания anat: respiratory organs.
~ здравоохранения health authorities.
~ прикрепления zool: adhesive organs (of flukes, etc.)
~ размножения anat: reproductive organs
оргастический orgastic.

ординатор resident physician, house p., assistant p.
ордовикский коралл ordovician coral.
орёл orn: eagle (Aquila).
орех bot: nut.
~ американский = о. бразильский.
~ бассия illipe (Bassia latifolia).
~ белый = диморфант.
~ болотный = о. водяной.
~ бразильский Brazil nut, cream n., Para n., nigger n., niggertoe (Bertolletia excelsa).
~ водяной water (chest)nut (Trapa natans).
~ волоцкий (волошский) walnut, English w.,Persian w.(Juglans regia).
~ гиккори hickory nut (Carya glabra).
~ грецкий = о. волоцкий.
~ земляной = арахис.
*~ индейский Indian walnut (Aleurites molbucana, Willd.)
~ калифорнийский = о. серый.
~ кедровый pine nut.
~ кола ombene nut.
~ лесной = лещина.
~ мускатный nutmeg (Myristica fragrans, Houtt.)
~ пекан pecan nut (Hicoria pecan,Brit.)
~ рвотный = чилибуха.
~ серый butternut, white walnut (Juglans cinerea, L.)
~ чёрный black walnut (J. nigra).
~ японский Japan walnut (J. sieboldiana).
ореховидный nutlike; anat: enarthrodial.
~ сустав anat: ball-and-socket joint, enarthrosis.
ореховка orn: nutcracker (Nucifraga).
ореховые (сем.) bot: walnut family (Juglandaceae).
ореховый bot: juglandaceous, of walnut.
орехоносный = орехоплодный.
орехоплодное дерево nut tree.
орехоплодный bot: nuciferous, cupuliferus.
орехотворка entom: gallfly, gallwasp.
~ виноградообразная Neuroterus quercus-baccarum.
~ корневая Biorrhiza pallida.
~ монетовидная Neuroterus numismalis.
~ шиповниковая mossy rose gallfly (Rhodites rosae, etc.)
~ шишковидная oak hedgehog gallfly (Andricus foecundatrix).
~ яблоковидная oak-apple gallfly (Diplolepis quercus-folii).
орехотворки (сем.) entom: gallflies (Cynipidae).

орехоцветные (пор.) bot: Juglandales.
орешек nutlet; pyrene.
~ дубильный bot: gall on oak tree.
~ чернильный = о. дубильный.
орешина bot: nut tree, see лещина.
орешкоплодные крестоцветные bot: nutlet-fruit crucifers. Cf. стручковые крестоцветные.
орешник bot: nut tree, see лещина.
ориентация в пространстве av med: spatial orientation.
ориентировочный аппарат anat: orientating apparatus.
ориньял = лось американский.
оркиш = полба.
орлёнок orn: eaglet.
орлик = водосбор.
*орлица orn: eagless.
орлы orn: eagles (Aquila).
орляк обыкновенный ichth: eagle ray (Myliobatis aquila, M. tobiei).
орнитин ornithine.
орнитозух zool: Ornitosuchus (extinct).
орнитолог ornithologist.
орнитологический (судовой) журнал bird log.
орнитология ornithology.
ороговелость corneous substance.
ороговелый cornified.
ороговение hornification, cornification, keratinization.
ороговеть cornify, keratinize.
оронтиум bot: golden club (Orontium).
оротовая кислота orotic acid.
орошать irrigate.
орошение irrigation.
орселевый лишайник bot: archil (Roccela usnea).
~ ягель = о. лишайник.
ортоодонтия orthodontics.
ортопед orthopedist, orthopedic surgeon.
ортопедическое отделение orthopedic department, orthopedic ward.
ортопедия orthopedics.
ортоперкуссия int: threshold percussion.
ортоплазия bio: orthoplasty.
ортопное path: orthopnea.
ортопристис ichth: pigfish (Orthopristis).
ортоптероидный комплекс (подотдел) entom: Polyneoptera.
ортотропизм bot: orthotropism.
ортотропный bot: orthotropous.
ортофория ophth: orthophoria.
О'Рурк O'Rourke.
орхидея bot: orchid.
орхидные (сем.) bot: orchis family (Orchidaceae).

орхидный bot: orchidaceous.
орцин pharm: orcin(ol).
оса entom: wasp (Diploptera, Vesparia).
~ древесная tailed wasp (Sirex gigans); see also рогохвост соснов.
~ ~ гигантская = рогохвост еловый.
~ общественная social wasp.
~ одиночная solitary wasp, eumenid.
~ стенная sand wasp (Odynerus).
осадок sediment, deposit, precipitate, silt; fur, lees (in wine).
~ из уратов urate deposit.
осаждальщики zool: sedimentation type.
осаждение sedimentation, deposition, precipitation, settling.
осарсол pharm: a Soviet preparation against whipworm.
освежать (края раны) surg: refresh, freshen (up).
освежающий refreshing.
освежение surg: debridement, freshening (up),
освежить p. a. of освежать.
осветитель illuminator.
осветление clarification, clarifying, decantation; defecation.
осветлитель clarificant.
осветлить p. a. of осветлять.
осветлять clarify; defecate.
осветляющий раствор chem: clarifying solution.
освещение illumination.
~ глазного дна ophthalmoscopy.
~ при затемнённом поле mcscop: dark ground illumination.
~ солнечными лучами insolation, solarization.
~ ультрафиолетовыми лучами ultraviolet irradiation.
освидетельствование (physical) examination.
освобождение верхушки (лёгкого) apicolysis.
~ нерва от рубцовой ткани neurolysis (loosening of adhesions).
~ от известковых солей decalcification.
~ ручек obstet: liberation of the arms.
осевая гиперметропия ophth: hypermetropia.
~ палочка zool: axostyle.
~ тракция obstet: axis traction.
осевое поле bot: pseudoraphe.
осевой axial, axile.
~ синус zool: axial sinus.

осевой скелет axial skeleton.
~ цилиндр anat: axis cylinder (of a nerve fiber).
осевоцилиндрический отросток neur: axon, axis cylinder process.
осевые органы embr: axial organs.
оседание setting, spatfall.
оседлый bot: sedentary.
~ макрофаг hist: fixed macrophage.
осёл zool: ass, donkey, burro, jackass (Asinus, Equus asinus).
~ домашний ass, donkey (Equus asinus).
осеменение insemination, pollination.
осенняя пятнистость phytp: late blight (on parsley, celera).
осётр sturgeon (Acipenser); see also русский осётр.
осетровые (сем.) ichth: sturgeon fam. (Acipenseridae).
осина bot: aspen, poplar (Populus).
~ американская quaking aspen, trembling asp, quiver leaf (P. tremuloides).
~ европейская European aspen, trembling poplar (P. tremula).
осиная талия path: wasp's waist.
осколок splinter, fragment.
осколочная рана mil: shell-splinter wound.
оскольчатый перелом surg: comminuted fracture, splintered f.
оскудение impoverishment, depletion, exhaustion.
оскулюм zool: osculum, vent (in sponges)
оскулярное отверстие zool: terminal opening.
ослабевание weakening, enfeeblement, attenuation.
ослабить p. a. of ослаблять.
ослабление weakening, attenuation, dilution, reduction; mitigation (pain).
~ болезненных проявлений abatement of disease symptoms, remission.
~ кровообращения path: reduction in circulation.
~ обоняния path: hyposmia.
~ памяти psych: hypomnesia.
~ тонуса abnormally low tonus, atonia hypotonicity.
ослабленное кровообращение path: reduced circulation.
ослабленный weakened, etc., cf. ослаблять.
ослаблять weaken, enfeeble, debilitate, attenuate; dilute, reduce; mitigate (pain).
ослёнок zool: colt, young donkey.
ослепление dazzling.
ослеплять dazzle; blind.
ослепляющий источник glare source.
ослизнение making slimy, gelatinization.
ослинник двулетный = энотера.
ослинниковые (сем.) bot: evening-primrose family (Oenotheraceae).
осложнение complication.
~ в связи с родами obstet: parturient complication.
~ со стороны глаз ocular complication.
~ ~ стороны желёз glandular c.
~ ~ стороны плевры pleural c.
~ ~ стороны сердца cardiac c.
~ ~ стороны сосудистой системы vascular c.
~ ~ стороны ушей aural c.
осложнённый complicated.
~ перелом surg: complicated fracture.
осман ichth: Diptychus.
осморегуляция osmoregulation.
осмориза bot: osmorrhiza (Osmorhiza, Washingtonia).
осмотическое давление osmotic pressure.
осмотр inspection, examination.
~ бронхоскопом bronchoscopy.
~ глаз ophth: inspection of the eyes.
осмысливать psych: comprehend.
осмыслить p. a. of осмысливать.
осмышление psych: comprehension.
оснащение rigging, equipment, armamentarium.
основа = основание.
основание base, basis.
~ лёгкого anat: basis pulmonis.
~ листа bot: leaf base.
~ мази pharm: ointment base.
~ моста anat: basis pontis.
~ носа anat: nasal floor.
~ околоцветника bot: base of perianth.
~ черепа anat: base of the skull.
основная азотновисмутовая соль pharm: subnitrate of bismuth.
~ артерия anat: basilar artery.
~ диета basic diet.
~ клетка basal cell.
~ кость anat: basilar bone.
~ ~ черепа = клиновидная кость.
~ масса пищи bulk of food.
~ осевая почка bot: leader bud.
~ пазуха anat: sphenoid sinus.
~ пища staple diet.
~ соль chem: subsalt.
~ фаланга anat: basilar phalanx.
основно-нёбная вырезка anat: sphenopalatine notch.

основно-нёбный нерв anat: sphenopalatine nerve.
~ -нижнечелюстная связка anat: sphenomandibular ligament.
~ -решётчатый anat: sphenoethmoid.
~ -скуловой anat: sphenozygomatic, sphenomalar.
~ -сошниковый anat: sphenovomerine.
~ -теменной anat: parietosphenoid.
основной basic, basal, basilar.
~ дитиосалициловый висмут pharm: bismuth dithiosalicylate.
~ зачаток embr: primordium.
~ обмен basal metabolism.
~ раствор lab: stock solution.
~ стебель bot: main axis.
~ фуксин basic fuchsin, magenta.
особь individual.
~ (из колонии) zooid.
осоед = кобец.
осознание опасности comprehension of danger, realization of danger.
осока bot: sedge (Carex).
~ песчаная sand sedge (C. arenaria).
осоковые (сем.) bot: sedge family (Cyperaceae).
осокорь bot: black poplar (Populus nigra)
осокоцветные (пор.) bot: Cyperales.
осообразный entom: wasp-like.
осот bot: sow-thistle, milk thistle (Sonchus); see also бодяк.
~ густой pastor's lettuce (S. congestus)
~ жёлтый field sow-thistle, perennial s.-t. (S. arvensis).
~ жёсткий = о. колючий.
~ колючий spiny leaved s.-t. (S. asper).
~ огородный common s.-t. (S. oleraceus).
~ полевой way thistle (Cirsium arvense); see also осот жёлтый.
~ розовый Canadian thistle (Circium arvense).
оспа infect: smallpox, variola; vet: pox.
оспенный variolar.
~ соскоб vet: detritus.
оспинка infect: peck.
оспопрививательное перо vaccination quill.
оссеин hist: ossein(e).
оссификация ossification.
останавливать кровотечение stop the flow of blood, stanch.
останавливающий развитие бактерий bacteriostatic.
остановившееся развитие bio: arrested development.
остановка stop, stoppage, arrest, standstill.
остановка в диастоле diastolic arrest.
~ ~ систоле systolic arrest.
~ дыхания respiratory standstill.
~ кровотечения hemostasis.
остатки выкидыша gyn: abortion remains.
~ жаберных щелей remnants of branchial clefts.
остаток residue, residuum, remnant, remainder; chem: radical.
остаточная моча residual urine, bladder residuum.
остаточный vestigial, rudimentary, residual.
~ азот residual nitrogen.
остеклённость vitrification, glassiness.
остеобласт hist: osteoblast.
остеогенез osteogenesis.
остеогенея = остеогенез.
остеогенный osteogenic.
остеодистрофия osteodystrophia, osteodystrophy.
остеоклазия surg: osteoclasis.
остеолит osteolith.
остеология osteology.
остеома path: osteoma.
остеомалятический таз path: osteomalacic pelvis.
остеомаляционный osteomalacial, osteomalacic.
остеомаляция path: osteomalacia.
остеомиелит path: osteomyelitis.
остеопороз osteoporosis.
остеопорозный osteoporotic.
остеофил rad: bone seeker.
остистая анестезия = спинномозговая анестезия.
остистое отверстие anat: foramen spinosum.
остистый anat: spinous; bot: awned, aristate, bearded; barbate, prickly.
~ отросток anat: spinous process, spine, processus spinosus.
остия ostium (of a crustacea).
остракода zool: ostracod(e).
остракум zool: prismatic layer, ostracum.
острая гемоглобинурийная лихорадка blackwater fever, hematuric f.
~ лучевая болезнь acute radiation sickness.
острица helm: pinworm, threadworm, seatworm (Enterobius vermicularis, Oxyuris vermicularis).
островки Лангерганса anat: pancreatic islets, islets of Langerhans.
островковая ткань islet-cell tissue.

островковый anat: insular.
островок anat: islet, island, insula.
острое облучение rad: acute exposure.
острозубый zool: centrodontous.
остроконечная кондилома ven:
fig wart, verruca acuminata, condyloma acuminarum.
остроконечный (sharp)-pointed, peaked, beaked, acuminate, mucronate.
остролист bot: holly (Ilex).
остролодки bot: Oxytropis, DC.
остромордая лягушка zool: (Rana terrestris).
остронос ichth: mullet Mugil saliens.
остро́-перо = расторопша.
остропёстр = расторопша.
остропестро́ = расторопша.
остропреходящее психическое расстройство acute transitory psychic disorder. [(of disease).
острота́ sharpness, acuity; acuteness
~ зрения visual acuity, acuity of vision.
~ ощущений sensory acuity.
~ слуха hearing acuity, auditory acuity.
острочелюстной zool: oxygnathous.
острый sharp, pointed; poignant, pungent; acute.
~ бред psych: acute delirium.
~ выступ cusp.
~ колит int: acute colitis.
~ конъюнктивит ophth: pinkeye, Koch-Weeks conjunctivitis.
~ лучевой синдром acute radiation
~ (на вкус) pungent. |syndrome.
~ рассол agr: tangy brine.
~ свод твердого нёба path: sharp vault of the hard palate.
~ токсический энцефалит path: acute toxic encephalitis.
~ эмоциональный шок psych: acute emotional shock. [fication.
остудневание gelatin(iz)ation, gelati-
остудневать gelat(iniz)e, gelatinate.
ость 1. anat: spine, spina; 2. zool: guard hair (of fur); 3. bot: awn, arista, seta, beard; barb. [sacculation.
осумкование encapsulation, encystation,
осумкованный encapsuled, encysted, saccu-
~ плеврит encapsulated pleurisy, |lated. blocked pleurisy.
осунувшийся thin, hollow-cheeked,
осфрадий zool: osphradium. peaked.
осциллярия = осциллятория.
осциллятория bot: Oscillatoria (algae).
осы (сем.) entom: wasps (Vespidae).

осыпание (зерна) bot: shattering.
осыпать(ся) bot: shatter. [spindle.
ось 1. axis; center line; 2. axle, shaft,
~ глаза anat: axis of the eye.
~ глазницы orbital cavity axis.
~ соцветия bot: rachis, axis of inflorescence.
~ цветка bot: floral axis, rachilla.
осьмизубые (сем.) zool: Octodontidae. Cf. нутрия. [(Octopus).
осьминог zool: octopus, devilfish
осязаемый palpable. [amnesia.
осязательная амнезия psych: tactile
~ галлюцинация psych: hallucination of touch.
~ клетка zool: tactile cell, tangoreceptor.
осязательное тельце hist: tactile corpuscle, touch c.
осязательный tactile, haptic.
~ сосочек tactile papilla.
от мозга к периферии cerebrifugal.
отава bot agr: aftercrop, eddish, earsh.
отбеливание = беление.
отбелка = беление. [fragments.
отбивать осколки chip, break off
отбившееся от стада животное stray.
отбить p. a. of отбивать.
отбор лётчиков selection of airmen.
отборочный тест av med: screening test.
отбросы waste, offal, refuse, garbage.
отвар decoct(ion).
~ из трав pharm: herb decoction.
отведение глаз ophth: abduction of the eyes.
~ (конечности от средней линии тела) abduction (of an extremity from the axis of the body).
отвёрнутый bot: revolute.
~ назад reflexed.
~ наружу reflexed.
отверстие hole, orifice, aperture, ostium, ostiole, foramen, hiatus, meatus, opening, port, vent, fenestra; see also зев.
~ мочеиспускательного канала (внутреннее, наружное) anat: orificium urethrae (internum, externum).
~ нефридия nephridiopore.
отверстный orificial, meatal, etc., cf. отверстие.
отвести p. a. of отводить.
*ответвление branch, tap; bot: stam shoot.

отвислая грудь pendulous breast, prolapsed b.
~ кожа (у быка) gill.
~ складка dewlap.
отвислое ухо flap ear.
отвислый живот path: pendulous abdomen.
отвлекать lead off, distract, divert.
отвлекающее средство revulsant, revulsive agent, derivative (agent).
отвлечение revulsion, derivation.
отвлечь p. a. of отвлекать.
отвод offtake, draw-off; outlet; outflow, efflux, discharge, draining (off); diversion, removal.
отводить carry off, drain, lead away, divert, remove, discharge; abduct, abduce.
~ книзу subduce, subduct.
отводок bot: offshoot, ratoon, wild seeding, see побег; agr: mount layer.
отводящая мышца anat: abductor.
~ ~ большого пальца (длинная, короткая) anat: abductor pollicis (longus, brevis).
~ ~ мизинца anat: abductor digiti quinti.
~ ручная шина surg: abduction arm splint.
отводящий abducting, abducent.
~ нерв anat: abducens, sixth cranial nerve.
~ путь anat: efferent duct, outlet, route of discharge.
отвращение aversion, antipathy, repugnance.
~ к браку psych: misogamy.
~ к еде apocleisis.
~ к мясу creatic nausea.
~ к пище apositia, cibophobia.
~ к полету av med: distaste for flying.
~ к труду aversion to work.
отвязывать surg: unbind, tie off, underbind, wean, untie.
отгоняющее мошкару средство pharm: repellent.
~ сон средство somnifugous agent.
отгоняющий насекомых insect-repelling.
отграничение demarcation.
отграничивающаяся часть кости surg: sequestrum.
отдалённое действие remote effect.
отдалённый от рта aboral.
отдача кислорода тканям liberation of oxygen to the tissues.
отделение partition, ablatio(n), detachment, detaching, separation, segregation, excision, precipitation, loosening, sublation; see also выделение.
~ больницы hospital department, h. ward.
~ жёлчи biliation.
~ желудка от спаек surg: gastrolysis.
отделение желудочного сока flow of gastric juice.
~ матки от спаек gyn: hysterolysis.
~ нерва от сращений surg: neurolysis.
~ плаценты obstet: placental separation.
~ (пленок) casting off, shedding, see отхождение.
~ ребра от грудины surg: desternalization.
~ слёз lacrimation.
~ тупым путём surg: blunt dissection.
~ фаллопиевой трубы от спаек gyn: salpingolysis.
отделить p. a. of отделять.
отдельная ягодка bot: coccus (of a composite fruit).
отдельность bio: fission.
отдельный листочек bot: leaflet.
~ цветок bot: single flower, floret.
отделяемое из мочеиспускательного канала urethral discharge.
отделять surg obstet: loosen, detach, separate, sever, partition.
отдирать strip.
отёк path: edema, dropsy.
~ гортани glottidial edema.
~ нижележащих частей dependent e.
отекать swell (up), form edema.
отелившаяся корова calved cow, down calver.
отелиться p. a. of телиться.
отематома path: othematoma.
отёчная болезнь = голодный отёк.
~ жидкость path: transudate.
~ крапивница path: edematosa urticaria.
~ припухлость конъюнктивы ophth: chemosis.
отёчный edematous, edematic, dropsical.
отечь p. a. of отекать.
отжечь p. a. of отжигать.
отжигание burning off, cauterization.
отжигать burn off, cauterize, burn down.
отиатр aural surgeon.
отиатрия aural surgery, otology.
отит path: otitis.
откашливание expectoration, coughing up.
откашливать expectorate, cough up.
откашливаться cough up, expectorate, hawk.
откашлянуть p. a. of откашливать.
откашляться p. a. of откашливаться.
откинувшийся recumbent (posture), decubital.
откладка яиц = кладка яиц.
откладывать икру = метать икру.

откладывать яйца oviposit.
откладывающий сахар metab:glycopexic.
отклонение deflection, deviation.
~ в сторону laterodeviation.
~ кзади reclination.
~ комплемента complement deviation.
отклоненный отросток anat: clinoid process.
отклониться p. a. of отклоняться.
отклонять(ся) deflect, deviate.
отклоняющийся (от нормы) abnormal.
открывание цвет(к)ов bot: tripping of flowers.
открываться bot: dehisce (of a fruit).
открывающийся круглой крышечкой bot: circumscissile (fruit).
открытая рана open wound.
~ форма туберкулёза open tuberculosis.
открытое опыление open pollination.
открытый open, patent.
~ вывих surg: compound dislocation.
~ перелом surg: compound fracture.
~ прикус odont: open bite.
~ пыльник bot: open anther.
отложение deposit(ion).
~ жира metab: adiposis, adiposity, adipopexis, lipopexia.
~ красящего вещества pigmentation.
отложить p. a. of откладывать.
отметавшая икру рыба spent fish.
отметина (белое пятно на лбу животного) blaze.
отметка mark, score, record.
~ по девятибальной системе av med: stanine score.
отметчик времени time marker.
отмирание withering away, dying away, departing.
~ ботвы bot: top necrosis.
отмирать wither away, die away, depart.
отмирающий moribund.
отморожение congelation, frostbite.
отмучивание elutriation, levigation.
отмучивать elutriate, levigate.
отмучить p. a. of отмучивать.
отмывать wash off.
отмытое ядро washed-off nucleus.
отмыть p. a. of отмывать.
отнерестившаяся рыба spent fish.
отнерестившийся атлантический лосось ichth: kelt.
отнимать take off (away), amputate.
~ от груди ped: wean, ablactate.
относительная сердечная тупость int: relative cardiac dullness.
отношение ratio; relation(ship).
~ биологического воздействия к физическому rad: biological-physical ratio.
~ хозяина и паразита host-parasite relationship.
отнятие taking off (away), amputation.
~ от груди ped: weaning, ablactation, delactation.
отнять p. a. of отнимать.
отогнутый recurved.
~ вниз retrorse.
~ назад retrorse.
отодрать p. a. of отдирать.
отоларинголог otolaryngologist.
отоларингология otolaryngology.
отолит ichth: otolith, earstone.
отология otology.
ото рта aborad.
отосклероз otosclerosis.
отощать waste away, emaciate.
отпадающий deciduous, caducous.
отпадение deciduation.
отпечаток impression, imprint.
~ большого пальца legl: thumb print.
~ пальца legl: fingerprint.
отпиливание surg: sawing off.
отпиливать surg: saw off.
отпилить p. a. of отпиливать.
отпочковать(ся) p. a. of отпочковывать(ся).
отпочковывать(ся) bot: bud off.
отправление function.
отпрепарировать anat: dissect off.
отпрыск 1. offspring; descendant; 2. bot: offshoot, runner, sucker, browse, flush, propagule, see also отросток, побег.
отпугивание repulsion. Cf. вещество отпугивающее насекомых.
отпугивающая жидкость repellant fluid.
отпуск лекарства pharm: dispensing [of a medicine.
~ по болезни sick leave.
отпускать лекарства pharm: dispense medicines.
отпустить p. a. of отпускать.
отр. = отряд.
отравление poisoning.
~ алкоголем alcohol poisoning.
~ атропином atropine p., atropism.
~ барбитуратом barbiturate p.
~ бензолом benzol p., benzolism.
~ болиголовом conium maculatum p., coniism.

отравление борной кислотой boric acid poisoning, borism.
~ бромом brominism.
~ вероналом poisoning from barbiturates, barbitalism.
~ газами gas poisoning.
~ грибами mushroom poisoning.
~ дурманом Datura stramonium poisoning, daturism.
~ индийской коноплей cannabis indica poisoning, cannabism.
~ ипекакуаной emetism.
~ камфорой camphor poisoning, camphorism.
~ карболовой кислотой carbolic acid poisoning, carbolism.
~ кислородом oxygen poisoning.
~ колбасным ядом botulism.
~ консервами canned food poisoning.
~ кротоновым маслом croton tiglium poisoning, crotonism.
~ лаком av med: dope poisoning.
~ мышьяком arsenic poisoning.
~ нитроглицерином glonoinism.
~ пищей food poisoning, bromatotoxism.
~ радием radium poisoning.
~ резорцином resorcinism.
~ ртутью mercury poisoning.
~ рыбой fish poisoning, ichthyotoxism.
~ сантонином santonin poisoning, santonism.
~ свинцом lead p., plumbism, saturnism.
~ синильной кислотой hydrocyanic acid poisoning, hydrocyanism.
~ скипидаром terebinthinism.
~ спорыньей ergot poisoning, ergotism.
~ стрихнином strychnin poisoning.
~ сурьмой stibialism.
~ хинином quininism, cinchonism.
~ щавелевой кислотой oxalic acid poisoning, oxalism.
~ ядом паука arachnidism.
отравлять poison.
отражать 1. reflect, mirror; 2. repel.
отражение reflection.
отразить p. a. of отражать.
отреагирование psych: abreaction, catharsis.
отрезание cutting off, lopping off, amputation, abscission, excision.
отреза́ть cut off, lop off, amputate.
отре́зать p. a. of отреза́ть.
отрезок RS-T RS-T segment (heart).
отрицательный результат (заражения) bact: negative take.
отродиться p. a. of отрождаться.
отродье bantling.
~ свиней pig breed.
отрождаться entom: to be hatched.
отрождение zool: hatching.
отросток 1. anat: process, apophysis, appendix; see also бугор, возвышение, вырост; 2. zool: arm (of an echinoderm); 3. bot: offshoot, shoot, runner, flush, provine, stolon, sucker, haustorium, rhizome; see also отпрыск, побег; 4. branch (piece), tap, spur.
~ молоточка anat: process of the malleus.
отростчатая клетка neur: dendritic cell.
отрубевидное шелушение derm: defurfuration, furfuraceous desquamation, branlike desquamation.
отрубевидный bot: furfuraceous.
отруби agr: bran.
отрубянистая оболочка agr: bran coat.
отрубяной agr: branny.
отрывание abruptio(n), tearing away.
отрывистое дыхание jerky respiration.
отрыгивание regurgitation.
отрыгивать eruct, belch, regurgitate.
отрыжка eructation, belching, regurgitation.
~ газами gaseous eructation.
отряд bio: order.
отсасывание suction, sucking off, drawing off, aspiration, pumping out; absorption.
отсасывать suck off, draw off; pump out; aspirate; absorb.
~ пипеткой pipette off.
отсечение части органа surg: resection.
отслаивание peeling (off), scaling (off), exfoliation, flaking off.
отслаивать(ся) peel off, scale off, exfoliate, flake off.
отслоить(ся) p. a. of отслаиваться
отслойка сетчатки ophth: detachment of retina, amotio retinae.
отсос крови sanguisuction, blood abstraction.
отсосать p. a. of отсасывать.
отстойник san: sludge tank.
~ -загниватель san: septic tank.
~ Имгофа san: Imhoff tank.
отстоящий от конца anteapical.
отступать от нормы deviate from normal.
отступить p. a. of отступать.
отсутствие аккомодации ophth: accommondation failure.
~ аппетита absence of appetite, anorexia, inappetence.
~ выделение молока path: agalactia.
~ грудины path: asternia.

отсутствие дыхания respiratory standstill.
~ жажды adipsia, adipsy, aposia.
~ желудочного сока achylia.
~ зрачка path: acorea.
~ зубов toothlessness, edentation.
~ кислотности path: anacidity.
~ конечностей path: amelia.
~ координации asynergy, asynergia, incoordination.
~ листьев bot: aphylly.
~ лихорадки afebrile conditions.
~ лица path: aprosopia.
~ матки ametria.
~ месячных path: amenorrhea.
~ обоняния path: anosmia.
~ пальцев path: adactylia, adactylism.
~ пигмента в покровах albinism(us), leukoderma, achromoderma.
~ пола agamia, asexuality.
~ пульса acrotism, pulselessness.
~ равновесия unbalance.
~ рецидива nonrelapse.
~ рефлексов physl: areflexia.
~ сегментного деления bio: amerism.
~ сердца acardia.
~ соляной кислоты path: inacidity.
~ сперматозоидов azoospermia.
~ спинного мозга path: amyelia.
~ ушей path: anotia.
~ хилуса path: achylia.
~ хрусталика ophth: aphakia.
~ черепа path: acrania.
~ чувства насыщения physl: acoria.
отсчет reading, indication.
~ координат av med: coordinate reading.
отсчитать p. a. of отсчитывать.
отсчитывание counting off; reading.
отсчитывать take reading, read (out, off).
оттаивать defrost.
оттаять p. a. of оттаивать.
оттекать flow off, run off.
оттечь p. a. of оттекать.
оттиск impression, imprint.
отток outflow, discharge, drainage.
~ (ассимилятов) bot: translocation.
~ крови (от) shifting of blood (from).
отторжение casting off, tearing (from).
~ некротического участка surg: disengagement of a necrotic section.
оттягивание книзу path: bearing down.
оттяжка = осветляющий раствор.
отупевший torpid, dull, apathetic, sluggish, indifferent.
отупение torpor, dullness, apathy, sluggishness.

отхаркивание expectoration.
~ гноя pyoptysis.
отхаркивать expectorate.
отхаркивающее средство pharm: expectorant.
отхаркнуть p. a. of отхаркивать.
отхождение discharge, outflow, escape, departure; casting off, shedding, sloughing (off, away), crumbling; desquamation; anat: origin.
~ вод obstet: bursting of waters.
~ газов passage of flatus.
~ кала = дефекация.
отхожее место = уборная.
отцветание bot: blossom fall, shedding.
отцедить p. a. of отцеживать.
отцеживать draw off, tap, drain, abduct
отцовское растение bot: pollen parent.
отцовство paternity.
отчаяние despair.
отчленение 1. see вычленение; 2. bot: abjunction.
отшнурование surg embr: snaring, constriction.
отшнуровать(ся) p. a. of отшнуровывать(ся).
отшнуровывать(ся) snare, tie off, constrict.
отщемить p. a. of отщемлять.
отщемление surg: squeezing off.
отщемлять squeeze off.
отщепить p. a. of отщеплять.
отщеплять split off, set free, cut (off).
отщипывать pinch out.
отыскивающий пищу в иле zool: mud-hunting.
офиуры = змеезвёзды.
офрис bot: southern twayblade (Listera australis, Lindl.)
офталмия ophthalmia.
офталмолог ophthalmologist.
офталмологический кабинет eye room.
офталмология ophthalmology.
офталмоскоп ophthalmoscope.
офталмоскопирование ophthalmoscopy.
офталмоскопические данные ophthalmoscopic findings.
офталмоскопическое обследование ophthalmoscopic examination.
офталмоскопия ophthalmoscopy.
официнальный препарат pharm: officinal preparation.
охладительная смесь chem: cooling mixture.
охладительное средство cooling agent.
охлаждение cooling (down), temperature fasting, chilling; refrigeration.

охотник 1. hunter, fowler; 2. beast of prey, predatory beast.
охрана диких животных wildlife con- [servation.
~ природы conservation, protection of natural resources.
~ труда labor protection.
охранительное торможение psych: protective inhibition.
охриплость hoarseness.
охрящевание chondrification, cartila- [gin(ific)ation.
оцеанитес orn: Wilson's petrel (Oceanites oceanicus).
оцелот zool: ocelot (Felis pardalis).
оценка результатов evaluation of results, interpretation of findings.
оцепенелость stiffness, torpor.
очаг focus, seat, nidus.
~ омертвения path: infarct.
очаговая инфекция focal infection.
~ пневмония int: lobar pneumonia.
очаговое поражение focal lesion.
очаговый симптом med: focal symptom.
очанка bot: eyebright (Euphrasia).
очень заразный highly contagious.
~ тонкий порошок very fine powder, impalpable powder.
~ чувствительный supersensitive.
очервление (in)vermination.
очервлённый кишечными паразитами angiostomic.
очин пера orn: quill, calamus.
очистительная клизма cleansing enema, evacuant enema.
очистительный облёт cleansing flight [(of bees).
очистить p. a. of чистить, очищать.
очистка раны surg: debridement.
~ сточных вод san: sewage treatment.
очиток bot: stonecrop, orpine (Sedum).
~ едкий mossy stonecrop, wallpepper, love entangle, biting stonecrop (S. acre).
~ пурпуровый live-forever, garden orpine, frogplant (S. purpureum).
очищать clean (up); purify, refine; cleanse, absterge, scavenge, purge, see опоражнивать.
~ кишечник purge.
~ (марлей или ватой) surg: cleanse by mopping, dab up.
очищающее средство pharm: detergent, abluent.
очищающий detergent, purifying, cleans- [ing.
очищение ablution, cleaning (up), etc., cf. очищать.
~ кишечника purgation.
очищение сырого лекарственного материала pharm: emundation.
очищенная рана surg: debrided wound.
очищенный мёд clarified honey.
~ мел pharm: prepared chalk, drop c.
~ от жира blubbered (seal, etc.)
очки ophth: spectacles, eyeglasses.
очковая змея = кобра.
~ оправа ophth: spectacle (trial) [frame.
очная ставка legl: confrontation.
очный цвет bot: pimpernel (Anagallis).
очувствлённый sensitized.
ошибнёвые (сем.) ichth: Ophidiidae.
ошпаривать scald, parboil.
ошпарить p. a. of ошпаривать.
ощелачивать = подщелачивать.
ощениться p. a. of щениться.
ощипанный orn: plume-plucked.
ощипывание 1. orn: deplumation; 2. bot: picking (of berries, etc.)
ощупать p. a. of ощупывать.
ощупывание palpation, feeling, groping.
ощупывать palpate, feel, grope.
ощутимое потение sensible perspiration.
ощутимый perceptible, tangible, palp- [able.
ощущать feel, heed, perceive, sense.
~ первые движения плода obstet: quicken.
ощущение physl: sensation, feeling.
~ биений сердца path: heart consciousness.
~ колыхания fluctuation, feeling.
~ ложного крена av med: "the leans."
~ опоясывания neur: girdle sansation.
~ падения av med: sensation of falling.
~ первых движений плода obstet: [quickening.
~ пикирования по вертикали av med: sensation of diving beyond the vertical.
~ подъема при развороте av med: sansation of climbing while turning.
~ полноты sansation of fullness.
~ противовращения av med: sensation of reversal of rotation.
~ противоположного наклона при скольжении av med: sensation of opposite tilt in a skid.
~ снижения при выходе из разворота av med: sensation of diving during recovery from a turn.
~ собственной неполноценности feeling of inadequacy, feeling of inferiority.

П

пава orn: peafowl hen; cf. павлин.
паварициӣ surg: agnail.
павиан zool: baboon (Papio ursinus).
павлин orn: peacock (Pavo cristatus).
павлиний глаз большой entom:
  butterfly Saturnia pyri.
павлиноглазка Шенка entom:
  butterfly Neoris schenki.
павлиноглазки (сем.) Attacidae.
павловская школа bio: Pavlov school.
пагрус ichth: Japanese porgy (Pagrus
  major).
падалица bot: windfall, drops, shack
падаль carrion. |(fruits).
падальник = питающийся падалью.
падать в обморок faint, swoon.
падди paddy, see рис красный.
падуб bot: holly (Ilex).
падучая neur: falling sickness, epilep-
пажитник = тригонелла. sy.
пазания bot: tanbark oak (Pasania acutiflora, Oerst., Quercus densiflora).
пазник коротококорневой bot: cat's-
  ear (Hypochoeris radicata).
пазуха листа bot: base of a leaf, axil
~ основной кости anat: air sinus,
  sinus sphenoidalis.
пазушная почка bot: axillary bud. [es.
пазушные побеги bot: axillary branch-
пазушный угол лист-черенок
  bot: axil.
пакет с перевязочным материалом
  dressing packet.
пакля oakum.
паламедея orn: anserine Palamedea.
палата ward.
палатная сестра ward sister.
~ уборщица wardmaid. [orderly.
палатный служащий ward attendant,
палеарктическая птица palearctic
  bird.
палёметс ichth: poppyfish, California
  pompano (Palomets simillimus). [tany.
палеоботаника paleobotany, fossil bo-
палеоботанический paleobotanical.
палеозойский paleozoic.
палеозоология paleozoology.
палеолимнологический
  paleolimnological. [(extinct).
палеомастодонт zool: Palaeomastodon
палеонисциды ichth: Palaeoniscoidei
палеонтолог paleontologist.|(extinct).
палеонтология paleontology.
палеоспондилус ichth: Palaeospondi-
  lus (extinct).
палеоспондилы ichth: Palaeospondyli
палеоцен paleocene. (extinct).
палеоэкология paleoecology.
палец anat: digit (finger or toe).
~ ноги toe.
~ руки finger.
палинология palynology. [sue.
палисадная ткань bot: palisade tis-
палисадный слой hist: bacillary
  layer. [во.
палисандр = палисандровое дере-
палисандровое дерево bot: kingwood
  (Jacaranda brasiliensis, Jacaranda
  chelonia, Grieseb.)
палиуриус = держи-дерево.
палия ichth: bull trout (Salvelinus
паллиатив palliative. lepechini).
паллиативное лечение palliative
  treatment.
*палоло (червь) palolo (worm),
  nmatamata (Eunice viridis).
палочка stick; bact: rod.
~ для прижигания pharm: caustic
  stick, caustic stylus.
~ ~ размазывания материала bact:
  streaking rod.
~ ~ размешивания lab: stirring rod.
~(инфекционного) аборта abortus
  bacillus (Brucella abortus).
палочки Меддокса ophth: multiple,
  Maddox rod.
палочковидная спикула (губок)
  zool: rhabdus.
~ форма (клетки) hist: staff form.
палочковидный rod-shaped, bacilli-
  form, staff-form.
*палочкоядерный stabnuclear.
палочники (отр.) entom: Phasmodea.
палошник = тимофеевка.
палтус ichth: halibut (Hippoglossus).
~ белокорый halibut (H. hippoglossus)
~ мелкий (или молодой) chicken
  halibut.
~ обыкновенный = п. белокорый.
~ синекорый = п. чёрный.
~ стрелозубый Atheresthes evermanni.
~ чёрный Reinhardtius hippoglossoides.

палудрин pharm: paludrine hydrochloride, chloroguanide hydrochloride.
пальма bot: palm.
~ ассаи bot: Para palm (Euterpe edulis).
~ кавказская = самшит.
~ нипа nipa palm (Nipa fruticans).
~ ореховая австралийская nut palm (Cycas media, R. Br.)
~ "рыбий хвост" fishtail palm (Caryota).
пальмеллевидное состояние bot: palmella condition.
пальмеллевидный bot: palmelloid.
пальметта bot: palmette.
~ капустная cabbage p., see п. сабаль
~ -сабаль sabal (Inodes palmetto, Walt.)
пальмира-пальма bot: palmyra palm (Borassus flabelliformis).
пальмовая ветвь bot: frond.
пальмовидный bot: palmatifid.
пальмовые (сем.) bot: palm family (Palmaceae).
пальмовый вор = краб-разбойник.
пальмоцветные (пор.) bot: Principes.
пальмы = пальмовые (сем.)
пальпабильный palpable.
пальпация palpation.
пальпировать palpate.
пальпитация palpitation.
пальцевидный отросток digitiform process, digitule.
пальцевое исследование per rectum int: rectal touch.
~ ~ per vaginam gyn: vaginal touch.
пальцевой digital, dactylar, dactylic.
пальцеобразный digitiform.
пальцеходящий zool: digitigrade.
пальце-стопоходящий zool: digitiplantigrade.
*пальцы мертвеца zool: dead-men's-fingers (Alcyonium digitatum).
пальчатая железа zool: finger gland.
~ трава = свинорой.
пальчатый digitate, dactylate, palmate, pedate.
~ злак = свинорой.
пампельмус = грейпфрут.
память psych: memory.
панамская пальма bot: palm Carludovica palmata.
панариций falon, paronychia, panaris; see also ногтоеда.
панацея panacea.
панда = енот.
пандан = панданус.
пандановые (сем.) bot: screw palm family (Pandanaceae).
панданус bot: screw palm.
панданусовый bot: pandanaceous.
пандемический pandemic.
пандемия pandemia, pandemy.
пандорина bot: Pandorina (alga).
панкраций bot: pancratium (Pancratium).
панкреатит pancreatitis.
панкреатическая железа anat: pancreas.
панкреатический сок pancreatic juice.
паннус path: pannus.
пантера zool: panther (Felis pardus panthera).
пантотеновая кислота pantothenic acid.
панцырная щука ichth: fresh-water gar, gar pike, alligator pike, (Lepidosteus).
панцырноголовые = стегоцефалы.
панцырные zool: 1. Polyplacophora (class of the phylum Mollusca), see хитоны; 2. Dinoflagellata.
~ гады = крокодилы.
~ моллюски (подкл.) zool: chitons (Polyplacophora, Loricata).
~ рыбы armor fishes (Placodermi).
панцырный armored, shelled, thecate.
панцырь 1. zool: armor, shell, carapace (of a turtle, etc.); 2. bot: case, frustule (of a diatom).
~ коловраток zool: lorica of rotifers.
~ черепахи zool: tortoise shell, turtle shell.
папаверин pharm: papaverine.
папаин papain, papyotin.
папайа bot: papaya, papaw tree (Carica papaya).
папилла bio: papilla.
папиллома path: papilloma.
папилломатозный papillomatous.
папирософбразный дренаж surg: cigarette drain.
папирус bot: papyrus, paper reed (Cyperus papyrus).
папкорн = кукуруза разрывная.
папоротник bot: fern, bracken, brake (Filicales); see also щитовник.
~ женский = кочедыжник.
~ -многорядник Christmas fern, dagger fern, canker brake (Polystichum acrostichoides, Schott.)
~ мужской male fern, bear's paw root (Dryopteris filix-mas, Schott.); pharm: aspidium.
~ орляк bracken, brake (Pteridium aquilinum).
~ щитовник = щитовник.
папоротники водяные (пор.) bot: water-fern order (Hydropteridales).

папоротники настоящие (пор.) bot: fern order (Filicales).
папоротниковые (кл.) bot: ferns and fern-allies (Filicinae).
~ (сем.) bot: fern family (Polypodiaceae)
папоротникообразные bot: pteridophytes (Pteridophyta).
папоротникообразный bot: pteridophytic, pteridophytous.
папула derm: papule, papula.
папулёзный papular.
папуляция derm: papulation.
пар steam; vapor.
параагглютинин lab: partial agglutinin, minor a., group a.
пара-аминобензойная кислота paraaminobenzoic acid.
~ -аминофенилмышьяковокислый натрий pharm: sodium para-aminophenylarsonate.
парабазальное тельце parabasal body (in protozoans).
парабиоз parabiosis.
парабионт parabiont.
парабиотический parabiotic.
парабулия psych: parabulia.
паравертебральная область anat: paravertebral region.
парагвайский чай = матѐ.
парадизка bot: paradise apple, see дусен.
паразит parasite.
паразитарное заболевание parasitosis.
паразитарный parasitic.
~ индекс parasitic rate.
~ сикоз derm: barber's itch, tinea barbae, tinea sycosis.
паразитизм parasitism.
~ в личиночной стадии zool: parasitoidism.
паразитирование parasitism.
~ на одном хозяине monoxeny.
паразитировать parasitize.
паразитирующий на жабрах (рыб) zool: branchicolous.
~ ~ нескольких хозяевах metoxenous.
~ ~ паразите biparasitic, superparasitic.
паразитические круглые черви zool: hookworms (Ancylostoma, Necator).
~ перепончатокрылые (подотдел) entom: parasitic hymenopters (Parasitica).
паразитический parasitic.
паразитическое простейшее parasitic protozoan.
паразитолог parasitologist.
паразитология parasitology.

паразитоноситель parasite carrier. parasitifer.
паразитоустойчивость parasite resistance.
парализованный paralized, palsied.
парализующий paralyzing, paralyzant.
паралитик paralytic.
паралитическая грудная клетка paralytic chest.
~ форма бешенства dumb rabies.
паралитический маразм paralytic marasmus.
паралич paralysis, palsy.
~ аккомодационной мышцы ophth: cycloplegia.
~ Белля Bell's palsy.
~ водолазов diver's paralysis.
~ всех четырёх конечностей quadriplegia, tetraplegia.
~ глазных мышц ophthalmoplegia.
~ диафрагмы phrenoplegia.
~ лицевого нерва facial nerve palsy, Bell's palsy.
~ нижних конечностей paraplegia.
~ одной конечности paralysis of a single limb.
~ одной стороны тела paralysis of one side of the body, hemiplegia.
~ от сдавления или прижатия pressure palsy.
~ подмышечного нерва axillary paralysis.
~ речи laloplegia.
параллельно-нервный лист bot: parallel-veined leaf.
паралогика psych: paralogism.
паралогический psych: paralogistic.
паралогия paralogia.
паралябракс ichth: rock bass (Paralabrax).
параметрий anat: parametrium.
параметрит gyn: parametritis, pelvic cellulitis.
параметритный parametritic.
парамецин paramecin (antibiotic).
парамикроб paramicrobe.
парамилон bio chem: paramylon.
парамимия psych: paramimia.
парамнезия psych: paramnesia.
параназальный синус anat: paranasal sinus.
паранекроз path: paranecrosis.
параноик psych: paranoic.
параноический psych: paranoid.
~ психопат paranoic psychopath.
паранойное состояние psych: paranoidism.
паранойный paranoid.
паранойя psych: paranoia.
паранотальный вырост entom: paranotum.
паранотум entom: paranotum.

параплегия paraplegia.
параподиальный parapodial.
параподий zool: parapodium.
параподия parapodium.
парапраксия psych: parapraxia.
парапроктит paraproctitis. [(extinct).
парапсиды zool: squamates Parapsida
парасимпатическая нервная система parasympathetic nervous system.
паратион chem: parathion.
паратиф path: paratyphoid.
парауретральный paraurethral.
парафенилсульфонокислая ртуть pharm: mercury paraphenylthionate.
парафимоз path: paraphimosis.
парафин paraffin.
парафиновый срез paraffin section.
парафобия psych: paraphobia.
парафренический psych: paraphrenic.
парафрения psych: paraphrenia.
парацентез surg: paracentesis, puncture, tapping.
парацентетический surg: paracentetic.
пардель = оцелот.
парез path: paresis.
~ **мимической мускулатуры** path: facial paresis.
парейазавр zool: extinct reptile Pareiasaurus.
парентеральный parenteral.
паренхима parenchyma.
паренхиматозные черви zool: Parenchymatosa, see плоские черви.
паренхиматозный parenchymatous.
паренхимная спикула bot: flesh
парестезия path: paresthesia. |spicule.
парестетический paresthetic.
паретическое слабоумие psych: paretic dementia.
париетальный parietal.
~ **листок** = пристеночный листок.
парижская зелень chem: Paris green, imperial, Schweinfurth, parrot green.
парить scald, parboil; saturate with steam.
паркериевые = папоротники водяные.
паркинсонизм = дрожательный паралич.
паркинсония колючая bot: Jerusalem thorn (Parkinsonia aculeata).
парнокопытные (отр.) zool: artiodactyls, even-toed hoofed mammals (Artiodactyla).
парнолистниковые (сем.) bot: caltrop family (Zygophyllaceae).
парнопалые zool: Paraxonia (extinct).
парно-перистосложный лист bot: abruptly pinnate leaf.
парнорезцовые грызуны (подотр.) zool: rodents Simplicidentata.
парные хромосомы pairing chromosomes.
паровая ванна phys-ther: steam bath.
пароксизм paroxysm: see also припадок, приступ.
пароксизмальный paroxysmal.
партеногенез parthenogenesis.
партеногенетическая спора bot: parthenospore. [genetic.
партеногенетический bio: partheno-
партеногенетическое образование женских особей thelyotoky.
партеногонидий parthenogonidium.
партенокарпический bio: parthenocarpic.
партенокарпия bot: parthenocarpy.
партенокарпный плод bot: pharthenocarpic fruit, nonpollinated fruit.
парус 1. zool: velum, craspedon (of a hydromedusa); 2. bot: dorsal standard, banner, vane, vexillum.
парусник zool: 1. by the wind sailor (Velella); 2. sailfish, spikefish (Istiophorus nigricans); 3. cf. below.
парусники (сем.) entom: swallow-tails and parnassians (Papilionidae).
парциальное давление кислорода av med: partial pressure of oxygen.
парша 1. derm: scald head, favus, (honeycomb) tetter; 2. vet: tetter, mange, impetigo; 3. phytp: scab; cf.
~ **груш** pear scab. вентурия.
~ **картофеля** common scab, corky s., po-
~ **яблок** apple s. (Venturia pomi).|tato s.
паршевое блюдечко derm: favus cup.
пары аммиака chem: ammonia vapor.
парэнтеральный parenteral.
паслён bot: nightshade, bane (Solanum).
~ **горькосладкий** bittersweet, woody nightshade (S. dulcamara).
~ **чёрный** black nightshade, houndsberry, garden huckleberry (S. nigrum).
паслёновое растение solanaceous plant. [family (Solanaceae).
паслёновые (сем.) bot: nightshade
паслёновый bot: solanaceous.
паслёноцветное растение bot: solanal.
паспалум bot: dallis grass (Paspalum
пассаж = перепрививка. | dilatatum).
пассивизм passivism.
пассивист passivist.

пассивная гиперемия path: passive congestion.
пассивное торможение = безусловное торможение.
пассифлора = страстоцвет.
пастбище pasture.
пастбищный pastoral, grazing, attr: pasture.
Пастер Pasteur.
пастерелла pasteurella.
пастереллёз pasteurellosis.
пастеризация pasteurization.
пастеризованное молоко pasteurized milk.
пастернак bot: parsnip (Pastinaca sativa).
пастись graze.
пастушки orn: rails, gallinules, coots (Ralli).
пастушковые куропатки orn: Mesoenades.
пастушок orn: rail, gallinule.
~ виргинский Virginia rail (Rallus virginianus).
~ водяной water rail (R. aquaticus).
~ мадагаскарский Mesoenatida.
пастушья сумка bot: shepherd's purse shovelweed (Capsella, Medic.); pickpocket, blind weed, lady's purse (Capsella bursa-pastoris).
пасть zool: mouth.
пастьба agr: grazing.
"пасущееся" животное grazer, grazing herbivore.
пасынок = водяной побег.
пасынкование bot: suckering.
пасюк = крыса пасюк.
патентованное средство patent medicine.
патиссон bot: custard squash, gourd, scallop (Cucurbita pepo).
патогенез pathogenesis.
патогенность pathogenicity.
патогенные свойства pathogenicity.
патогенный pathogenic.
~ микроорганизм bact: nosophyte.
патогистологический histopathologic.
патогномонический pathognomonic.
патолог pathologist.
патологическая анатомия pathologic anatomy, morbid anatomy.
~ гистология pathologic histology.
~ диплопия ophth: pathologic diplopia.
~ лживость psych: pathologic lying, pseudologia phantastica.
~ психология abnormal psychology.
~ химия pathological chemistry.
патологические роды obstet: morbid labor.
патологический перелом pathologic fracture.
патологическое изменение pathologic change.
~ опьянение pathologic intoxication.
~ состояние pathological state, diseased condition, morbid c.
патология pathology.
~ конечностей acropathology.
~ лётной глухоты aviation deafness pathology.
патологоанатом pathologoanatomist.
патологоанатомический pathologic-anatomy.
патулин patulin.
паук spider (Araneida).
~ домовой house spider (Tegenaria domestica).
~ -краб zool: spider crab (Hyas, Inachus, Macropodia, Maia, Libinia).
~ -крестовик Araneus diadematus.
~ -птицеед bird spider (Avidularia)
~ ~ яванский Java bird spider (Selenocosmia).
~ -серебрянка водяной Argyroneta aquatica.
пауки (отр.) zool: spiders (Araneida, Araneae).
пауко- arachno-.
паукобоязнь psych: arachnephobia.
паукообразная клетка hist: spider cell.
~ обезьяна zool: spider-like monkey (Ateles).
паукообразные zool: arachnids (Arachnoidea).
паукообразный spiderlike.
пауроподы (отр.) zool: Pauropoda.
паутина web, cobweb.
паутинная бородавка zool: spinneret.
~ железа zool: spinning gland.
~ (мозговая) оболочка anat: arachnoid, arachnoidea encephali.
~ оболочка спинного мозга anat: arachnoid of spine (arachnoidea spinalis).
паутинник тминный entom: caraway webworm (Depressaria nervosa).
паутинный arachnoidal.
~ червь = совка хлопковая.
паутинообразный arachnoid.
паучник bot: 1. spiderwort (Tradescantis); 2. spider flower, spider plant (Cleome spinosa, Jacq.)
паучниковые (сем.) bot: spiderwort family (Commelinaceae).
паучок entom: small spider.
~ цитрусовый красный citrus red spider (Tetranychus mytilaspidis).
пах anat: groin, inguinal region.
пахизандра = молочай японский.
пахионовы грануляции anat: Pacchionian bodies, arachnoidal granulations.

паховая гранулёма path: groin ulceration, granuloma inguinale.
~ грыжа path: inguinal hernia.
~ железа anat: inguinal gland.
~ связка = пупартова связка.
паховое кольцо abdominal inguinal ring.
паховый канал anat: inguinal canal.
пахта buttermilk.
пахтанье = пахта.
пахучий odoriferous, strong-smelling, aromatic.
~ колосок = душистый колосок.
пациент patient.
Пачини Pacini.
пачиниевы тельца hist: Pacinian corpuscles.
пачули bot: patchouli (Pogostemon patchouli, Pellet.)
пашенный bot: arable-field (arvensus).
пебрина pebrine disease (of silkworms).
певчая гортань orn: syrinx.
~ птица orn: songbird; see also настоящие певчие.
певчий дрозд orn: song thrush.
педераст psych: pederast.
педерастия psych: pederasty, pedication.
педиаструм bot: Pediastrum (algae).
педиатрист pediatrist, pediatrician.
педиатрия pediatrics.
педикулёз derm: pediculosis.
педипальпа zool: pedipalp.
педогенез zool: pedogenesis.
педофилия psych: pedophilia.
педофобия psych: pedophobia.
пезиза = пецица.
Пейер Peyer.
пейеровы бляшки anat: Peyer's plaques.
Пейтон Payton.
пекан bot: pecan, see орех пекан.
~ горький = гиккори болотный.
пекарские дрожжи baker's yeast.
пектин pharm: pectin.
пектиновый pectic.
пелагическая икра pelagic fish eggs.
~ рыба pelagic fish.
пелагический моллюск zool: pteropod.
пелагическое животное surface swimmer.
пеламида ichth: Sarda.
пеламидовые (сем.) ichth: Cybiidae.
пеламидра веслохвостая zool: yellow-belied sea snake (Pelamidrus olaturus).
пеларгония "герань" bot: geranium of gardens (Pelargonium, Ait.)
пеликан orn: pelican (Pelecanus).
пеликаны (сем.) orn: pelican family (Pelecanidae).

пеликозавры zool: Pelycosauria (extinct), see звероподобные.
пелингас = пиленгас.
пеллагра path: pellagra, Italian leprosy.
пеллагрик pellagrin.
пеллагрозный pellagrous.
пелликула zool: pellicula.
пельвеометрия = тазоизмерение.
пельтандра bot: arrow arum (Peltandra).
пельтигера bot: Peltigera lichens.
пелюшка = горошек полевой.
пелягодрома orn: frigate petrel (Pelagodroma marina hypoleuca).
пелядь ichth: whitefish Coregonus peled.
пемфигоидальный path: pemphigoid.
пемфигус path: pemphigus.
пена foam, froth, spum.
пендинка path: Oriental sores, Aden ulcer (due to Leishmania tropica).
пендинская язва = пендинка.
пенёк stump, stipe, stem (of a mushroom).
пенетрант zool: penetrant, see стрекательная клетка.
пенетрирующий penetrating.
пение singing.
пенис anat: penis.
пенисный penile.
"пенистая" клетка foamy cell.
пенициллин penicillin.
пенициллиум bot: Penicillium (fungi).
пеннатулида zool: pennatulid (coral).
пенница entom: meadow spittlebug.
~ слюнявая entom: spittlebugs Philaemus spumarius.
пенницы (сем.) entom: spittlebugs, frog-hoppers (Cercopidae).
пенообразование foaming, frothing, spurging.
пеночка = пеночка обыкновенная.
~ -веснячка orn: wood warbler, wood wren (Phylloscopus trochilus).
~ -камышовка marsh warbler (Hypolais).
~ кузнечик marsh warbler (Phyloscopus collybita).
~ обыкновенная willow warbler, willow wren, Brit: chiff-chaff (Phylloscopus trochilus, P. sibilatrix).
пентоза chem: pentose.
пентоземия pentosemia.
пентозонуклеиновая кислота pentose nucleic acid.
пентоксил pentoxyl.
пентстемон bot: beardtongue (Penstemon, Mitch.)
пеньки (зачатки вновь отрастающих перьев) orn: bristle.

пенящийся foaming, frothing, spurging.
пеон = пион.
пепелица phytp: disease of grape vine, fungus Uncinula necator, Bor.
пепельник = зольник.
пепельно-серый cineraceous.
пепельный cinereous.
пеперминт pharm: peppermint.
пепино bot: pepino, see груша дынная.
пеприлис ichth: starfish (Peprilis).
пепсин pepsin.
пепсинировать pepsinate.
пепсиновая железа anat: peptic gland.
пептическая язва peptic ulcer.
пептонат висмута pharm: peptonized bismuth.
пептонизироваться peptonize.
пептонная вода bact: peptone water.
первая пара ног entom: first legs.
~ помощь med: first aid.
~ сигнальная система first signaling system (Pavlovian cortical system in man and animal associated with the sense organs that respond to external stimuli). Cf. вторая с.с.
первенец first-born.
перверзия perversion.
перверзная психопатия perversive psychopathy, psychopathia sexualis.
первитин pharm: pervitin.
первичная кишка embr: archenteron, archigaster, coelenteron, primary gut, progaster; foregut.
~ кость primary bone.
~ ксилема bot: protoxylem.
~ культура bact: primary culture.
~ менорреа gyn: primary amenorrhea.
~ образовательная ткань bot: meristem.
~ полоска embr: primitive streak.
~ чешуйка bot: first glume.
~ энтодерма embr: primitive entoderm, primary entoderm.
~ язва ven: primary sore, hard sore.
~ ямка embr: primitive pit.
первично-беременная primigravida.
~-бескрылые насекомые apterygota.
первичноводные животные Anamnia.
первичное освидетельствование original examination.
первичнокишечный embr: archenteric.
первичноназемные животные Amniota.
первичнопокровные (подкл.) bot: Archichlamydeae subclass.
первичнополостные черви (тип) zool: roundworms (Nemathelminthes).
первичноротые (подразд.) zool: Protostomia.
первичносумчатые грибы bot: Protascales.
первичнотрахейные (кл.) zool: Protracheata, Onychophora.
первичные грибы = архимицеты.
~ маховые перья orn: primary feathers.
~ членистоногие zool: subphylum Proarthropoda.
первичный больной = перворазный больной.
~ диагноз primary diagnosis.
~ желобок embr: primitive groove.
~ корень bot: primary root, primordial root.
~ позвоночник embr: primitive backbone.
~ рот zool: gastropore, blastopore, primitive mouth.
~ узелок embr: primitive knot.
~ шок primary shock.
первовозрастная стадия личинок entom: instar form of larvae.
первое крыло entom: first wing.
~ ребро anat: subclavicula.
первозвери zool: Prototheria, see клоачные звери.
первозданные воды eternal waters.
первоначальная концентрация original concentration.
перворазный больной first-admission patient.
первороженица obstet: primipara.
первоцвет bot: primrose, cowslip (Primula); bear's ear (P. auricula).
~ аптечный wild p., butterweed, herb Peter (P. officinalis, P. veris).
~ высокий oxlip, cup-and-saucer (P. elatior).
~ истинный = п. аптечный.
~ кортузоидный bear's ear primrose (P. cortusoides, var. amoena).
~ лекарственный = п. аптечный.
~ "медвежье ухо" = п. кортузоидный.
первоцветные (пор.) bot: Primulales.
~(сем.) bot: primrose family (Primulaceae).
первый желудок жвачных = преджелудок.
~ оборот = заключающий тело оборот.
~ отдел желудка = преджелудок.
~ тон сердца first heart sound.
~ шейный позвонок anat: first cervical vertebra, atlas.
перга bot: beebread.
"пергаментная кожа" parchment skin.

перебой 1. int: irregularity (of heart action); 2. av med: beat (of propellers); 3. interruption, disruption (of service, etc.)
переболевший оспой infect: variolated.
перебранный pharm: garbled.
переваливающаяся походка path: waddling gait.
переваривание digestion.
переваривать digest.
переваримость digestibility.
переваримый digestible.
переварить p. a. of переваривать.
перевести на инвалидность put (a patient) in disabled category.
перевиваемая опухоль transplanted tumor.
перевиваемый рак transplantable cancer.
перевивка 1. bact: subinoculation; 2. graft, transplantation.
перевитой intorted.
перевитые стебли bot: tangled stems.
переворачивание inversion.
перевязать p. a. of перевязывать.
перевязка 1. surg: dressing (change); ligation; binding, tying; 2. zool: see тигровый хорёк.
~ артерии surg: ligation of an artery.
~ пуповины obstet: tying of the cord, cord dressing.
~ сосуда = кровоостанавливающая перевязка сосуда.
перевязочная surg: dressing room.
~ сестра surg: dressing room nurse.
~ сумка surg: dressing case.
перевязочные ножницы surg: bandage scissors, bandage shears.
перевязочный материал surg: dressings.
~ пункт surg: dressing station.
~ стол surg: dressing table.
перевязывать surg: dress; ligate; bind, tie.
перевязь (для руки) surg: (arm) sling.
перегиб flexion, kink(ing).
~ кпереди bending forward, anteflexion.
~ матки кпереди gyn: anteflexion of the uterus.
~ мочеточника ureteral kink.
~ под углом angulation.
~ прохода bend of the canal.
перегибаться кзади retroflex.
перегнать p. a. of перегонять.
перегной humus.
перегнойная земля humous soil.
перегнуться p. a. of перегибаться.
перегонный куб still.

перегонять distil(late).
перегородка septum; partition; baffle.
~ (в стручке) bot: pith diaphragm.
перегородочный septal.
перегрев(ание) overheating, superheating.
перёд наличника entom: anteclypeus.
передаваемость infect: transmissibility.
передатчик = переносчик.
передача мыслей на расстояние thought transference, telepathy.
~ половых признаков genet: sex linkage.
передающийся infect: transmissible.
~ посредством воды infect: waterborne.
передвижение locomotion, movement, shift.
переднегрудной entom: prothoracic.
переднегрудь entom: prothorax.
переднее крыло entom: primary wing, anterior w., front w., hemelytron.
переднежаберные моллюски (подкл.) zool: Prosobranchia (mollusks).
переднезадняя ось anat: anteroposterior axis.
~ горизонтальная ось тела anat: antero-posterior horizontal axis of the body.
переднеспинка entom: pronotum.
переднечерепной anat: precranial, sincipital.
передние два холмика четверохолмия anat: pregeminum.
передний front, fore, pre-; anat: anterior.
~ боковой anterolateral.
~ зуб (резец) anat: incisor, front tooth, fore-t.
~ конусовидный конец helm: cephalic cone (of Trematoda).
~ корешок (нервов) anat: anterior root (of nerves), motor r., ventral r.
~ край крыла entom: costal margin of the wing.
~ мозг embr: forebrain, anterior brain vesicle, prosencephalon.
~ нерв грудной клетки (боковой, срединный) anat: (lateral, medial) anterior thoracic nerve.
~ отдел желудка zool: first compartment of the stomach (of a ruminant), rumen, paunch.
~ родничок anat: anterior fontanel(la), fonticulus major, fonticulus quadrangularis.
~ спинной anterodorsal.
~ ~ плавник ichth: first dorsal fin.
~ (спинномозговой) корешок anat: ventral root.

передняя глазная камера = передняя камера глаза.
~ грудь entom: prothorax.
~ доля гипофиза anterior hypophyseal lobe.
~ дуга позвонка anat: anterior arch of the vertebra.
~ камера глаза anat: anterior chamber of the eye.
~ кишка entom: fore-intestine, foregut.
~ комиссура головного мозга anat: precomissure.
~ лапа zool: forepaw; anterior leg.
~ лапка = п. лапа.
~ латеральная борозда anat: anterolateral spinal sulcus.
~ нога foreleg.
~ ножка entom: foreleg.
~ синехия ophth: anterior synechia.
~ срединная щель anat: anterior median fissure (of the spinal cord).
~ центральная извилина (мозга) anat: ascending frontal gyrus, precentral g., g. centralis anterior.
~ часть брюшка entom: preabdomen.
~ ~ вымени zool: fore-udder.
~ ~ конечности anat: fore-limb.
~ ~ копыта zool: toe.
~ ~ наличника entom: anteclypeus.
~ ~ основной кости anat: presphenoid.
~ ~ ручной кисти anat: fore-hand.
~ ~ спинки entom: pronotum.
~ ~ тела fore-body.
~ яма черепа anat: precranial fossa, anterior cranial fossa.
"переедание" overeating.
переживание psych: (usually hard emotional) experience.
~ навязчивых идей psych: rumination.
пережигание cautery, cauterization.
~ межплевральных сращений surg: thoracocautery.
пережим = перетяжка.
пережуй-личко = волчеягодник.
перезимовать overwinter.
перезимовка (over)wintering.
перезимовывание поколений entom: overwintering of generations.
перезрелость overripeness, overmaturity.
перезрелый overripe, overmature, hypermature.
переисследование reinvestigation.
перекармливание overfeeding, overnutrition, supernutrition, superalimentation.
перекармливать overfeed.
перекати-поле bot: babies'-breath, tumbleweeds (Gypsophila paniculata; Eryngium campestre; Statice; Goniolimon, Limonium, etc.)
перекись chem: peroxide.
~ водорода hydrogen peroxide.
~ марганца manganese peroxide.
перекладина anat: beam, trabecula.
перекорм = перекармливание.
перекормить p. a. of перекармливать.
перекоррегированный overcorrected.
перекрашивание mcscop: overstaining.
перекрёст cross(ing), intersection, chiasma, decussation; genet: crossing-over.
~ зрительных нервов anat: decussation of the optic nerve, optic chiasm, chiasma opticum.
~ (нервов) anat: chiasma.
~ петель anat: decussation of the fillet.
~ пирамид anat: pyramidal decussation.
перекрестить(ся) p. a. of перекрещивать(ся).
перекрёстная адсорбция reciprocal adsorption.
~ диплопия ophth: heteronymous diplopia, crossed diplopia.
~ совместимость genet: cross-compatibility.
~ стерильность genet: cross-sterility.
перекрёстное оплодотворение bio: cross-fertilization, xenogamy, allogamy.
~ опыление bot: cross pollination, heterogenous p.
перекрёстные реакции chem: cross reactions.
перекрёстный рефлекс neur: crossed reflex, consensual reflex.
перекрещивание факторов genet: crossing over.
перекрещивать(ся) cross, intersect, decussate.
перекручивание 1. twisting; 2. looping.
перекрученный twisted.
перекрывающийся imbricate(d), overlapping.
перелеска (голубая) = печёночница обыкновенная.
перелёт flight.
перелётная птица migratory bird.
переливание surg: transfusion.
~ крови blood transfusion.
переливать surg: transfuse.
перелов overfishing.
переловить ichth: overfish.
перелой ven: gonorrhea.
перелойный ven: gonorrheal.
перелом 1. surg: fracture; 2. crisis, apostasis, turning point (of disease).

перелом основания черепа fracture of the cranium base.
~ позвоночника fracture of the spine.
~ с вдавлением depressed fracture.
~ со смещением кости subgrundation.
~ тела кости shaft fracture.
~ челюсти fracture of maxillary bone.
переломанный surg: fractured.
перемежающаяся лихорадка collq: chills and feveri, shakes.
~ невралгия тройничного нерва face ague, brow ague, tic douloureux.
~ олигурия с полиурией path: anisuria.
~ хромота path: intermittent claudication, angina cruris, dysbasia intermittens angiosclerotica.
перемежающееся поседение derm: ringed hair. [convulsions
перемежающиеся судороги intermittent
перемена положения postural change.
переменный душ alternating douche. [ty, unsteadiness
переменчивость mutability; changeabil-
перемещение воды и питательных веществ bot: translocation.
~ хромосомы genet: chromosome translocation.
перемычка между центриолями embr: centrodesmos.
перенаселение overpopulation.
перенаселённость = перенаселение.
перенаселённый overpopulated.
перенасытить p. a. of перенасыщать.
перенасыщать supersaturate.
перенесение реагирования = отреагирование. [diseases
перенесённые заболевания previous
перенос transfer, transport(ation), migration, transmission, vection.
~ болезнетворного начала metastasis.
~ инфекции transmission, vection.[sion.
~ насекомыми infect: insect transmis-
~ через воздух infect: aerial transmission.
переносчик vector, carrier, transmitting agent, transmitter.
переношенная беременность cf. задержавшиеся роды.
переопод peraeopod (of a crustacean).
переосвидетельствование reexamina-
переохлаждение supercooling. |tion.
переоценка своей личности psych: overestimation of one's own personality.

перепел orn: quail (Coturnix).
~ обыкновенный common quail (Coturnix communis).
перепёлка orn: quail hen.
перепись населения census.
переплетаться interlace. [roots.
переплетение корней bot: matting of
переполнение filling beyond capacity, overflow. [venous pooling.
~ вен path: engorgement of veins,
~ кровью path: hyperemia, engorgement.
перепонка membrane, diaphragm, pellicle, velum, web.
перепончатая ампула anat: membrane-
~ нога orn: palmated foot.| ous ampulla.
~ часть мочеиспускательного канала anat: membraneous urethra.
перепончатокрылое entom: hymenopter(on).
перепончатокрылые (отр.) entom: hymenopters; bees, wasps, ants, etc. (Hymenoptera). [ous.
перепончатокрылый entom: hymenopter-
перепончатоногие web-footed birds (Steganopodes).
перепончато-хрящевая часть трубы cartilaginous portion of the tube (ear).
перепончатые пальцы path: web fingers; see also синдактилия.
перепончатый membran(ace)ous, diaphragmatic, pellicular, velar, webbed.
~ лабиринт anat: membranous labyrinth.
~ покров (спорангия) bot: membranous indusium, velum. [decayed.
перепревший bot: fusty, rotten,
перепрививка mcbio: subinoculation.
переработка (re)processing, reworking, assimilation.
перераздражение лабиринта av med: overstimulation of the labyrinth.
перерезание мягких тканей лигатурой surg: seriscission.
~ пуповины obstet: cutting of the umbilical cord, omphalotomy.
перерезанный transected.
перерезать пуповину obstet: cut the umbilical cord.
перерезка нерва surg: neurotomy.
перерод agr bot: degenerative crop.
переродившийся degenerate.
переродиться p. a. of перерождать-
перерождаться degenerate. ся.
пересадить p. a. of пересаживать.
пересадка surg: transplantation, grafting.

пересадка животной ткани surg: zoolplasty, transfer of zoografts.
~ кожи skin grafting, dermanaplasty.
~ кости surg: bone transplantation, bone grafting.
~ растений replanting.
~ роговицы transplantation of cornea.
~ ткани tissue transplantation.
~ чужой кожи surg: dermatoheteroplasty.
пересаживаемая животная ткань zoograft.
пересаживать transplant, graft.
~ растение replant.
пересадить p. a. of пересаживать.
пересев bot: reseeding, replanting; bact: subculture, subculturing, reinoculation, transfer.
пересевать cf. пересев.
пересевная культура bio: subculture.
переслаивать overlay.
пересмешник orn: mockingbird.
переспелость = перезрелость.
переспелый = перезрелый.
перестойный bot: overmature, overripe.
перестройка макронуклеуса hemixis (in infusorians).
переступень bot: white bryony (Bryonia alba).
перетяжка necking-in, necking-off, narrowing; constriction, snare.
переутомление extreme fatigue.
~ глаз eye fatigue, eye overstrain, overuse of the eyes.
~ от боевых действий mil: combat fatigue.
переутомленный от боев mil: combat-fatigue(d).
перехват = перетяжка.
~ (отделяющий голову) cervical sinus (in crustacea).
~ Ранвье node of Ranvier.
переходная клетка hist: transitional cell.
~ складка конъюнктивы anat: retrotarsal fold.
~ ячейка transitional cell (bees).
переходник lab: adapter.
переходные годы женщины turn of life, menopause, climacteric.
перец bot: pepper.
~ арабский bot: akola, negro pepper (Xylopia aethiopica, A. Rich.)
~ водяной = горец.
~ гвоздичный bayberry (Pimenta acris).
~ душистый pimento (Pimenta officinalis).
~ жгучий hot pepper (Capsicum annum).
~ кайенский cayenne pepper (C. annum, var. acuminatum).
перец стручковый bush red p. (Capsicum annum, C. frutescens).
перечная мята pharm: peppermint.
перечник bot: Iberis amara; pepperwort, peppergrass, tonguegrass (Lepidium).
~ зонтичный candytuft (Iberis umbellata).
~ полевой cow cress, field peppergrass (Lepidium campestre, R. Br.)
перечное дерево bot: pepper plant (Piper nigrum).
~ зерно bot: peppercorn.
~ масло pimento oil.
перечноцветные (пор.) bot: Piperales.
перечные (сем.) bot: pepper family (Piperaceae).
перечный peppery, piperitus.
~ гриб peppery lactarius (Boletus piperatus, Bull.)
перешеек anat: isthmus.
перешеечный anat: isthmian.
перешнуровать(ся) p. a. of перешнуровывать(ся).
перешнуровывать(ся) constrict, ligate, undergo segmentation.
переяровизация agr: revernalization (of seeds).
периблема bot: periblem.
перибронхит path: peribronchitis.
периваскулярный anat: perivascular.
перивентрикулярная область anat: periventricular region.
перивителлиновое пространство bio: perivitelline.
перигепатит path: perihepatitis.
перидинея bot: peridinean (flagellated plants Peridineae).
перидонт = корневая оболочка зуба.
перикамбий bot: paricycle.
перикардиальный anat: pericardiac, -al.
перикардит path: pericarditis.
перикарион neur: perikaryon.
перикарпий bot: pericarp.
перилла bot: perilla (Perilla ocymoides)
перимедулярная зона bot: medullary sheath.
периметр perimeter.
периметрий anat: perimetrium.
периметрический perimetric.
периневрий hist: perineurium.
период вынашивания икры ichth: egg-bearing season.
~ изгнания obstet: expulsion period, second stage.
~ оплодотворения entom: flight time.
~ поворота плода obstet: rotation stage of labor.

период покоя aestivation (period).
~ половой активности sexually active period.
~ полувыведения rad: effective half-life.
~ предвестников заболевания prodromal period, premonitary period.
~ размножения zool: breeding season.
~ раскрытия obstet: stage of dilatation, first stage.
~ роста growing period.
~ спаривания mating time, pairing t.
~ течки zool: estrus, heat, rut.
~ токования = п. спаривания.
периодическая мания psych: periodic mania, recurrent mania.
~ рвота path: cyclic vomiting.
периодический запой psych: dipsomania.
периост anat: periosteum.
периостальный рефлекс physl: periosteal reflex.
периостит path: periostitis.
периоститный periostitic.
периострак(ум) zool: periostracum.
перипласт bio: periplast.
перисарк zool: perisarc.
периспиракулярные железы = стигмальные железы.
периспориевые (пор.) bot: Perisporiales order (fungi).
перистальтика physl: peristalsis.
~ желудка gastric peristalsis.
~ с нарушенным ритмом anisoperstalsis.
перистальтический peristaltic.
перистая мышца anat: pennate muscle.
~ ость bot: plumose awn.
перистое рыльце bot: plumose stigma.
~ строение pinnation.
перистожаберный zool: pterygobranchiate.
перистоопределенный pinnatipartite.
перистолистный bot: pinnately leaved.
перистолопастный лист bot: pinnately lobed leaf.
перистом zool: peristome.
перистомальная спираль (инфузорий) adoral spiral zone.
перистонервный bot: feather-veined.
перистораздельный bot: pinnatipartite, pinnatifid, pinnately divided.
перисторазрезной = перистораздельный.
перисторассечённый = перистораздельный.
перисторасщепленный = перистораздельный.
перистосложный bot: pinnately compound.
*перистые диатомеи bot: Pannatae
~ жабры gill plume.
перистый pinnate; feathery, plumose, plumarius.
~ лист с двумя парами листочков bot: bijugate leaf.
~ ~ с увеличенной конечной лопастью bot: lyrate leaf.
~ усик entom: plumose antenna.
перитониальное сращение path: peritoneal adhesion.
перитонит path: peritonitis.
перитрих mcbio: peritrichate.
перитрофическая мембрана entom: peritrophic membrane.
периферическая нервная система anat: peripheral nervous system.
периферический восприниматель physl: exteroceptor.
периферическое зрение peripheral vision.
~ кровообращение peripheral circulation.
~ сердце obs: peripheral heart.
~ сосудистое расстройство peripheral circulatory failure.
перифитон periphyton.
перифитонный periphytic.
перицикл bot: pericycle.
перкарина ichth: Percarina.
перкуссионный молоточек percussion hammer, plexor.
перкуссия percussion.
перкутанно per cutem (through the skin)
перкутировать percuss, tap.
перкуторно by percussion.
перкуторный звук percussion note.
перламутр pearl, nacre, mother-of-p.
перламутровая раковина nacreshell; gold-lip, silver-lip, gold edge (Margaritana maxima).
перламутровый слой zool: nacreous layer, mother-of-pearl.
перловица zool: nacreshell, pearly mussel (Uniondae).
перловник bot: melic grass (Melica).
~ голубой blue moor grass (Aira caerulea).
пермоцинодон zool: Permocynodon (extinct).
пернамбук bot: red sandalwood (Adenanthera pavonina).
пернатая дичь game bird, wild fowl.
пернициозная анемия pernicious anemia.
перо feather, plume.
~ лука bot: scallion, onion top.

перозис orn: perosis.
перонин pharm: benzylmorphine hydrochloride.
перообразный plumose.
пероральное применение oral administration.
персеверация psych: perseveration.
персея опушённая swamp bay (Persea pubescens, Sarg.)
"персидская манна" = верблюжья колючка.
персидский порошок Persian insect powder.
персик bot: peach (Prunus persica).
~ с неотделяющейся косточкой clingstone peach.
персикария bot: smartweed (Persicaria).
персимон = хурма.
персонал personnel, staff.
перстневидный хрящ anat: cricoid cartilage.
перстне-трахеальная связка anat: ligamentum cricotracheale.
~ -черпаловидная мышца (боковая, задняя) anat: cricoarytenoid muscle (lateral, posterior).
~ -щитовидная мышца anat: cricothyroid muscle.
~ ~ связка anat: ligamentum cricothyreoideum.
перувианский бальзам pharm: Peruvian balsam, Indian balsam.
перфорация perforation.
~ головки плода obstet: transforation.
перфузионная жидкость perfusate.
перфузируемая печень perfused liver.
перхоть derm: dandruff, dander, scurf.
перцина ichth: log perch (Percina caprodes).
перчатка (губка) glove sponge (Euspongia tubulifera).
" перышко" bot: see колеоптиль.
Перье Perier.
*перья plumery, feathers.
~ коченя orn: saddle feathers.
пёс zool: dog (Canis).
песец = полярная лисица.
пескарь обыкновенный ichth: quab (Gobio gobio).
пескожил zool: lugworm (Arenicola).
песколюб 1. bot: sea reed, marram, matgrass (Ammophila, Host.); 2. zool: gerbil
~ песчаный = тростник песчаный.
пескоройка zool: ammocoete larva.
"песок под веками" av med: dry gritty feeling under the eyelids.
песочная ванна sand bath. Cf. лечение песочными ваннами.
песочник orn: common sandpiper (Tringa).
пестик 1. bot: pistil: 2. lab: pestle (for mortar).
~ удлинённым столбиком bot: dolichostylous pistil.
пестичное растение bot: pistillate plant, angiosperm.
пестичные (тип) bot: Gynoeciatae, see покрытосеменные.
пестичный цветок bot: pistillate flower.
пёстрокрылка = муха плодовая средиземноморская.
~ цитрусовая orange fly (Trypeta ludens).
пёстрокрылки (сем.) entom: Trypetidae.
пёстрые семена bot: mottled seeds.
пёстрый pied, motley, variegated, brindled; very irregular (distribution)
пестряк bot: golden aster (Chrysopsis).
пестрянка виноградная entom: moth Theresia ampelophaga.
пестрянки (сем.) entom: Zygaenidae.
пестрятка ichth: parr (Salmo salar).
песчаная баня lab: sand bath.
песчаник = бычок-песочник.
песчанка 1. zool: gerbil; sand lance, lent; 2. ichth: sand eel (Ammodytes); 3. bot: see тростник песчаный.
песчанковые (сем.) ichth: sand eels (Ammodytidae).
песчаный bot: sandy, of sand (arenarius).
~ колосок = волоснец песчаный.
~ тростник = тростник песчаный.
пёсья вишня = физалис.
петехиальная сыпь petechial eruption, mulberry rash.
петехия path: petechia.
петидин pethidine.
петлистая сеть meshwork.
петля loop; surg: snare; anat: fillet, lemniscus.
~ Генле anat: loop of Henle, medullary loop (renal).
~ кишечника anat: intestinal loop, convolution.
~ с культурой bact: infected loop.
петрификация petrifaction.
петрушка bot: parsley.
~ зеленная curly p. (Petroselinum sativum crispum, P. hortense, Hoffm.)
~ корневая (turnip-)rooted p. (P. hortense tuberosum).
~ кудрявая = п. зеленная.
~ садовая = п. зеленная.
~ собачья = кокорыш.
петсай Pe-Tsai (Chinese cabbage).

петунья bot: petunia (Petunia).
петух orn: cock, rooster; male bird.
петуший гребень cockscomb, cock's crest; anat: crista falli.
~ гребешок bot: celosia, cockscomb (Celosia).
петушиная грудь path: pigeon chest.
~ походка path: prancing gait, steppage gait.
петушки = касатик.
пецица bot: fungus Peziza; shield-like peziza (Peziza coutellata); scarlet cup (P. coccinea); cup fungus (P.akrautia).
печёночная артерия anat: hepatic artery.
~ вена anat: hepatic vein.
~ двуустка helm: liver fluke (Distomum hepaticum).
~ долька hist: hepatic lobule.
~ доля anat: hepatic lobe.
~ пиявка helm: liver fluke (Distomum hepaticum).
~ тупость int: hepatic dullness.
~ хлоазма derm: chloasma hepaticum, liver spots.
печёночник bot: hepatica, liverwort.
печёночники (кл.) bot: liverworts (Hepaticae).
печёночница обыкновенная bot: liverleaf, hepatica, noble liverwort (Hepatica, Mill.)
печёночного происхождения hepatogenous.
печёночно-двенадцатиперстная связка anat: ligamentum hepatoduodenale.
~ -желудочная связка anat: gastrohepatic ligament.
~ -жёлчный hepatobiliary.
~ -лёгочный hepatopneumonic.
~ -почечный hepatorenal.
печёночный вырост zool: hepatic caecum.
~ мох bot: hepatica, liverwort.
~ проток anat: hepatic duct.
~ сосальщик zool: liver fluke (Fasciola hepatica).
печень anat: liver..
~ трески cod liver.
пещеристая пазуха anat: cavernous sinus.
~ ткань hist: erectile tissue.
~ часть мочеиспускательного канала anat: spongy portion of urethra, cavernous urethra.
пещеристое тело cavernous body, corpus cavernosum.
~ ~ мочеиспускательного канала corpus cavernosum urethrae.
пещеристое тело полового члена corpus cavernosum penis.
пещеристый cavernous, spongious, spongy, honeycombed.
пещерная саламандра zool: Oedipus, Hydromantis.
пиассава = канатная пальма.
пивное сердце path: beer heart.
пивные дрожжи bot: brewer's yeast, barm (Saccharomyces cerevisiae).
пигидий entom: pygidium.
пигмент pigment.
~ изнашивания pigment associated with wearing out of organism,lipofuscin.
пигментация pigmentation.
пигментированный pigmented.
пигментная клетка hist: pigment cell.
пигментное родимое пятно path: nevus pigmentosus.
пигментный pigmental, pigmentary.
~ бокал zool: pigment cup (ocellus).
пиголица = чибис.
пигостиль zool: pygostyle.
пиелит = пиэлит.
пиелография pyelography.
пиемический pyemic.
пиемия hem: pyemia.
пижма bot: tansy (Tanacetum).
пизанг bot: plantain (Musa paradisiaca)
Пикар Piccard.
пикногонида zool: pycnogonid (Pycnogonidae).
пикнолепсия neur: pyknolepsy.
пикнометр pycnometer.
пикульник bot: hemp nettle (Galeopsis).
~ колючий hedgehog (G. tetrahit).
~ ладанниковый hemp nettle (G. ladanum).
пикша ichth: 1. haddock, dickie (Melanogrammus aeglefinus); 2. see мерланг черноморский.
пила saw.
~ -рыба ichth: sawfish (Pristis).
пиленгас ichth: mullet Mugil so-iuy.
пилидий zool: pilidium, nemertine larva.
пилильщик entom: sawfly (Prionidae).
~ берёзовый северный Croesus septentrionalis.
~ вишнёвый бледноногий Priophorus padi.
~ ~ слизистый pear slug (Caliroa cerasi).
~ грушевый sawfly (Haplocampa brevis).
~ ~ укороченный Micronematus abbreviatus.
~ еловый spruce sawfly (Nematus abietinus).

пилильщик земляничный curled rose sawfly (Allantus cinctus, Emphytus cinctus).

~ крыжовниковый gooseberry sawfly, currant worm (Pteronidea ribesi).

~ ~ бледный Pristiphora pallipes.

~ лиственничный larch sawfly (Lygaeonematus erichsonii).

~ листовой грушевый pear web-spinning sawfly (Neurotoma flaviventris).

~ малинный raspberry sawfly (Monophadnoides rubi).

~ рапсовый turnip fly (Athalia colibri).

~ рыжий wheat-stem sawfly (Cephus pygmaeus).

~ сосновый pine sawfly (Lophyrus pini, Diprion pini).

~ ~ рыжий Neodiprion sertifer.

~ стеблевой stem sawfly (Cephidae).

~ -ткач web-spinning s. (Pamphilidae).

~ ~ общественный Lyda erytrocephala.

~ ~ сосновый одиночный Lyda hieroglyphica.

~ хлебный wheat sawfly-borer, corn sawfly (Cephus pygmaeus).

~ чёрный stem borer Trachelus tabidus.

~ яблонный European apple sawfly (Hoplocampa testudinea).

~ ясеневый белоточечный Macrophya punctum-album.

пилильщики (подотр.) entom: sawflies (Symphyta, Chalastrogastra).

пилка для ампул ampule saw.

пилоболус bot: Pilobolus (fungus).

пилонос ichth: saw shark (Pristiophorus)

пилорический клапан entom: pyloric valve.

~ придаток ichth: pyloric appendage, caecum.

~ сфинктор anat: pyloric sphincter.

пилороспазм path: pylorospasm.

пилоростеноз path: pylorostenosis.

пильчатый bot: serrate, dentate (leaf).

~ усик entom: serrate antenna, saw-like a.

пилюли Бло pharm: chalybeate pills, pills of ferrous carbonate.

~ с сабуром pharm: pills of aloes.

пилюльная доска pharm: pill board.

пилюля pharm: pill, pilule, pellet, see таблетка.

пилящий шум int: sawing murmur.

пимелеметопон ichth: fat-head (Pimelometopon pulcher).

пимпла entom: ichneumon-fly Pimpla examinator.

пинагор lumpsucker, lumpfish (Cyclopterus lumpus).

пинагоровые = круглопёрые.

пинанг = арековая пальма.

пингвин orn: penguin (Spheniscidae).

пингвины orn: 1. impennates, penguins (superorder Impennes), see плавающие; 2. penguins (order Sphenisci).

пиния bot: Italian stone-pine (Pinus pinea).

пиннулярия bot: Pinnularia (alga).

пинта derm: pinta disease, spotted disease (tropical).

пинцет для глазного яблока eyeball forceps.

~ ~ предметных стекол mcscop: slide forceps.

~ ~ радужной оболочки ophth: iris forceps.

~ ~ снятия скобок surg: clip remover.

~ ~ удаления инородных тел surg: foreign body forceps.

~ ~ эпиляции ресниц ophth: cilia forceps.

пинцирование (пинцировка) agr bot: nipping, pinching.

пиодермия pyoderma.

пион bot: peony (Paeonia).

пионефроз path: pyonephrosis.

пионефрозный pyonephrotic.

пиопневмоторакс path: pyopneumothorax.

пиоррея path: pyorrhea.

пиосальпинкс gyn: pyosalpinx.

пиоцианин imm: pyocyanin.

пиперазин pharm: piperazine.

пипетка pipette.

~ с тормозом braking pipette.

пиповые (сем.) zool: Pipidae family (batrachians).

пипчак vet: capped hock.

пипы = пиповые.

пирамида pyramid.

пирамидальный pyramidal.

пирамидка anat: pyramis, see каменистая часть.

пирамидки почки anat: renal pyramids.

пирамидный путь anat: corticospinal tract.

пирамидон pharm: pyramidon, aminopyrine.

пиреноид bot: pyrenoid.

пиреномицетные лишайники bot: Pyrenolichenes.

пирономицеты bot: pyrenomycetes (Pyrenomycetes).

пиретрин pyrethrine.

пиретрум pharm: pellitory, pyrethrum; bot: see ромашка далматская.

~ девичий = девичья трава.

пиридоксин pyridoxine.

пириметамин pharm: pyrimethamine.
пиримидин pyrimidine.
пиритиамин chem: pyrithiamine.
пировиноградная кислота pyruvic acid.
пируват chem: pyruvate.
писк cheep, peep, chirp.
пискнуть p. a. of пищать.
писсуар san: urinal.
пистия bot: water lettuce (Pistia).
писчая судорога neur: penman's spasm, writer's cramp, chirospasm.
~ ~ у машинисток neur: typist's cramp.
писчий спазм = писчая судорога.
писчик recorder; recording pen.
письменник красивый bot: queen of orchards (Grammatophyllum speciosum).
питание 1. diet, see пища; 2. nutrition, nourishment, nourishing, alimentation.
~ волос trichotrophy.
~ зародыша embryotrophy.
~ растений plant nutrition.
~ через желудочный свищ gastrostogavage, gastrogavage.
~ ~ прямую кишку rectal alimentation.
питательная артерия anat: nutrient artery.
~ среда lab: culture medium, nutrient m.
~ ~ из печени bact: liver medium.
питательное вещество nutrient.
питательность nutritive value, nutritional v.
питательные соли bot: manurial salts.
питательный nutritious, nutritional, nutrient, nutritive, nourishing, alimentary, pabular.
~ бульон bact: nutrient broth.
~ желток embr: food yolk.
~ кубик bot: soil block.
~ полип zool: feeding polyp.
~ раствор bot: hydroponics solution.
~ сосуд anat: nutrient vessel.
питать feed, nourish, diet; supply.
питаться feed on; prey upon.
питающая ткань nurse tissue.
питающий полип feeding polyp.
~ пузырёк embr: trophoblast.
питающийся грибками mycetophagous.
~ донным материалом zool: bottom-feeding.
~ древесиной wood-eating, xylophagous.
~ животной пищей zoophagous.
~ живыми организмами biophagous.
~ кровью zool: sanguivorous.
~ личинками zool: larvivorous.
питающийся микробами microbivorous.
~ молоком galactophagous.
~ неорганическими веществами prototrophic.
~ одним видом пищи monophagous.
~ падалью zool: necrophagous, scavenger, carrion-eating, saprophagous.
~ растительной пищей zool: phytophagous.
~ рыбами piscivorous.
~ улитками snail-eating.
питомник (для молодых устриц) ambulance.
питоцин pitocin.
питуитрин pharm: pituitrin.
питьевая вода drinking water, potable water.
пиурия path: pyuria.
пихта bot: fir (Abies).
~ бальзамическая balsam fir, fir-balsam (A. balsamea, Mill.)
~ канадская see пихта бальзамическая.
~ серебристая silver fir (A. picea).
пихтовый bot: firry.
пища food, foodstuff, nutriment, pabulum.
~ богатая белками high protein diet.
пищать cheep, peep, chirp.
пищеварение digestion.
пищеварительная вакуоль zool: digestive vacuole, food v.
~ полость stomach cavity.
~ трубка anat: digestive tube.
пищеварительное средство digestant.
пищеварительный лейкоцитоз hem: digestive leukocytosis.
~ сок digestive juice.
~ тракт digestive tract, alimentary canal.
пищевая аллергия food allergy.
~ кашица (в желудке) contents of the stomach, chyme.
~ лихорадка path: food fever.
~ химия food chemistry.
~ цепь bio: food chain.
пищевод anat: gullet, esophagus.
пищеводный esophageal.
пищевое животное food animal.
~ отравление food poisoning, bromatotoxism.
~ растение food plant.
пищевой комок alimentary bolus.
~ объект bio: food object, food form, food item.
~ химик food chemist.
~ цикл food cycle.
пищевые отношения zool: food relation.
~ потребности food requirements, nutritional requirements.

пищевые продукты foodstuff, victuals.
~ ресурсы zool: food supply.
пищуха zool: pika, cony, little chief hare (Ochotona princeps, etc.)
*~-сверчок orn: wall creeper (Certhia familiaris).
пищухи (сем.) zool: pikas, cony family (Ochotonidae).
пиэлит path: pyelitis.
пиэлитный pyelitic.
пиэмия path: pyemia.
пиявица criocerid (Lema melanopa).
пиявка zool: leech, hirudinean (Hirudo)
~ венгерская leech (H. officinalis).
~ медицинская medicinal leech (Hirudo medicinalis).
~ немецкая = п. медицинская.
~ обыкновенная = п. венгерская.
пиявки (кл.) zool: leeches (Hirudinea).
пиявочка zool: young leech.
плавательная нога zool: swimming leg, pleopod.
~ ножка zool: swimmeret.
плавательный zool: natatory, natatorial.
~ колокол zool: swimming bell, nectophore, nectocalyx.
~ пузырь zool: air bladder, swim(ming) bladder, fish sound.
плавающее помутнение ophth: floating opacity.
плавающие (надотр.) orn: natants, penguins (Natantas), see пингвины 1.
плавающий лист bot: pad.
плавник 1. zool: flipper, fin, flapper; 2. flotsam (material).
плавниковый луч zool: fin-ray.
плавникообразная мембрана (хвоста церкарий) membranous ala.
плавунец entom: diving beetle (Dytiscidae).
плавунчик orn: phalarope (Phalaropus; Lobipes; Steganopus).
плазма plasma.
~ крови blood plasma.
плазмаген plasmagene.
плазматическая клетка hist: plasma cell.
плазматические (подтип) zool: Plasmodroma.
плазматический фактор hem: plasma factor.
плазмодесмы bio: protoplasmatic connections.
плазмодий 1. hist: plasmodium; 2. zool: Plasmodium (genus of protozoa).
плазмодиофора капустная bot: Plasmodiophora brassicae, Wor.
плазмоид plasmoid.
плазмолемма plasmolemma.
плазмолиз plasmolysis.
плазмолизоваться plasmolyze.
плазмопара bot: Plasmopara (fungus); see also мильдью.
плазмоцид pharm: plasmocide.
плазмоцит hist: plasmocyte.
плакун-трава = дербенник иволистный.
плакучий bot: weeping, pendant, drooping.
пламенные клетки zool: flame cells, flame bulb (in Turbellaria).
пламя flame.
планария zool: planarian.
планктер plankter.
планктический planktonic.
планктолог planktologist.
планктон plankton.
*~ солоноватых вод hypalmiroplankton.
~ текучих вод bio: potamoplankton.
планктонная диатомея bot: plankton diatom (alga).
~ икра drifting eggs.
~ сетка plankton net.
планктонное животное zooplankton organism.
~ растение phytoplankter.
планктонные бактерии и грибы saproplankton.
планктонный planktonic.
планктонологический planktological.
планктоноядное животное plankton feeder.
планктоноядный plankton-eating.
пластида bot: plastid.
пластика surg: plastic operation, -plasty.
~ век ophth: tarsoplasty, blepharoplasty.
~ влагалища gyn: vaginoplasty, elytroplasty.
~ волчьей пасти uraniscoplasty.
~ глаза ophthalmoplasty.
~ губы labioplasty, cheiloplasty.
~ желудка gastroplasty.
~ кисти руки chiroplasty.
~ кожи dermatoplasty.
~ кости osteoplasty.
~ лба metopoplasty.
~ лица facioplasty.
~ матки uteroplasty.
~ мочеиспускательного канала urethroplasty.
~ мочеточника ureteroplasty.
~ мужского члена penoplasty, phalloplasty.
~ мышц myoplasty.
~ наружного уха otoplasty.
~ нёба palatoplasty.
~ носа rhinoplasty.
~ ~ и губы rhinocheiloplasty.
~ половых органов genitoplasty.
~ промежности perineoplasty.
~ прямой кишки proctoplasty.
~ ~ кишки и мочевого пузыря proctocystoplasty.
~ рта stomatoplasty.

пластика сустава arthroplasty.
~ суставной связки syndesmoplasty.
~ сухожилия tenoplasty.
~ трахеи tracheoplasty.
~ фасции fasciaplasty.
~ хряща chondroplasty.
~ челюсти gnathoplasty.
~ черепа cranioplasty.
~ шейки матки tracheloplasty.
~ щеки maloplasty.
~ ~ и губы genycheiloplasty.
пластинка plate, lamina, lamella.
~ гребешка orn: comb blade.
~ гриба bot: gill.
~ для выстукивания = плессиметр.
~ из кровяного агара bact: blood-agar plate.
~ ~ лакмусового агара bact: litmus-agar plate.
~ крыла entom: wing membrane.
~ листа bot: leaf blade.
~ позади рта metastoma (in crustacea).
~ четверохолмия anat: lamina quadrigemina.
~ Энгельмана hist: lateral disk.
пластинниковые (сем.) bot: fungi Agaricaceae.
пластиножаберные (подкл.) ichth: elasmobranches (Elasmobranchii, Plagiostomi), see акуловые.
пластинчатая разводка = посев на чашки.
~ структура lamellosity.
пластинчатожаберное zool: lamellibranch.
пластинчатожаберные (кл.) zool: lamellibranches (Lamellibranchiata, Bivalva), see двустворчатые.
~ (подкл.) = пластиножаберные.
~ моллюски (кл.) zool: bivalved mollusks (Lamellibranchiata, Pelecypoda, Bivalva).
пластинчатожаберный моллюск lamellibranch mollusk.
пластинчатоклювые orn: anserines, geese, swans, ducks (Anseres).
пластинчатость lamellosity.
пластинчатоусые entom: lamellicorns (Scarabaeidae).
пластинчатый laminated, lamelliferous.
~ гриб bot: agaricaceous fungus, agaric, gill-bearing fungus (Agaricini).
~ усик entom: lamellate antenna.
пластическая операция = пластика.
~ хирургия plastic surgery, see also пластика.
пластичность plasticity.
пластрон zool: plastron.
пластырная мыщца головы anat: splenius capitis muscle.
~ ~ шеи splenius cervitis, s. colli.
пластырь plaster.
~ стручкового перца pharm: capsicum plaster.
плата за больничное лечение hospital fee.
платан bot: sycamore, buttonwood, plane-tree (Platanus).
~ американский American plane-tree (P. occidentalis).
~ восточный eastern plane-tree, London plane (P. orientalis).
~ европейский = п. восточный.
платановые (сем.) bot: plane-tree family (Platanaceae).
платигастеры (сем.) entom: Platygasteridae.
платизма anat: platysma (myoides).
платиновая игла lab: platinum needle.
~ петля lab: platinum loop.
платная койка pay bed.
платный больной pay patient.
плаун bot:lycopodium, club moss (Lycopodium). Cf. равноспоровые плауны, разноспоровые плауны.
~ аптечный = п. булавовидный.
~ булавовидный common club moss, running club moss, coral evergreen, staghorn evergreen, buckhorn, wolf's claws, (L. clavatum).
~ сплюснутый running evergreen, trailing e., ground pine, ground cedar Christmas green, creeping jenny (L. complanatum).
~ темный tree club moss, flat-branch ground pine, running pine (L.obscurum).
плаунное семя = плауновое с.
плауновое "семя" bot: lycopod spores.
плауновые (кл.) bot: clubmoss class (Lycopodiinae).
~ (пор.) bot: clubmoss order (Lycopodiales).
~ (сем.) bot: clubmoss family (Lycopodiaceae).
плаунообразные bot: Lycopsida.
плацента placenta, sporophore.
плацентарное млекопитающее = высшее м.
плацентарные zool: placentals (Placentalia), see высшие звери.
плацентарный шум obstet: placental souffle.
плацентное млекопитающее = высшее м.
плащ mantle, see also мантия.

плащ мозга anat: pallium.
плащевой отдел мозга = надсегментарный отдел мозга.
плащеносная акула ichth: Chlamydoselachus anguineus.
плева anat: membrane, pellicle.
плевательница spitoon, cuspidor, sputum cup.
плевел bot: darnel (Lolium).
~ английский = п. многолетний.
~ многолетний common darnel, perennial ryegrass, English bluegrass (L. perenne).
плевра pleura.
плевральная жидкость pleural fluid.
плевральный мешок anat: pleural sac.
плеврэктомия surg: pleuretomy.
плеврит path: pleurisy.
плевробранхия zool: pleurobranchia.
плеврококк bot: Pleurococcus (epiphyte algae).
плевросигма bot: Pleurosigma (algae).
плезиозавры (подкл.) zool: Plesiosauria (extinct reptiles).
плейокотилия bot: pleicotyly.
плейрит entom: pleuron.
плейстон pleuston.
плейстонный pleustonic.
плектасковые грибы bot: Plectascales.
племенная кобыла breed mare.
племя tribe.
~ свиней pig breed.
плёнка film.
~ зерна bot: hull, husk.
~ прицветника bot: bract husk.
плёнкоцветные = пленчатоцветные.
плёночка bot: lodicule. [palea.
плёнчатая чешуя bot: membranaceous
плёнчатоцветные (пор.) bot: Glumiflorae, Graminales (order).
плеопода zool: swimmeret, pleopod.
плеоцитоз pleocytosis.
плероцеркоид helm: pleurocercoid, sparganum.
плесень bot: mold.
плеск clapotage.
плесневелость moldiness, mustiness.
плесневение molding.
плесневый moldy, musty.
~ грибок bot: mold fungus (Mucor, Aspergillus, Penicillium, Oidium).
плессиметр plate for plessesthesia.
плетевой побег bot: running vine.
плеть bot: runner.
плеуропогон bot: semaphore grass (Pleuropogon).
плечевая артерия anat: brachial artery
плечевая вена anat: brachial vein.
~ кость anat: humerus, shoulder bone.
~ мышца anat: brachialis (anticus) muscle. [humeralis.
~ поперечная жилка entom: vena
плечевое предлежание obstet: shoulder presentation.
~ сплетение anat: brachial plexus, brachiplex.
плечевой scapular.
~ нерв anat: brachial nerve.
~ отросток anat: acromion.
~ пояс anat: shoulder girdle, pectoral girdle, limb girdle.
~ сустав anat: shoulder joint.
плече-локтевой сустав anat: humerolunar joint.
~ -лучевая мышца anat: brachioradialis muscle, supinator longus.
~ -лучевой сустав anat: humeroradial joint.
плеченогие zool: brachiopods (Brachiopoda).
плечо anat: shoulder.
плешивость baldness, acomia, alopecia, calvities, see облысение.
плешивый bald, etc., cf. плешивость.
плимутрок agr orn: Plymouth rock.
плиоценовая флора Pliocene flora.
пловучесть buoyancy.
плод fruit; embr: fetus; bot: carp.
~ бобовых bot: pod.
~ кофейного дерева bot: coffee drupe.
~ паслёновых bot: solanberry.
~ при аборте gyn: abortive fetus, aborted fetus, abortus.
~ шиповника bot: rose hip.
плодик bot: mericarp.
плодить(ся) multiply, propagate.
плодная оболочка embr: fetal membrane.
плодный in crop.
~ мешок fetal sac, gestation sac.
~ покров embr: fetal integument.
плодовая ветвь bot: fruit spur.
~ почка bot: fruit bud.
плодовед bot: pomologist.
плодовитость fecundity, fertility.
плодовитый prolific, fecund.
плодовод fruit grower.
плодоводство bot: fruit-growing (industry), pomology.
плодовое дерево bot: fruit tree.
~ ложе bot: torus.
плодовые культуры bot: horticultural crops.
плодовый сад bot: orchard.
плодожорка fruit moth, tortricid moth (Totricidae); see also листовёртка.

плодожорка восточная персиковая oriental fruit moth (Laspeyresia molesta).
~ гороховая pea moth (L. dorsana, L. nigricana).
~ грушевая pear m. (Carpocapsa pyrivora).
~ желудёвая acorn m. (Laspeyresia splendana).
~ льняная flax-plant m. (Phalonia epilinana).
~ орешниковая nut m. (Laspeyresia amplana).
~ сливовая plum m. (L. funebrana).
~ сосновая European pine shoot m. (Evetria margoratana).
~ яблоневая lesser apple-worm (Laspeyresia pomonella); codling moth (Carpocapsa pomonella).
плодоизгнание gyn: causing abortion.
плодолистик bot: carpel.
плодоложе bot: fruit receptacle.
плодоножка bot: fruit-stalk, carpophore, pedicle, stem.
плодоносец bot: fruit-body.
плодоносить bot: bear fruit, fructify, teem.
плодоносный bot: fruit-bearing, fructificative, fruiting.
плодоносящая ветвь bot: fruit spur.
~ стадия fruiting stage.
плодоносящее дерево bearing(-age) tree.
плодоносящий = плодоносный.
~ побег bot: fruiting cane.
плодоношение bot: fruit bearing, fructification, fruiting.
плодородие fecundity, fertility, prolificacy, fruitfulness.
плодосумчатые грибы bot: Caproasci.
плодоядные летучие мыши (подотр.) zool: frugivorous bats (Megachiroptera).
плодоядный frugivorous, fruit-eating.
плодуха bot: fruit spur.
плодушка bot: fruit spur.
плодущий гибрид fertile hybrid.
плоёный с веерообразными складками bot: plicate.
пломба odont: filling.
пломбирование odont: filling.
пломбированный зуб filled tooth.
пломбировать odont: fill (the tooth).
плоская грудь flat chest.
~ капсюля rad: planar implant.
~ кость flat bone.
~ рыба flatfish.
~ стопа orthop: flat foot.
плоские черви zool: flatworms, platyhelminthes (1. phylum Platodaris; 2. subphylum Platyhelminthes).
плоский вкус blank taste (of a wine).
~ персик bot: peen-to (Persica platicarpa).
~ сустав anat: gliding joint.
~ таз obstet: flat pelvis, platypelloid pelvis.
~ эпителий hist: squamous epithelium.
плоскогрудость path: flattening of the chest.
плоское копыто vet: flat hoof.
плоскоклеточный hist: planocellular.
~ рак path: squamous cell carcinoma.
плоскоореховатая структура bot: flat nutty structure.
плоскостопие orthop: flatfoot, pes planus.
плоскотел сиамский entom: grain beetle Lophocateres pusillus.
плоскотелка entom: square-necked grain beetle (Cathartus gemellatus); foreign g. b. (Ahasverus advena).
плоскоход грушевый entom: pear-twig beetle (Xyleborus pyri).
~ непарный shot-borer beetle (Xyleboros dispar).
плотва ichth: roach (Rutilus rutilus).
~ аральская Aral-Lake roach (Rutilus r. aralensis).
~ сибирская Siberian r. (R. r. lacustris).
плотная часть протоплазмы hist: plasmagel.
плотно прижатый adpressed.
~ прилегающий adpressed.
плотнорогие = олени.
плотность density.
плотный клубок hist: close skein.
плотоядное zool: carnivore.
плотоядные (отр.) zool: flesh-eaters (Carnivora).
~ жуки (подотр.) entom: carnivorous beetles (Adephaga).
*плотоядный zool: carnivorous.
~ зуб zool: carnassial tooth.
плохо вправляющийся вывих surg: recurrent dislocation.
~ очищенный (о губке) gurried.
плохое питание malnutrition.
~ самочувствие discomfort, ill-feeling.
~ усвоение malassimilation.
площадка для воздушных ванн platform for air baths.
площица = вошь лобковая.

плумбаго = свинцовка.
плювиалис orn: golden plover (Pluvialis).
плюска bot: cupule, cup.
плюсна anat: metatarsus, instep; zool: cannon, shank.
плюсневая кость anat: metatarsal bone (any of 5).
плющ канадский bot: yellow parilla, common moonseed (Menispermum canadense); see also
~ обыкновенный English ivy (Hedera helix).
плющелистный bot: ivy-leaved.
плюющая кобра zool: spitting cobra, black-necked c. (Naja nigricollis).
плянера bot: water elm (Planera aquatica).
пляска св. Витта = хорея.
плясовое бешенство neur: dancing disease.
плятионихус zool: squeaker crab (Platyonichus ocellatus).
*плаутус orn: garefoul (Plautus impennis).
пневая поросль bot: stump offshoots.
пневматическая кость orn: pneumatic bone.
пневматический отметчик av med: pneumatic marker, pneumatic pointer.
пневматофор float.
пневматоцеле path: pneumatocele, pneumo(no)cele.
пневмо- pneumo-.
пневмограмма pneumogram.
пневмограф pneumograph.
пневмококк pneumococcus.
пневмокониоз pneumonoconiosis.
пневмомассаж air massage.
пневмонический path: pneumonic.
пневмония path: pneumonia.
пневмоперитонеум pneumoperitoneum.
пневмосклероз int: pneumosclerosis.
пневмотахограмма pneumotachogram.
пневмоторакс pneumothorax.
пневмоэнцефалография pneumoencephalography.
пнейматофор zool: pneumatophore, air sac, float.
пнеймо- pneumo-.
пнеймокониоз = пневмокониоз.
пнеймотиф infect: pneumotyphoid.
по желанию ad lib(itum), as desired.
~ отцовской линии patrilineal.
побег bot: shoot, burgeon, offset, spear, provine, wand, see also
~ от корня bot: root sucker, rootstock, tiller.
~ прироста bot: continuance shoot, terminal shoot.
~ хмеля hopbind, hopbine.
побеговьюн зимующий entom: European pine-shoot moth (Evetria buoliana).
~ летний Evetria duplana.
~ смолёвщик resin gall-moth (Evetria resinella).
~ срединный почки Evetria turionana.
побелить p. a. of белить.
побитость (плода) agr bot: bruise (of a fruit).
побитый морозом bot: frostbitten.
побледнение pallor.
~ ткани blanching of tissue.
побледнеть p. a. of бледнеть.
побочная пластинка hist: lateral disk.
~ ~ Энгельмана Engelmann's lateral disk.
побочное действие side effect, by-effect.
побуждение stimulus, stimulation, motivation, motive, incentive.
побурение browning.
~ цитрусовых phytp: lemon brown rot.
повадка zool: habits, habitus.
повальная болезнь epidemic.
повальный выкидыш vet: epizootic abortion.
поваренная соль common salt, table s.
поведение behavior.
поведенческий behavioral, behavioristic.
поверхностная вена руки, внутренняя anat: basilic vein.
~ ~ руки, наружная anat: cephalic vein.
~ плёнка surface film.
поверхностное дыхание shallow breathing.
~ изъязвление erosion.
~ нагноение path: fester.
~ охлаждение surface cooling.
~ распространение surface spread.
поверхностные рыбы surface fish.
поверхностный опоясывающий слой (мозга) anat: molecular layer, stratum zonale cerebri.
~ сгибатель пальцев anat: flexor digitorum sublimis.
поверхность (зуба) обращенная к языку anat: lingual surface.
повий = дереза.
повилика bot: dodder, love-vine, strangle weed (Cuscuta).
~ американская = п. полевая.
~ клеверная large-grained dodder (C. trifolii, Bab. & Gibs).
~ крупная люцерновая large alfalfa d. (C. indecora, C. approximata, Bab.)
~ крупносемянная = п. клеверная.

повилика льняная flax dodder (Cuscuta epilinum, Weihe).
~ люцерновая alfalfa d. (C. cupulata).
~ полевая greater d. (C.arvensis).
~ тимьянная lesser d., clover d. (C. epithymum, Murr.)
повислый лист bot: depressed leaf.
повитель = вьюнок полевой.
повой bot: bindweed (Convolvulus).
~ бирюзовый = смилакс ланцетовидный.
~ заборный hedge b., wild morning [glory (C. sepium).
повойничек bot: waterwort (Elatine).
повойничковые (сем.) bot: waterwort family (Elatinaceae).
поворачивающий голову cephalogyric.
поворот turn(ing), version.
~ кнаружи supination.
~ на головку obstet: cephalic version.
~ ~ ножку obstet: podalic version.
~ ~ ягодицы obstet: pelvic version.
~ по Бракстон Хиксу obstet: Braxton Hicks version.
повреждение lesion, injury, damage.
~ излучением radiation injury.
~ нерва nerve injury.
~ от ожога burning lesion.
~ при аборте gyn: abortion injury.
~ слухового нерва acoustic nerve lesion.
~ спины back injury.
~ сухожилия tendon injury.
~ черепа cranial injury.
повседневные наблюдения daily observations.
повторная ампутация surg: reamputation.
~ операция surg: reoperation.
~ перегонка redistillation.
повторное вливание reinfusion.
~ исследование re-examination.
~ оплодотворение superfetation.
~ освидетельствование re-examination.
~ пережевывание пищи path: rechewing of food.
~ поступление (в больницу) readmission, re-entry.
~ скрещивание genet: recrossing.
повторный больной second-admission patient (also 3rd, 4th, etc. admission).
~ вывих surg: redislocation, recurrent dislocation.
повышение вязкости hem: hyperviscosity.
~ кровяного давления rise in blood pressure.
~ сопротивляемости imm: epiphylaxis.
~ температуры temperature rise.

повышенная возбудимость path: erethism.
~ деятельность overactivity, hyperactivity, superactivity.
~ ~ блуждающего нерва path:vagotonia.
~ ~ щитовидной железы path: hyperthyroidation.
~ ~ эндокринных желез path: hypercrinia, hyperendocrinism.
~ кислотность superacidity.
~ острота hyperacuity.
~ подвижность hypermotility.
~ секреция hypersecretion.
~ ~ инсулина hyperinsulinism.
~ токсичность hypertoxicity.
~ утомляемость undue fatigability.
~ функция hyperfunction.
~ ~ щитовидной железы hyperthyroidism.
~ чувствительность hypersensitivity, hypersusceptibility, hyperesthesia.
~ ~ к холоду hypercryalgesia.
~ щелочность hyperalkalinity.
повышенно радостное настроение psych: euphoria.
повышенное возбуждение overexcitement.
~ давление hypertension, high (blood) pressure.
~ настроение (болезненное) psych: elevated mood, (abnormal) high spirits, euphoria.
~ питание overnutrition.
~ раздражение overirritation; overstimulation.
~ содержание воздуха abnormal(ly high) presence of air, emphysema.
~ ~ холестерина в крови metab: hypercholesterolemia.
повышенный иммунитет hyperimmunity.
~ обмен веществ hypermetabolism.
~ рефлекс overactive reflex, reinforced reflex.
повязка band, bandage; sling.
~ Карлейля Carlisle dressing.
~ с мазью salve dressing.
поганка 1. orn: grebe (Colymbidae); 2. bot: toadstool, amanita.
~ бледная bot: death cup (Amanita phalloides, Fr.)
~ весенняя bot: destroying angel (Amanita, Armillaria vera).
поганки 1. bot: see поганки; 2. orn: grebes (Colymbi).
поги porgy (Calamus bajonado; C. catamus; Chaetodipterus faber; etc.)
погибать perish, die, succumb.

погибший от холода cold-killed.
поглаживание effleurage, stroking (movement).
поглотитель углекислоты carbon dioxide absorbent. [capacity.
поглощающая способность absorbing
поглощение absorption, intake, uptake.
~ кислорода oxygen intake.
погоныш orn: rail, marsh fowl (Porzana porzana). Cf. пастушки.
пограничный невроз borderline neurosis. [sympathicus.
~ симпатический ствол anat: truncus
погребальщик undertaker, mortician, funeral counsellor.
погребение burial, interment.
погребная гниль storage rot.
погремок bot: yellow rattle, rattlebox (Rhinanthus, R. crista-galli).
погружаться submerge.
погружение immersion.
~ под воду submergence.
погружённое растение submerged weed.
погружённый submersed, submerged.
погружная ванна plunge bath.
погружной шов surg: buried suture, sunk suture.
под головкой anat: subcapital.
~ кожей (живущий) zool: cuticolous.
подавленное настроение psych: depression, state of dejection; blues.
подавленность = подавленное настроение.
подавляющая иммунность epistatic
подагра gout, podagra. immunity.
подагрическая боль gouty pain.
~ конституция gouty habit.
~ почка gouty kidney.
подагрический gouty, podagral.
~ диатез goutiness.
подагрическое отложение gouty depo-
подбел = андромеда. sit.
подберёзовик bot: edible mushroom Boletus versipellus, Bull.
подбирать (пищу) zool: scavenge.
подблоковый нерв anat: infratrochlear nerve.
подбородок anat: chin, mentum.
подбородочная ость anat: mental spine, genial tubercle.
подбородочно-подъязычная мышца anat: geniohyoid muscle.
~ -язычная мышца anat: genioglossus, geniohyoglossus.
подбородочное возвышение anat: mental protuberance.
подбородочный anat: mental, genial.
подбугровая область anat: hypothalamus, subthalamic region.
~ часть (промежуточного мозга) = подбугровая область.
подвергаться be subjected to. ся.
подвергнуться p. a. of подвергать-
подверженность susceptibility (to), liability, predisposition.
подверженный susceptive (to), liable, predisposed.
подвешивание за голову orthop: cephalic suspension.
подвешивающая повязка surg: suspensory sling. [binder.
~ ~ для женских грудей mammary
~ шина surg: suspension splint.
подвздошная артерия anat: iliac
~ кишка anat: ileum. artery.
~ кость anat: ilium, flank bone.
~ мышца anat: iliacus.
~ ость anat: iliac spine.
~ ямка anat: iliac fossa, f. iliaca.
подвздошно-бедренная связка anat: iliofemoral ligament.
~ -гребешковое возвышение anat: iliopectinal eminence.
~ -крестцовое сочленение anat: sacro-iliac joint. [artery.
~ -ободочная артерия anat: ileocolic
~ -паховой нерв anat: ilioinguinal nerve. [tric nerve.
~ -подчревный нерв anat: iliohypogas-
~ -поясничная артерия anat: iliolumbar artery.
~ ~ мышца anat: iliopsoas muscle.
~ ~ связка anat: iliolumbar ligament.
~ -седалищный anat: iliosciatic.
~ -слепокишечная заслонка anat: iliocecal valve.
подвздошный anat: iliac, ilial.
~ гребень anat: iliac crest, cresta iliaca.
подвид bio: subspecies.
подвижная клетка для размножения hist: swarmer.
~ печень (почка и т.п.) path: floating liver (kidney, etc.)
подвижное растение mobile plant.
подвижной столик mcscop: mechanical stage. [portability.
подвижность mobility, motility; trans-
~ глазного яблока eyeball mobility.
подвижный на своём основании bio: evertible.

подвижный хрящ path: floating cartilage.
подвисочная ямка anat: fossa infratemporalis.
подвисочный гребень anat: infratemporal crest.
подводное опыление bot: hydrophilous pollination.
подводный underwater, subaquatic, submarine.
подвой bot agr: rootstock, matrix, tree stock.
подвывих surg: subluxation, semiluxation.
подглоточник entom: hypopharynx.
подглоточный узел entom: subesophageal ganglion.
подголовник av med: head rest.
подгон bot agr: second growth, undergrowth.
подготовительное лечение preparatory treatment.
*подгрудок zool: gill (in a bull).
подгрызающий червь = гусеница совки озимой.
поддающийся анализу analyzable.
поддерживающая клетка hist: sustentacular cell.
~ связка (члена, яичника) anat: suspensory ligament (of penis, ovary).
поддерживающие клетки hist: prop cells.
поддержка support, prop.
поддиафрагмальный anat: subphrenic, subdiaphragmatic.
поддуговая ямка anat: subarcuate fossa.
подёнка entom: Mayfly (Ephemeroptera); green drake (Ephemera vulgata).
подёнки (отр.) entom: Mayflies (Ephemeroptera, Agnatha).
подергивание twitching.
подергивать(ся) twitch.
поджаберный subbranchial.
поджелудочная железа anat: pancreas.
~ секреция pancreatic secretion.
поджелудочно-двенадцатиперстная артерия anat: pancreaticoduodenal artery.
поджелудочный anat: pancreatic.
~ сок pancreatic juice.
поджилки hock (of a horse).
подземный побег bot: subterranean shoot, underground shoot.
подкаменщик ichth: bullhead (Cottus gobio).
~ сибирский Siberian b. (C. sibiricus).
подкаменщиковые (сем.) ichth: bullheads (Cottidae).
подкидыш ped: foundling.
подкислить p. a. of подкислять.
подкислять acidify.
подкл. = подкласс.
подкладное судно san: bedpan.
подкласс bio: subclass.
подклювье orn: mandible.
подключичная артерия anat: subclavian artery.
подключичный anat: subclavian, infraclavicular.
~ ствол anat: trunkus subclavius (lymphatic).
подковонсовые (сем.) zool: bat family Rhinolophidae.
подковообразная почка path: horseshoe kidney.
подкожная вена бедра, большая anat: vena saphena magna.
~ ~ нижней конечности, большая anat: great saphenous vein, vena saphena magna.
~ ~ нижней конечности, малая small saphemous vein, vena saphena parva.
~ ткань anat: subcutaneous tissue, tela subcutanea, hypodermis.
~ фасция anat: fascia subcutanea.
~ эмфизема path: subcutaneous emphysema.
подкожно hypodermically.
подкожное введение (лекарства) hypodermic administration.
~ впрыскивание hypodermic injection.
~ кровоизлияние path: purpura.
подкожные оводы (сем.) entom: Hypodermatidae.
подкожный hypodermic, subdermal, subcutaneous, cuticulous.
~ жировой слой blubber (of a whale, etc.)
подколенная артерия anat: popliteal artery.
~ область anat: popliteal space.
~ ямка anat: popliteal fossa.
подколенный мускул anat: popliteus.
подколенок hock (of a cow); shank (of a bird).
подколокольная часть zool: subumbrella (of a medusa).
подкопытные zool: Subungulata (extinct)
подкорковое белое вещество anat: subcortical white matter.
подкорковый слой bot: subcortical layer, medullary l., cambium.
подкормка auxiliary nutrition, additional n.
~ пчёл bee feeding.
подкрадывающаяся болезнь insiduous disease.
подкрыльцовая артерия anat: axillary artery.
~ вена anat: axillary vein.
~ впадина = подмышечная в.

подкрыльцовая дуга anat: axillary arch.
~ железа anat: axillary gland.
~ линия (передняя, средняя, задняя) anat: linea axillaris (anterior, media, posterior).
~ складка anat: axillary fold.
~ ямка = подмышечная впадина.
подкрыльцовый нерв anat: axillary nerve, circumflex nerve.
подлежащая слизистая lining mucosa.
подлежащий заявке reportable, obligatory-notice (disease, etc.)
подлесник bot: sanicle, black snakeroot (Sanicula).
подлесок bot: underbrush, undergrowth.
подлихорадочный subfebrile.
подложечная область anat: epigastrium.
~ ямка anat: infrasternal depression, epigastric fossa, scrobiculus cordis.
подлопаточная артерия anat: subscapular artery.
~ мышца anat: subscapularis.
~ ямка anat: subscapular fossa.
подлопаточный нерв anat: subscapular nerve.
подмаренник bot: bedstraw, cleavers (Galium).
~ жёлтый yellow b., our Lady's b. (G. verum).
~ мягкий white b., wild madder (G. mollugo).
~ настоящий = п. жёлтый.
~ цепкий (spring) cleavers, goosegrass, catchweed (G. aparine).
подмышечная впадина (ямка) anat: axilla, armpit.
~ железа anat: axillary gland.
~ линия midaxillary line.
~ областьanat: axillary area.
подмышка = подмышечная впадина.
подниматель заднепроходного отверстия anat: levator ani.
~ прямой кишки anat: levator ani.
поднимающая мышца anat: levator (muscle).
~ нёбо мышца anat: levator veli palatini, levator palati.
подногтевой anat: subungual, hyponychial.
подобный лимфатической железе lymphoglandula-like, limphoid.
подоболочечное пространство anat: subpial space (brain).
подокарповые (сем.) bot: Podocarpaceae.
подопытное животное experimental animal, test animal.
подопытное лицо experimental person, test person.
~ растение test plant.
подорожник bot: plantain, ribwort (Plantago).
~ большой common p., whiteman's foot (P. major).
~ ланцетовидный ribgrass, ripplegrass, English plantain, ribwort plantain (P. lanceolata).
~ песчаный sandwort (P. arenaria, P. indica).
~ приморский seaside plantain (P. maritima).
~ снежный = пуночка.
~ средний hoary p. (P. media)
подорожниковое растение bot: plantaginaceous plant.
подорожниковые (сем.) bot: plantain family (Plantaginaceae).
подорожниколистный bot: plantain-leaved (plantaginifolius).
подосиновик bot: rough-stemmed boletus (Boletus scaber).
подостемовые (сем.) bot: riverweed family (Podostemaceae).
подостем(он) bot: riverweed, waterweed (Podostemum, Michx.)
подостемум = подостемон.
подостная мышца anat: infraspinatus.
~ ямка anat: infraspinous fossa.
подострый subacute.
подотр. = подотряд.
подотряд bio: suborder.
подофил bot: May apple, mandrake (Podophyllum).
подошва anat: sole, vola.
~ (брюхоногих) zool: sole (of gastropods).
~ гидры zool: pedal disk of a hydra.
подошвенная (артериальная) дуга anat: plantar arch.
~ мышца anat: plantaris.
~ связка anat: plantar ligament.
подошвенный апоневроз anat: plantar aponeurosis.
~ рефлекс sole reflex.
подпаутинное пространство anat: subarachnoid space.
подпестичный bot: hypopetalous, hypogynous.
подпищеводный anat: subesophageal, infra-esophageal.
подповерхностный распластанный корень bot: subsurfacial splitted root, tracing root.
подподбородок entom: submentum.
подпор. = подпорядок.
подпороговый раствор subliminal solution.
подпорядок bio: suborder.

подпочва subsoil.
подпрыгивающий пульс int: jerky pulse
подпушек fluff, down, fuzz, lint, delint.
~ на семенах хлопчатника bot: delint.
подразд. = подраздел.
подраздел bio: subdivision.
подращивание growing (for a short time)
подращивать grow (for a short time).
подрод bio: subgenus.
подродовой bio: subgeneric.
подрост 1. bot: earsh, eddish, second growth; low cover; 2. young stock (cattle).
порытый undermined.
подсачивать bot: tap (the tree).
подсвекольник = амарант колосистый.
подсвинок = молодая свинья.
подсев reseeding, interplanting; seeding growth.
подсед 1. vet: malanders; 2. bot: undergrowth.
подсем. = подсемейство.
подсемейство bio: subfamily.
подсемядольное колено bot: mesocotyle, caulicle, hypocotyl.
подсерозный subserous.
подсеять reseed, interplant.
подскорлупная оболочка яйца putamen.
подсластить p. a. of подслащивать.
подслащивать sweeten, edulcorate.
подслизистая оболочка anat: tunica submucosa.
~ ткань anat: submucosa.
подснежник bot: snowdrop (Galanthus).
~ золотой = мать-и-мачеха.
подснежниковые (сем.) bot: amaryllis family (Amaryllidaceae).
подсознание psych: subconsciousness.
подсознательный subconscious.
подсолнечная ржавчина phytp: sunflower rust (Puccinia helianthi).
подсолнечник bot: sunflower (Helianthus).
~ гигантский полуклубневой gigantic sunflower, Indian potato (H. giganteus, var. subtuberosus).
~ кормовой feeding s. (H. annuus).
~ красный red s. (H. multiflorus).
~ межеумок mean s. (H. annus, var. intermedia).
подсосный ягненок agr: teg.
[slashed t.
подсоченное дерево tapped tree,
подсочить p. a. of подсачивать.
подсочка bot: tapping, slashing, turpentining.
подставка stand(ard), support, rest mount(ing), bracket; bot: receptacle.
~ для головы head rest.
подставка для красящихся препаратов lab: staining stand.
~ ~ ног foot rest.
подстилающий lining, basal.
подстилка litter.
подсчет = счет.
~ крови blood count.
подсыхание drying (off).
подтип bio: subphylum.
подтропический subtropical.
подтянутые бока zool: tucked flanks.
подузелковый subnodal.
подура entom: poduran.
подуст ichth: Chondrostoma.
подушечка Pulvillus.
~ ржавчины phytp: rust pustule.
подушечковый entom: pulvillar.
подушечница продолговатая = пульвинария чайная.
[pulvinate.
подушкообразный bot: cushion-shaped,
подчелюстная (слюнная) железа anat: submaxillary gland.
[artery.
подчревная артерия anat: hypogastric
подчревное сплетение anat: hypogastric plexus.
подшёрсток zool: underfur.
подщелачивание chem: alkalizing.
подщелачивать chem: alkal(in)ize.
подъельник = вертляница.
[gland.
подъязычная железа anat: sublingual
~ кость anat: hyoid, os hyoideum, lingual bone.
[gland.
~ слюнная железа anat: sublingual
подъязычно-подбородочный anat: hyomental.
~ -язычная мышца anat: hyoglossus.
подъязычное мясцо anat: caruncula sublingualis.
[glossal.
подъязычный anat: sublingual, hypo-
~ нерв anat: hypoglossal nerve, twelfth cranial nerve.
[lial.
подэндотелиальный anat: subendothe-
подэпендимный anat: subependymal.
поедание eating, devouring; predation.
~ перьев (болезнь птиц) feather-eating.
поедающий ил zool: mud-eating.
поездная болезнь train sickness.
пожелтение yellowing; bot: yellow disease.
пожилой middle-aged, elderly.
~ человек middle-aged man.
пожирающий клетки bio: cytophagous.
поза attitude, posture.
позадиматочная складка anat: rectouterine plica.

позвонок anat:vertebra, spinal bone.
позвоночная артерия anat: vertebral artery.
позвоночник = позвоночный столб.
позвоночное zool: vertebrate.
~ животное vertebrate.
~ отверстие anat: vertebral foramen, foramen vertebrale.
позвоночные zool: vertebrates, back-boned animals (Vertebrata,Craniata), see черепные.
позвоночный anat: vertebral, spinal.
~ столб anat: backbone, vertebral column, spinal c.,columna vertebralis.
поздне-зимний рис late-winter rice.
позднеспелый agr: lately ripening.
поздний плод bot: late fruit, behindhand.
позднонерестующий ichth: late-spawning.
поздноцветущий bot: late-flowering.
поздняя гниль phytp: late blight.
познабливание path: chilliness.
позология med: posology.
позыв к рвоте =
~ на рвоту retching, gag.
поильник feeding cup.
поимка capture.
поиски пищи zool: foraging, searching for food.
пойкилотермный zool: poikilothermic, cold-blooded.
поймать p. a. of ловить.
пойнтер zool: pointer (Canis familiaris avicularius).
пойти в стрелку bot: spear.
показание indication.
~ к операции surg: operative indication
показания эксперта legl: expert testimony.
показано med: indicated.
~ оперативное удаление surgical removal (is) indicated.
показывание demonstration, exhibition, exhibiting, showing.
~ мимо neur: past pointing (in Barani test).
покалывание path: pricking, tingling.
покатые плечи sloping shoulders.
покашливание hacking cough, semicough.
поклёванный pecked (by birds).
покой dormancy.
поколачивание phys-ther: tapping, tapotement; Brit: clapping,claquement.
поколение generation.
покосно-луговая лихорадка vet: leptospirosis.
покоящаяся клетка hist: resting cell.
~ спора bot: resting spore, akinete.
покоящееся состояние resting condition.

покраснение erubescence, reddening, blush.
~ сердцевины дерева phytp: red heartwood.
покров cover, sheath(ing), mantle, blanket, coating; involucre; integument, tegmen, tegmentum, investment.
~ соруса bot: indusium.
~ цветка = околоцветник.
покровитель zool: host.
покровительственная окраска protective coloration, assimilative c.
покровная ткань cover tissue, dermatogen.
покровное стекло lab: cover glass, cover slip.
покровные клетки hist: covering cells, supporting cells, deckzellen.
покровный cover(ing),tegmental, etc.,cf. покров.
покровосеменные (кл.) bot: Chlamydospermatophyta.
покрывало bot: spatha.
покрывальце volva, veil, cup (of a mushroom).
покрывание листвой = облиствение.
покрывать (овцу) tup.
покрытая хитоном куколка entom: obtected pupa.
покрытосемянные bot: angiosperms (Angiospermae).
покрытосемянный bot: angiospermous.
покрытый ареолами areolated.
~ волдырями blistery.
~ жёсткими волосами (или щетинками) hispid.
~ корочкой crusted.
~ кустарником bushy.
~ мелкими шипами spinulate.
~ папулами derm: papuliferous.
~ перьями orn: plumigerous.
~ плотным пушком hoary.
~ пухом downy.
~ пушком pubescent.
~ редкими волосками hispidulous.
~ родимыми пятнами path: nevose.
~ серым пушком canescent.
~ скорлупой (или коркой) crustaceous.
~ сосочками papillate.
~ тонкой пленкой pelliculate.
~ червеобразными полосочками vermiculate.
~ чешуйками lepidote.
~ шерстью wooled, woolen.
~ щетинками hispid, setose.
покрыть p. a. of покрывать.
покрышка covering; anat: tegmentum.
покушение на самоубийство attempted suicide.

пол 1. sex; 2. floor.
полая вена (верхняя, нижняя) anat: vena cava (superior, inferior).
~ стопа path: pes cavum.
полба bot: one-grained wheat, einkorn (Triticum monococcum).
~ настоящая spelt, German wheat, dinkel w. (T. spelta).
полбяное растение bot: speltoid plant.
поле зрения field of vision.
полевая мышь field mouse (Agricola agrarius, Microtus arvalis); meadow mouse (Apodemus agrarius).
полевица bot: bentgrass (Agrostis).
~ белая redtop, silky bentgrass, marsh b., gray hairgrass (A. alba).
волосовидная astoria bent, brown-top grass, Rhode Island bent (A. tenuis, A. capillaris).
~ зимняя silk grass, hairgrass, flyaway grass, ticklegrass (A. scabra).
~ каменистая fiorin (A. stolonifera).
~ нежная = п. волосовидная.
~ обыкновенная fine bent (A.vulgaris).
~ приморская seaside bent, creeping b. (A. maritima).
~ серобурая букетная cloud grass (A. nebulosa, Boiss.)
~ шелковистая = п. белая.
полевицевые (подсем.) bot: bentgrass subfamily (Agrostideae, Kunth).
полёвка обыкновенная = полевая мышь.
~ рыжая bank vole (Evotomys glareolus).
полевое животное field dweller.
полевой воробей = красноголовый в.
~ госпиталь mil: field hospital.
~ лазарет = п. госпиталь.
~ слизень zool: slug Agriolimax agrestis.
полёгший bot: beated down, tumbled.
полемониевые (сем.) bot: polemonium family (Polemoniaceae).
полемониум bot: Greek valerian, Jacob's ladder (Polemonium caeruleum).
поленика bot: arctic dwarf raspberry, plumboy (Rubus arcticus).
ползание "мурашек" neur: formication, paresthesia, creeping sensation.
ползающее животное creeper, crawler, sprawler.
ползающие гребневики (сем.) zool: crawling ctenophores (Platyctenidae).
ползун ichth: Anabas.
ползучая лихорадка path: slow fever.
~ сыпь derm: creeping eruption.
~ язва path: creeping ulcer, serpiginous ulcer.
ползучее растение bot: creeping plant, crawling p., repent p. Cf. стелящееся растение.
ползучий bot: creeping (repens).
~ сорняк bot: crabgrass.
полиартрит path: polyarthritis.
полибласт hist: polyblast.
поливалентная вакцина bact: polyvalent vaccine.
поливное растение agr: irrigated plant.
полигамный polygamous.
полигландулярный polyglandular.
полиглутаминовая кислота polyglutamic acid.
полидипсия path: polydipsia, anadipsia
полиев пузырь zool: Polian vesicle.
поликистозный polycystic.
поликлады = многоветвистые турбеллярии.
поликлиника polyclinic.
полимастия path: polymastia.
полимиксин pharm: polymyxin.
полимикстный bio: polymixic.
полиморфизм polymorphism.
полиморфный polymorphic, polymorphous.
полиневрит polyneuritis, multiple neuritis.
полиневритический психоз polyneuritic psychosis.
полинемида ichth: threadfin (Polynemidae).
полиноида zool: polynoid.
полиомиелит path: polymyelitis.
полиопия ophth: polyop(s)is, multiple vision.
полип zool: polyp, hydranth; path: polyp.
полипедиды zool: Polypedidae (batrachians).
полипептидный polypeptide.
полипид (мшанки) zool: polypide.
полиплоидия polyploidy.
полипнейстическая лопасть zool: polypneusic lobe.
полиповидный polypoid.
полипорус bot: polypore fungi (Polyporus); see also трутовик.
~ берёзовый phytp: birth-tree polypore (P. betulinus, Fries.)
~ киноварный cinnabar p. (P. cinnabarinus).
~ разноцветный yellowish wood rot (P. versicolor).
~ серный sulfur-colored p. (P. sulphureus).
~ шероховатый P. squarrosus, Huds.
полисахарид polysaccharide.
полисерозит path: polyserositis.
полисифония bot: red algae Polysiphonia; P. fibrillosa, etc.

полиспороз polysporosis.
Политцер Politzer.
полиурический polyuric.
полифагия zool: polyphagia.
полифилетический polyphyletic.
полихета entom: bamboo worm (Clymenella torquata).
полихеты = многощетинковые кольчецы.
полихромазия polychromasia.
полихроматофильный эритробласт polychromatophylic erythroblast.
полицейский врач police surgeon.
Полицер Politzer.
полицитемия path: polycythemia.
полиэмбриония entom: polyembryonia.
полковой врач regimental surgeon.
поллардированное дерево pollard tree.
поллиний bot: pollinium.
поллюция physl: pollution, nocturnal emission.
полная клапанная закупорка path: stop valve obstruction.
~ петля bact: loopful.
~ сердечная блокада path: complete heart block.
~ симметрия pansymmetry.
~ синехия ophth: total synechia.
полное дробление embr: total cleavage.
~ цветение bot: full bloom.
~ число лейкоцитов hem: total white [count.
полнокровие plethora. Cf. местное полнокровие.
полнокровный plethoric.
полнота в ушах av med: (feeling of) fullness in the ears.
полный антиген complete antigen.
~ выдох complete exhalation.
~ набор хромосом genet: complete complement of chromosomes.
~ перелом surg: complete fracture.
~ упадок сил prostration.
~ цикл развития entom orn: egg-to-egg cycle.
~ человек fat man.
~ шприц syringeful.
половая болезнь sexual disease.
~ борозда embr: genital furrow.
~ губа = срамная г.
~ железа gonad; germ gland.
~ зрелость = половозрелость.
~ клетка germ cell.
~ неразвитость path: sex infantilism.
~ особь кормидия = гонозоид.
~ охота = течка.
~ психопатия sexual psychopathy.
~ функция sexual function.
половая хромосома genet: sex chromosome.
половое бессилие path: impotence.
~ влечение libido.
~ возбуждение vet: see течка.
~ извращение path: sexual perversion.
~ отверстие zool: porus genitalis.
~ отклонение sexual deviation.
~ размножение sexual reproduction, amphigony, gamogenesis.
~ сношение sexual intercourse, coitus, copulation.
~ удовлетворение (или удовольствие) sexual gratification.
половозрелость puberty, pubescence, eugamy.
половозрелый puberal, pubescent, eugamic; hebetic.
половой sexual, gamic, genital.
~ акт coital act.
~ атрий zool: genital atrium (in worms).
~ бугорок embr: genital tubercle, genital eminence.
~ подбор bio: sexual selection.
~ проток anat: gonaduct.
~ процесс sexual process, sexuality.
~ член anat: penis.
половые органы anat: sex organs, [genitals.
положение position, posture.
~ между пронацией и супинацией semipronation.
~ на животе ventricumbent position.
~ ~ спине dorsal position.
~ плаценты bot: placentation.
~ плода position of the fetus.
~ при камнесечении urol: lithotomy position.
~ с высокоприподнятым тазом surg: high-pelvic position.
положительный геотропизм bot: positive geotropism.
~ результат (заражение) lab: positive take.
~ фототропизм bot: positive phototropism.
полоз zool: racer (snake of genera Zamenis, Elaphe, Coluber, etc.)
поломка breaking (off, away), injury, damage.
полорогие (сем.) zool: hollow-horned fam. (Cavicornia).
полоса band; strip, strap; stripe; streak.
~ поглощения absorption band.
полосатая гиена zool: striped hyena (Hyaena hyaena).
~ мышца anat: striated muscle.

полосатик = рорквал.

полосатое тело anat: corpus striatum, striate body.

полосатый тюлень ribbon seal (Phoca fasciata).

полоска strip, stripe, streak, band, vitta.

~ липкого пластыря adhesive strip, plaster strip.

~ марли strip of gauze.

полоскание 1. gargling (rinsing the pharynx); 2. gargle (solution).

~ для горла throat wash.

~ ~ рта mouth wash.

полоскать (горло) gargle.

полоскун = енот.

полостная жидкость perivisceral fluid.

полостной cavitary.

полость cavity.

~ амниона embr: amniotic cavity.

~ брюшины anat: peritoneal cavity, cavum peritonei.

~ глотки pharyngeal cavity.

~ гортани laryngeal cavity.

~ грудной клетки anat: thoracic cavity.

~ дробления embr: segmentation cavity.

~ жабр zool: marsupium.

~ желудка gastric cavity.

~ матки uterine cavity, cavum uteri.

~ носа anat: nasal cavity.

~ плавательного колокола zool: nectocyst, nectosae.

~ плевры anat: pleural cavity.

~ пульпы odont: pulp cavity

~ рта anat: oral cavity, cavum oris; zool: camerostom (in hydrachnids).

~ сердца anat: heart cavity.

~ сосцевидного отростка anat: mastoid antrum, tympanic antrum (ear).

~ тазобедренного сустава anat: hip-joint cavity.

~ тела body cavity.

~ цирруса cirrus lumen.

полосчатость striation.

полосчатый striped (lengthwise), vittate.

полоть agr bot: weed.

полуагональное состояние semiagonal state, semimoribund state.

полубессознательное состояние dazed condition.

полубессознательный semiconscious.

полуванна half-bath.

полувдох mid-inspiratory position.

полувлажный semihumid.

полуводный semiaquatic.

полувыбой ichth: half-spent.

полувыведение rad: cf. период полувыведения.

полудревесинное волокно bot: metaxylem.

полудревесный zool: semi-arboreal.

полудремотное состояние semidream-like state.

полужесткокрылые = настоящие п.

полужидкий semiliquid.

полузасушливый semiarid.

полузлокачественный path: semimalignant.

полузонтик bot: cyme (inflorescence).

полузонтиковый cymose.

полузонтичный cymose.

полуклетка semicell.

полукоматозный psych: semi-comatose.

полукружная артерия anat: arcuate artery.

полукружной канал semicircular canal (ear).

полукуколка entom: semipupa.

полукустарник bot: subshrub, undershrub.

полулуние crescent.

полулунная кость запястья anat: lunate bone, semilunar bone.

~ складочка anat: semilunar fold.

полулунный клапан anat: semilunar valve.

полумахровый bot: semidouble.

полумера palliative.

полумягкий коралл alcyonarian, false coral.

полунепарная вена anat: hemiazygos vein.

полунепрерывный semicontinuous.

полуночник = козодой.

полуобезьяны zool: lemurs (Prosimiae)

полуостистый bot: semiawned, half-awned.

полупаразит semiparasite.

полуперепончатая мышца anat: semimembranosus muscle.

полупериод half-cycle; rad:half-life.

~ биологического выведения rad: biological half-life.

полуплод bot: half-fruit.

полуполба = эммер.

полупроницаемая перепонка semipermeable membrane.

полупроницаемый semipermeable.

полупух half-down.

полураскрытый erecto-patent (of insect wings).

полурыл ichth: halfbeak, ballyhu (Hemirhamphus).

полурыловые (сем.) ichth: halfbeak fishes (Hemiramphidae).

полусгибание semiflexion.

полускверхедный agr bot:subclavate.

полусогнутый semiflexed.

полусознательный psych:semiconscious.
полусон(ный) subwaking.
полустерильность semisterility.
полусустав anat: hemiarthrosis.
полусухожильная мышца anat: semitendinosus.
полусухожильный anat: semitendinous.
полутвёрдый semihard; semisolid.
полухордовые (подтип) zool:Hemichorda.
получатель recipient.
~ крови blood recipient.
полученные данные 1. data received; 2. findings.
полушарие большого мозга anat: cerebral hemisphere.
~ головного мозга = п. большого мозга.
полушаровидный semiglobular, semispherical.
полушник bot: quillwort (Isoëtes).
полушниковые = расходниковые.
полынь bot: wormwood (Artemisia);see also божье дерево, чернобыльник.
~ горькая wormwood, absinthe, absinthium (A. absinthium).
~ древовидная sagebrush (A. arbuscula)
~ звездчатая beach wormwood, old woman, dusty miller (A. stelleriana).
~ кустарниковая southernwood (A. abrotanum).
~ противоглистная wormseed (Chenopodium anthelminticum, Gray).
~ холодная prairie sagewort, wild sage.
~ цитварная santonica wormwood (A. cinae).
Поль Pol.
пользоваться хорошим здоровьем enjoy good health.
полюс pole.
~ глаза lens pole.
полярная камбала ichth: eel-back flounder (Liopsetta putnami).
~ лисица zool: arctic fox, polar fox, white f. (Alopex lagopus).
~ медуза zool: arctic medusa (Cyanea arctica).
~ треска = сайка.
полярность polarity.
полярные акулы (сем.) ichth:Scymnidae.
полярный медведь = белый м.
помацентрида ichth: demoiselle (Pomacentridae).
помела = грейпфрут.
померанец bot: bitter orange (Citrus aurantium), bigardia.
померанцевая корка pharm:orange peel.
помесный hybrid.
помесь bio: hybrid, blendling, bastard.
помёт zool: 1. shedding(s), dung, droppings, castings; 2. litter, see приплод
помёт хищных животных lesses.
пометка об операции operative note.
помешанный = сумасшедший.
помешательство psych:derangement, insanity.
помешивание stirring.
помещать в больницу hospitalize.
помещение (больного) в больницу hospitalization.
помидор bot: tomato (Solanum lycopersicum).
помогающий assisting, adjuvant,synergist.
помолог bot: pomologist.
помология = плодоводство.
поморник orn: skua (Stercorarius).Cf. чайка.
×поморники (сем.) orn: Stercoracidae.
помощь на дому home service.
помрачение сознания psych: clouding of consciousness, caligation.
помутнение opacification, cloudiness,
~ роговицы ophth: corneal opacity, macula corneae, nebula.
~ стекловидного тела ophth: vitreous opacity.
~ хрусталика ophth: linticular opacity, cataract.
помятость (плода) agr bot: bruise (of a fruit)
понести become pregnant.
понижающий жизнедеятельность apobiotic, depressant.
~ потоотделение adiaphoretic, anaphoretic.
~ тонус antitonic.
понижение слуха hearing depression, impairment of hearing.
~ температуры fall of temperature.
пониженная возбудимость hypoexcitability.
~ деятельность hypoactivity, hypofunction.
~ ~ надпочечных желёз path: hypoepinephry.
~ секреция path: hyposecretion.
~ температура subnormal temperature, lowered temperature.
~ функция hypofunction.
~ ядовитость hypotoxicity.
пониженное давление hypotension.
~ питание undernutrition, subnutrition, undernourishment.
~ потоотделение adiaphoresis.
~ содержание углекислоты в крови metab: acapnia.
пониженный обмен веществ hypometabolism.
пониклый drooping, nodding (ear); see плакучий.
понимание показаний приборов av med: instrument comprehension.
~ текста reading comprehension.

понимание читаемого = п. текста.
понос path: diarrhea, flux.
понтедериевые (сем) bot: pickerelweed family (Pontederiaceae).
понтедерия bot: pickerelweed (Pontederia).
понурость головы vet: drooping of head.
поперечная жилка entom: cross-vein (of the wing).
~ исчерченность cross-striation.
~ кость zool: transversum.
~ мышца живота anat: transversus abdominis.
~ ~ промежности (глубокая, поверхностная) anat: transversus perinei (profundus, superficialis).
~ ободочная кишка anat: transverse colon.
~ пазуха anat: transverse sinus.
~ связка запястья anat: carpi transversum ligament.
~ щель мозга = боковая борозда мозга.
поперечно-горизонтальная ось anat: lateral-horizontal axis.
~ -полосатая мышечная ткань hist: striated muscle tissue.
~ ~ мышца anat: (cross-) striated muscle.
поперечное предлежание obstet: transverse presentation, cross birth.
поперечные височные извилины (мозга) anat: transverse temporal gyri, Heschl's g.
поперечный отросток anat: transprocess, transverse process.
~ разрез surg: transection.
поплавок (водоросли) bot: pneumatocyst (of an alga).
поповник bot: chamomile (Anthemis); see нивяник.
~ кавказский телесноцветный (Pyrethrum carneum).
поползень orn: nuthatch, tree creeper (Sitta).
~ белобрюхий white-breasted n. (S. europaea caesia)
~ -ямщик = п. белобрюхий.
пополнение zool: recruit stock, incoming year class.
поправиться p. a. of поправляться.
поправляться = выздоравливать.
попугаи (сем.) orn: parrot family (Psittacidae)
попугай orn: parrot.
~ длиннохвостый =
~ каролинский parrakeet (Conurus carolinensis).
попугайчик Бурке Bourke's parrakeet.
попугайчики-неразлучники orn: lovebirds (Agapornis).
популяция population.
пор. = порядок.
пора pore.

поражаемость affectability, vulnerability, injury rate.
поражать affect, afflict, injure, involve.
поражение affection, affliction, lesion, injury, involvement.
~ верхушки apical lesion (of a lung).
~ глаз eye lesion.
~ головного мозга cerebral affection.
~ дыхательного аппарата respiratory lesion.
~ желёз adenosis, adenopathy.
~ клапанов сердца valvular heart disease.
~ кости bone affection, osteopathy.
~ лёгких pulmonary affection, lung lesion.
~ лишаём derm vet: licheniasis.
~ молнией lightning stroke.
~ на одной стороне тела hemilesion.
~ нервной системы nervous breakdown.
~ поджелудочной железы pancreatic affection.
~ позвонков spondylopathy.
~ почек kidney lesion, renal impairment.
~ сердечной мышцы myocardial lesion.
~ сердца cardiac failure.
~ сетчатки ophth: retinal lesion.
~ языка glossopathy.
поражённая ткань invaded tissue.
*поражённое гнилью дерево doted tree.
~ растение attacked plant.
поражённый блефаритом ophth: blepharitic.
~ головнёй phytp: smutted.
~ опрелостью derm: intertriginous.
~ отитом otitic.
~ паразитами parasitized.
~ ржавчиной phytp: rusted.
~ сифилисом ven: syphilized.
~ чесоткой derm: scabbed.
поразить p.a. of поражать.
поранение = повреждение, ранение.
пористость porosity, poriness.
пористый porous, poriferous.
поровая трубка zool: foraminal tubule (in sponges).
поровое отверстие zool: foraminal aperture.
поровой канал bot: aperture.
порог болевого ощущения threshold of feeling (ear).
~ раздражения physl: threshold of stimulation.
~ слышимости threshold of audibility.
*пороговый threshold, luminal.
порода agr: breed, stock, race.
порождать beget, engendre, generate; bring into being, bring about, produce.

порождающее пластиду включение клетки plastidome.
порозность = пористость.
порок failure, defect, fault, crack; vice.
~ аортальных клапанов path: aortic valve failure.
~ развития глаза eye malformation.
~ сердца heart failure, cardiac f.
поронотус ichth: dollar fish, pumpkinseed (Poronotus triacanthus).
поросая свинья farrowed sow.
поросёнок zool: piglet, pigling.
~ диких свиней zool: young wildboar.
пороситься zool: farrow (of a sow).
поросль bot: undergrowth, brushwood.
поросость pregnancy (of a sow).
поросячий помёт zool: farrow, pig litter.
пороховой ожог powder burn.
порошистая парша картофеля phytp: powdery scab.
порошица zool: anus (of rotifera).
порошковдуватель pharm: powder blower, pulverflator.
порошок 1. powder (pulverized solid); 2. pharm: (single dose) powder.
~ против насекомых insect powder.
~ против потения ног foot powder.
поррей bot: leek.
портняжная мышца anat: sartorius.
португальская устрица zool: Portuguese oyster (Ostrea angulata).
португальский кораблик zool: Portuguese man-of-war (Physalia).
портулак bot: purslane (Portulaca); common p., "pusley".
~ крупноцветный rose moss (P. grandiflora).
портулаковые (сем.) bot: purslane fam. (Portulaceae).
поручейник bot: water parsnip (Sium).
поручейница bot: brookgrass (Catabrosa. Beauv.)
порфира bot: red algae: laver, slack, limu, amanori, amori (Porphyra).
~ бахромчатая pink laver, slack, sloke, che choy (P. laciniata).
порча 1. spoilage, deterioration, staling; 2. evil spell, evil eye.
порывистое дыхание panting.
порядок 1. bio: order (Ordo); 2. skate.
посадить на диету put on a diet.
посадка на сучок и т.п. entom orn: perching.
~ с торможением av med: arrested landing.
посадочный материал agr bot: stock.
посев bot: seeding, sowing, seed planting; bact: culture, inoculation.
посев испражнений stool culture.
~ крови bact: blood culture.
~ мочи urine culture.
~ на среды inoculation of media.
~ ~ сыворотке seroculture.
~ ~ чашки plate culture, Petri dish c., plating.
~ отделяемого влагалища vaginal culture.
~ штриховым методом streak inoculation.
посевной bot: sown (sativus).
~ материал mcbio: inoculum.
посегментный zool: metameric, segmental.
поселение entom: ecesis.
посещаемость attendance.
посконник bot: thoroughwort, mistflower, joe-pye weed (Eupatorium).
~ горный upland boneset (E. sessilifolium).
~ коноплёвый hemp agrimony (E. cannabinum).
~ прободённый thoroughwort, boneset (E. perfoliatum).
посконь bot: male hemp plant, common hemp.
послабление laxation.
после- post-, after-, see also пост-.
~ еды after a meal, postprandial.
~ полового созревания postpubescent.
~ приёма пищи postcibal.
послебрачный postconnubial.
послевакцинальный энцефалит path: postvaccinal encephalitis.
послеварочное потемнение (картофеля) after-cooking darkening (of potatoes).
послегипнотический posthypnotic.
послегриппозный post-influenza.
послед obstet: placenta, afterbirth.
последействие aftereffect.
последняя причина ultimate cause.
последовые схватки obstet: afterpains, post-partum tormina.
последовый период obstet: placental stage, third s. of labor.
последствие, -ия sequela.
последующая головка obstet: aftercoming head.
~ запись follow-up note.
~ культура bact: subculture.
последующее вкусовое ощущение neur: aftertaste.
~ восприятие neur: afterperception.
~ зрительное ощущение aftervision.
~ кровотечение path: consecutive hemorrhage.
~ лечение aftertreatment.
~ наблюдение follow-up observation.
~ ощущение aftersensation.
~ ~ давления afterpressure.
~ слуховое ощущение neur: afterhearing, aftersound.

последующий звук neur: aftersound.
~ образ afterimage.
~ уход aftercare, aftertreatment.
послежелтушный postictal, posticteric.
послеинфекционный энцефалит path: postinfectious encephalitis.
послекризисные явления path: epicrisis.
послекризисный path: epicritic.
послелихорадочный postfebrile.
посленерестовый ichth: post-spawning.
послеоперативный = послеоперационный. [surgical fever.
послеоперационная лихорадка surg:
послеоперационное лечение surg: postoperative course.
послеоперационный surg: postoperative.
~ уход surg: postoperative care.
послепищеварительный postdigestive.
послеродовая закупорка труб gyn: pueperal tubal occlusion.
послеродовое кровотечение obstet: post-partum hemorrhage.
~ очищение obstet: lochia. [natal.
послеродовой puerperal, postpartum, post-
~ период obstet: puerperium, puerperal
~ психоз puerperal psychosis. |period.
послетифозный posttyphoid.
послетравматический posttraumatic.
послеуборочный agr: postharvest.
послеузловой neur: postganglionic.
посмертное изменение postmortem alteration.
~ разложение postmortem decomposition.
посмертные данные postmortem findings.
посмертный posthumous, postmortal, postmortem, postnecrotic.
пособие по болезни sickness benefit,
пост- post-, see also после-. |sick pay.
постабдомен zool: postabdomen.
постанальный zool: postanal.
постапоплектический postapoplectic.
постганглионарный neur: postganglionic.
постгеморрагическая анемия posthemorrhagic anemia. [mic.
постгипогликемический posthypoglyce-
постгипоксический парадоксальный эффект av med: posthypoxic paradox effect.
постельный больной bed patient.
~ клоп bed bug.
~ режим bedrest.
~ уход bed care.
постенница bot: pellitory, wall cress (Parietaria).
~ лекарственная pellitory-of-the-wall (P. officinalis).

постенносеменные (пор.) bot: Parie-
постенный parietal. |tales, Violales.
~ слой hist: parietal layer (of cells).
постит posthitis.
постконвульсивный postconvulsive.
постлярвальный zool: postlarval.
постментум entom: postmentum.
постнатальный postnatal. [filling.
постоянная пломба odont: permanent
постоянная ткань permanent tissue.
постоянный зуб anat: permanent tooth.
~ катетер urol: indwelling catheter, retention c.
постоять на носках alight on the
пострадавший injured, casualty. |toes.
посттравматическое нарушение posttraumatic personality disorder.
постулат postulate.
поступательное движение (плода) = выступательное д.
поступление admission.
постэмбриональный postembryonic.
пот sweat, perspiration (fluid).
потамопланктон bio: potamoplankton.
потатор = пьяница.
поташник = солянка. [tion, sudation.
потение sweating, perspiring, perspira-
потентность physl: potency.
потеря аппетита loss of appetite, anepithymia.
~ болевого чувства insensibility to
~ в весе weight loss. |pain, analg(es)ia.
~ видовых особенностей despeciation.
~ голоса aphonia.
~ зубов loss of teeth, dedentition.
~ памяти loss of memory, amnesia.
~ речи path: speechlessness, aphasia,
~ сил adinamia. alalia.
~ слуха hearing loss.
~ сознания psych: loss of consciousness, mental blankness.
~ способности писать буквы literal
~ ~ писать слова verbal a. |agraphia.
~ ~ писать фразы amnemonic a.
~ ~ стоять path: astasia.
~ ~ ходить abasia.
~ тактильного чувства atactilia.
~ чувствительности loss of sensation,
потеть sweat, perspire. |anesthesia.
потливость diaphoresis, hidrosis, sweating.
~ (чрезмерная) path: hyper(h)idrosis, hidrorrhea, ephidrosis, sudatoria, sudo-
потница derm: miliaria, |resis.
prickly heat, heat rash.
потовая железа anat: sudoreferous gland,
~ ~ кожи sudoriparous g. |sweat g.

потовый ход anat: sweat duct.
потогонная ванна phys-ther: sweat
bath.
потогонное лечение diaphoretic
treatment, sweat cure. [sudorific.
~ средство diaphoretic, hidrotic,
потогонный diaphoretic, hidrotic,
sudoriferous, sudorific.
потомки progeny, issue; pl. of
потомок.
потомок descendant, offspring.
потомство progeny, offsprings.
потоотделение sweating, secretion of
sweat, perspiration.
потребитель пищи feeder, food consumer.
потребление алкоголя alcohol consump-
~ корма zool: feed intake. tion.
~ пищи food consumption, f. intake. [irement
потребность в кислороде oxygen requ-
потрескивание crepitation, crackling.
потрескивающий хрип crepitant rale.
потроха = внутренности.
*потрошение emboweling, evisceration.
*потрошить agr zool: embowel, gib, paunch,
Потт Pott. eviscerate, gut.
потуги straining (oneself); obstet:
birth pangs.
потужные усилия (во время дефека-
ции straining (at stool), tenesmus.
потускнеть p. a. of тускнеть.
потягивание pulling, tugging.
похмелье hangover, queasiness, postalco-
holic state. Cf. опохмеляться.
походка gait.
~ в виде косьбы mowing gait.
~ косца = п. в виде косьбы.
~ мелкими шажками small step gait.
походные шелкопряды (сем.) entom:
Thaumatopoea. [(unit).
походный госпиталь mil: mobile hospital
похожий на кровь bloodlike. [clinous.
~ на материнскую линию genet: matro-
похоронное бюро funeral bureau.
похороны funeral.
похотник anat: clitoris.
похудание thinning, growing lean.
похудеть p. a. of худеть. [Spadiciflorae.
початкоцветные bot: Spathiloflorae,
початок bot: 1. spadix; 2. ear (of maize).
почвенная вытяжка agr: soil extract.
~ зоология soil zoology.
~ культура lab: soil culture.
~ углекислота soil carbon dioxide.
почвенное насекомое soil insect.
почвенные условия soil environment.

почвенные факторы agr: edaphic factors.
почвенный attr: soil; bio: soil-
почвовед soil scientist. |inhabiting.
почвоведение soil science, edaphology.
почвоистощающая культура agr: soil-
depleting crop.
почвообразование pedogenesis.
*почесуха path: pruritis.
почечка 1. zool: gemmule; 2. bot: budlet.
почечная артерия anat: renal artery.
~ глиста helm: kidney worm.
~ киста path: cystic kidney.
~ колика urol: renal colic.
~ лоханка anat: renal pelvis.
~ пазуха anat: renal sinus.
~ пирамида anat: renal pyramid.
~ чашечка (большая, малая) anat:
renal calyx (major, minor). [genous.
почечного происхождения nephro-
почечное очищение renal clearance.
~ тельце anat: renal unit, nephron.
почечнокаменная болезнь int:
nephrolithiasis.
почечные столбики anat: renal
columns (of Bertin).
~ чешуи bot: bud scales, cataphyll.
почечный 1. anat: renal, nephric; 2. bio:
~ больной nephritic. |gemmaceous.
~ камень urol: renal calculus.
~ отёк renal dropsy.
~ песок urol: renal sand.
~ цилиндр mcscop: renal cast.
почечуйная трава = горец почечуйный. [gemma.
почка 1. anat: kidney; 2. bot: bud, burgeon,
почкование bio: budding, gemmation.
почковая разновидность bot: sport,
bud variation.
почковидный kidney-shaped, reniform,
~ лист bot: kidney-shaped leaf. |nephroid.
~ тазик kidney basin, curved b.
почковый червь смородины = моль
смородинная. [fumiferana).
почкоед entom: spruce budworm (Tortrix
почконосный bot: gemmiferous.
почкообразный = почковидный.
почкосложение bot: praefoliation.
почти беспрерывный subcontinuous.
~ взрослый организм subadult.
~ грушевидной формы subpyriform.
~ древовидный subarborescent.
~ квадратный subquadrate.
~ одинаковой формы plesiomorphic.
~ параллельный subparallel.
~ равный subequal.

почти сердцевидной формы subcordate.
~ сидячий bio: subsessile.
*пощипывание tingling, pickling.
поярок teg wool.
пояс belt, zone.
~ зостеры bot: zosteran belt.
поясковый zool: clitellar.
поясная извилина (мозга) anat: gyrus cinguli.
поясница anat: loin.
поясничная артерия anat: lumbar artery.
~ боль path: lumbago.
~ мышца (большая, малая) anat: psoas (major, minor).
поясничное сплетение anat: lumbar plexus, lumbiplex.
~ утолщение anat: lumbar enlargement.
пояснично-крестцовое сочленение anat: lumbosacral joint.
~ ~ сплетение anat: lumbosacral plexus.
~ -рёберный lumbocostal.
~ -спинная фасция anat: lumbodorsal fascia.
поясничные позвонки anat: lumbar vertebrae, vertebrae lumbales.
поясничный прокол surg: lumbar puncture, rachicentesis.
~ проток anat: truncus lumbalis.
поясок zool: clitellum, girdle.
Правац Pravaz.
правая ориентация right-handedness.
правильный прикус odont: anatomic occlusion.
правое предсердие anat: atrium cordis dextrum.
~ сердце path: pulmonary heart, cor pulmonale.
правозавёрнутый dextral.
правозакрученноесть dextrotorsion.
правозакрученный right-hand coiled, dextrotorsal.
правша right-handed person.
правый dextral.
~ желудочек (сердца) anat: right ventricle of the heart.
~ лимфатический проток anat: right lymphatic duct.
~ с левым животным ultradextral (shell)
практикующий врач practicing physician, (general) practitioner.
практический врач = практикующий врач.
праща surg: sling.
пращевидная повязка = праща.
преанальный zool: preanal.
превентивный prevent(at)ive.
превратить(ся) p. a. of превращать(ся)
превращаться в студень gelatinate.
~ в эфир etherify.
превращение transformation, conversion.
~ артериальной крови в венозную dearterialization.
~ в костный мозг medullization.
превращение в порошок pulverization.
~ венозной крови в артериальную arterialization.
~ куколки во взрослую форму entom: pupal-adult transformation.
преганглионарный neur: preganglionic.
прегнандиол pregnanediol.
предварительное сообщение preliminary report.
предварительные схватки obstet: preliminary pains.
предварительный диагноз tentative diagnosis, presumptive d., provisional d.
предвестник precursor, premonitory sensation.
предвзятое представление psych: preconceived notion, preconception.
предглотка anat: prepharynx.
предглоточная полость zool: buccal tube, prepharynx (of a fluke).
предгрудинник = предгрудник.
предгрудник zool: omosternum (in amphibians).
преддверие anat: vestibule antechamber, approach.
~ влагалища anat: vestibule of the vagina, atrium vaginae.
~ рта anat: vestibule of the mouth, vestibulum oris.
~ уха anat: vestibule of the ear.
предел выносливости endurance limit.
предельная величина limit value.
преджелудок zool: rumen, paunch (of a ruminant); orn: proventriculus, forestomach; entom: gizzard.
предконвульсивный preconvulsive.
предкуколка entom: nymph.
предкуколочный период nymphal stage.
предлежание obstet: presentation.
~ головки cephalic presentation.
~ колена knee presentation.
~ нескольких частей compound presentation.
~ ножек obstet: footling presentation.
~ плаценты placental presentation.
~ подбородка chin presentation.
~ пуповины presentation of cord, funic p
~ рта mouth presentation.
~ ручки arm presentation.
~ щеки cheek presentation.
предлежать obstet: present.
предлежащая часть obstet: presenting part.
предлихорадочный antefebrile.
предметное стекло mcscop: (glass) slide object carrier.
~ ~ с лункой depression slide.

предметное стекло с углублением
mcscop: hollow(-ground) slide,
excavated s., concavity-type s.
преднамеренное убийство legl: first
преднерестовый ichth: prespawning.
преднизон prednisone. degree murder.
предобморочное состояние
precoma(tous state).
предобразование preformation.
предок ancestor, forefather. [tion.
предохранительная прививка vaccina-
предохранительные ремни av med:
safety belts.
предплечный anat: antibrachial.
предплечье anat: antibrachium, forearm.
предплюсна anat: tarsus.
предплюсневой anat: tarsal.
предплюсне-плюсневый сустав anat:
tarsometatarsal ligament.
предподбородок entom: praementum.
предпозвоночная фасция anat:
prevertebral fascia.
предпочка embr: fore-kidney, head k.
предпочтительная локализация
abode of predilection.
предрак precancer.
предраковый precancerous.
предрасполагающая причина
predisposing cause, antecedent c. [cive.
предрасполагающий predisposing, condu-
предрасположение к болезням
predisposition to diseases, taint.
предрасположенность predisposition,
~ к раку cancerism. diathesis.
предрасположенный (к) predisposed (to).
предромальный vet: precursory.
предросток bot: prothallium, prothallus,
gametophyte; proembrio (of algae).
предротовой preoral. [treatment.
предсезонное лечение preseasonal
предсердие anat: atrium cordis.
предсердно-желудочковое отверстие
anat: atrioventricular orifice.
~ -желудочковый клапан anat: atrioven-
предсердный anat: atrial. | tricular valve.
предсказание prediction, prognosis.
предсмертный ante-mortem.
предсозревание bot: yellow ripeness.
предсонное состояние predormition.
представитель бентоса bottom dweller.
~ планктона planktont.
~ того же рода bio: congener.
~ фауны faunal form. [tal representation.
представление psych: idea, notion, men-
предстарческий психоз presenile
psychosis.

предстательная железа anat:
prostrate (gland).
~ маточка anat: prostatic utricle.
~ часть мочеиспускательного
канала anat: prostatic urethra.
предуборочный agr: preharvest.
~ период agr: preharvest(ing period).
предузловой antenodal; neur: pregang-
предупредительная окраска | lionic.
warning color(ation).
предупредительно-оздоровительные
мероприятия prophylaxis & sanitation.
предупреждающий prevent(at)ive.
~ трупное разложение necrosozoic.
предупреждение 1. warning;
2. prevention.
~ беременности = п. зачатия.
~ болезни disease prevention.
~ зачатия contraception; birth control.
~ несчастных случаев accident
prevention. [foreboding.
предчувствие psych: premonition,
предшественник predecessor; precursor.
предшествующий агонии preagonic.
~ взрослой стадии zool: preimaginal.
~ высыпанию path: preeruptive.
~ злокачественному перерождению
premalignant.
~ нагноению presuppurative.
~ образованию хряща embr: prochondral.
~ половой зрелости prepuberal.
~ рвоте prevomiting.
преждевременная зрелость precocity.
~ старость presenility. [tion.
преждевременное старение presenila-
преждевременно родившийся prematu-
~ состарившийся presenile. | rely born.
преждевременные роды obstet:
premature labor, premature delivery,
partus immaturus.
прежнее заболевание past disease.
преимагинальный entom: preimaginal.
преканкрозный precancerous.
прекапилляр hist: precapillary.
прекращение cessation, ceasing,
stop(ping), abeyance.
~ дыхания path: cessation of respiration, respiratory standstill, r. failure.
~ менструаций gyn: | asphyxia.
menostasia, suppressed menstruation.
~ молока agalorrhea. [anuresis.
~ отделения мочи path: anuria, anury,
~ перистальтики path: aperistalsis.
~ слюноотделения path: aptyalism,
aptyalia.

прекращение функции afunction, defunctionalization.
преломляющая сила (или способность) хрусталика ophth: dioptric power of the lens.
прелость fustiness.
прелый fusty.
премолярный зуб zool: premolar tooth, fore-molar.
пренатальный prenatal.
Пренс Prince.
преобладание preponderance.
преобладающий preponderant.
препарат pharm: preparation, drug; lab: mount.
~ железа iron preparation.
~ крови blood preparation.
~ -мазок streak preparation, smear p.
~ -отпечаток lab: impression preparation, contact p.
~ ткани tissue specimen.
препарировать prepare.
препаровальная ванночка lab: dissecting dish.
~ игла lab: microscopic needle, dissecting n., teasing n.
~ лупа lab: dissecting lens.
препаровочная игла = препаровочная игла.
препуций anat: prepuce.
препятствующий агглютинации anti-agglutinating.
~ атрофии anatrophic.
~ гемолизу antihemolytic.
~ кариесу odont: anticarious.
~ кровотечению anthemorrhagic.
~ нагноению antipyogenic, antipyic.
~ образованию камней antilithic.
~ развитию тепла thermoinhibitory.
прерывистый шов surg: interrupted suture, noose s.
пресбиопический ophth: presbyopic.
пресбиопия ophth: presbyopia.
пресбиофренический psych: presbyophrenic
пресбиофрения psych: presbyophrenia.
прескутум entom: praescutum.
пресмыкающееся zool: reptile.
пресмыкающиеся (кл.) zool: reptiles (Reptilia), see рептилии.
пресмыкающийся adj zool: reptilian.
пресная вода fresh water, sweet w.
пресноводный fresh-water, limnetic.
пресный fresh (water); unleavened, lenten (bread).
пресс press, prelum.
прессорный рефлекс pressor reflex.
преступная небрежность в работе med: criminal negligence, malpractice.
преступность 1. criminality; 2. rate of crimes.
претарз entom: praetarsus.
префронтальная лоботомия prefrontal lobotomy.
преходящая мания psych: transitory mania.
преходящее разложение transitory decomposition.
преходящий transient, fugitive (pain, etc.)
прецентральная борозда anat: precentral fissure.
преципитат precipitate.
преципитин precipitin.
преципитирующийся на холоду cold-precipitable.
презклamптический preeclamptic.
приакантус ichth: catalufa (Priacanthus arenatus).
приапизм path: priapism, persistent erection.
прибавление 1. addition (to); 2. appendage, appendix.
~ в весе weight gain.
прибавлять в весе put on weight.
приближённо количественный semiquantitative.
приближённый анализ proximate analysis.
прибор для взятия проб sampler.
~ ~ встряхивания bact: shaking machine.
~ ~ стерилизации sterilizing outfit.
прибрежная рыба shore fish.
приведение physl: adduction (of muscles).
~ в неподвижное состояние rendering motionless, immobilization.
~ глаз ophth: adduction of the eyes.
привес животных agr: animal gain(s).
привести p. a. of приводить.
прививаемость опухолей survival of tumors.
прививать = делать прививку.
прививка 1. med: vaccination; 2. agr bot: grafting.
~ врасщеп bot: cleft grafting.
~ мостиком agr bot: bridge grafting.
~ оспы smallpox vaccination.
~ пня agr bot: stump grafting.
~ черенками agr bot: scion grafting.
прививочная лимфа imm: inoculation lymph.
~ почка agr bot: oculus.
привидениевые (отр.) entom: Phasmodea.
привитая шизофрения "inoculated" schizophrenia (in persons who had an organic lesion of the brain in the past).
привить p. a. of прививать.
привнесенный adventitious.
приводить adduct.
приводящая мышца (большая, длинная, малая, короткая) anat: adductor (magnus, longus, minimus, brevis).
~ ~ большого пальца anat: adductor pollicis.
приводящее движение (мышцы) adduction movement (of a muscle).
приводящий physl: adducting, adducent.

привой agr bot: scion.
привратник anat: pylorus.
привратниковый anat: pyloric.
привходящий intercurrent, accessory.
привыкание habituation.
~ к камфоре camphor habit.
привычка habit; addiction.
~ кусать ногти nail biting habit.
привычный аборт path:habitual abortion
~ алкоголизм psych: inebriety.
~ вывих path: habitual dislocation.[belt.
привязной ремень av med:restraining
~ ~ грудного типа av med: lap-type safety belt.
~ ~ плечевого типа av med: shoulder-type safety belt.
пригибать (ботву и т.п.) bend over (the tops, etc.)
приглушение dullness, blunting. Cf. притупившийся.
пригнуть p. a. of пригибать.
пригодность для питья potability.
приготовление к операции surg: operative preparation.
~ лекарств pharm:preparation of medic-
~ настойки pharm:tincturation. |aments.
~ срезов hist:microtomy, section-cutting.
придатки anat:adnexa, annexa, appendages.
~ матки anat:uterine appendages, adnexa
придаток appendix, appendage, sacculus.
~ мозга anat:hypophysis cerebri. |uteri.
~ на рубчике (семени) bot:caruncle, strophiole. [(of a hydrachnid)
~ ротового аппарата entom:capitulum
~ семенника epididymis.
~ яичка anat: epididymis. [gland.
придаточная железа anat:accessory
~ полость носа anat: nasal accessory sinus.
~ почка bot:adventitious bud, accessory b.
придаточное крыло entom orn: bastard
~ перо orn:aftershaft. |wing, alula.
придаточные железы entom:collateral glands. [appendicular.
придаточный adnexal, appendiculate,
~ корень bot:adventitious root.
придонная рыба bottom-dwelling fish.
придонный benthopelagic, demersal.
приём 1.reception, acceptance, admittance; 2.ingestion, intake (of food, medicine, etc.); 3.technique, manner, mode, way; 4. dose; 5.time(two tablets at a time).
~ (больных в больницу) admission (of patients to a hospital).
~ внутрь = приём 2.
приём пищи food intake. [occlusion.
приемлемый прикус mil:serviceable
приёмная врача physician's office, doctor's o.
приёмная (лечебного заведения) admission room.
приёмные часы office hours.[building.
приёмный покой admission room, a.
прижатие кровеносного сосуда surg: angiopressure.
~ сосуда пинцетом surg:forcipressure.
прижатый appressed.
прижечь p. a. of прижигать.
прижигание cauterization, cautery.
~ едкими веществами chemical cautery.
~ ракалённым железом actual cautery.
~ химическими веществами chemical cautery. [galvanocautery.
~ электричеством electrocautery,
прижигатель cauter(ant).
прижигать cauterize, burn in, sear.
прижигающее средство caustic.[stain.
прижизненная окраска intravitam
прижизненное иссечение (для исследования)biopsy, excision.
~ наблюдение biopsy, observation.
прижизненный intra-vitam, during life.
призменная диоптрия prism diopter.
признак indicant, indication, sign, stigma. Cf. предчувствие[pregnancy.
признаки беременности obstet:signs of
~ внутриутробного плода ped: fetalism.
прикладная ботаника economic botany.
~ психология applied psychology.
~ химия applied chemistry.
прикладывание application.
"прикованный" к постели bedridden bedfast. Cf. коечный больной.
прикорневое побурение phytp: bottom rot.
прикорневой лист radical leaf.
прикрепительный орган bot:hapteron (of algae).
прикрепление attachment.
~ кишок surg: enteropexy. [rosis.
~ мышцы attachment of a muscle, aponeu-
~ толстой кишки surg: colonopexy.
прикреплённый fastened, attached; sessile, sedentary, stationary; fringing(alga, etc.)
~ тыльной частью bot:dorsifixed
прикроватный столик bedtable.|(anther).
прикус odont: occlusion, bite.
~ при покойном положении челюстей restbite.

прикусовый odont: occlusal.
прилаживание adaptation, adjustment.
прилежащие тела entom: corpora allata.
прилежащий к грудине anat: adsternal.
~ ~ подъязычной кости anat: adhyoid.
прилив afflux(ion), affluence.
~ крови flush, rush, congestion, hyperemia.
~ ~к животу abdominal pool.
"прилив" (первая стадия пневмонии) engorgement, infarction.
приливный affluent.
прилипало ichth: suckfish, suckerfish (Remora); shark sucker (Echeneis).
прилипальце = липкая подушечка.
прилипание adhesion, sticking, agglutination.
прилипающий adhesive, sticky, viscid, glutinous.
прилистник bot: stipule; scale leaf.
~ листочка bot: stipel (of a compound leaf).
прилистниковый bot: stipular, stipulate.
приманка bait, lure.
приманочное вещество bait(ing matter)
примачивание application of lotion, moisture.
примачивать apply lotion, moisture.
применение банок cupping.
~ инструментов instrumentation.
~ кокаина cocainization.
~ кровесосных банок wet cupping.
~ линимента linition.
~ морфия morphinization.
~ наркотиков у душевнобольных psych: medicinal restraint.
~ паллиативных средств palliation.
~ пластыря emplastration.
~ эфира etherization.
применять антисептику antisepticize.
примёр agr bot: hasting, early-ripening variety.
примесь крови admixture of blood.
примидон pharm: primidone.
примордиальный bio: primordial.
примочить p. a. of примачивать.
примочка pharm: lotion.
примула = первоцвет.
примыкание adjoining, abutting, connection, union.
принадлежащий к тому же роду bio: congeneric.
принадлежности для подкожных инъекций hypodermic outfit.
принесённый bio: allogenetic.
принести p. a. of приносить.
принимать роды obstet: deliver (to assist at the birth).
приноровление adaptation, accommodation.
приносить плоды bear fruit.
приносящий канал zool: incurrent canal, ostium (in sponges).
принудительное питание forced feeding.
~ скармливание = п. питание.
~ скрещивание bot: controlled pollination.
принявшееся растение rooted plant.
принятие положения assumption of position.
приобретённая адаптация acquired adaptation.
~ цветовая слепота acquired color blindness.
приобретённое слабоумие psych: dementia.
приостанавливающий развитие болезни cutting short a disease, abortive.
припадать на колено to kneel.
припадок path: seizure, fit; see also приступ.
припаривание fomentation (application of heat and moisture).
припаривать apply poultice, foment, stupe.
припарить p. a. of припаривать.
припарка pharm: poultice, cataplasm, fomentation, stupe.
~ из льняного семени pharm: linseed poultice.
припасть p. a. of припадать.
приплод zool: litter, offsprings.
приподнятость elevation; psych: elation
припудренный bot: pulverulent.
припудривание powdering, inspergation.
припудривать bepowder, powder, dust.
припудрить p. a. of припудривать.
припухание (little) tumescence.
припухлость little swelling. tumidity. turgidity.
~ кожи cutaneous swelling.
прирастание adhesion.
прирастающий adhesive.
приращение языка к стенке ротовой полости path: adhesion of the tongue to the side of the mouth.
приращённый рубец adherent scar.
природный natural, native; see врождённый.
прирождённый native.
прирост accretion, increment; amount of growth; agr: weight gain.

прирученный agr: tame, domesticated.
присасывание sucking up, sucking in.
присасывательная нога entom: suctorial leg. [suctorial d.
~ пластинка zool: adhesive disk,
~ ямка bothrium (of a tapeworm).
присасывательные щели helm: bothria.
присасывательный диск = присасывательная пластинка.
приседать на корточки squat.
присемянник = околоплодник.
присесть p. a. of приседать.
присоединение connection, union.
~ аминовой группы chem: aminating.
присоска = присосок.
присосок zool: sucker, sucking disk, cup.
~ в форме чаши zool: acetabulum, cup.
приспособительная реакция adaptive reaction, adaptation r.
приспособить p. a. of приспособлять.
приспособление adaptation, accomodation, adjustment; device.
~ к холоду cold acclimation.
~ хрусталика physl: accomodation.
приспособляемость adaptability, ophth: accomodation power.
приспособлять к зимним условиям winterize.
пристенный parietal.
пристеночный parietal.
~ листок anat: peritoneum parietale.
~ ~ плевры anat: parietal pleura.
Пристли Priestly.
пристрастие (к) predilection (to) preconceived liking, philia, fondness (for).
~ (к алкоголю, наркотикам) addiction
~ к животным zoophilism.
~ ~ спиртным напиткам alcoholism, overindulgence in alcohol.
приступ attack, paroxysm, seizure, fit, spell; see also припадок.
~ болей по ходу нерва neuralgia.
~ грудной жабы int: anginal attack.
~ кашля fit of coughing, coughing spell.
~ рвоты vomiting spell.
~ резкой боли twinge.
~ удушья choking spell.
~ эпилепсии = эпилептический припадок.
присутствие бактерий в крови presence of bacteria in blood, bacteremia.
присущий организму enorganic.
присыпать dust.
присыпать p. a. of присыпать.

присыпка pharm: dusting powder, externally used powder.
притворство (dis)simulation, pretense, feigning, sham.
притворяшка entom: spider beetle (Ptinidae).
~ волосистый Ptinus villiger.
~ -вор white marked spider beetle (Ptinus fur).
~ шелковистый golden spider beetle (Niptus hololenchus).
притертая пробка ground stopper.
притупившийся blunt, dull, indifferent, insensitive, desensitized.
притупление blunting, dullness, obtusion.
притупление перкуторного звука loss of resonance.
притуплённый bot: retuse, premorse.
~ (звук) flat (sound).
притуплять(ся) blunt, dull, obtund.
притупляющий нервную чувствительность nerveobtudent.
приусадебный огород agr: home garden.
приходить в сознание recover consciousness.
приходящий ambulatory, ambulant.
~ больной outpatient.
прихрамывать limp.
прихрамывающая походка path: halting gait.
прицветник bot: bract, spathe; see also маленький высохший прицветник.
~ на вторичной оси bot: bracteole, bractlet.
прицветниковый bot: bracteal.
прицепляющийся bot: climbing.
причина cause, reason.
причинный момент causal condition.
причудливый плод bot: odd fruit.
пришивание желудка к брюшной стенке surg: gastropexy.
~ органа к брюшной стенке ventrifixation.
~ придатков матки adnexopexy.
прищипка agr bot: nipping.
прищипнуть p. a. of прищипывать.
~ завязь agr bot: nip in the bud.
прищипывать agr bot: nip, pinch out.
приют asylum.
проанура zool: Proanura (extinct amphibians).
проба lab: 1. test, assay, trial, probe; 2. sample.
~ азотной кислотой nitric-acid test.
~ воздуха air sample.
~ крови lab: blood sample, b. smear.

проба мочи urinalysis.
~ на белок albumin test.
~ ~ брожение fermentation test.
~ ~ вкус tasting, gustation.
~ ~ всплывание legl:hydrostatic test.
~ ~ координацию coordination test.
~ ~ всхожесть agr bot:germination test.
~ ~ кровяную группу blood-group test.
~ почек renal test.
~ Рену lab: Renoux test.
~ с азотной кислотой nitric-acid test.
~ ~ водой urol:water elimination test.
~ ~ двумя стаканами ven: two-glass test.
~ ~ тремя стаканами three glass test.
~ сахарной толерантности sugar tolerance test.
~ толерантности tolerance test.
~ функции печени liver function test.
~ ~ почек renal function test.
пробенецид probenecid.
пробивание пыльника bot:protrusion of anther.
пробивать яичную скорлупу orn: chip.
пробирка lab: test tube, beaker.
~ с бульоном bact: bouillon tube, broth t.
~ ~ закраиной flange-type test-tube.
~ ~ косой средой bact: sloped tube.
~ ~ косым агаром bact: sloped agar tube.
~ ~ культурой bact: culture tube.
~ ~ сывороточной средой bact: serum tube.
пробка 1. stopper, plug; 2.bot: cork.
~ для изолирования от шумов otolar: antiphone.
~ из ушной серы ceruminal plug.
пробковая ткань bot: phellema.
пробковидный cork-like, suberous.
пробковый corky; suberous.
~ камбий bot: cork cambium.
пробная диета test diet.
~ линза ophth: trial lens.
пробник sampler.
пробный завтрак test breakfast.
~ прокол surg:exploratory puncture.
~ шрифт ophth:test type,Snellen chart.
пробование tasting;trying; see also проба.
прободающие волокна Шарпея hist: perforating fibres of Sharpey.
прободение path: perforation.
~ язвы желудка perforating gastric ulcer.
прободённая язва path: perforated ulcer.
прободённые фораминиферы (подотр.)zool: perforate foraminifers (Perforata).
прободной path:punctured, ruptured.
пробоотбиратель lab: sampler.
пробормотать p. a. of бормотать.
пробуждение после гипноза psych: dehypnotization.
провал памяти spotty memory defect.
проведение санитарно-гигиенических мероприятий sanitation, hygienization.
провентилировать p. a. of вентилировать.
провентрикулюс zool:proventriculus.
проветривание ventilation, airing.
проветривать air, ventilate.
проветрить p. a. of проветривать.
провитамин provitamin.
проводимость conduction.
проводниковая анестезия surg: conduction anesthesia.
проводящая ткань conducting tissue.
проводящий путь conduction path.
проволочная пила surg: wire saw.
~ трава bot: wire grass (Aristida).
~ шина surg: wire splint, wiring.
~ ~ для ног surg: breeches splint.
проволочник entom: wireworm. (larva of the click beetle).
~ кукурузный cornstalk borer (Elasmopalus lignosellus).
~ пшеничный wheat wireworm (Agriotes mancus).
проволочное сито lab: wiresieve.
проволочный зонд surg: wire probe.
~ пульс path: wiry pulse.
~ червь = проволочник.
прогестерон progesterone.
проглатывание swallowing, ingestion.
проглоттида helm: proglottid.
проглоченный swallowed, ingested, engorged.
прогнатизм path: prognathism.
прогнатический prognathic,prognathous.
прогноз psych: prognosis.
~ успеха av med: prediction of success.
прогностический prognostic.
прогоняющий сон somnifugous.
прогорклость rancidity,rankness.
прогорклый rancid, rank, saprogenic.
прогрессивная мышечная атрофия path:wasting palsy, progressive muscular atrophy.
~ ~ дистрофия path: progressive muscular dystrophy.

прогрессивный паралич progressive paralysis, dementia paralytica, general paralysis (of the insane).
прогрохоченный agr: screened.
прогул absenteeism.
продолговато-мозговой anat: oblongatal, myelencephalic.
продолговатый лист bot: oblong leaf.
~ мозг anat: myelencephalon, afterbrain, medulla oblongata.
продольная борозда (затылочной кости) anat: sagittal sulcus (occipital).
~ ~ сердца anat: ventricular groove, sulcus longitudinalis.
~ щель мозга anat: longitudinal fissure of the cerebrum.
продольный longitudinal, anteroposterior.
~ разрез surg: longisection.
продромальное явление med: prodrome.
продромальный prodromal, prodromous, prodromic, premonitory, precursory.
продувание барабанной полости ventilating the tympanum.
~ по Полицеру otolar: politzeration.
~ среднего уха ventilating the middle ear.
~ уха воздухом ventilating the ear.
продукт product; produce.
~ выделения physl: secretory product.
~ обмена веществ metabolic product, metabolite, metastate.
~ отделения physl: secretory product.
~ питания foodstuff.
~ разложения = продукт распада.
~ распада decomposition product, decay product; catabolin, catabolite.
~ фотосинтеза bot: photosynthate.
продуктивность productivity, productiveness, yield, efficiency.
продуктивный productive, efficient.
продукция production.
~ растений plant production.
продуцент producer.
продуцирование producing, production.
продуцирующий молоко lactigenic, galactopoietic.
~ пепсин pepsinoferous, pepsinogenous.
~ слизь muciferous.
продырявленная пластинка anat: cribriform plate, lamina cribrosa.
продырявленный perforated, fenestrated foraminated, see дырчатый.
проекционное волокно anat: projection fibre.
проекция projection.
проехидна zool: proechidna (Zaglossus).
прожаривать roast thoroughly.
прожарить p. a. of прожаривать.
прожевать p. a. of жевать.
прожилка entom: vein.
прозектор anat: dissector.
прозекторская anat: dissecting room.
прозенхима bot: prosenchyma.
прозерпинака bot: mermaid weed (Proserpinaca).
прозрачный transparent, clear, hyaline.
проигра = весенний облёт пчёл.
произведение потомства prolification.
произведённый на месте autogenetic.
производители zool: brood stock.
производитель producer, sire, getter; ichth: spawner.
~ кислорода oxygenator.
производительность productivity, efficiency.
производить produce.
производящая шёлк железа silk-spinning gland.
производящий кислород oxygenating.
произвольно-двигательный voluntomotory.
произвольный voluntary.
произношение pronunciation.
происходящий во время родов obstet: intranatal.
происхождение origin, descent, extraction, genesis, parentage, lineage, primordium.
~ болезни pathogenesis.
~ из среднего зародышевого листка bot: mesoblastic origin.
пройти p. a. of проходить.
прокажённый leper.
проказа leprosy, Hansen's disease.
прокаинпенициллин procaine penicillin.
прокалывание иглой surg: needling.
~ насквозь transfixion.
прокалывать насквозь surg: transfix.
прокалывающий орган zool: piercer.
прокамбиальный тяж bot: procambial strand.
прокарпий bot: procarp.
прокипятить boil thoroughly; p. a. of кипятить.
прокислость sourness.
проклёвывание orn: chipping, hatch(ing).
прокол puncture.
~ амниона gyn: amnion puncture.

прокол артерии surg: arteriopuncture.
~ барабанной перепонки otolar: myringotomy.
~ живота surg: abdominal puncture, paracentesis, abdominocentesis.
~ сердца surg: cardiopuncture; cardiocentesis.
~ толстых кишок = колоцентез.
проколлаген procollagen.
прокоттус ichth: Procottus.
проксимальный proximal.
проктит path: proctitis.
пролапс prolapse, prolapsus.
пролежень bedsore, decubitus ulcer.
пролес zool: proles.
пролеска bot: 1. squill (Scilla); 2. mercury (Mercurialis).
~ многолетняя dog's m. (M. perennis).
~ однолетняя boys-and-girls (M. annua).
проливной profuse.
~ пот path: drenching sweat.
пролин proline.
пролиферационная способность proliferative capacity.
пролиферация proliferation.
пролиферировать proliferate.
промежностная цистотомия hypocystotomy.
промежностный anat: perineal, anoperineal.
промежность anat: perineum.
промежуточное вещество hist: interstitial substance, intercellular s.
промежуточномозговой embr: diencephalic.
промежуточный intermediate, interstitial, interjacent.
~ мозг anat: betweenbrain, diencephalon.
~ продукт bio: intermediate.
~ ~ углеводного обмена metab: carbohydrate intermediate.
~ хозяин bio: intermediate host.
промиэлоцит embr: promyelocyte.
промикропс ichth: spotted jewfish (Promicrops guttalus).
промороженный frostbound.
промывалка wash-bottle.
промывание washing (out), irrigation, lavation, lavage, ablution.
~ бронхов bronchial lavage.
~ желудка gastric lavage.
~ ~ зондом tube lavage.
*~ ~ через свищ gastrostolavage
~ почечной лоханки urol: pelvic lavage.
~ пузыря urol: bladder lavage.
~ уха ear irrigation.
промывать wash (off, out), lave, absterge.
промысел кораллов coral fishery.
промытый washed.
промыть p. a. of **промывать.**
промышленная гигиена industrial hygiene.
~ психология industrial psychology.
промышлять пищу zool: obtain food, hunt for food.
пронатор anat: pronator.
~ квадратный p. quadratus.
~ круглый p. (radii) teres.
пронзённый bot: streaked.
пронизанный свищами path: infistulated.
проникать penetrate.
проникающая рана surg: penetrating wound.
проникающий запах penetrating odor.
проникновение penetration.
проникнуть p. a. of **проникать.**
пронимфальный период entom: pronymphal stage.
проницаемость permeability, penetrability.
~ капилляров capillary permeation, capillary filtration.
проницаемый pervious.
пропедевтика propaedeutics.
пропедевтическая клиника propaedeutical clinic.
пропедевтический курс propaedeutical course.
пропионат chem: propionate.
пропионовая кислота propionic acid.
прописать p. a. of **прописывать.**
прописывание лекарства prescribing of medicine.
прописывать prescribe.
пропись pharm: prescription.
пропитанный кровью blood-soaked.
пропитать p. a. of **пропитывать.**
пропитывание impregnation, soaking.
пропитывать impregnate, soak, treat.
пропласток agr: seam.
прополаскивание rinsing, washing off.
прополаскивать rinse, wash off.
прополис propolis, bee glue.
прополоскать p. a. of **полоскать.**
пропотевать sweat, perspire.
пропотеть p. a. of **пропотевать.**
проприорецептор anat: proprioceptor.
проприоцептивное ощущение av med: proprioceptive sense.
проприоцептор anat: proprioceptor.
проприоцепция proprioception.
пропфшизофрения = привитая шизофрения.

прорастание bot: germination, sprouting. [burgeon.
прорастать bot: germinate, sprout, spire,
прорастающий bot: germinating, sprouting.
прорасти p. a. of **прорастать.**
проращивание bot: germination.
прорезаться p. a. of **прорезываться.**
прорезывание eruption, emergence.
~ **головки** obstet: disengagement.
~ **зубов** dentition, teething, eruption (of molars). [milk d.
~ **молочных зубов** primary dentition,
~ **постоянных зубов** secondary dentition, permanent d.
прорезываться erupt, emerge.
проросток bot: germinant, sprout, spire; germchit; germ plant; sporeling.
просачивание transudation, infiltration.
просачиваться transude, infiltrate.
просверливание зуба tooth boring.
просвет lumen.
~ **артерии** anat: arterial lumen.
~ **евстахиевой трубы** anat: lumen of the eustachian tube.
просветление clearing, clarifying, clarification.
просветлить p. a. of **просветлять.**
просветлять clear, clarify.
просветляющее средство chem: clarifying agent, clarificant.
просвечиваемость яйца gleam of egg.
просвечивание transillumination; translucence.
~ **рентгеновскими лучами** roentgenoscopy.
просвечивающий pellucid.
просвирняк bot: mallow (malva), see **мальва.** [(M. rotundifolia).
~ **круглолистный** round-leaved m.
~ **курчавый** curled m. (M. crispa).
~ **мускусный** musk m. (M. moschata).
~ **обыкновенный** common m., cheeses, cheeseflower (M. neglecta), see **алтей.**
проселяхии ichth: Proselachii (extinct).
проскурняк = алтей.
просо bot: millet (Panicum miliaceum).
~ **африканское** bot: African millet (Eleusine coracana, Gaertn.)
~ **большое** guinea grass (Panicum maximum).
~ **венгерское** Hungarian m., see п. итальянское.
~ **волосное** old witch grass (P. capillare).
~ **гвинейское = п. большое.**
~ **жемчужное** bajree (Pennisetum glaucum).
~ **итальянское** spiked m., German m., Hungarian m. (Setaria italica).
просо куриное chicken panis grass, prickly grass (P. crus-galli), see ежовник петушье просо.
~ ~ **японское = ежовник хлебный.**
~ **мучнистое = ежовник хлебный.**
~ **настоящее** millet, broomcorn m., proso, Russian m. (P. miliaceum).
~ **негритянское** Egyptian m. (Pennisetum typhoideum, Rich.)
~ **нежное = п. парагвайское.**
~ **парагвайское** Para grass (P. molle).
~ **посевное = п. настоящее.**
~ **развесистое** barnyard m. (P. miliaceum effusum, Alf.)
~ **татарское = п. итальянское.**
~ **тростниковое** bulrush m., see п. негритянское.
~ **черноплёнчатое** blackhull m. (P. miliaceum nigrum).
просовидная высыпь derm: miliary eruption.
просовидный millet-seed like, miliary.
просовые (подсем.) bot: panic-grass subfamily (Paniceae, R. Br.)
просочиться p. a. of **просачиваться**
простата anat: prostate.
простатит path: prostatitis.
простатитный path: prostatitic.
простатический anat: prostatic.
простатный anat: prostatic.
простая асцидия zool: sea squirt.
простейшее zool: protozoan (Protozoa).
простейшие (тип) zool: Protozoa.
простейший (организм) bio: protist.
~ **растительный организм** protophyte.
простерилизованный фильтрацией lab: filter-sterilized.
простое митотическое деление genet: equation dividing.
простой глаз zool: ocellus, simple eye.
~ **лист** bot: simple leaf.
~ **пестик** bot: simple pistil, carpel.
~ **плоский таз** obstet: simple flat pelvis.
~ **сустав** anat: simple articulation.
~ **эфир** chem: ether.
простомиум prostomium.
пространственное восприятие psych: space perception.
пространство между соседними зубами odont: interproximal space, interdentium.
прострация prostration.
прострел 1. int: myalgia, myositis; 2. bot: pasque-flower.

прострел грубошерстистый 1. bot: pasque-flower (Pulsatilla hirsutissima)
~ **раскрытый** bot: pasque-flower, prairie-smoke, Hartshorn plant (P. patens, Mill.)
простуда path: common cold.
простудиться p. a. of **простуживать-[ся.**
простудное недомогание cold misery.
простуж(ив)аться catch cold.
проступать exude.
~ **(о сыпи)** derm: erupt, break out, effloresce.
проступить p. a. of **проступать.**
простынное обертывание phys-ther: sheet bath.
просянка derm: millet seed rash.
просяные = просовые.
протанопический ophth: protanopic.
протанопия ophth: protanopia.
протаргол pharm: protargol, strong silver-protein.
протеевые (сем.) bot: protea family (Proteaceae).
протез orthop: prosthesis.
протеи (сем.) zool: Proteidae.
протеин protein.
протеиназа proteinase.
протеинотерапия protein therapy, proteotherapy.
протей zool: proteus.
протекающий приступами path: fitful.
протел zool: aard-wolf (Proteles cristatus)
протеоза proteose.
протеолитический proteolytic.
протерандричный prot(er)androus, protandric.
протероринус ichth: Proterorhinus.
против- anti-, counter-, contra-, see **анти.**
против поноса (средство) antidiarrhe-[al.
противоаллергический antiallergic.
противобродильное (средство) antiferment. [antizymotic.
противобродильный antifermentative,
противовенерический antivenerial.
противоводяночный ant(i)hydropic.
противовоспалительное (средство) antiphlogistic.
противовоспалительный antiphlogistic.
противовращение counterrotation, reversal of rotation.
противовытяжение surg: counterextension
противогазовая защита mil: gas defence.
противоглистное средство = глисто-[гонное.
противогнилостный antiputrefactive, antiseptic.
противогнойное средство antipyogenic.
противогнойный antipyogenic, antipyic.
противогрибковый antimycotic, fungicide.
противодиабетическое средство antidiabetic.
противоестественный unnatural.
противозавиток anat: ant(i)helix (ear).
противозачаточное (средство) contraceptive.
противозачаточные меры contraception, birth control.
противоинфекционное (средство) antiinfective.
противокислотное средство antacid.
противокислотный antacid.
противокозелковый anat: antitragic.
противокозелок anat: antitragus.
противокомплементный anticomplementary.
противолихорадочное (средство) antifebrile, febrifuge.
противолихорадочный antifebrile, fever-controling, febrifugal.
противоличиночное средство larvicide.
противолишайный antiherpetic.
противоломо́тный antiarthritic.
противомалярийный antimalarial.
противоневритное (средство) antineuritic.
противообщественный psych: antisocial.
противоокислитель antioxidant.
противоопухолевая резистентность antitumoral autodefense.
противоотверстие surg: counteropening.
противоотёчный antiedemic.
противопаразитное средство antiparasitic.
противоперегрузочный костюм av med: anti-g suit.
противопоказание path: contraindication, contraindicant.
противопоказанный contraindicated.
противопоказывающий (симптом) contraindicant.
противопоносный antidiarrheal.
противопоставляющая мышца anat: opponens pollicis, flexor ossis metacarpi pollicis.
~ ~ **мизинца** anat: opponens digiti [quinti.
противопростудное (средство) cold reliever.
противорвотное (средство) antiemetic.

противорвотный antiemetic.
противоречащий требованиям гигиены unhygienic.
противосифилическое (средство) antisyphilitic, antiluetic.
противосонное (средство) anthypnotic
противостоящий зуб odont: opposing tooth.
противосудорожное средство antispasmodic, antispastic.
противосудорожный antispasmodic, antispastic.
противосыворотка antiserum.
противотело antibody.
противотиаминовый эффект antithiamine effect.
противотифозная прививка antityphoid inoculation.
противотифозный antityphoid.
противотрипсиновый antitryptic.
противотуберкулёзный antitubercular.
противотуляремийная вакцина antitularemia vaccine.
противоцынготное (средство) antiscorbutic.
противоцынготный antiscorbutic.
противочахоточный antiphthisic.
противочесоточное (средство) antiscabetic, antipruritic, antipsoric.
противочесоточный antiscabetic.
противочумная сыворотка antiplague serum
противочумный antiplague.
противошум av med: ear deafener.
противоядие pharm: antidote.
противоядное действие antidotism.
противоядный antidotal.
протирание mopping.
протист bio: protist.
протистолог protozoologist.
протистология protozoology.
протовератрин pharm: protoveratrine.
протогиничный bot: proterogynous.
протогиния bot: proterogyny.
протогиппус zool: Protohippus (extinct).
протозоа zool: protozoa.
протозойный protozoal.
протозоолог protozoologist.
протозоология protozoology.
проток anat: duct, passage.
~ **жёлчного пузыря** anat: cystic duct.
~ **околоушной железы** anat: parotid duct.
~ **поджелудочной железы** anat: pancreatic duct.
~ **подъязычной железы** anat: sublingual duct.
проток придатка (общий извитой) anat: epididymal duct, ductus epididymidis.
протококковые (пор.) bot: Protococcales order (algae).
протокол вскрытия autopsy report, a. record.
протоксилема bot: protoxylem.
протомерит zool: protomerita.
протомонады (отр.) zool: Protomonadina
протоморфные животные zool: protomorphic animals(Protomorpha), see **одноклеточные животные.**
протонема bot: protonema.
протонефридиальная система water-vascular system.
протонефридиальный anat: protonephridial.
протонефридий protonephridium.
протоплазма protoplasm.
протоплазматический protoplasmic.
протоплазменный protoplasmic.
протопласт protoplast.
протоптерус ichth: Protopterus.
проторакс zool: prothorax.
проторозавр protorosauride.
проторозавры zool: Protorosauria (extinct reptiles).
прототип prototype, archetype.
прототроктес ichth: Prototroctes muraena.
протохлорофилл bot: protochlorophyll.
протоцилиаты (подкл.) zool: protociliates, opalines (Protociliata).
протрава chem: caustic (substance), pickle, mordant.
протрагированный protracted.
протрактор zool: protractor.
протромбин prothrombin.
протромбинемия prothrombinemia.
протяжённость корней bot: root extension.
профаза hist: prophase.
профессиональная болезнь occupational disease.
~ **медицина** occupational medicine.
~ **неврастения** professional neurasthenia.
~ **судорога** handicraft spasm, professional s.
профессиональное облучение rad: occupational exposure.
профессиональный невроз occupational neurosis.
профилактика prophylaxis.
профилактическая медицина preventive medicine.
профилактический поворот obstet: prophylactic version.

профилактическое лечение preventive treatment.
~ мероприятие prophylaxis; preventive measure.
профпутёвка psych: hospital certificate stating the occupations permissible for a discharged mental patient.
профузное маточное кровотечение gyn: uterine flooding.
профузный profuse.
профундаль profundal.
проходимость евстахиевой трубы gyn: Eustachian tube patency.
проходимый passable.
проходить (о болезни) cease, disappear subside.
проходная рыба migratory fish.
проходящий по середине брюшка entom: midventral.
процедить p. a. of процеживать.
процедура procedure.
процеживание filtering, straining, screening.
процеживать (per)colate, filter, strain, screen.
процент всхожести agr bot: germination percentage
~ смертности mortality (rate)
процеркоид helm: procercoid.
процесс process (course of a phenomenon)
прощупать p. a. of прощупывать.
прощупываемый palpable.
прощупывание palpation, indagation.
прощупывать palpate, grope.
проэритробласт proerythroblast.
проявление 1. manifestation, appearance; 2. developing (photo).
прудовая рыба pondfish.
прудовик zool: mollusk Limnaeus.
~ малый water snail (Limnaeus truncatulus)
~ обыкновенный L. stagnalis.
~ ушковый L. auricularius.
~ яйцевидный L. ovatus.
прудовый планктон bio: heleoplankton.
пружинящий палец path: trigger finger, jerk f., sweep f.
прус entom: Calliptamus italicus.
~ богарный C. turanicus.
~ туранский = п. богарный.
прусик = прус.
пруссак entom: German cockroach.
прутовник = дрок испанский.
прыгательная нога entom: hopping leg, leaping l.
прыгающие zool: salientians (Salientia).
прыгающий zool: saltigrade, leaping.
прыгун 1. ichth: mud skipper, walking goby (Periophtalmus); 2. entom: skipper (Piophila casei).
прыгунчик zool: insectivorous African animal Macroscellida; 2. Cf. next term.
прыгунчики (сем.) entom: locusts Tetrididae.
прыжок без разбега standing jump.
прыткая ящерица zool: agile lizard (Lacerta agilis).
прыщ derm: pimple, small pustule or papule.
прядильные железы = шелкоотделительные железы.
прядильный орган zool: spinneret.
прямая кишка anat: rectum.
~ мышца живота anat: rectus abdominis muscle.
~ наследственность direct heredity.
~ пазуха anat: straight sinus, s. rectus
прямое деление (клетки) hist: direct nuclear division, simple fission, amytosis.
~ скрещивание genet: direct crossing.
прямой антагонизм direct antagonism.
~ каналец anat: straight tubule, tubulus rectus (renal).
прямокишечная артерия anat: hemorrhoidal artery.
прямокишечное зеркало rectal speculum.
прямокишечные (отр.) zool: rhabdocoeles (Rhabdocoela).
прямокишечный anat: rectal.
~ зонд rectal tube.
~ наконечник rectal tip.
прямокрылое orthopteran, orthopterous insect.
прямокрылые (отр.) entom: orthopterans: grasshoppers, crickets, etc. (Orthoptera, Saltatoria).
прямослойность bot: straight-grain (of xylem).
прямостоячее растение bot: upright plant.
прямостоячий erect, upstanding, upright, orthotropous.
~ колос bot: erect head.
прямостоящая семяпочка bot: orthotropous ovule.
прямошовные мухи entom: straight-seamed flies (Orthorrhapha).
прямые мочевые канальцы anat: collecting tubes.
пряность spice.
псалтырь anat: psalterium.
псаммома path: psammoma, brain-sand tumor.
псевдафикус entom: Pseudaphycus malinus.
псевдо- pseudo-.
псевдоакация = акация белая.
псевдогермафродит pseudohermaphrodite, androgyne, androgynus, androgyna.
псевдогермафродитизм pseudohermaphroditism.
псевдогермафродитический pseudohermaphroditic, androgynous.
псевдодеменция psych: pseudodementia.
псевдозухии zool: Pseudosuchia (extinct).

псевдоизохроматическая таблица ophth: pseudoisochromatic plate.
псевдоконгидрин pseudoconhydrin.
псевдолейкемия pseudoleukemia.
псевдомутовка bot:false whorl.
псевдонарцисс = нарцисс жёлтый.
псевдопаренхиматозный pseudoparenchymatous.
псевдоподия = ложноножка.
псевдорабдит zool: pseudorhabdite.
псевдоредукция pseudoreduction.
псевдореминисценция psych: pseudoreminiscence.
псевдосколекс zool: pseudoscolex.
псевдотрахея entom: pseudotrachea.
псевдотсуга bot: Pseudotsuga taxifolia.
псевдотуберкулёз pseudotuberculosis.
псефенус entom: psephenid.
псилотовидные = псилотовые.
псилотовые (тип) bot: Psilopsida, Tmesopsida.
псилофиты (кл.)bot:Psilophytineae (extinct).
пситтакоз psittacosis,parrot disease.
псих collq: loose term meaning mentally unbalanced or deranged person.
психагогический psychagogic.
психагогия psychagogy.
психалгия psychalgia.
психастеник psychasthenic man.
психастенический psychasthenic.
психастеничка psychasthenic woman.
психастения psychasthenia.
психач = псих
психачка = псих
психиатр psychiatrist,psychiater, alienist.
психиатрическая больница mental hospital, lunatic asylum.
психиатрическое обследование psychiatic examination.
~ отделение psychiatric department.
психиатрия psychiatry,psychiatrics.
психизм psychism.
психика psyche.
психиноз psychinosis.
психическая аберрация mental aberration.
~ аура neur: psychic aura.
~ вялость mental lethargy.
~ депрессия mental depression.
~ неполноценность mental deficiency.
~ неустойчивость mental instability.
~ угнетённость mental depression.
психически здоровый mentally sound.
психический возраст mental age.
~ эквивалент psychic substitute (of an epileptic seizure).
психическое беспокойство = беспокойство.
~ возбуждение psychic excitement.
~ выздоровление mental healing.
~ заболевание mental disease.
~ расстройство mental disorder, psychic dysfunction.
~ состояние mental state.
псих(о)- psych(o)-.
психоанализ psychoanalysis.
психоаналитик psychoanalyst.
психоаналитический psychoanalytic.
психобиолог psychobiologist.
психобиологический psychobiological.
психобиология psychobiology.
психовать collq: conduct oneself like or feign a crazy person.
психогальванометр psychogalvanometer.
психогенез psychogenesis.
психогения psychogenia.
психогенный psychogen(et)ic.
психогигиенический psychohygienic.
психогноз psychognosis.
психогностика psychognosis.
психограмма psychogram.
психографический psychographic.
психодиагностика psychodiagnostics.
психодинамика psychodynamics.
психодинамический psychodynamic.
психоз psychosis.
~ беременных gestational psychosis.
~ на почве голодания = голодный психоз.
~ ~ почве предшествующего заболевания consecutive insanity, egressing i.
~ от алкоголизма alcoholic psychosis.
~ ~ истощения exhaustive psychosis.
~ после инфекции postinfectious psychosis.
~ при отравлении intoxication psychosis.
психолог psychologist.
психологическая пригодность av med: psychological fitness.
психологическое обследование psychologic screening.
психология 1. psychology;2.mentality.
~ подсознательного depth psychology.
психометрический psychometric.
психометрия psychometry,psychometrics.
психомоторика psychomotor system.
психомоторное напряжение psychomotor tension.
психоневроз psychoneurosis.
психоневрологический psychoneurologic.

психоневротик psychoneurotic.
психоневротический psychoneurotic.
психономика psychonomics.
психономический psychonomic.
психопат psychopath.
психопатический psychopathic.
психопатия psychopathy.
психопатка female psychopath.
психопатолог psychopathologist.
психопатологический psychopathological.
психопатология psychopathology.
психопатоподобный psychopath-like.
психополовой psychosexual.
психопрофилактика psychoprophylaxis.
психореакция psychoreaction.
психоритмия psychorhythmia.
психоррея psychorrhea.
психосенсорный psychosensory.
психослуховой psychauditory.
психосоматический psychosomatic.
психотерапевт psychotherapeutist.
психотерапевтический psychotherapeutic.
психотерапия psychotherapy.
психотехника psychotechnics.
психотехнический кабинет department of psychotechnics.
психотический psychotic.
психофизика psychophysics.
психофизиологический psychophysiologic.
психофизиология psychophysiology.
психофизический psychophysical.
психохирургия psychosurgery.
псоралея bot: scurf-pea (Psoralea).
псориаз path: psoriasis.
псориазный path: psoriatic.
пташка orn: finch.
птелея bot: water ash(Ptelea trifoliata)
птенец chick(en), nestling.
птерегат entom: pteregate.
птеригий ophth: pterygium.
птеригоподий ichth: clasper.
птеробранхии (кл.) zool:Pterobranchia, see граптолитовые.
птерогат pterogate (ant).
птеродактиль zool: pterodactyl, see птерозавры.
птеродрома orn: petrel of the genus Pterodroma
птерозавры zool: pterosaurs, pterodactyls (Pterosauria).
птеромалиды (сем.) entom:Pteromalidae.
птеропода zool: pteropod.
птеростигма entom: pterostigma.
птилидий bot:Ptilidium (liverworts).
птилидий бахромчатый P. ciliare, Hamp.
~ красивый scale-moss liverwort (P. pulchrinum).
птилота bot: Ptilota (alga).
птихохейлюс ichth: white salmon (Ptychocheilus lucius).
птица bird. [Cf. удоды.
~ -носорог orn:tropical bird Bucerotes.
птицевод agr: poultryman.
птицеводство agr: poultry.
птице-звери prototheria.
птицетазовые zool: Ornithischia (extinct reptiles).
птицы orn: birds (Aves).
~ -мыши orn: Colli.
птичий ornithic, avian, of birds.
~ помёт bird dung, guano.
~ туберкулёз fowl tuberculosis.
птичья холера fowl cholera.
~ чума fowl plague.
птоз ophth: ptosis.
птомаин ptomaine.
птотический ophth: ptotic, ptosed.
пуба zool: air cell (of an egg).
пубертатная железа anat: puberty gland.
пубиотомия surg: pubic section.
пуговчатый шов surg: button suture.
пуголовка ichth: Benthophilus.
пудель poodle (Canis familiaris genuinus).
пузанок ichth: Caspian and Black Sea herring(Alosa).
пузырёк 1.pharm: small bottle, vial;2. follicle, vesicle, utricle; bubble.
пузыреногие (отр.) entom: thrips (Thysanoptera).
пузыреножка краснохвостая = тля оранжерейная.
~ цитрусовая = эутрипс цитрусовый.
пузыристый bullate, bullous, blistered, puckered, see пузырчатый.
пузырная вена anat: vesical vein.
пузырновлагалищный anat:colpocystic.
~ свищ gyn: colpocystosyrinx.
пузырное сплетение anat: vesical plexus.
пузырно-прямокишечная складка anat: rectoversical plica, sacrogenital fold.
пузырный занос obstet: hydatid(iform)-mole.
~ проток anat: cystic duct, ductus cysticus.
~ треугольник anat: bladder triangle.
пузырчатая глиста = эхинококк.
~ головня phytp: low smut (Tilletia tritici).

пузырчатая мокрая головня high smut.
~ ржавчина сосны phytp: pine-blister rust.
~ стадия ленточной глисты helm: bladder worm, cyst w.
~ сыпь path:blister teller,pemphigus.
~ форма cystic form.
*пузырчатка bot: bladderwort(Utricularia)
пузырчатковые (сем.)bot:bladderwort family (Lentibulariaceae). [blister.
пузырчатость листьев phytp: leaf
пузырчатые хрипы bubbling rales.
пузырчатый blistered,vesicular,bladdery blebby, see пузыристый.
~ глист helm: bladder worm, hydatid, cysticercus.
~ лишай vet: blister tetter.
~ червь = финка.
пузырь 1.bag; 2.anat:bladder;vesicle; 3.path: bleb,bulla,blister.
~ с горячей водой hot-water bag.
~ со льдом icebag. [bile,Blume).
пуласан bot: pulassan (Nephelium muta-
пулевая рана surg:bullet wound.
пулевые щипцы surg: bullet forceps.
пульверизатор atomizer, comminuter.
пульверизация pulverization, communution.
пульверизовать chem: pulverize,
пульвиллы entom: pulvilli. |comminute.
пульвинария чайная entom: motile soft scale Pulvinaria floccifera.
пульпа pulp.
пульпарный pulpar, pulpal.
пульпозный pulpous, pulpy, pultaceous; see also рыхлый.
пульс pulse, pulsus.
~ высокого напряжения path: high tension pulse. [pulse.
~ низкого напряжения low tension
~ при пороках митрального клапана mitralized pulse.
~ пуповины embr: funic pulse.
~ с перебоями intermittent pulse.
пульсация pulsation,beating,throbbing.
пульсировать pulsate,beat,throb.
пульсовое давление pulse pressure.
пульсовой дефицит path:pulse deficit.
~ удар pulse beat.
пулярдка poulard, spayed hen.
пума zool: puma, see кугуар.
пункт punctum,point;station.
~ первой помощи first-aid-station.
пунктат specimen obtained by puncture.
пунктация stippling.

пунктация при малярии hem: malarial stippling.
пункция surg: puncture; paracentesis.
~ живота surg: abdominal tapping.
пуночка orn: snow bunting (Plectrophenax nivalis).
пупавка bot: see 1. завязь огурцов; 2. ромашка.
пупарий entom: puparium. [ligament.
пупартова связка anat: inguinal
пуплёнок bot: cuke, see завязь огур-
пуповина embr: umbilical cord, |цов. funicle, funis.
пуповинный obstet: funic.
пупок 1.anat:navel,umbilicus,omphalos; 2.zool:umbo (in mollusks).
пупочная артерия anat: umbical artery. [h.,omphalocele.
~ грыжа surg: umbilical hernia,annular
~ связка (боковая, средняя)anat: umbilical ligament (lateral,median).
~ складка (боковая, срединная) anat:(lateral,median)umbilical fold.
пупочнобрыжеечный проток embr: omphalomesenteric duct,umbilical d.
пупочное кольцо anat: umbilical ring, annulus umbilicalis.
~ отверстие anat: umbilical aperture.
пупочный anat: omphalic, umbilical.
~ канатик = пуповина.
пурин purine.
Пуркинье Purkinje.
пурпура purpura.
пурпурная бактерия purple bacterium (Bacterium prodigiosum).
пускание ростков bot: sprouting, prolification.
пускать капли instill.
~ почки bot: gemmate.
~ ростки bot: sprout.
*пустельга orn: kestrel,windhower (Cerchneis, Falco tinnunculus).
пустить p. a. of пускать.
пустоцвет bot: unfertile flower.
пустула pustule, pock, blain.
пустулёзный derm: pustular.
пустырник обыкновенный bot: leonurus (Leonurus villosus, Desf.,or Cardiaca vulgaris, Moench.)
путассу ichth: Micromesistius.
пути заражения infection ways.
~ оттока outflow,outlet,drainage path.
путридный putrid.
путь way,pathway, course, tract, tractus.

путь Монакова anat: tractus rubrospinalis.
пуффин = буревестник.
пух down, fuzz, pappus.
пуховое крыло orn: down feather.
пуховой downy.
пухоед entom: bird-louse, poultry-louse (Mallophaga).
~ быка ox-l. (Trichodectes scalaris).
~ домашней птицы head-l. of fowls (Lipeurus heterographus).
~ кошки cat-l. (Trichodectes subrostratus)
~ кур hen body-l. (Menopon biseriatum).
~ собаки dog-l. (Trichodetes canis).
пухоеды entom: bird-lice (Mallophaga).
пухонос дернистый = оленья трава.
пучеглазие exophthalmos, exophthalmus, goggle-eye.
пучеглазый path: goggle-eyed.
пучение tympanites, meteorism, flatulence.
пучковатый fasciculate, fascicled.
пучковая трава bot: little bluestem (Andropogon scoparius, Michx.)
пучковый fascicular.
~ лук bunch onion, scallion.
пучкожаберные (отр.) ichth: Lophobranchii, Syngnathiformes.
пучок bundle, bunch, cluster, band, fascicle, fasciculus, funicle, funiculus.
~ Бурдаха = клиновидный п.
~ Голля = нежный п.
~ листьев поверх плода bot: topknot.
~ лубяных клеток bot: phloem strand.
~ нервов anat: nerve tract.
~ спор(ангиев) bot: sorus, fruit dot (of ferns).
пушистая бородка downy beard.
пушистый tomentose, tomentous, pubescent, fluffy, fuzzy, fimbriate, villous, see опушённый.
пушица bot: cotton grass, bog cotton, wool grass (Eriophorum).
пушкиния bot: pushkinia (Pushkinia scilloides, Adams)
пушная дичь fur game.
пушной зверь fur animal.
пушок naps, down, fuzz, pubescence, tomentum, fur, bloom (on peaches, etc.)
пуэрилизм psych: puerilism.
пуэрильный ped: puerile.
пуэрперальный obstet: puerperal.
пфлюк-салат = салат срывной.
пчела entom: bee (Apis mellifera).
~ домашняя = пчела.
~ -матка queen bee.
~ медоносная honeybee.
~ плодущая рабочая entom: pseudoqueen.
~ работница working bee.
пчела рабочая working bee.
пчелиная куколка zool: pupa of a bee.
~ матка queen, female bee.
пчелиные паразиты (сем.) entom: bee-lice (Braulidae).
пчелиный бой bee fighting, struggle of bees.
~ воск beeswax, yellow wax.
~ клей bee glue, propolis.
~ яд bee venom.
пчеловодство agr: beekeeping.
пчелоед = щурка золотистая.
пчельник beehouse.
пшеница wheat (Triticum).
~ английская duckbill w., piolard w. (T. vulgare, var. turgidum).
~ белозёрная white wheat.
~ белоколосая white wheat.
~ дикая wild w. (Aegilops triuncialis)
~ карликовая club w. (T. compactum).
~ краснозёрная red-kernelled w.
~ -спельта = полба настоящая.
пшеничный крахмал pharm: wheat starch.
пшено husked millet.
пыжина bot: wad.
пыжьян ichth: whitefish Coregonus lavaretus pidschian.
пылевая инфекция dust-infection.
~ клетка lab: dust cell.
~ профессия dust occupation.
пылевидный фунгисид fungicidal dust.
пылевое заболевание dust disease.
пылинка bot: pollen grain.
пыльная головня = г. пыльная.
пыльник bot: anther.
пыльниковый мешок bot: anther sheath, pollen sac.
пыльца bot: pollen.
пыльцевая трубка bot: pollen tube.
пыльцевое зерно bot: pollen grain.
пыльцевой анализ bot: pollen analysis, pollen studies.
~ родитель bot: pollen parent.
пыльцевход семяпочки bot: germ pore, micropyle.
пыльцеед entom: pollen-eater.
~ волосистый Omophlina hirtipennis.
~ восточный O. orientalis.
~ горчичный O. pilicollis.
~ дагестанский Podonta daghestanica.
~ протей O. proteus.
пыльцееды (сем.) entom: pollen-eaters (Alleculidae).
пыльценоситель bot: pollen carrier.
пыльценосный bot: pollen-bearing, polliniferous.
пырей bot: wheatgrass (Agropyrum, Agropyron, Gaerthn.)

пырей американский slender w., western w. (A. tenerum).
~ западный bluejoint (A.)
~ нежный = п. американский.
~ обыкновенный = п. ползучий.
~ ползучий witchgrass, couchgrass, quitchgrass, quickgrass, speargrass, quackgrass (A. repens).
~ ситниковый sea couchgrass (A. junceum).
~ тонкий = п. американский.
пытливость inquisitiveness.
пышно разрастаться luxuriate.
~ расти bot: flourish.
~ цвести bot: flourish.
пьявица entom: leaf-beetle of the genus Lema.
~ обыкновенная L. melanopus.
~ просяная L. dilecta.
~ рисовая L. suvorovi.
~ синяя L. cyanella.
пьяная трава = термопсис.
пьяница = голубика.
пьяница drunkard, alcoholic.
пьянство inebriety, habitual drunkenness
пьяный хлеб temulent corn; cf. фузариум розовый.
пэановский зажим surg: Pean's haemostatic forceps.
Пэпин Papin.
Пьи-де-Дом Puy-de-Dome.
пяденица entom: geometrid, geometer, measuring worm, looping caterpillar; march moth.
~ волосистая Biston hirtarius, Lycia h.
~ зимняя winter moth (Operophtera, Cheimatobia brumata).
~ крыжовниковая gooseberry moth (Abraxas grossulariata).
~ лиственная Hybernia defoliaria, Erannis, Anisopterix aescularia.
~ люцерновая Tephrina arenacearia.
~ -обдирало orange moth (Erannis defoliaris); mottled umber m. (Hibernia defoliaria).
~ пушистая Anisopterix aescularia.
~ сосновая pine looper m. (Bupalus piniarius).
~ тутовая Apocheima cinerarius.
пяденицы entom: geometrids, measuring worms (Geometridae).
пястная ладонная артерия anat: volar metacarpal artery.
пястно-фаланговый сустав anat: metacarpophalangeal joint.
пястный anat: metacarpal.
пясть anat: metacarpus.

пятидневная лихорадка = волынская лихорадка.
пятизубчатый bot: quinquedentate.
пятикруговые bot: Pentacyclicae.
пятикрылый bot: pentapterous (fruit).
пятилепестный цветок bot: pentapetalous flower.
пятилетка bot: five-year old, quinquennial (wood).
пятилетний quinquennial.
пятилистное растение bot: quinquefoliate plant.
пятилопастный bot: quinquelobate, quinquelobed.
~ лист bot: five-lobed leaf.
пятилучевая морская звезда bot: five-finger (Potentilla).
пятипалый pentadactyle.
пятипестиковый bot: pentagynian, pentagynous.
пятистворчатый bot: quinquevalve, quinquevalvular.
пятисуставчатый pentamerous.
пятитычиночный цветок bot: pentandrous flower.
пятиусый five-bearded.
пятка 1. anat: heel; 2. zool: hock (horse); shank (cock).
пятна беременности gyn: chloasma gravidarum.
~ Филатова-Коплика Koplik's spots.
пятнистая болезнь = 1. верльгофова болезнь; 2. пебрина.
~ горячка vet: petechial fever.
~ древесница zool: Dendrobatus tinctorius.
~ камбала spotted flounder (Psettichtys melanostictus).
~ саламандра zool: spotted salamander (Ambystoma maculatum).
~ сельдь ichth: ma-iwashi (Clupanodon).
~ сыпь derm: macular rash; erythema.
пятнистость maculation, spots, spottiness, blemish, smudge, smears; phytp: mosaic disease, spot disease.
~ всходов phytp: early leaf blight.
~ краев листьев phytp: marginal plant chlosis.
~ листьев phytp: angular leaf spot, leaf blotch, leaf spot (tiness).
~ ~ свёклы = церкоспороз.
~ ~ томатов phytp: tomato leaf spot, early blight of tomato.
~ стручьев phytp: spot blight.
пятнистый maculated, maculose, spotted, spotty, blemished, blotched, smudged, smeared.
~ лист bot: dotted leaf.
~ олень zool: axis deer (Cervus axis).
~ тиф = пятнистая горячка.

пятнистый тюлень leopard seal (Phoca vitulina).
пятно spot, blotch, macula, patch.
~ спермы spermatic stain.
пяточная кость anat: heel bone, calcaneus, os calcis.
пяточный anat: calcaneal.
~ бугор anat: calcaneal tubercle, tuber calcanei.

Р

раб entom: slave (ant).
рабда zool: rhabdus, acerate (in sponges)
рабдит zool: rhabdite; rhammite (in ciliata).
рабдитная личинка helm: rhabdite larva.
рабдолит zool: rhabdolit.
рабдом entom: rhabdom.
рабдомер zool: rhabdomere.
рабдоплевра zool: Rhabdopleura.
рабдосфера rhabdosphere.
рабовладелец entom: slaveholder (ant).
рабовладельчество entom: slaveholding (ants).
работа мозга psych: cerebration.
~ с перебоями (о сердце) irregular heart action.
работоспособность working capacity, efficiency; fitness for work.
рабочая пчела entom: worker bee.
рабочий стол bench (in a lab).
рабство entom: slavery (ants).
равновесие equilibrium, balance.
~ обмена веществ metabolic equilibrium
равнодушие psych: indifference, equanimity, apathy.
равнодушный indifferent, equanimous, apathetic.
равнокрылые entom: jugate lepidopterans (Jugatae).
~ хоботные (отр.) entom: cicadas, leafhoppers, aphids, scale-bugs, etc. (Homoptera).
равномерно-суженный таз obstet: generally contracted pelvis.
~ -увеличенный таз obstet: generally enlarged pelvis.
равноногие раки (отр.) zool: pillbugs, sowbugs, wood lice, etc. (Isopoda).
равноногий рак pillbug, sowbug.
равноногое = равноногий рак.
равноперистый bot: paripinnate.
равноресничные (отр.) zool: Holotricha.
равносегментный homeomerous.
равноспоровые плауны (сем.) bot: clubmoss family (Lycopodiaceae).
равностворчатый zool: equivalve.
радиально-симметричные (разд.) zool: Radialia.
радиальный radial.
радиационное поражение radiation injury.
радиация radiation.
радиевая игла radium needle.
~ капсюля radium seed.
~ терапия radium therapy.
радиирующая боль referred pain.
радикальная операция грыжи surg: hernioplasty.
радикулит path: radiculitis.
радиоактивная ванна radiactive bath.
~ игла needle implant.
радиоактивность radioactivity.
радиоактивный инсектицид radioactive insecticide.
~ препарат r.preparation, r.drug.
радиобиолог radiobiologist.
радиобиологический radiobiologic.
радиобиология radiobiology.
радиодерматит radiodermatitis.
радиолог radiologist.
радиологическая безопасность radiological safety.
радиологическое отделение radiology department.
радиология radiology.
радиолокаторный наблюдатель av med: radar observer.
радиолярии (отр.) zool: radiolarians (Radiolaria).
радиоляриевый zool: radiolarian.
радиолярия zool: radiolarian(Radiolaria).
радио-медиальная жилка entom: vena radio-medialis.
радиометрический анализ radiometric analysis.
радиоскоп radioscope.
радиоскопия radioscopy.
радиоснимок radiograph.
радиосопротивление radioresistance.
радиостерилизация radiosterilization.
радиостойкость radioresistance.
радиотерапевт radiotherapeutist
радиотерапевтический radiotherapeutic.

радиотерапия radiotherapy.
радиотермия radiothermy.
радиочувствительность radiosensitivity
радиус radius; entom: vena radialis.
радужина = радужка.
радужка ophth: iris.
радужная оболочка ophth: iris.
~ форель rainbow trout (Salmo irideus).
радужница entom: long-horned leaf beetle (Donaciidae).
радула 1.zool: radula, lingual ribbon (of a mollusk); 2.bot: Radula complanata (liverwort).
раж = неистовство.
разбавление = разведение 1.
разбитость ног vet: foundering (of a horse).
развеваемость (почвы) bot: erodibility (of soil) by wind.
разведение 1.breeding, raising; cultivation, culture; 2.dilution, thinning
~ в себе genet: inbreeding.
~ пиявок breeding of leeches, hirudiniculture.
~ рыбы fish-rearing.
~ сыворотки serum dilution.
развернуть(ся) p. a. of развертываться.
развёртывание листа, цветка bot: leaf expansion, flower exploding.
развёртывать(ся) bot: unfurl, expand.
развести cf. разведение.
разветвление branching, ramification; bifurcation, fork, splitting.
~ артерии arterial ramification.
~ второго порядка bot: secondary branching.
разветвляться branch, ramify; bifurcate, fork, split.
развиваться develope, evolve.
развивающееся в вакуоль включение клетки bio: vacuome.
развивающийся в присутствии железа bio: siderophilic.
~ из мёртвого организма necrogenous, necrogenic.
~ ~ соматических клеток embr: somatogenic
развилина crotch.
развилка fork, bifurcation; see also вилочка.
развитие зародыша embryon development, embryogeny.
~ зубов development of teeth, odontogeny.
~ листвы = облиствение.
~ лишая derm: lichenization.
~ нервной ткани embr: neurogeny.
~ органа development of an organ, organogeny, organofaction.
~ отёка path: edematization.
~ плода embr: fetation.
~ раковой опухоли canceration.
развитие скелета skeletogeny.
~ склероза path: sclerogeny.
~ сосудов embr: angiogeny.
~ с промежуточным хозяином heteroecism.
~ тканей embr: histogeny.
~ яйца embr: ovification.
развиться p.a. of развиваться.
разводить cf. разведение.
разводка bact: culture, see культура.
~ на картофельной среде potato culture.
~ ~ косой среде slant culture.
разволокнение separation into fibers, fraying, fringing.
разврат lewdness, depravity, lasciviousness, fornication, excessive venery.
разгар (цветения) bot: flush.
разгибание extension.
разгибатель anat: extensor.
~ большого пальца ноги (длинный, короткий) anat: extensor hallucis (longus, brevis).
~ ~ пальца руки (длинный, короткий) anat: extensor pollicis (longus, brevis).
~ пальцев (длинный, короткий) anat: extensor digitorum (longus, brevis).
~ плеча anat: arm extensor.
разгибать extend.
разгибающий мускул anat: extensor.
разговор во сне neur: somniloquence, somniloquism.
разграничение delimiting, defining, separating, marking off.
раздавливающие щипцы surg: crushing forceps.
раздваивать split in two parts, bifurcate.
раздвоение splitting in two parts, bifurcation, dichotomy.
~ нёба = раздвоенное нёбо.
раздвоенное нёбо path: cleft palate.
раздвоенный bifurcate, dichotonized.
~ язык path: bifid tongue.
разд. = раздел.
раздел division.
разделение scission.
~ дыхательного горла anat: bifurcation of the trachea.
~ надвое bipartition, dichotomy.
разделённый на десять сегментов decempartite.
~ на доли или лопасти lobose.
~ ~ дольки partitioned.
~ ~ камеры chambered.
~ ~ пять частей quinquepartite.
~ ~ семь частей septempartite.
~ ~ сегменты meristic, segmented.

разделённый перегородками septate.
разделительная пластинка septal plate.
раздельнолепестные bot: choripetalous (Choripetalae).
раздельнополость bio: sexuality.
раздельнополый dioecious.
раздельный пестик bot: apocarpous pistil.
раздетый unclothed.
раздражающее средство 1. stimulant, stimulating agent; 2. irritant.
раздражающий 1. stimulating; 2. irritative
раздражение 1. stimulation; 2. irritation.
~ брюшины path: peritoneal irritation.
~ глаз eye irritation.
~ горла throat irritation.
~ гортани laryngeal irritation.
~ дыхательных путей respiratory tract irritation.
~ кожи skin irritation.
~ шумом stimulation by noise.
раздражимость irritability.
раздражимый irritable.
раздражитель 1. stimulus, stimulant; excitant; 2. irritant
раздражительная слабость нервной системы neurasthenia.
раздражительность psych: irascibility, fretfulness.
раздражительный irascible, fretful.
раздробление comminution, crushing, fractionation, fragmentation.
~ дозы rad: dose fractionation.
~ черепа плода obstet: basiotrypsy, cranioclasis, cranioclasty.
раздроблённая доза rad: fractionated dose.
раздроблённый перелом surg: comminuted fracture.
раздробляющий clastic, crushing.
~ камень urol: calculifragous.
раздувальные мехи bellows.
раздумывание psych: brooding.
раздумье psych: brooding.
разжижать fluidize, liquefy.
разжижающий желатин bact: gelatinolytic.
разжижение fluidization, liquefaction; dilution, thinning, watering down.
~ крови path: hydremia.
~ мякоти phytp: glassiness (in apples).
разинька zool: clam.
разлагать(ся) decompose, disintegrate, decay, dissociate, break up.
разливание по бутылкам lab: bottling.
~ ~ пробиркам tubing (of media).
разливать по бутылкам lab: bottle.
~ ~ колбам flask.
разлитое торможение psych: diffused inhibition.
разлитой diffuse.
различная величина зрачков ophth: anisocoria.
различная преломляющая сила (глаз) anisometropia.
различнозернистый varigrained.
разложение decomposition, disintegration, dissociation, breaking up.
разложившийся decayed.
разложиться p. a. of разлагаться.
размачивание steeping, maceration.
размачивать steep, macerate.
размельчение pharm: trituration.
размер кладки zool: clutch size.
разминание phys-ther: petrissage, kneading massage.
размножать(ся) multiply, reproduce, breed, proliferate, propagate.
~ почкованием mcbio: gemmate.
~ самосевом bot: reseed itself.
размножающийся бесполым способом bio: agamogenetic, monogenous.
~ дроблением bio: fissiparous.
~ половым путём bio: amphigenetic,
~ почками bot: gemmiparous.
~ почкованием bio: gemmate.
размножение multiplication, reproduction, breeding, proliferation, propagation.
~ делением = p. дроблением.
~ дроблением bio: fissiparity, scissiparity.
~ клеток cell multiplication.
~ отводками bot: layering.
~ семенами bot: (propagation by) seedage.
размно́житься p. a. of размножаться
размозжение surg: smashing, bashing, crushing.
~ основной кости = сфенотрипсия.
размозжить surg: smash, bash, crush.
размолотый ацетат целлюлозы alphacel.
размораживать defrost, unfreeze.
разморозить p. a. of размораживать
размочаленные (ветром) листья bot: ragged leaves.
размыкательное сокращение physl: opening contraction.
размягчаться soften.
размягчение softening.
~ артерии path: softening of an artery, arteriomalacia.
~ костей path: bone softening, osteomalacia.
~ спинного мозга path: myelomalacia.
разновес balance weights.
разновидность bio: variety, subvariety, subspecies.
разновозрастный лес all-aged forest.
разноголосые (подотр.) orn: suborder Diacromyodi.
разнодольчатый inequilobate.

разножгутиковые bot:Heterocontae (algae).
разнозернистый anisomerous.
разнокрылые (подотр.) entom: frenate lepidopterans (Frenatae).
разнолепестное растение heteropetalous plant.
разнолистный bot:alternate-leaved (alternifolius).
разнонитчатая структура heterotrichous habit.
разнообразный variform, diverse.
разнорасовый брак miscegenation.
разнореснитчные (отр.) zool: Heterotricha.
разнореснитчный entom: heterotrichous.
разнородность heterogeneity.
разнородный heterogenous.
разноспоровые плауны (сем.) bot: spikemoss family (Selanginellaceae).
разноспоровый bot: heterosporous.
разностный порог differential threshold.
разнотычинковое растение bot: heterandrous plant.
разнотычиночный цветок bot: heterostaminous flower.
разноформенность heteromorphism.
разноформенный heteromorphic.
разнощитковые zool: Heterostraci (extinct).
разноядные (подотр.) entom: herbivorous beetles (Polyphaga).
разовая доза pharm: single dose.
разогнуть p. a. of разгибать.
разрастание в носу growth in the nose.
~ плодоножки bot: aril.
~ половых органов path:growth of the genitals.
~ рака carcinomatosis.
~ слизистой path: papillomatosis.
~ щитовидной железы path:enlargement of the thyroid gland, goiter, goitre.
~ эпителия path: epithelization.
разращение path:(out)growth, vegetation.
~ аденоидной ткани path: adenoid, hypertrophied lymphoid tissue.
разрежение rarefication.
~ кости path: osteoporosis.
разрежённая посадка agr bot: spaced planting.
разрез surg: cut, incision, section.
~ белочной оболочки surg: albugineotomy.
~ для уменьшения напряжения surg: relief incision.
~ ободочной кишки surg: colotomy.
~ трупа autopsy.
разрезанный до срединной жилки bot: pinnatisect.
разрезной лист bot:laciniated leaf.
разрешающая способность mcscop: resolving power, resolution.
разрешающее средство pharm: repellent.
разрешение 1.clearance, permission, authorization; 2.see родоразрешение; 3. see разрешающая способн.
разрешённое к продаже молоко certified milk.
разрисованный лист bot:patterned leaf.
разрушать destroy, break down, demolish, ruin.
разрушающий волосы decalvant.
~ клетки cytolytic, cytocidal.
~ костную ткань path: osteolytic.
~ лейкоциты hem: leucocytolytic.
~ лимфатическую ткань path:lymphatolytic.
~ ткань path:histolytic.
~ ~ зобной железы thymolytic.
~ ~ опухоли oncolytic.
~ ~ печени hepatolytic.
~ ~ яичка orchilytic.
~ ~ яичника ovariolytic.
~ хрусталик ophth: phacolytic.
~ эпителий path: epitheliolytic.
разрушение лейкоцитов hem: leucocytolysis.
~ осевого цилиндра neur: axolysis.
~ структуры destruction.
~ эритроцитов hem: erythrocytic destruction.
разрыв surg: rupture, rhexis, tear, rent, laceration.
~ артерии path:rupture of an artery, arteriorrhexis.
~ барабанной перепонки av med: ear drum rupture.
~ заднего прохода surg: anal fissure.
~ матки gyn: uterine laceration.
~ мышцы path: muscular rupture.
~ плодных оболочек obstet vet: breaking of waters.
~ промежности obstet:perineal tear, p. laceration.
~ пузыря surg: vesical tear.
~ связки surg: sprain fracture.
~ хромосомы chromosome breakage.
разрывание rupturing, tearing apart, divulsion.
разрыхлившийся = рыхлый.
разум psych: intellect, mind; reason.
разъедание corrosion, etching.
разъедать corrode, etch.
разъедающий corrosive, anabrotic.
разъединение psych: sejunction.
разъесть p. a. of разъедать.

райграсс bot:ryegrass;see also плевел
~ высокий tall oatgrass(Arrhenatherum elatius).
~ итальянский = плевел многоцветный.
~ многоукосный = плевел многоцветный.
~ французский French r.,see р. высокий.
райка = парадизка.
район обитания zool: area, range.
~ хвойных bot: coniferous region.
райская птица orn: bird of paradise (Paradisea).
*райские зерна bot: cardamon.
рак 1.oncol: cancer;2.zool:crayfish,crawfish(Astacidae; Palinuridae); 3.bot: canker.
~ -богомол zool: Squilla mantis.
~ глаза eye sarcoma,ophthalmomelanoma.
~ дерева bot: tree canker, gangrene.
~ заднего прохода anal carcinoma.
~ картофеля bot:potato canker.
~ клубней картофеля bot: wart disease of potatoes.
~ копыта (у лошади)vet: canker.
~ курильщиков smoker's cancer.
~ ~ трубки claypipe cancer.
~ лиственницы larch canker,l.blister.
~ -отшельник hermit crab,shore hermit (Pagurus).
~ речной crayfish, see рак 2.
~ трубочистов chimney-sweepers' cancer.
~ шейки матки cervical carcinoma.
ракита bot: goat willow (Salix caprea); brittle w.(S.fragilis).Cf. ива.
ракитник bot: broom (Cytisus).
~ белый tagasaste (C.proliferus,var. albus, Kirchn.)
~ золотой дождь golden chain,laburnum (C.laburnum)
~ побежистый = р. белый.
раковая клетка cancer cell.
~ опухоль cancerous tumor.
~ ткань cancer tissue.
раковина shell, conch.
~ личинки двустворчатого моллюска dissoconch.
~ с крабом crab-inhabited shell.
раковинные амёбы (отр.) zool:shelled Lobosa (Testacea, Thecamoebaea).
~ мягкотелые (подтип) zool: conchiferous mollusk (Conchifera).
раковинный anat: pinnal.
~ гребень anat: turbinated crest.
раковоподобный cancroid, cancerlike.
раковые камешки zool: crab's-eyes, crab's-stones.
раковый cancerous.

раковый больной cancer patient.
~ нарост phytp: tree wart,rind gall.
~ очаг cancer focus.
~ сок cancer juice,c.milk.
~ узелок cancer nodule.
ракообразное zool: crustacean.
ракообразные zool: crustaceans (Crustacea).Cf. высшее ракообр.
ракоскорпионы (кл.)zool:Palaeostraca, see меростомовые.
ракохилюс ichth: alfiona (Rhacochilus toxotes).
ракушечный attr: shell.
ракушка = двустворчатый моллюск.
ракушковые рачки (отр.)zool: minute crustaceans Ostracoda.
ракши orn: coraciforms:kingfishers, hornbills, etc.(Coraciae).
раматный жевательный аппарат zool: ramate jaws.
рами = крапива китайская.
рамнецветниковые (сем.)bot: mistletoe family (Loranthaceae).
рана wound; sore;see also ранение.
~ брюшной стенки surg: abdominal wall injury.
~ груди chest wound.
~ кисти руки hand wound.
~ нанесённая с целью самоубийства suicidal wound.
~ промежности perineal wound.
раневое отверстие mil:wound entrance.
раневой сепсис sepsis due to a wound.
ранение mil surg:wound, w.case, w. casualty,injury;see also рана.
~ головы head injury.
~ осколком брони выбитым пулей av med: bullet splash wound.
раненый wounded.
ранимый injurable.
ранить surg: wound.
раннее зацветание (или цветение) bot: early blossoming.
~ слабоумие psych: dementia precox.
раннемолочная стадия bot:premilk stage (of grain).
раннеспелость bot:earliness of ripening.
раннеспелый bot:early ripening.
ранний bot:early,precocious.
~ детский возраст infancy.
ранник bot:see многоножка обыкновенная.
ранняя гниль phytp:early blight,target spot of potatoes).
ранула path: ranula.
ранулярный path: ranular, ranine.
рапа bittern (brine).
рапо́рт psych: hypnotic rapport.

рапс bot: rape (Brassica napus, etc.)
рапсовое масло rape(seed) oil.
~ семя bot: rapeseed.
рапунцель = валерианница овощная.
раса race; strain (of animals).
раскалённая петля surg: hot snare.
раскалывание хроматиды chromatid
break. [(effusus).
раскидистый bot: (loosely) spreading
раскрывание по швам bot: septicidal
dehiscence.
~ стручка bot: dehiscence (of a pod).
раскрывать(ся) bot: unfurl, expand (of
a leaf, bud, etc.)
раскрывающийся отверстием в
каждой камере bot: loculicidal (fruit).
раскрывшийся цветок tripped flower.
раскрытие пыльников bot: dehiscence of
раскрытое состояние patency. |anthers.
раскрытый patent.
раскрыть p. a. of раскрывать.
расовое вырождение cacogenics,
расовый ствол racial stock. |dysgenics
распад decay, decomposition, dissolution,
disintegration; catabolism.
~ лейкоцитов hem: leucolysis. [fraying.
~ на волокна separation into fibers,
~ органического вещества biolysis.
~ почечной ткани nephrolysis. [ting cell.
распадающаяся клетка hist: disintegra-
распатор surg: raspatory, xyster.
распластать flatten out.
расплод zool: hatch, brood (bees).
распознавание discernment,
distinguishing, identification, discrimi-
~ болезни diagnosis. nation.
~ по несходству differential diagnosis.
расположение жилок bot: venation.
~ пучками fasciculation.
расположенный внутри слоя темпе-
ратурного скачка midthermocline.
~ впереди присоска preacetabular.
~ за головой postcephalic.
~ кнаружи от ветвей кишечника
extracecal. [cecal.
~ между выростами кишечника inter-
~ ~ мозгом и пищеводом brain esopha-
~ ~ сегментами intersegmental. |geal.
~ над ногой epipodial. [genital.
~ перед генитальным сегментом pre-
~ ~ ротовым отверстием prostomial.
~ ~ семенниками pretesticular.
~ позади генитального сегмента
postgenital.
~ ~ ротового отверстия metastomial.

расположенный позади семенников
posttesticular. [tromedian.
~ посередине брюшной стороны ven-
~ после присоска postacetabular. [sal.
~ почти на спинной стороне subdor-
расправить p. a. of расправлять.
расправлять (крылья) zool: spread
(the wings).
распределение внимания av med:
division of attention.
~ по поясам zonation.
распределительная хроматография
partition chromatography.
распростёртая прикрепительная
система bot: prostrate system (of algae)
распространение propagation,
spread(ing), expansion.
~ семенами bot: dissemination.
распространённая водянка path:
anasarca.
распространённый spread, scattered,
~ вид bio: dispersed species. |diffuse.
~ рефлекс spreading reflex.
распространяющийся divaricate.
распукование bot: breaking (of buds).
распускание bot: unfolding, breaking (of
buds), exploding (of flowers).
распускаться cf. распускание.
распустившийся вполне bot: full-blown.
распуститься p. a. of распускаться
распухший turgid, swollen, tumid.
распушённость fuzziness.
распущенность intemperance,
licentiousness, dissoluteness,
libertinism, debauchery.
распыление pulverization, atomization.
распылитель pulverizer, atomizer,
nebulizer.
распятие neur: crucifixion attitude.
рассада agr: young plants, seedlings.
рассаживание agr bot: resetting.
рассасывание resorption, resolution.
~ кости deossification, osteolysis,
ossifluence. [soluble ligature.
рассасывающаяся лигатура surg:
рассев dissemination, sowing.
рассеивание dissemination, scattering.
~ семян bot: dissemination.
~ спор bot: dissemination of spores.
рассеивать семена bot: disseminate.
рассекать surg: dissect.
~ на четыре части quadrisect.
~ посредине medisect.
~ сухожилие surg: tenotomize.
рассечение dissection.

рассечение девственной плевы gyn: hymenotomy.
~ диафрагмального нерва surg:phrenicotomy.
~ капсулы surg: capsulotomy.
~ клитора gyn: clitorotomy.
~ ключицы surg: clavicotomy.
~ нерва surg: nerve section.
~ пополам hemisection.
~ рубца surg: cicatricotomy, uletomy.
~ стенки влагалища gyn: elytrotomy.
~ стриктуры surg: coarctotomy, stricturotomy.
~ суставных связок surg: desmotomy.
~ таза surg: pelviotomy.
~ трахеи surg: tracheotomy.
~ угла глазной щели surg: canthotomy.
~ уздечки surg: frenotomy.
~ фасции surg: fasciotomy.
~ хряща surg: chondrotomy.
~ шейки матки gyn: hysterotracheletomy.
рассечённый partite, parted.
~ лист bot: incised leaf.
рассечь p. a. of рассекать.
рассеянный diffused, scattered, disseminated; dissipated.
~ склероз path: multiple sclerosis.
расслабление relaxing,relaxation, slackening, lassitude.
~ артерии path: arteriomalacia.
~ сосудов path: vasorelaxation.
~ сфинктера path:sphincteric incontinence.
расслабленный relaxed.
расслаивание delamination.
расслоение stratification,lamination, (ex)foliation.
рассол brine.
расстилающийся diffuse.
расстояние между зрачками ophth: interpupillary distance.
~ нормального чтения ophth:reading distance.
~ ясного слуха hearing distance, ear reach.
расстройство derangement, disorder, disturbance, impairment.
~ артикуляции речи dysarthria,logophasia.
~ всасывания malabsorption.
~ гармонии движений incoordination of muscular action,ataxia.
~ глотания dysphagia.
~ голоса phonopathy.
~ движений athetosis, dyskenesia.
~ деятельности почек renal disturbance
~ дыхания respiratory impairment, r. distress, dyspnea.
~ желудка gastric disturbance, upset stomach.
~ жирового обмена lipodistrophy.
расстройство зрения dysopia,visual disturbance.
~ иммунитета dysimmunity.
~ компенсации compensation disturbance.
~ координации asynergy, faulty coordination.
~ кровообращения circulatory disturbance.
~ ~ с застоем congestive failure of circulation.
~ кровяного давления dysarteriotony.
~ менструации menstrual disturbance, emmeniopathy.
~ обмена веществ metabolic disturbance.
~ образования млечного сока dyschylia.
~ осязания tactile disturbance.
~ от недоедания undernutrition d.
~ памяти dysmnesia.
~ письма dysgraphia.
~ питания nutritive disturbance, trophopathy.
~ пищеварения indigestion,digestive disturbance, dyspepsia.
~ пузыря vesical disturbance.
~ речи speech disturbance, alalia, dyslalia, dysphasia; psych: mental alalia.
~ секреции инсулина dysinsulinism.
~ ~ молока dysgalactia.
~ сердечной деятельности cardiac disturbance, c. disorder.
~ ~ деятельности во время беременности gravidocardiac disturbance.
~ согласованности движений мышц path: incordination of muscular action, ataxia.
~ тонуса dystonia.
растапливать melt, thaw.
раствор solution.
~ для заделки или консервирования hist: mounting solution.
~ Добелла pharm: Dobell's solution.
~ индикатора rad: tracer solution.
~ носителя rad: carrier solution.
растворение dissolving,(dis)solution.
~ бактерий bacteriolysis.
растворённое вещество solute.
растворимость (dis)solubility, dissolvability.
растворимый (dis)soluble, dissolvable.
~ в жирах liposoluble.
~ ~ спирту chem: alcohol-soluble.
~ ~ уксусной кислоте acetosoluble.
~ ~ эфире ether-soluble.
~ крахмал soluble starch.
растворитель (dis)solvent.

растворить p. a. of растворять.
растворять (dis)solve.
растворяющий мочевую кислоту urisolvent.
~ слизь mucolytic.
~ ураты uratolytic.
растение bot: plant.
~ в симбиозе с муравьями myrmecophyte.
~ опыляемое животными zoidiophilous plant.
~ прикрепляющееся к животным epizoophyte.
~ процветающее при низких температурах cryophyte.
~ с плавающими листьями floating-leaved plant.
~ -хозяин host plant.
растениеведение phytology.
растениеведческий phytologic(al).
растениеводство plant growing, p. breeding, p. raising.
растениеводческий plant-growing, etc.
растениеед = растениеядное животное.
растениеядное животное plant-eating animal, plant-eater, vegetarian a., phytophagous a., phytovorous a.
растениеядность vegetarianism.
растереть p. a. of растирать.
расти grow.
растирание rubbing down (on); chafing; abrasion.
~ в порошок pharm: trituration.
растирать rub down (on); chafe; abrade.
~ в порошок pharm: triturate.
растительная клетка plant cell.
~ ткань plant tissue.
~ функция vegetal function.
растительное масло vegetable oil.
~ царство plant kingdom.
растительность vegetation, plantage.
растительный plantal, vegetational.
~ анаэробный микроорганизм bact: anaerophyte.
~ белок phytalbumin.
~ микроорганизм bact: microphyte.
~ паразит biophyte.
~ ~ кожи bact: dermatophyte.
~ покров vegetative cover.
~ полюс embr: vegetal pole.
~ эктопаразит ectophyte.
~ эндопаразит entophyte.
растопить p. a. of растапливать.
расторопша bot: milk thistle (Silybum marianum, Gaertn.)
растрескаться p. a. of растрескиваться.

растрескивание dehiscence.
растрескиваться dehisce.
растрескивающийся вдоль bot: septicidal.
~ плод bot: dehiscent fruit.
~ по верхнему шву пестика bot: loculicidal.
растущая на скале водоросль bot: rockweed, lithophyte.
растущий гроздями или кистями bot: clustery.
~ на нижней стороне hypogenous.
~ ~ стебле bot: cauline.
~ от основания bot: basifugal.
растягивающая нёбо мышца anat: tensor veli palatini, tensor palati, dilator tubae.
растяжение 1.distension, stretching out; sprain; 2.anat: lacertus.
~ плечевого сустава surg: shoulder wrench.
~ пузыря path: bladder distension.
растяжимость distensibility.
расхищающее (посевы) животное marauding animal.
расход энергии physl: energy expenditure.
расходка (у оленей) = течка.
расходник bot: quillwort (Isoëtes).
расходниковые (сем.) bot: quillwort family, (Isoëtaceae).
расходящийся = раскидистый.
расхождение disunion, divarication; divergence, discrepancy, discord; dissent, disagreement.
расцвести p. a. of расцветать.
расцветать bot: come into bloom, blossom.
расцветший bot: new-blown, blossoming.
расчеловечение dehumanization (human degradation in Soviet slave camps).
расчес(ывание) scratching.
расчленение dismemberment, dissection.
расчленённый венчик bot: disarticulated corolla.
расчленять dismember, dissect.
расширение expansion, distension, stretching, dilatation, extension.
~ артерии path: dilatation of an artery, arteriectasis, aneurysm.
~ бронхов path: bronchiectasis.
~ вен path: dilatation of veins, varicosity, phlebectasia.
~ ~ семенного канатика path: varicocele.
~ вследствие скопления газов int: flatulent distension.
~ желудка path: dilatation of the stomach, gastrectasis.

расширение зрачка ophth: pupil dilatation, mydriasis.
~ лёгких physl: lung expansion.
~ пищевода path: dilatation of the oesophagus.
~ просвета артерии path: aneurysm.
~ сердца path: cardiac dilatation, heart d.
~ сосудов path: vasodilatation.
расширенная часть цветоложа bot: disk.
расширенный bot: dilated (dilatatus).
~ зрачок ophth: mydriatic pupil, dilated p.
~ листообразный черешок bot: phyllode, phyllodium.
~ препарат hist: cleavage dilatation.
расширяющая зрачок мышца anat: dilator pupillae.
расщелина грудины path: cleft sternum.
~ нёба = волчья пасть.
расщепить(ся) p. a. of расщепляться.
расщепление 1. splitting, fission; fissure, cleavage; see распад; 2. surg: scission; 3. psych: sejunction, splitting.
~ белка protein cleavage, proteolysis; albuminolysis.
~ жира lipolysis, adipolysis.
~ мошонки path: scrotal fissure.
~ нёба = расщелина нёба.
~ позвонков path: bifid spine, spina bifida.
~ признаков genet: filial segregation.
~ сахара glycolysis.
~ хроматиды chromatid break.
~ хромосомы chromosome break.
расщеплённая губа = заячья губа.
~ хромосома split chromosome.
расщеплённоногие (отр.) zool: opossum shrimps (Schizopoda, Mysidacea).
расщеплённый split, etc., cf. расщепление.
~ на десять частей decemfid.
~ ~ пять частей pentafid, quinquefid.
~ ~ шесть частей sexifid.
~ язык path: cleft tongue, split t.
расщепляемость fissility.
расщеплять(ся) split, etc., cf. расщепление.
расщепляющий белки proteolytic.
~ глюкозиды glucosidolytic.
~ жиры lipoclastic, fat-splitting, adipolytic, lipolytic, steatolytic.
~ сахар glycolytic.
расщепляющийся fissile.
расщипывать (ткань) hist: tease.
рата bot: rata (Metrosideros robusta).
ратанг bot: rattan (Calamus ratang, C. tenuis).
ратания pharm: ratany; bot: see крамерия.
раувилоид pharm: rauwiloid (a preparation of Rauwolfia serpentina).
раувольфия pharm: Rauwolfia serpentina.
рафидиум = актинаструм.
рафия bot: palm Raphia taedigera.
рахит ped: rachitis, rickets.
рахитические четки derm: rachitic rosary, rachitic beads, beading of ribs.
рахитический rickety.
рахитичная грудь path: rachitic chest.
рахитичный таз acanthopelvis, acanthopelyx, pelvis spinosa.
рахитоми zool: Rhachitomi (extinct amphibians).
рахицентрон ichth: sergeant fish (Rachycentron canadum).
рацемическое соцветие bot: simple inflorescence, raceme, flower cluster.
"рачьи шейки" = горец змеиный.
рваная рана surg: lacerated wound, torn w.
рваный lacerate(d).
рвать path: vomit.
рвота path: vomiting, emesis, vomitus.
~ беременных morning sickness, vomitus matutinus, hyperemesis gravidarum.
~ грудных детей hyperemesis lactentium.
~ жёлчью path: bilious vomiting.
~ кофейной гущей coffee-ground vomiting.
~ после наркоза postanesthesia vomiting.
рвотная масса vomitus, vomited matter, vomit.
рвотное (средство) emetic, vomitory.
рвотный emetic, vomitive.
~ газ vomiting gas.
~ камень pharm: tartar emetic, antimony and potassium tartrate.
рдест bot: pondweed, water weed (Potamogeton).
~ гребенчатый sago, fennel-leaved p. (P. pectinatus).
~ курчавый curly-leaved p. (P. crispus).
рдестовые (сем.) bot: pondweed family (Zosteraceae, Potamogetonaceae).
реа orn: rhea, South American ostrich (Rhea).
реагин reagin.
реактив chem: reagent.
реактивная бумага chem: test paper.
реактивный психоз reactive psychosis, situational p.
реакционная способность reaction capacity, r. ability.

реакция reaction; response.
~ Вассермана ven: Wassermann's test.
~ ~ со спинномозговой жидкостью spinal Wassermann's test.
~ животного на условия zoapocrisis.
~ карбоксилирования chem: carboxyl reaction.
~ короткого замыкания psych: trigger reaction, trigger-type pathologic affect.
~ выпадения хлопьев flocculation test.
~ Дика imm: Dick test.
~ оседания (эритроцитов) (erythrocyte) sedimentation test.
~ поведения psych: conduct reaction.
~ помутнения turbidity reaction.
~ "тревоги" physl: alarm response.
ребёнок child, infant, baby.
~ вскармливаемый грудью ped: nursing baby.
~ ~ рожком ped: bottle-fed baby.
~ родившийся в срок full-term baby.
~ отнятый от груди weanling.
рёберная борозда anat: costal groove, sulcus costae.
~ дуга anat: costal arch.
~ плевра anat: pericardiac pleura.
рёберно-грудинное сочленение anat: costo-sternal joint.
~ -ключичная связка anat: costoclavicular ligament.
~ -средостенная пазуха anat: sinus costomediastinalis.
~ -шейный ствол anat: costocervical trunk.
рёберное дыхание costal respiration.
рёберные ножницы surg: rib shears.
рёберный anat: costal.
~ край anat: costal margin.
~ угол anat: costal angle.
~ хрящ anat: rib cartilage, costal c.
ребристый costate, lirate.
ребро anat: rib, costa.
рёбрышко (на раковине) zool: lira.
ребяческий psych: childish, anile.
ребячество psych: childishness, anility.
~ (старческое) = впадение в детство.
рёв roaring.
ревакцинация imm: renewed vaccination.
ревенная настойка pharm: tincture of rhubarb.
ревенный bot: rheic.
~ порошок pharm: powdered rhubarb.
~ сироп pharm: syrup of rhubarb.
~ экстракт pharm: powdered extract of rhubarb.

ревень bot: rhubarb (Rheum).
~ овощной pieplant, pontic r. (R. rhaponticum).
~ черешковый = р. овощной.
ревматизм path: rheumatism.
ревматик rheumatic.
ревматин = салициловокислый салицилхинин.
ревматическая кривошея rheumatic torticollis.
ревматоидный rheumatoid.
револьвер для трех объективов mcscop: triple nose piece. [revolving n.
~ ~ четырёх объективов quadruple
~ (микроскопа) lab: nosepiece.
револьверная оправа mcscop: revolving nosepiece.
ревун zool: squaller, bawler (Mycetes).
регемолиз rehemolysis.
регенерация regeneration.
регенерировать regenerate.
регионарная анатомия regional anatomy.
регистратор record keeper (male).
регистраторша record keeper (female).
регистратура record department.
регитин regitine (a vasodilator compound).
регрессивный regressive.
регрессия regression.
~ признаков genet: filial regression.
регулировка control, regulation.
~ (условий) питания nutritional control.
регулирующий рост growth-regulating.
~ сахарный обмен glycoregulatory.
регулы physl: menses.
регуляция physl: regulation.
редис = редиска.
редиска bot: radish (Raphanus sativus, var. radicula, Pers.)
редия zool: redia.
редкая бородка scanty beard.
~ листва bot: sparse foliage.
~ растительность thin vegetation.
редкий травостой loose grasses.
редукционное деление hist: meiosis, reduction division.
~ ~ клеток genet: reductional cell division.
редукция хромосом genet: chromosome reduction.
редуцированный глаз reduced eye.
редька bot: summer-and-winter radish (Raphanus sativus DC.)
~ дикая corn r., wild r. (R. raphanistrum).
~ зимняя winter r.
~ летняя summer r.

редька масличная Chinese r.
~ полевая = р. дикая.
~ стручковая rat-tailed r., serpent r. (R. sativus, var. caudatus).
~ японская daikon (R. sativus major, var. Daikon).
режим 1. regimen; 2. regime, conditions, mode of work, of upkeep, etc.
режуха bot: rock cress (Arabis).
~ гибкая bushy pondweed (Najas flexilis).
режущая боль cutting pain.
режущий zool: sectorial (tooth, etc.)
резаная рана incised wound.
резеда bot: reseda, mignonette (Reseda).
~ душистая scented m., sweet r. (R. odorata).
~ жёлтая yelloweed, weld, dyeweed, gaude
~ красильная = р. жёлтая. (R. luteola)
резедовые (сем.) bot: mignonette family (Resedaceae).
резекция surg: resection.
~ ребра costotomy.
~ сустава arthrectomy.
резервная щёлочность крови reserve alkalinity of blood.
резерпин reserpine.
резец anat: incisor, nipper.
резецировать surg: resect.
резина rubber.
резиновая дренажная трубка rubber drain.
~ пробка rubber stopper.
~ трубка rubber tubing.
резиновый баллон rubber bulb.
~ колпачок rubber cap.
~ круг rubber air ring, ring air cushion.
резистентность resistance, autodefense.
~ капилляров capillary resistance.
резистентный resistant.
*~ к мышьяку arsenfast.
резистенция resistance.
резкая боль sharp pain, pang.
~ слабость adynamia.
резко выраженная лихорадка sthenic fever.
резкость sharpness, acuity.
резонанс resonance.
резонёрство psych: reasoning, moralization.
резорбция = ресорбция.
резорцин pharm: resorcinol.
резорцинмоноацетат pharm: resorcinol monacetate
результат заражения lab: take.
резус zool: rhesus monkey (Macacus rhesus)
резуха = режуха.
резцовые зубы anat: incisor teeth; central nippers (in horse).
резцовый odont: incisal.
~ гребень, канал и т.п. anat: incisive crest, canal, etc.

резь в животе gripe(s), colic.
реинвазия reinvasion, reinfestation.
реиннервированная мышца reinnervated muscle.
реинфекция reinfection.
рейнклод bot: reine claude, gage, greenage (Prunus domestica, var. cereola)
Рейно Raynaud.
рекомпрессия av med: recompression.
реконвалесцент convalescent (person).
ректальная аэрофагия rectal aerophagia.
~ биопсия rectal biopsy.
~ жаберная полость rectal gill chamber (of dragonflies, etc.)
~ щёточка rectal brush.
ректальные железы entom: rectal glands.
ректороманоскопия proctosigmoidoscopy.
ректосигмовидная кишка rectosigmoid.
ректосигмоидэктомия surg: rectosigmoidectomy.
ректоскопия rectoscopy.
ректум anat: rectum.
релаксация relaxation.
реликт relict.
реликтовый relict.
ремиссия remission.
ремнелепестник козлиный bot: orchis (Himanthoglossum caprinum, Spreng., or Orchis hircina, Schmalh.)
ремнец обыкновенный helm: cestode Ligula intestinalis.
ремонтантный bot: remontant, perpetual.
ренин renin.
ренклод = рейнклод.
рентген roentgen.
~ в ткани tissue roentgen.
~ -эквивалент roentgen equivalent.
рентгенизация roentgenization.
рентгенметр rad: r-meter, roentgenometer.
рентгеноанатомия roentgen anatomy.
рентгеновская пластинка x-ray plate.
~ трубка x-ray tube, roentgen t.
~ установка x-ray unit, x-ray apparatus, x-ray machine.
рентгеновские лучи x-rays, roentgen rays.
рентгеновский аппарат = рентгеновская установка.
~ кабинет x-ray department, x-ray room.
~ ожог x-ray burn.
~ снимок x-ray picture, x-ray photograph, roentgenogram.
~ ~ пузыря cystogram.
~ экран x-ray screen.
рентгеновское исследование x-ray exploration.
~ ~ матки hysterography.
~ ~ мочевых путей urography.

рентгеновское исследование почечной лоханки pyeloscopy.
рентгенограмма = рентгеновский снимок.
~ тазовой полости pelycogram.
рентгенография roentgenography.
~ мочеточника ureterography.
~ плода fetography.
рентгенолог roentgenologist.
рентгенология roentgenology.
рентгенопросвечивание roentgenoscopy.
рентгеноскоп roentgenoscope.
рентгеноскопия roentgenoscopy.
рентгеноснимок = рентгеновский снимок.
рентгеностереофотограмметрический roentgen stereophotogrammetric.
рентгенотерапия roentgentherapy, x-ray therapy.
рентгенотехник x-ray technician, radiographer.
Рену Renoux.
реокардиограмма rheocardiogram.
реология rheology.
реопланктон bio: rheoplankton, potamoplankton.
реотаксис rheotaxis.
реотактический rheotactic.
реотропизм rheotropism.
репа bot: turnip (Brassica rapa).
~ венгерская = кольраби.
~ дикая navew, bird's rape (B. r. napifera).
~ индейская Indian t.(Arisaema triphyllum, Torr.)
~ кормовая field t.(B.r.)
~ масличная t.rape(B.r.oleifera.DC.)
~ овощная garden t.(B. r.)
~ огородная = р. овощная.
*~ семиголовая Italian rab(B.r.gemnifera)
~ столовая = р. овощная.
репарация path: repair.
репей = репейник.
репейник bot: beggar's-lice, bur, see лопушник большой.
репейница entom:butterfly Pyrameis cardui.
репица хвоста tail head,dock(of a horse)
репник морщинистый wild turnip (Rapistrum rugosum, All.)
репница = белянка репная.
реповидный turnip-shaped, napiform.
репозиция reposition.
репродуктивный reproductive.
рептилии zool:reptiles,see пресмыкающиеся.
рептильный zool adj: reptilian.
репчатый корень bot: napiform root.
репяшок bot: agrimony.cocklebur,harvest lice (Agrimonia).
реснитчатая мышца ciliary muscle.
реснитчатое тело ophth:ciliary body.
ресница anat: eyelash, cilium.
ресничка cilium.
ресничная артерия anat:ciliary artery.
~ клетка hist: whip cell.
~ корона anat: ciliary crown.
~ мышца anat: ciliary muscle.
ресничное тело anat: ciliary body.
ресничные (кл.) zool: ciliates (Ciliata, Infusoria).
~ черви (кл.) zool:ciliated worms (Turbellaria).
ресничный покров ciliated envelope.
ресорбция resorption.
респираторный respiratory.
респирометр respirometer.
рестионовые (сем.) bot:Restionaceae.
реституция restitution.
ретенционная киста path:retention cyst.
ретенция retention.
ретикулоклеточная саркома reticulum cell sarcoma.
ретикулоцит hem: reticulocyte.
ретикуло-эндотелиальный reticulo-endothelial.
ретикулярная ткань hist:reticular tissue.
ретина ophth: retina.
ретинальный retinal.
ретинограмма retinogram.
ретиноскоп ophth: retinoscope.
ретиноскопия ophth: retinoscopy.
ретракция сгустка hem: clot retraction.
ретроантероградная амнезия psych: retroanterograde amnesia.
ретробульбарный anat: retrobulbar.
ретроградная амнезия psych: retrograde amnesia.
~ память psych: retrograde memory.
ретроперитонеальная область anat: retroperitoneum.
ретроперитонеум anat: retroperitoneum.
рефлекс reflex.
~ Бабинского neur:Babinski's sign, great toe s.
~ зева faucial reflex.
рефлексогенный reflexogenic.
рефлекторная возбудимость reflex excitability.
~ дуга anat: reflex arc.
~ задержка reflex inhibition.
~ рвота при раздражении уха ear vomiting.
~ тошнота reflex nausea.
рефлекторное вздрагивание startle reflex.
~ движение reflex movement.
~ действие reflex effect.
~ явление reflex phenomenon.

рефлекторный паралич neur: reflex
рефракция refraction. palsy.
рецепт pharm: prescription, recipe.
рецептакуля bot: receptacle.
рецептор receptor. [apparatus.
рецепторный аппарат anat: receptory
рецептурная книга pharm: formulary.
рецессивный recessive.
~ аллеломорф genet: recessive allelomorph.
рецидив relapse, backset, recidivation.
~ малярии malarial relapse.
~ рака recurrent cancer.
рецидивировать recur, relapse.
рецидивирующая инфекция recurrent infection.
рецидивист recidivist.
рецидивность recidivity.
реципиент donee, recipient (of blood, etc.)
речевая спутанность psych: speech confusion.
речная выдра zool: true otter, common o. (Lutra vulgaris, L. lutra).
*~ крачка orn: common tern (Sterna
~ мартышка = чайка |hurindo).
обыкновенная.
~ минога zool: river lamprey (Lampetra fluviatilis).
~ чайка = чайка обыкновенная.
речной fluvial, of rivers, fluviatilis.
~ рак zool: crayfish, crawfish (Astacus,
речь speech. |Cambarus, Potamobius, etc.)
"решето" = увирандра.
решётчатая кость anat: ethmoid bone, middle turbinate bone, os ethmoidale.
~ пазуха anat: ethmoid sinus.
~ пластинка anat: cribriform plate.
решётчатое пятно anat: cribriform spot.
решётчато-костный anat: ethmoidal.
~ -лобный anat: ethmofrontal.
~ -сошниковый anat: ethmovomerine.
решётчатый lattice(d), cribiform, clathrate, ethmoid.
~ гребень ethmoid crest.
ржавая крапчатость bot: rusty mottle.
ржавчина phytp: rust, fusiform rust, see ржавчинник. [(Cronartium ribicola).
~ белой сосны white-pine blister r.
~ бурая пшеничная Puccinia triticina.
~ ~ ржаная P. dispersa.
~ весенняя spring r., golden-yellow r.
~ кукурузы corn r. (P. glumarum).
~ лука onion smut (Urocystic cepulae).
~ льна flax r.
~ мятлика bluegrass r.
~ ржи rye smut (U. occulta).

ржавчина спаржи asparagus r.
~ стеблей риса rice bunt.
~ хлебная black stem r., black r. of grain (P. graminis).
~ яблочная apple r., cedar apple (Gymnosporangium).
ржавчинная мокрота rusty expectoration, prune-juice sputum. [les).
ржавчинники phytp: rust fungi (Uredina-
ржавчинные грибки = ржавчинники
ржание zool: neigh (of a horse).
ржанка orn: ringed plover, ring dotterel (Charadrius hiaticula).
~ александрийская Kentish plover (C. alexandrinus).
~ глупая dotterel (Endormias morineblus).
~ обыкновенная golden plover (Charad-
ржаной хлеб rye bread. |rius pluvialis).
ржать zool: neigh. [cleic acid.
рибонуклеиновая кислота ribonu-
рибонуклеопротеид ribonucleoprotein.
рибофлавин riboflavin, vitamin B_2, vitamin G, lactoflavin.
ригидность rigidity.
Ридж Ridge. [root fibril.
ризоид bot: rhizoid, root hair, filament,
ризома bot: rhizome, see корневище.
ризоморф bot: rhizomorph.
ризоподиальный zool: rhizopodial.
ризоподия zool: rhizopod(ium).
ризосфера bot: rhizosphere.
ризофора = мангровое дерево.
риккетсиоз(ное заболевание) rickettsial disease.
риккетсия сыпного тифа typhus rickettsia (Rickettsia mooseri).
ринит path: rhinitis.
~ у детей snuffles.
риноскоп otolar: rhinoscope. [whisky n.
ринофима path: rhinophyma, toper's nose,
ринхоспора bot: beak rush (Rhynchospora).
рипус ладожский Ladoga-Lake whitefish (Coregonus albula infraspecies ladogensis).
рис bot: rice (Oryza sativa).
~ болотный lowland r., water r. (Zizania aquatica).
~ водяной = р. болотный.
~ дикий wild rice, see р. болотный.
~ индейский Indian r., see р. болотн.
~ канадский Canada r., see р. болотн.
~ красный brown r., paddy.
~ необрушенный = р. красный.
~ неполированный = р. красный.
~ суходольный upland rice (Oryza sativa sp. montana).

рис сырец = р. красный.
рискованный объект для операции surg: poor operative risk.
рислинг Riesling (grapes and wine).
рисовая головня phytp: rice smut.
~ птица orn: reedbird, bobolink (Dolichonyx oryzivorus).
рисовидка bot: mountain rice, red rice (Oryzopsis, Michx.)
рисовые (подсем.) bot: rice subfamily (Oryzeae, Kunth).
рисовый корень bot: rice-root epicampes.
~ стул path: rice-water stools.
риссоля ichth: cusk eel (Rissola marginata).
рисунок мозговых извилин anat: gyral pattern.
ритм галопа gallop rhythm, cantering rhythm.
~ сердца physl: rhythm of the heart.
ритмическое сокращение systole.
рифовые (сем.) ichth: Pomacentridae.
рихардия = калла эфиопская.
рицинник bot: castor bean, castor-oil plant (Ricinus communis).
ришта = гвинейский червь.
Робертсон Robertson.
робиния = акация белая.
рог horn.
~ спинного мозга anat: horn of the spinal cord.
рогатая акула ichth: bullhead shark (Heterodontus).
рогатик bot: coral fungus (Clavaria).
рогатиковые (сем.) bot: Clavariaceae.
рогаткаichth: bullhead Myoxocephalus.
~ северная North-Atlantic b. (M. scorpius).
~ четырёхрогая M. quadricornis.
рогатые (подотр.) zool: horned animals (Pecora).
рогатый horned, corniculatus.
~ жаворонок orn: shore lark (Otocorys alpestris).
~ скот horned cattle.
рогач = жук-рогач.
роговая мука agr: horn meal.
~ оболочка = роговица.
~ ткань hist: horny tissue.
роговидный hornlike.
~ вырост cornu.
роговица ophth: cornea.
роговичный ophth bio: corneal.
роговник = мартиния.
роговое вещество horny substance.
роговой horny, keratic, keratose, corneous.
~ коралл zool: antipathid.
рогоз bot: cat-tail flag, reedmace, macereed, tule (Typha).
~ узколистный narrow-leaved cattail (T. angustifolia).
рогоз широколистный flag, cattail (T. latifolia).
рогозовое растение typhaceous plant.
рогозовые (сем.) bot: cat-tail family (Typhaceae).
рогозуб = австралийский р.
роголистник bot: hornwort, coontail (Ceratophyllum).
роголистниковое растение ceratophyllous plant.
роголистниковые (сем.) bot: hornwort family (Ceratophyllaceae).
рогоподобный hornlike, corneous.
рогохвост entom: horntail, wood wasp (Sirex).
~ голубиный pigeon h. (Tremex columba).
~ еловый yellow wood wasp, giant sirex (S. gigas).
~ ольховый Xyphydria camelus.
~ сосновый steel-blue woodwasp (Sirex juvencus).
рогохвосты (сем.) entom: horntails (Siricidae).
рогульки = живокость посевная.
рогульник bot: water chestnut.
род bio: genus (Genus); brood, stock.
родильная горячка obstet: childbed fever, puerperal fever.
родильница obstet: puerpera (woman who has recently been delivered).
родильное отделение obstetric department, maternity d.
родильный дом maternity hospital.
~ покой obstet: delivery room.
~ психоз = послеродовой п.
родимения bot: red algae: dulse, etc. (Rhodymenia); sea kale, waterleaf, dulse (R. palmata).
родимое пятно birthmark, nevus.
родинка mole.
родительский parental.
родительское растение parental plant.
родить p. a. of рожать.
родничок anat: fontanel(la).
родной брат (сестра) sib, sibling.
родные братья и сёстры sibship.
родовая деятельность obstet: labor.
родовое положение bio: generic status.
родовой 1. bio: generic; 2. obstet: parturient.
~ акт = роды.
~ канал anat: parturient canal, birth c.
~ паралич obstetrical palsy, birth p.
родовспомогательное средство obstet: parturifacient.
родовые боли obstet: labor pains.
~ пути = родовой канал.

родовые схватки obstet: labor pains.
рододендрон bot: rhododendron, rosebay, azalea (Rhododendron).
~ индийский = азалия.
родолия entom: rodolia ladybug (Rodolia cardinalis).
родопсин ophth: rhodopsin, visual purple.
родоразрешение obstet: parturition, partus, delivery, childbirth.
~ кесаревым сечением Cesarean delivery. [operative delivery.
~ оперативным вмешательством
~ посредством поворота version delivery.
~ щипцами forceps delivery.
родственник relative.
~ по восходящей линии ancestor.
родственное заболевание allied
~ скрещивание inbreeding. |disease.
роды obstet: parturition, partus, parturiency, delivery, labor, childbirth, confinement, childbed, lying-in, accouche-
~ двойней twin delivery. ment.
~ мёртвым плодом missed labor.
~ после смерти роженицы postmortem delivery.
~ при атонии матки powerless labor.
~ ~ головном предлежании head delivery.
~ ~ затылочном предлежании occipital delivery.
~ ~ ножном предлежании footling d.
~ ~ помощи операции instrumental delivery. [cross birth.
~ ~ поперечном положении плода
~ ~ ягодичном предлежании breech-delivery, partus agrippinus.
роение swarming (of bees).
рожа infect: erysipelas; vet: wild fire.
~ свиней vet: swine erysipelas. [deliver.
рожать obstet: give birth, parturiate,
рожающая во второй раз obstet: secun-
~ впервые obstet: primipara. |dipara.
рождаемость birth rate, natality.
рождающая личинок larviparous.
рождение birth, childbirth, childbearing, texis, delivery.
~ живого ребёнка live birth.
~ мёртвого плода stillbirth.
~ ребёнка после смерти роженицы postmortem delivery. [in w
роженица obstet: parturient woman, lying-
рожистая крапивная лихорадка vet: erysipeloid.
рожистое воспаление = рожа.
рожистый erysipelatous. [спорынья.
рожки bot: 1. fruits of algaroba; 2. see

рожковое дерево bot: algaroba (Ceratonia siliqua).
рожок ped: nursing bottle, feeding b.
~ (большой, малый) anat: cornu (greater
рожь bot: rye (Secale cereale). |lesser).
~ дикая = волоснец песчаный.
~ ивановская spring r.
~ озимая winter r.
~ яровая spring r.
роза bot: rose (Rosa).
~ альпийская = рододендрон.
~ дамасская damask r. (R. damascena).
~ дикая dog r. (R. canina) see шиповник
~ китайская Chinese hibiscus, shoe-black plant (Hibiscus rosa-sinensis).
~ коричная cinnamon (R. cinnamomea).
~ многоцветная вьющаяся rambler (R. multiflora, Thunb.) [Thunb.)
~ морщинистая rugose r. (R. rugosa,
~ мохнатая cabbage r., moss r. (R. centifolia). [Thory).
~ нуазетовая noisette r. (R. noisettiana,
~ прерийная prairie r. (R. blanda. Ait.)
~ ржавая = шиповник эглантерия.
~ собачья = р. дикая.
~ степная = р. прерийная.
~ центифольная = р. мохнатая.
~ чайная tea r., China r. (R. odorata).
розан китайский = роза китайская
розанные (пор.) bot: Rosales.
розелла bot: rosella, Jamaica sorrel (Hibiscus sabdariffa).
розеола path: roseola.
розеолёзная сыпь rose rash.
розеолы при брюшном тифе infect: typhoid spots.
розетка брюссельской капусты bud of Brussels sprouts.
розмарин bot: rosemary (Rosmarinus).
~ аптечный old man (R. officinalis).
розовая вода pharm: rose water.
~ гниль phytp: pink rot. [montagui).
~ креветка pink shrimp (Pandalus
~ лихорадка rose cold, rose fever.
~ чайка ross's gull (Rhodostethia rosea).
розовое дерево bot: torchwood (Amyris
~ масло rose oil. balsamifera).
розовые (подсем.) bot: rose sub-family (Rosoideae).
~ (сем.) bot: rose family (Rosaceae).
розовый коробочный червь хлопчатника pink bollworm (Pectinophora gossypiella). [onocrotalus.
~ пеликан orn: pelican Pelecanus
розоцветные (пор.) bot: Rosales.

розоцветные (сем.) = розовые (сем)
роиться swarm, hive, cluster.
рой swarm, cluster.
~ -первак first swarm, prime s.(of bees)
рокет-салат bot: rocket salad, arucola, tira (Eruca sativa, Mill.,or Brassica eruca.L.)
роландова борозда = центральная б.
роликовый пинцет ophth: roller forceps
рольмопс rollmop.
ромашка bot: chamomile (Anthemis).
~ аптечная wild c., matricaria (Matricaria chamomilla).
~ благородная large c.(A. nobilis).
~ вонючая Mayweed, stinking c., dogfennel (A. cotula).
~ далматская pyrethrum (Pyrethrum cineraryfolium,Anacyclus pyrethrum).
~ дикая = р. аптечная.
~ красильная yellow c., golden marguerite (A. tinctoria).
~ лекарственная = р. аптечная.
~ немецкая аптечная Anacyclus officinarum, Hayne.
~ непахучая scentless mayweed (Matricaria inodorata).
~ обыкновенная = р. аптечная.
~ римская Roman c.,see р. благородн.
~ розовая pyrethrum roseum, bunach (Chrysanthemum coccineum, Willd.)
~ собачья = р. вонючая.
~ чихачёвская turfing daisy(Pyrethrum Tchihatchewii, Hort.)
~ шерлаховокрасная = р. розовая.
*ромб ichth: turbot (Bothidae); summer flounder,chicken halibut (Paralichthys dentatus).
Ромберг Romberg.
ромбический лист bot: rhombic leaf.
ромбовидная мышца (большая, малая) anat: rhomboideus(major,minor).
~ ямка anat: fossa rhomboidea.
ромбовидный мозг embr: hindbrain, rhombencephalon.
ронкадор ichth: spot-fin croaker (Roncador stearnsi).
рорквал zool: rorqual,sei,pollock whale (Balaenoptera borealis).
Роршах Rorschach.
роса dew.
росистый dewy.
росичка bot: fingergrass, crabgrass (Digitaria, Heist.)
~ кровяная crabgrass (D. sanguinalis).
росной ладан pharm: benzoin, gum benjamin (Styrax).
росноладанная кислота benzoic acid.

россомаха zool: wolverine,wolverene, glutton (Gulo gulo, G.borealis, G. luscus).
рост 1.growth; 2.height.
~ бактерий bacterial growth.
~ волос на крестце sacral growth of hair.
~ выше нормы overheight.
~ клеток cell enlargement.
ростец bot: thallus.
ростильня lab: germination dish.
ростовая почка bot:growth bud,leader b.
ростовое вещество growth substance.
ростовой побег bot: continuance shoot, terminal s., leading s.
росток bot: sprout, propagule,propagulum, seedling,spire.
ростральная лейкотомия rostral leucotomy.
рострум zool: rostrum(of Crustacea), beak(of daphnids).
росянка bot: sundew, daily dew, dew plant (Drosera).
~ круглолистная round-leaved s., lustwort (D. rotundifolia).
росянковые (сем.)bot: sundew family (Droseraceae).
рот mouth.
ротанг bot: palm Calamus.
ротовая пластинка embr: oral plate.
~ полость anat: oral cavity.
~ присоска helm: oral sucker,mouth-s.
ротовое впячение zool: cell-mouth.
~ отверстие mouth opening.
ротовой oral,stomatic,buccal,oscular.
~ конус (гидры)zool: manubrium, hypostome (of a hydra).
~ придаток palpus(of a bivalve mollusk).
ротовые органы entom: mouth-parts.
ротоногие раки (отр.)zool: mantis shrimps (Stomatopoda).
роторасширитель surg: mouth gag.
рохля (скат) guitar fish (Rhinobatus schegelii).
роющая нога = копательная н.
роющая форма zool: burrower.
р-р = раствор.
ртутная мазь pharm:mercurial ointment.
ртутное втирание pharm: m.inunction.
ртутный паралич neur: m. palsy.
~ пластырь pharm: mercurial plaster.
ртуть mercury, Hg.
~ растёртая с жирами pharm: extinguished mercury.
"рубашка"bot: dry scales(of onion,etc.)
рубец 1.scar,cicatrix; 2.weal, wale; 3.zool:rumen,paunch; 4.tripe.
~ в лопасти листа bot: leaf scar.
рубить chop, hack.
рубление chopping, hacking, hachement.
руброспинальный тракт anat:tractus rubrospinalis.

рубцевание cicatrization, scarring,
рубцеваться cicatrize, scar. |ulosis.
рубцовая ткань hist: scar tissue, cicatricial tissue. [contraction.
рубцовое затягивание path:scarring
~ сужение path:cicatricial narrowing.
рубцовые сосочки (плевы) anat: carunculae hymenales.
рубцовый scarry, cicatricial. [pion.
~ заворот век ophth:cicatricial entro-
рубчик bot:hilum, small scar, stigma.
рудбекия bot:coneflower(Rudbeckia).
~ волоокая oxeye, black-eyed susan, yellow daisy (R. hirta).
~ шерстистая = р. волоокая.
~ шершавая = р. волоокая.
рудимент rudiment.
рудиментарный rudimentary, vestigial.
рука anat: 1. arm, brachium; 2. hand, see кисть руки. [accoucheur's h.
~ акушера path:obstetrician's hand,
рукав 1.hose; sleeve; 2.zool: rumen, paunch.
рукоблудие psych: self-abuse, onanism.
рукокрылые (отр.) zool: chiropters, bats (Chiroptera).
рукокрылый zool:chiropteran, of bats.
руконожка zool: lemur Chiromis madagascarensis.
рукопёрые (сем.)ichth: Lophidae.
рукоятка bio: manubrium, proboscis.
~ (грудины) anat: manubrium.
~ молоточка anat: malleus handle.
рукояточный manubrial.
рулевое перо orn: rectrix.
рулевой жгутик zool:trailing flagellum
рулёк helm: accessory piece.
рулетка = измерительная рулетка.
румянец erubescence, bloom(on fruits).
румянка bot: alkanet, anchusa, bugloss (Anchusa).
румянящийся bot: erubescent(fruit, etc.)
рунец = кровососка овечья.
руппия bot:ditchgrass, widgeongrass
русская баня Russian bath. |(Ruppia).
русский гусь orn:Russian goose(domestic)
~ осётр ichth: Russian sturgeon (Acipenser güldenstaedtii).
рута bot: rue (Ruta); common rue, herb-of-grace (R. graveolens).
~ стенная wall r. (R. muricata).
рутовые (сем.) bot: rue family (Rutaceae).
ручейник entom:caddis-fly.
~ мелкий microcaddis f.(Hydroptilidae).
ручейники (отр.) entom: caddis-flies (Trichoptera).

ручка 1. anat: small hand (fetus, baby, infant); 2. handle.
ручная ванна phys-ther: arm bath;
~ кисть anat: hand. maniluvium.
~ шина surg: hand splint.
ручное тазоизмерение obstet:digital pelvimetry.
ручьевая форель ichth: brook trout (Salvelinus fontinalis).
р-ция = реакция. [dontidae).
рыба-бабочка butterfly-fish (Chaeto-
~ -гадюка viper fish (Chauliodus).
~ -дракон dragonfish (Pegasus).
~ -единорог unicorn fish (Bregmaceros maulellandi).
~ -лоцман Naucrates ductor.
~ -молот Sphyrna zygaena.
~ обитающая в русле channel fish.
~ объячеена fish is gilled.
~ -пилот pilot fish (Naucrates ductur).
~ -призрак long-finned ghostfish (Dolichopterix).
~ -прилипало Echenoidea.
~ -сабля = сабля-рыба.
~ -скелет skeletonfish (Sternoptix).
~ со зрелой икрой female in full roe.
~ способная раздуваться в шар bur fish. [phum).
~ -фонарь lantern fish (Diaphus; Micto-
~ -хирург surgeon fish(Acanthurus).
рыбацкий узел surg: reef knot.
рыбец ichth: Vimba.
рыбёшка small fish, fry, minnow.
рыбий piscine, of fishes.
~ жир cod-liver oil.
~ клей fish glue, isinglass.
рыбная промышленность fishing industry.
рыбные консервы canned fish.
рыбный бульон bact: fish-broth.
~ запах fishy odor.
~ привкус fishy flavor.
рыбовидный fishlike.
рыбовод fish farmer, fish culturist.
рыбоводное хозяйство fish husbandry, fish culture project.
рыбоводный fish-cultural.
~ завод fish hatchery, fish farm.
рыбоводство pisciculture, f.culture.
рыбозмей zool: Ichthyophis.
рыболовная ягода pharm: cocculus indicus.
рыболовный fishing, piscatorial.
рыболов-пигмей ichth:pygmy angler (Aceratias).
рыбоподобный ichthyoid, fishlike.

рыборазведение fish farming.
рыбоядный fish-eating, ichthyophagous, piscivorous.
рыбы ichth: fishes (Pisces).
рыбьи вши fishlice (Branchiura); see also короткохвостые раки.
рыбья пиявка zool: acanthodella (Acanthodella pelidina, Pisicola geometra).
рыгать belch, eructate.
рыгнуть p. a. of рыгать.
рыжай = краснодев.
рыжей bot: false flax (Camelina, Crantz).
~ посевной Western false f., Dutch f., large false f., gold-of-pleasure, dodder seed, garden rocket (C. sativa).
рыжик bot: 1. orange milk mushroom, delicious milky cap (Lactarius deliciosus, Fr.); 2. see рыжей.
рык roaring (of a lion).
рыло zool: snout, muzzle.
рыльнокопытная болезнь = ящур.
рыльце bot: stigma, snout.
рыльцевый bot: stigmatic.
рыскун-трава = вереск.
рысь zool: lynx, bobcat, wildcat (Felis lynx).
рыхлая соединительная ткань hist: areolar tissue.
~ ткань hist: areolar tissue.
рыхлоголовый bot: loose-head.
рыхлоколосый agr bot: lax-spiked.
рыхлокочанный bot: loose-head.
рыхлокустовая трава bot: bunch grass.
рыхлый friable, crumbly, loosely packed, packless, pultaceous; see also пульпозный.
~ клубок hist: loose skein.
рычание roaring (of a lion).
рэдфиш redfish (Pimelometopon pulcher; Sciaenops ocellatus).
рябина bot: European mountain ash, rowan, [illegible] (Sorbus aucuparia, L., or Pyrus aucuparia, Gaertn.); chokeberry.
~ американская American m.a., dogberry, roundwood, missey-moosey (P. americana).
~ домашняя service-tree (P. domestica).
~ канадская serviceberry (Amelanchier canadensis, Medic.)
~ клуглолистная whitebeam (Sorbus aria)
~ крымская = р. домашняя.
~ обыкновенная = рябина.
~ садовая = рябина.
рябинолистник bot: false spiraea (Sorbaria sorbifolia, A.Br.)
рябишник = пижма.
рябки (пор.) orn: Pterocletes.
рябой poked, pitted, marked with pustules.
рябчик orn Brit: hazel-grouse, hazel-hen, wood hen (Bonasa betulina, Tetrao bonasia).
рядовка скрытная = зелёнка.
ряпушка обыкновенная ichth: whitefish Coregonus albula.
ряска bot: duckweed, duck's-meat (Lemna).
~ многокоренная water flaxseed, large duckweed (Spirodela polyrhiza).
~ трехдольная star duckweed, ivy-leaved d. (L. trisulca).
рясковые (сем.) bot: duckweed family (Lemnaceae).

С

с with, see also снабжённый.
~ бахромчатым неровным краем lacerate-fimbriate.
~ ветвящимся талломом bot: trichothallic.
~ волнистым краем repand.
~ высоким содержанием белка high-protein.
~ ~ содержанием жира high-fat.
~ выступающей нижней челюстью prognathic.
~ гладкой раковиной smooth-shelled.
~ глубоким пупком zool: umbilicate (shell, etc.)
~ густыми ветвями или листьями bot: fastigiate.
~ двумя коготками biunguiculate.
~ ~ кольцами biannulate.
~ жилкованием entom: veined.
~ закрученными назад или вниз краями revolute.
~ илистым дном muck-bottom.
~ килем bio: keeled, ecarinate.
~ клешнями zool: chelate, labidophorous.
~ колючими зубчиками serrate-spiny.
~ крышечкой operculate.
~ крышкой operculate.
~ листьями объемлющими стебель bot: perfoliate.
~ мелкими шипиками bot: spinulose, spinulated.
~ миндалевидными глазами almond-eyed.
~ нарушенным ритмом перистальтики anisoperistaltic.

с немногими оборотами bio:paucispiral
~ ~ семенами bot: few-seeded.
~ неправильно зазубренным краем erose.
~ неравными створками zool:inequivalve
~ одним вздутием zool:aphelenchoid.
~ ~ коготком zool:uniunguiculate.
~ ~ семенем bot: one-seeded.
~ перепончатым краем scarious-margined.
~ прижатыми щетинками bio:strigose.
~ прицветником bot:bracteate,bracted.
~ продольными ложбинками bot: subcanaliculate.
~ пупкообразным вдавлением umbilicated.
~ пустым кишечником zool: empty-gutted.
~ равными створками zool:equivalve.
~ раскрытым зевом bot: ringent.
~ сухой тонкой перепонкой bot: scariose, scarious.
~ тонкой трубочкой расширяющейся в плоскую воронку bot: salverform, salver-shaped.
~ точечными бороздками striato-punctate.
~ тремя органами каждого вида bot: three-merous,3-merous (of a flower).
~ ~ семенами bot: three-seeded, 3-seeded.
~ узкими остроконечными долями bot: laciniate, slashed.
~ ушками auriculate.
~ хвостообразным придатком caudate.
~ хохолками bot: floccose.
~ цельной чашечкой bot:gamosepalous.
~ черешком bot:petiolate, petioled.
сабадилла bot: sabadilla (Sabadilla officinarum,Brandt.)
сабаль-пальметта = пальметта-сабаль.
сабина = можжевельник казацкий.
саблевидная нога path: bowleg,genu varum.
саблезубая рыба-гадюка saber-toothed viperfish (Chauliodus sloanei).
саблерот ichth: scimitar-mouth (Gonostoma elongatum).
сабля-рыба cuttlass fish,ribbon fish (Trichiurus lepturus).
сабур bot: aloe;pharm:aloe pulp,a.pith.
сабуровый pharm: aloetic.
сагиттальная борозда anat:sagittal sulcus.
~ пазуха anat:sagittal sinus.
саговая пальма bot: sago palm (Metroxylon rumphii,Phoenix larve).
саговая селезёнка path:sago spleen.
саговник bot:sago palm(Cycas revoluta).
саговники (пор.)bot:Cycadales.
саговниковые (кл.) bot:Cycadophyta.
саджа orn: bird Syrrhaptes paradoxus. Cf. рябки.
садизм psych: sadism.
садист psych: sadist.
садист(иче)ский sadistic.
садовая улитка zool: garden snail (Helix aspersa).
садовод horticulturist.
садоводство horticulture.
садовое растение horticultural plant.
садовый слизень zool: shell-less slug Arion.
садок zool:live box,retainer,live car, minnow pail.
сажка = головня.
сазан = карп.
Сазерленд Sutherland.
сайга zool: antelope Saiga tatarica.
сайда ichth: saithe, coalfish,pollack, pollock (Pollachius).
сайдяной полосатик = ивасиевый полосатик.
сайка ichth:arctic cod(Boreogadus saida).
сайра ichth: Cololabis.
*сайсл bot: yaxci(Agave sisalana,Perr.)
саккулина zool:crustacean Sacculina.
салаамовы судороги neur: Salaam spasm.
салака = балтийская сельдь.
саламандра salamander.
саламандровые (подотр.)zool: salamandrines (Salamandroidea).
саламандры (сем.) zool: salamander family (Salamandridae).
саланган = стриж-саланган.
саланкс ichth: small fish Salangichthys microdon.
саланксовые (сем.)ichth:Salangidae.
салат bot: lettuce, milkweed, salad (Lactuca).
~ кочанный head l., cabbage l.
~ латук lettuce (L. sativa).
~ морской = морской салат.
~ огородный листовой loose-leaved l.
~ рапунцель = валерианница овощная.
~ -розель = розелла.
~ ромэн celery l., Cos l.
~ срывной cut-leaved l.,cutting l., bunching l.
~ -эндивий = эндивий.
~ эскариоль curled l.,Batavian endive (L. scariola crispa).

саливация salivation.
салигаллол = салициловокислый
пирогаллол. [cornia).
саликорния bot: glasswort, samphire (Sali-
салипирин pharm: salipyrin, antipyrine
salicylate.
салистый tallowish.
салит pharm: borneol salicylate.
салиформин pharm: formin salicylate,
urotropin s.
салициловокислый антипирин pharm:
antipyrine salicylate, salipyrazolone.
~ висмут (основной) Bismuth
subsalicylate.
~ литий lithium salicylate.
~ магний magnesium salicylate.
~ натрий sodium salicylate.
~ ~ -кофеин caffeine and sodium
salicylate.
~ пирогаллол pyrogallol disalicylate.
~ салицилхинин salicyl-quinine
salicylate.
~ феноколл phenocoll salicylate.
~ хинин quinine salicylate.
салмонелла salmonella.
салмонеллёзная инфекция salmonella
infection.
сало lard. колл.
салоколл = салициловокислый фено-
салол pharm: salol, phenyl salicylate.
салуфер pharm: sodium silicofluoride.
сальварсан pharm: salvarsan,
arsphenamine.
сальвиниевое растение bot: water
fern (Azolla, Salvinia).
сальвиниевые (сем.) bot: salvinia
family (Salviniaceae).
сальвиния bot: salvinia (Salvinia, Adans.)
~ плавающая S. natans, All. [sebaceous g.
сальная железа anat: fat gland,
~ ~ века anat: tarsal gland,
Meiboimian g. [sebaceous plug.
~ пробка derm: comedo, blackhead,
сальник (большой, малый) anat:
omentum (great, lesser). [nella)
~ высокогорный bot: tallow-weed (Acti-
сальниковая грыжа surg: omentocele,
epiplocele.
~ полоска anat: taenia omentalis.
~ сумка anat: omental bursa. [foramen.
сальниковое отверстие anat: epiploic
сальниковый anat: omental, epiploic.
~ отросток anat: appendix epiploica.
сальное дерево = китайское сальное дерево.

сальный lardy, sebaceous, tallowy.
сальпинготомия gyn: salpingotomy.
сальпы (кл.) zool: salpas (Salpae).
сальсифи = козлобородник.
~ испанский = испанский золотой
корень.
самая короткая глазная мышца
anat: brevissimus oculi, see
нижняя косая глазная мышца.
самбук = бузина.
самец zool: male, buck.
~ парнокопытных zool: even-toed male,
самка female. bull.
~ (ластоногих) cow.
~ павлина peahen.
само- self-, auto-, see авто-, ауто-.
самоанализ psych: morbid introspection,
self-examination. [bility.
самовнушаемость psych: autosuggesti-
самовнушение psych: autosuggestion,
self-suggestion.
самовозгорание spontaneous combustion.
самовскрытие bot: self-tripping (of
a flower).
самогипноз psych: autohypnosis, self-
hypnosis, idiohypnotism.
самогон(ка) moonshine (alcohol).
самодержащийся крючок surg:
automatic retractor. [invasion.
самозаражение autoinfection; auto-
самозаряжающаяся ловушка self-
resetting trap (for animals).
самоизворот obstet: spontaneous evolu-
самоизлечение self-healing. |tion.
самоизреживание bot: selfthinning,
autothinning.
самоизувечение legl: self-mutilation.
самокалечение 1. legl: self-mutilation;
2. zool: autotomy.
самолёт с герметизированной
кабиной av med: pressure-cabin plane.
самонаблюдение psych: introspection.
самонадувание среднего уха av med:
autoinflation of the middle ear.
самонесовместимость bot: self-
incompatibility. [ination, s.-accusation.
самообвинение legl psych: self-incrim-
самообеспложивание self-sterility.
самооплодотворение bio: self-
fertilization, autogamy. [autogamy.
самоопыление bot: self-pollination,
самоопылённая линия bot: intrainbred
самоотравление autointoxication. |line.
самоотсечение self-amputation.
самоочиститель san: autoeductor.

самоочищение self-purification; bot: self-pruning, natural pruning, autolopping
самопереваривание path: autodigestion, autolysis.
самоплодный bot: self-fruitful.
самоповорот obstet: spontaneous version.
самопожирание autophagy, self-consumption.
самопроизвольное кровотечение spontaneous hemorrhage.
саморастворение autolysis.
саморастрескивающийся плод bot: dehiscent fruit.
самосев bot: natural seeding; seeding growth.
самосевный клевер bot: volunteer clover
самосовместимость self-compatibility.
самосогревание сена hay heating.
самосохранение self-preservation.
самостерильность self-sterility.
самостоятельные роды obstet: spontaneous labor.
самостоятельный independent, self-supporting, self-existing, self-contained, autonomous.
самострел mil legl: soldier having a self-inflicted gunshot wound.
самоубивающий пояс ent agr: autocide belt (against harmful insects).
самоубийственный suicidal.
самоубийство legl: suicide.
самоуничижение psych: self-humiliation.
самочувствие "self-feeling", "self-sensation", patient's impression of his own condition; у него хорошее (плохое) с. he feels well (bad).
самшит bot: boxtree, common boxelder (Buxus sempervirens).
самшитовые (сем.) bot: box family (Buxaceae).
санаторий sanatorium, health resort.
санаторное лечение sanatorium treatment.
санация = оздоровление.
сандальное дерево sandalwood, see кампешевое дерево.
сандарак bot: sandarac(h), arar, gum-tree (Callitris quadrivalvis, Thuja articulata
санитар (male) orderly, attendant.
~ -носильщик stretcher-bearer.
санитария sanitation; sanitary science.
санитарка (female) orderly, attendant.
санитарная карета = с. машина.
~ машина ambulance (car)
~ повозка = с. машина.
~ полевая сумка mil: first-aid kit.
~ служба sanitary service, public health s.
санитарная техника sanitary engineering.

санитарное мероприятие sanitation measure, public-health m.
~ просвещение health education.
санитарный врач health officer, sanitarian.
~ надзор sanitary supervision.
~ поезд ambulance train.
~ работник sanitarian, (public-)health worker.
~ самолёт ambulance plane, air ambulance.
санталовое масло pharm: santal oil.
санталовые (пор.) bot: Santalales.
сантехника = санитарная техника.
сантил pharm: santabyl salicylate.
сантолина кипарисовидная bot: lavender cotton, santolina (Santolina chamaecyparissus).
сантонин pharm: santonin.
сантониновокислый натрий pharm: sodium santoninate.
сап infect vet: glanders, farcy, equinia.
сапинд bot: soapberry (Sapindus).
сапиндовые (сем.) bot: soapberry family (Sapindaceae).
сапиндоцветные (пор.) bot: soapberry order (Sapindales).
сапная опухоль farcy bud.
~ палочка bact: glanders bacillus.
сапный glanderous.
~ узелок glanders nodule.
саподилла bot: chikoo, sapodilla (Achras zapota, or A. sapota).
сапожничья грудь path: cobbler's chest.
сапонин saponin.
сапотовые (сем.) bot: sapodilla family (Sapotaceae).
сапрозойный zool: saprozoic.
сапролегниевый bot: saprolegnious, saprolegoniaceous.
сапролегния bot: water mold, Saprolegnia (fungus).
сапропель sapropel.
сапрофит bio: saprophyte.
сапрфитный saprophytic.
сапсан обыкновенный orn: peregrin falcon, duck hawk (Falco peregrinus).
сарана = краснодев.
~ большая turban lily (Lilium martagon).
~ мелколистная coral l. (L. tenuifolium)
саранка = сарана большая.
саранча entom: locust, short-horned grasshopper.
~ азиатская = с. перелётная.
~ восточная перелётная Locusta migratoria manilensis.
~ итальянская Italian l. (Calliptamus italicus).
~ марокская Maroc l. (Dociostaurus maroccanus).
~ обыкновенная = с. перелётная.

саранча перелётная migratory locust (Locusta migratoria, Pachytylus migratorius).
~ пустынная schistocerca(Schistocerca gregaria).
~ среднерусская Locusta migratoria rossica.
~ тропическая перелётная Locusta migratoria migrotorioides.
саранчовые (надсем.) entom: locusts (Acridoidea).
сарган ichth:garfish(Belone);hound fish (Tylosurus).
саргановые (сем.)ichth: garfishes (Belonidae).
саргасса bot: sargasso, ginbaso (Sargassum) brown algae; mo, moku (S. enerve); gulfweed (S.filipendula).
сарго ichth: sargo (Haemuliidae).
сардель = шпрот черноморский.
сардина ichth: sardine, pilchard (Sardina).
сардинка ichth: pilchard (Sardinella).
саркодовые zool: Sarcodina, see ложноножковые.
сарколемма anat: sarcolemma.
сарколемный sarcolemmic.
саркома path: sarcoma.
саркоматоз path: sarcomatosis.
саркофаги (сем.) entom: sarcophagids (Sarcophagidae).
саррацениевые (сем.) bot: pitcher-plant family (Sarraceniaceae).
саррацения bot: pitcher plant(Sarracenia).
сарсапариль = смилакс ланцетовидный.
сарцина bact: Sarcina.
сарцинный sarcinic.
сатинированный satiny.
сатурнизм saturnism, plumbism.
сафлор bot: safflower,false saffron, bastard saffron(Carthamus tinctorius).
сахалинский осётр ichth: red sturgeon, green s.(Acipenser medirostris).
сахар sugar.
сахарная белка zool: petaurist,flying squirrel (Petaurus sciureus).
~ кривая sugar curve.
~ пальма bot: sugar palm(Arenga saccarifera,etc.)
сахарное мочеизнурение = сахарный диабет.
сахарный sugary, saccharinus.
~ бульон lab: sugar broth.
~ диабет path: diabetes mellitus.
~ корень bot: sugar root, skirret (Sium sisarum).
~ обмен bio:saccharometabolism,sugar metabolism.
сахарный тростник sugar cane (Saccharum officinarum).
сахароза saccharose, sucrose.
сахаромицеты mcbio: saccharomyces (Saccharomycetes).
сахароносы bot: sugar plants.
сахарообменный bio: saccharometabolic.
сачок lift net, dip net, pusher.
сбегающий bot: decurrent.
сближающий шов surg: coapting suture.
сближение apposition,rapprochement.
сближенный connivent.
сбор pharm: species.
~ анамнеза collection of anamnesis.
сборный вид bio:collective species.
~ плод bot: aggregate fruit.
сбраживание fermentation.
сбраживающий fermentative.
сбрасывание bot: shedding, dropping, abscission; see also самоочищение.
~ листовых черешков bot: leaf petiole abscission.
Жсбрасывать кожу zool: cast, (the skin, shell, etc.)
~ листья bot: shed leaves.
сбривать san: shave (off).
сбритьр. a. of сбривать.
сброс цвета bot: blossom drop.
сбросить p. a. of сбрасывать.
сброшенная шкурка zool:exuvia(molt).
свайник-великан helm: kidney worm, palisade w. (Eustrongylus gigas).
~ -гигант = с.-великан.
~ двенадцатиперстной кишки =кривоголовка двенадцатиперстная.
сведа bot:seablite (Suaeda, Forsk.)
сведе́ние contracture.
~ зрительных осей ophth:convergence.
~ челюстей vet: trismus.
свежая катаракта ophth: existing cataract.
свежевать agr: flay, dress.
свежевылинявший zool: freshly molted.
свежевыпущенная кровь freshly drawn blood.
свежее помутнение ophth: macula corneae.
свежеизолированный lab: recently isolated.
свёкла bot: beet (Beta vulgaris).
~ кормовая fodder b., stock b.
~ листовая leaf b.,sea-kale b.,chard, silver b., mangold.
~ листовая шпинатная spinach b.
~ сахарная sugar b.
~ столовая table b., garden b.

свекловица bot:beetroot,see свёкла.
свекловичный сахар beet sugar.
свекольник bot: mangold, see свёкла листовая.
сверлило корабельный timber beetle (Lymexylon navale).
сверлильщик entom: borer,shot-hole b.
~ плоскоголовый бронзовый берёзовый bronze birch-borer(Agrilus anxius).
~ рисовый стеблевой шенобиус rice-stem borer (Schoenobius incertellus).
~ робиниевый locust borer (Cyllene robinia).
~ сосновый плоскоголовый flat-headed pine borer(Chalcophora virginiensis).
сверлящая боль boring pain, telebrating p.
~ губка zool: Cliona.
сверлящее ракообразное zool: gribble (Limnoria lignorum).
сверлящие органы zool: piercing organs
сверлящий дерево wood-boring.
~ тростник entom: cane-boring.
свёрнутый в кольцо bot: circinate.
~ (по длине)bot: convolute,rolled-up longitudinally.
свернуться p. a. of свертываться.
свёртываемость coagulability.
~ крови blood coagulation.
свёртываемый coagulable.
свёртывание coagulation, curdling, clotting.
~ крови blood coagulation.
свёртыватель coagulant.
свёртывать(ся) 1.furl,coil,roll(up), curl;2.coagulate,curdle,clot.
сверхдикротический пульс = дикротический пульс.
сверхиммунный hyperimmune.
сверхкомплектная почка bot:supernumerary bud.
сверхпаразит zool: hyperparasite.
сверчковые (надсем.)entom: crickets (Grylloidea).
сверчок entom: field cricket (Gryllus domesticus).
~ чёрный tree cricket (Oecanthus nigricornis).
светляк entom: fire-fly,glow-worm(Lampyris).
светобоязливый photophobic; bot: heliophobic.
светобоязнь photophobia,intolerance of light; bot: heliophobia.
световая ванна phys-ther:light-bath.
~ ловушка light trap.
световое восприятие light perception.
~ чувство light sense.
световой конус light reflex (in the ear).
~ раздражитель photic stimulus.
светолечение light treatment.
светолюбивое растение bot:light-demanding plant,heliophyte.
светолюбивый bot:light-demanding, heliophilous.
светопреломляющая среда глаза ophth:light-refracting medium of the eye.
светопреломляющий орган zool: light-refracting organ.
светящаяся медуза zool:luminescent medusa (Pelagia noctiluca).
светящееся животное phosphorescing animal.
светящесязубый удильщик ichth: shining-toothed angler(Dolopichthys).
светящиеся клетки photogenic cells, light-producing c.
светящийся luminous, lumenescent.
~ ночью noctilucous.
свеча Беркефельда bact: Berkefeld filter.
свечение luminescence, glow.
~ от живых организмов bioluminescence.
свечка pharm: suppository.
свечное дерево bot:candle-berry tree, see лаковое дерево 2.
свивание гнезда orn: nidification.
свидетельство 1. evidence; 2.certificate.
~ о здоровьи health certificate.
~ о рождении birth certificate.
~ о смерти death certificate.
~ о состоянии здоровья health certificate.
свидина bot: red dogwood, cornel. gaiter (Cornus sanguinea).
свиетения bot: mahogany (Swietenia mahagoni).
свинарник agr: pigpen,pigsty.
свиная краснуха vet: erysipeloid.
~ печень pig liver.
Свиней Sweeney.
свинец lead, Pb.
свинка 1.infect: mumps; 2.zool:small pig, piglet; 3.entom:see долгоносик свекловичный.
свиноводство agr: pig breeding.
свиное сало lard.
свиной porcine.
~ желудок hog stomach.
~ жир hog's lard.
~ ~ с бензойной смолой pharm: benzoinated lard.

свиной солитер = вооружённый цепень.
~ финноз vet: pork measles.
~ хлев agr: pigpen, pigsty.
свиноматка sow, she-swine.
свинорой bot: wire grass, dog's-tooth g. (Cynodon dactilon, Pers.); see also бермудская трава.
свицовая вода pharm: lead water.
~ кайма path: lead line.
~ колика = колика живописцев.
~ мазь Гебры pharm: diachylon ointment.
~ примочка pharm: lead lotion.
свинцовка bot: leadwort (Plumbago).
свинцовое отравление lead poisoning.
свинцовый паралич neur: lead palsy, saturnine p.
~ пластырь pharm: lead plaster, litharge p.
~ сахар pharm: sugar of lead.
~ уксус pharm: vinegar of lead.
свинчатковые (сем.) bot: leadwort family (Plumbaginaceae).
свиньи (сем.) zool: swine family (Suidae)
свинья swine, pig, sow (Sus scrofa domestica).
свиристель orn: waxwing (Bombycillidae, Ampelidae).
~ богемская Bohemian w. (Bombycilla garrula pallidiceps).
~ кедровая cedar w. (B. cedrorum).
~ обыкновенная = с. богемская.
свисающий = плакучий, пониклый.
~ язык zool: lolling tongue.
свистулька trumpet fish (Fistularia).
свистуха = свиязь.
свистящие хрипы path: sibilant rales.
свистящий звук whistling sound, stridor.
свить p. a. of вить.
свищ path: fistula, sinus; flaw.
~ (в орехе) bot: wormhole (in a nut).
~ грудной железы path: mastosyrinx.
~ заднего прохода anal fistula.
~ молочной железы milk fistula.
~ слюнной железы salivary fistula.
~ толстой кишки surg: colostomy.
свиязь orn: widgeon, duck Anas penelope.
свободная полоска anat: taenia libera.
свободное переопыление bot: open pollination.
свободноживущий free-living.
свободно лежащий loose-lying.
свободнолепестный bot: choripetalous, apophyllous.
свободнолистный bot: aposepalous, chorisepalous.
свободноколоцветниковый bot: apophyllous.
свободно плавающий free-swimming.
свободноподъязычные = челюстножаберные.
свободные иглокожие (подтип) zool: Eleuthrozoa.
свободный макрофаг hist: free macrophage.
~ от бактерий free from germs, sterile.
~ ~ растений plant-free.
свод anat: fornix, cul-de-sac.
~ конъюнктивы ophth: fornix of the conjunctiva.
сводовый anat: fornical.
сводообразная извилина = сводчатая извилина.
сводчатая извилина (мозга) anat: fornicate gyrus, g. fornicatus.
связка anat: ligament, commissure, frenu(lu)m, retinaculum.
~ век frenulum of the eyelid.
~ яичника, собственная ligamentum ovarii proprium.
связкообразный anat: ligamentous.
связник bot: connective, commissure.
связочный anat: ligamentous.
связующий bio: annectent.
связывание азота bot: nitrogen fixation.
~ комплемента complement fixation, c. binding.
сгиб bend, crease.
сгибание flexion.
~ в сторону gyn: lateroflexion.
~ колена genuflexion.
сгибатель anat: flexor.
~ большого пальца ноги (длинный, короткий) anat: flexor hallucis (longus, brevis).
~ ~ пальца руки (длинный, короткий) anat: flexor pollicis (longus, brevis).
~ пальцев (длинный, короткий) anat: flexor digitorum (longus, brevis).
~ руки arm flexor.
сгибательная контрактура path: permanent flexion.
~ поверхность anat: flexion surface.
~ сторона anat: flexor aspect.
сгибать(ся) bend, flex.
сгибающая мышца мизинца (короткая) anat: flexor digiti quinti brevis.
сгуститель inspissator.
сгустить(ся) p. a. of сгущать(ся).
сгусток clump, clot, curd, coagulum, grume.
~ крови blood clot.
сгущать(ся) condense, inspissate, thicken.

сгущение condensation, inspissation, thickening, pycnosis.
~ крови path: hemoconcentration, blood clotting.
сгущенное молоко evaporated milk.
сдавление compression. [compression.
~ головного мозга path: cerebral
сдавленный (com)pressed, narrowed, flattened. [together.
сдавливание compression, pressing
сдалбливание surg: chiseling off.
сдирать strip.
~ кожу (с животных) flay, strip.
сдор vet: crow, frill, mesentery.
*сеанс seance, sitting.
*себастомус ichth: corsair (Sebastomus
себоррея derm: seborrhea. |rosaceus).
себоррический seborrheic, seborrheal.
себорройный = себоррический.
северная качурка orn: Leach's fork-tailed petrel (Oceanodroma l.leucorrhoa).
~ лайка = упряжная собака.
~ олуша orn: northern gannet (Sula bassana). [gus).
~ сельдь Atlantic herring (Clupea haren-
северный олень zool: reindeer (Rangifer tarandus).
*~ ~ американский caribon (R.caribon).
севооборот agr bot: crop rotation.
севрюга ichth: starred sturgeon (Acipenser stellatus).
сегмент segment, entom: somite, arthromere.
~ брюшка zool: uromere.
~ ноги zool: podomere.
~ тела zool: arthromere.
сегментационное ядро hist: segmentation nucleus.
сегментация segmentation.
сегментированный segmented.
сегментоядерный segmentonuclear.
сегнетова соль pharm: potassium and sodium tartrate, Seignette's salt, Rochelle s.
седалище anat: huckle, ischium.
седалищная вырезка (большая, малая) anat: (greater, lesser) sciatic
~ кость anat: ischium, seat bone. |notch.
~ корешковая невралгия radicular sciatica.
~ ость anat: sciatic spine.
седалищно-пещеристая мышца anat: ischiocavernosus muscle.
~ -прямокишечная ямка anat: ischiorectal fossa.
седалищный бугор anat: ischial tuberosity.
седалищный нерв anat: sciatic nerve, nervus ischiadicus.
седаш = посконник коноплёвый.
седентарный sedentary. [type.
седиментаторы zool: sedimentation
седловидная голова path: saddle head.
~ ракушка zool: saddle oyster (Anomia).
седловидноголовый path: clinocephalous.
седловидный нос path: saddle nose.
~ сустав anat: saddle joint.
седловина zool: saddle.
сёдлышко zool: ephippium.
сёдлышковый zool: ephippial.
сезам bot: sesame, til, blue plant, ajonjoli, benne (Sesamum indicum).
сезамовая трава bot: gamagrass, sesamegrass (Tripsacum).
сезамовое масло benne oil.
сезамовые (сем.) bot: sesame family (Pedaliaceae). [tion.
сезонное изменение seasonal varia-
сейвал = ивасиевый полосатик.
сеймуриоморфа zool: Seymouriomorpha (extinct reptiles).
сейсмотерапия shaking cure.
сейурус orn: water thrush (Seiurus).
сейшельская пальма bot: palm Lodoicea seychellarum.
секач zool: old bull (old male fur seal).
секвестр sequestrum.
секвойя bot: sequoia (Sequoia, DC.)
~ вечнозелёная redwood (S. sempervirens). [see веллингтония.
~ гигантская big tree (S. gigantea),
секрет secretion (substance), secreta.
~ сальной железы sebaceous secretion.
секретарь orn: secretary bird (Sagittarius serpentarius).
секретное лекарственное средство pharm: secret medicine, nostrum.
секреторная железа anat: secretory gland.
~ жидкость physl: secretory liquid.
~ иннервация secretory innervation.
~ способность secretory ability.
секреторное средство secretagogue.
секреторный аппарат anat: secretory apparatus.
~ нерв anat: secretory nerve.
~ орган anat: secretory organ, secernment.
~ сосуд anat: secretory vessel.
секреция secretion.
~ жёлчи biliary secretion, bile secretion.

секреция мочи urine secretion.
сексологический sexologic.
сексология sexology.
сексуальность sexuality.
сексуальный sexual.
сектор Зоммерса Sommer's sector.
секционная комната = прозекторская.
секционный зал autopsy room, postmortem r.
~ инструмент anat: dissector.
~ стол anat: autopsy table, postmortem t.
секция section, sectio.
селагинелла bot: spikemoss (Selaginella).
~ крючковатая rainbow moss (S. uncinata, [Spring.)
~ плауновидная selago s. (Selaginella selaginoides).
селагинеллевые (сем.) bot: spikemoss family (Selaginellaceae).
селёдка ichth: herring, see сельдь.
селезёнка anat: spleen, lien.
селезёночная артерия anat: lienal artery, splenic a.
~ вена anat: splenic vein.
селезёночник bot: golden saxifrage (Chrysosplenium).
селезёночно-костномозговой anat: splenomedullary.
селезёночнопочечный lienorenal.
селезёночный splenic.
~ индекс path: spleen rate.
селезень orn: drake, male duck.
селективная локализация rad: selective localization (of an isotope).
селекционер bot: plant breeder.
селекционная станция bot: plant-breeding station.
селекция bot: selection, plant breeding.
селене ichth: horsehead, humpbacked butterfish, blunt-nosed shiner, pug-nosed s. (Selene vomer).
✶селитра salpeter, niter.
селитренная бумага pharm: salpeter paper.
сельдёвая акула ichth: mackerel shark, porbeagle (Lamna cornubica, L. nasus).
сельдевидная рыба big-eyed herring (Elops saurus; Pomolobus pseudoharengus).
сельдевидный herring-like, clupeoid.
сельдевые (сем.) ichth: herring family (Clupeidae).
~ акулы (сем.) ichth: mackerel sharks [(Lamnidae).
сельделов = чайка серебристая атлантическая.
сельдеобразные (отр.) ichth: Clupeiformes.
сельдеобразный = сельдевидный.
сельдерей bot: celery (Apium graveolens).
~ болотный marshwort (A. nodiflorum).
~ корневой (turnip-)rooted c., knob c., celeriac.
~ листовой = с. срывной кудрявый.
~ салатный celery.
~ срывной кудрявый soup c., smallage.
~ черешковый celery.
сельдь ichth: herring, Atlantic h. (Clupea harengus); spring h., river h., alewife, (Pomolobus pseudoharengus); etc.
сельдяной король ichth: ribbon-fish (Regalecus).
~ полосатик zool: fin whale, finback (whale) (Balaenoptera physalus).
сельский врач rural physician.
сельскохозяйственная ботаника economic botany.
сельскохозяйственные животные farm livestock, farm animals.
сем. = семейство.
сёмга = лосось.
семеводный spermiducal.
семеед seed-eating weevil, ovuliferous [scale.
~ берёзовый birch-seed weevil (Apion simily).
~ грушевый = с. яблонный.
✶~ клеверный clover-seed cater weevil (Apion apricons).
~ кориандровый coriander-seed weevil.
~ миндальный almond w. (Eurytoma amygdali).
~ плодовый fruittree w. Oxystoma [pomonae.
~ рябиновый Callimome aucupariae.
~ эспарцетовый Eurytoma onobrychidis.
~ яблонный apple-tree w. (Gallimome druparum).
семейная болезнь familial disease.
~ эритробластическая анемия familial erythroblastic anemia.
семейно-наследственный heredofamilial.
семейный анамнез family history.
семейство bio: family (Familia).
семена опийного мака mawseed.
семенная артерия, внутренняя anat: internal spermatic artery, ovarian a. (in female).
~ ~, наружная anat: external spermatic artery, cremasteric a.
~ бороздка bot: seed-furrow.

семенная железа anat: seminal gland.
~ жидкость seminal fluid.
~ камера bot: seed cavity.
~ коробочка bot: seedcase, seed vessel.
~ льняная коробочка bot: flax boll.
~ нить seminal filament, spermatic f.
~ оболочка bot: seedcoat.
семенник 1. zool: spermary, testis; 2. bot: seed plant; mother tree.
семенниковый testicular.
семенное дерево bot: mother tree.
~ растение bot: seed plant.
семенной seminal, spermic.
~ бугорок anat: seminal colliculus.
~ (извитой) каналец anat: seminiferous tubule (of the testis).
~ каналец zool: sperm ductule.
~ канатик anat: spermatic cord.
~ клубочек bot: seedball (beet, etc.)
~ проток anat: seminal duct, spermatic d.
~ пузырёк anat: seminal vesicle; hist: seed sack.
семенные папоротники bot: Pteridospermae (extinct).
~ растения bot: seed plants, phanerogams, Spermatophyta.
семеновод agr bot: seed grower.
семеноводство seed growing, s. breeding.
семеножка bot: funicle, seed stalk, ovule s.
семенонос bot: seed plant.
семеноносец bot: placenta.
семеноносный bot: seed-bearing.
семеприёмник vet: seminal receptacle; zool: spermatheca.
семечко bot: pip, pyrene.
семечковые плоды bot: pip fruits.
семильон bot: Semillon (grape and wine).
семиология semiology, symptomatology.
семиотика semiotics.
семиреченский лягушкозуб zool: Ranodon sibiricus.
семитычинковый bot: heptandrous.
семотилюс ichth: northern creek chub (Semotilus atromaculatus atromaculatus)
семья (пчелиная) colony (of bees).
семя 1. physl zool: semen; 2. bot: seed.
~ без белка exalbuminous seed.
~ капусты coleseed.
семявыносящий проток anat: deferent duct, ductus deferens.
семядольный bot: cotyledonous.
~ след bot: cotyledonary trace.
~ стебель bot: fundamentum.
~ узел bot: cotyledonary node.
семядоля bot: seedlobe, cotyledon, seminal leaf.
семяед = семеед.
семяизвергательный канал = семяизвергающий проток anat: ejaculatory duct.
семянистый bot: seedy.
семянка bot: achene, nut, mericarp (of umbelliferous plants).
семяножка = семеножка.
семяносец bot: placenta.
семяносное растение bot: spermatophyte phanerogam.
семяобразующий seminific.
семяпочка bot: ovule, seed bud.
семяприёмник = семеприёмник.
семяприёмниковый zool: spermathecal.
семяпровод vas deferens, ductus d.
сенега bot: mountain flax (Polygala senega); pharm: (rattle-)snake root.
сензитивный бред отношения psych: sensitive delusion of reference.
сенильный senile.
сенна bot: senna (Cassia acutifolia, C. angustifolia).
сенная болезнь = с. лихорадка.
~ лихорадка hay fever, pollenosis.
~ палочка mcbio: hay bacillus.
сенной настой hay infusion.
сеноеды (отр.) entom: book-lice, etc. (Copeognatha).
сенокосец daddy longlegs (Phalangium cornutum).
сенокосцы (отр.) zool: harvestmen, "daddy longlegs" (Phalangida, Opiliones).
сеноставки = пищухи.
сенсибилизация sensitization.
сенсибилизировать sensitize.
сенсибилизирующая эритроциты субстанция erythrocyte sensitizing substance.
сенсилла entom: sensilla.
сенсорная функция sensory function.
сенсорный стимул sensory stimulus.
сепсис path: sepsis.
септа bio: septum.
септицемия 1. path: septicemia; 2. entom: flasheria.
септическая лихорадка septic fever, septicemia.
септический психоз septic psychosis.
септорий septoria (fungus).
сера 1. sulfur, S; 2. see ушная сера.
серая гниль grey mould (Botrytis sp.)
~ крыса hooded rat.
~ куропатка = куропатка.
~ пластинка anat: gray plate, lamina cinerea.
~ спайка anat: medicomissure, commissura media s. mollis.
~ цапля orn: gray heron (Ardea cinerea).
сердечная аритмия cardiac arrhythmia.

сердечная астма int: cardiac asthma.
~ блокада path: heart block.
~ мышца anat: cardiac muscle.
~ петля embr: cardiac loop.
~ слабость path: cardiac weakness.
~ сорочка anat: pericardium.
~ тупость int: cardiac dullness.
сердечник 1.collq: cardiac, cardiopath; 2.collq: cardiologist; 3.bot: core, caudex; 4.bot: bitter cress (Cardamine).
~ луговой lady smock, cuckooflower (C. pratensis).
сердечного происхождения cardiogenic.
сердечное вдавление anat: impressio cardiaca.
~ средство pharm: cardiac stimulant.
~ ушко = ушко сердца.
сердечно-мышечный myocardial.
~ -сосудистая недостаточность int: cardiovascular insufficiency.
~ -сосудистое средство pharm: cardiovascular agent.
сердечнотонический cardiotonic.
сердечный больной = сердечник 1.
~ отёк path: cardiac dropsy.
~ приступ path: heart attack.
~ толчок cardiac impulse.
~ тон heart sound.
~ шум heart murmur.
~ ~ плода obstet: fetal souffle.
сердце anat: heart, cor.
сердцебиение heart beating, h. throbbing
сердцевидка zool: cockle (mollusk) (Cardium).
~ обыкновенная common cockle (C. edule).
сердцевидно-заострённый лист bot: heart-shaped acuminate leaf.
сердцевидный heart-shaped, cordate, cordiform (cordiformis).
~ лист bot: heart-shaped leaf.
~ морской ёж zool: heart urchin (Echinocardium, Echinocyamus).
сердцевина bot: core, pith, medulla, heartwood, xylem.
~ волоса hist: hair marrow.
~ цветоложа bot: pith of receptacle.
сердцевинная гниль phytp: heart rot.
~ ~ сельдерея pithiness in celery.
сердцевинное пятно в древесине bot: pith fleck.
сердцевинный bot: pithy, medullary.
~ луч bot: wood ray.
сердцелистный bot: with heart-shaped leaves (cordifolius).
сердцеобразный = сердцевидный.

серебрение hist: argentation.
серебристая чайка orn: herring gull (Larus a. argentatus).
серебристый лосось ichth: salmon smolt.
~ угорь silver eel.
серебро silver, Ag.
серебряная пломба odont: silver filling.
серебрянка ichth: Argentina silus.
серебрянковые (сем.) ichth: Argentinidae.
"серебряное дерево" = левкадендрон.
середина medium. | catkin (inflorescence).
серёжка 1.zool: wattle; 2.bot: ament,
серийный срез hist: serial section.
серин serine.
сериография seriography.
серифус kingfish, queenfish, white croaker (Seriphus politus).
серна zool: Caucasian antelope, chamois, gazelle (Rupicarpa rupicarpa).
серная бактерия sulfur bacterium.
~ ванна phys-ther: sulphur bath.
~ мазь pharm: sulphur ointment.
~ печень pharm: liver of sulphur.
~ пробка otolar: plug of cerumen.
сернистый chem: sulphurous.
~ углерод = сероуглерод.
сернокислая магнезия = английская соль.
сернокислый натрий pharm: sodium sulfate.
~ хинин pharm: quinine sulfate.
серные пары san: sulfur fumes.
серный chem: sulfuric.
~ источник sulfur spring.
серовато-голубой мох = плаун.
~ -зелёный лист bot: glaucous leaf.
серое вещество (мозга) anat: gray matter, substantia grisea.
~ ~ спинного мозга anat: spinal gray.
~ мозговое вещество anat: cinerea.
~ ртутное масло pharm: gray oil, oleum cinereum.
серозная жидкость serous fluid.
~ оболочка anat: serous membrane, (tunica) serosa.
серозногнойный path: seropulent.
серозное отделяемое path: serous drainage.
серознокровянистая жидкость path: serosanguineous fluid.
серознофибринозный path: serofibrinous.
серозный serous, serumal.

серозный плеврит = выпотной п.
серолог serologist.
серологическая реакция serum-test.
серологическое средство serological affinity.
серология serology.
серомукоид seromucoid.
серотерапия serotherapy, serum treatment.
серотонин hem: serotonin.
сероуглерод chem: carbon disulfide.
серп мозжечка anat: falcula, falx cerebelli.
серпазил pharm: serpasil.
серпигинозная язва path: serpiginous ulcer, creeping u.
серпин pharm: serpine.
серповидная клетка sickle cell.
~ связка anat: falciform ligament.
серповидноклеточная анемия sickle-cell anaemia.
серповидный sickle-shaped, falciform, falcate, falcular, crescent(falcatus).
серрановые (сем.) ichth: Serranidae.
Сертоли Sertoli.
сертолиевы клетки hist: Sertoli cells.
серусодержащий sulfur-bearing.
серушка ichth: roach Rutilus rutilus fluviatilis.
серфы (надсем.) entom: Serphoidea-proctotrupidae.
серый бугор anat: tuber cinereum.
~ буревестник sooty shearwater (Puffinus griseus).
~ варан zool: Varanus griseus. Cf. варановые.
~ волк zool: gray wolf(Canis nubilus).
~ гусь = гусь серый.
~ дельфин zool: cowfish(Grampus griseus).
~ журавль orn: gray crane(Grus grus).
~ (калифорнийсикй) кит California gray whale(Rhachianectes glaucus).
~ кит zool: gray whale (Eschrichtius glaucus).
~ порошок pharm: gray powder.
~ суслик zool: Siberian marmot (Citellus pygmaeus).
серьезная операция surg: major operation.
серьезное осложнение path: major complication.
сесамовидная кость anat: sesamoid bone.
сестон seston.
сестонный sestonic.
сестра-диететичка dietary nurse.
~ -обследовательница public health nurse
~ помощи на дому visiting nurse, community nurse.
~ стажерка student nurse, probationer n.
~ -хозяйка = экономка.
сестринский набор (инструментов) nurses' case.
сетевидный netlike, retiform.
сетка network, grid, screen.
~ (второй отдел желудка) zool: reticulum, agitator, honeycomb bag.
~ для защиты от комаров mosquito net.
~ ядра hist: linin network.
сеткообразный retiform.
сетной планктон net plankton, mesoplankton.
~ фитопланктон net phytoplankton.
сеточка reticulum.
сеттер setter (Canis familiaris sequax).
сетчатая иннервация netted-venation.
~ масса цитоплазмы spongioplasm.
~ оболочка ophth: retina.
сетчатка ophth: retina.
сетчатоволокнистый fibroreticulate.
сетчатокрылое насекомое neuropterous insect, neuropteron.
сетчатокрылые (отр.) entom: neuropterons: horned corydalus, lacewing-flies, ant-lions, etc. (Neuroptera).
сетчатокрылый neuropterous.
сетчатость netting, reticulation.
сетчатый reticular, reticulate, retiform.
~ хрящ anat: reticular cartilage.
сеть венозных сосудов anat: venous network.
~ канальцев яичка anat: rete testis.
~ капилляров anat: capillary network.
сечение section.
~ ахиллова сухожилия surg: achillot(enot)omy.
сеченовское торможение Sechenov inhibition.
сеянец bot: seedling.
сеяный bot: sown (sativus).
сжатие скорлупы shell shrinkage.
~ сосудов vasoconstriction.
сжигание трупов = кремация.
сжимаемость compressibility.
сжиматель anat: sphincter.
~ влагалища anat: sphincter vaginae, compressor vaginae, bulbocavernosus.
~ глотки anat: constrictor of pharinx.
сзывать цыплят = клохтать.
си-айлэнд = хлопок приморский.
сиалия orn: bluebird(Sialia sialis).
сибиреязвенная палочка bacillus anthracis.
сибиреязвенный inf: anthracic.
сибирская двуустка = кошачья д.
~ язва Siberian plague, anthrax, charbon, woolsorter's disease, malignant pustule, milzbrand, splenic fever.

сибирский осётр ichth: Siberian
sturgeon (Acipenser baeri).
~ четырёхпалый тритон Siberian newt
(Hynobius keyserlingii).
сибирскоязвенный anthracic.[groove.
сибсонова борозда anat: Sibson's
сива = фасоль мелкая лимская.
сивашник = бычок-травяник.
сивка = ржанка обыкновенная.[rula).
сивоворонка orn: roller (Coracias gar-
сивуч zool: (Steller's) sea lion
(Eumetopias jubatus).
сивушное масло fusel oil. [tus).
сиг ichth: whitefish (Coregonus lavare-
~ амурский Amur w. (C. ussuriensis).
~ байкальский Baikal w.(C.l.baikalens
~ валаамка Valaam w.(C.l.widegreni).is)
~ волховский Volkhov w. (C.l. baeri).
~ лудога Ludoga w. (C. l. ludoga).
~ невский морской Neva w.
(C. l. lavaretus). [lavaretoides).
~ озёрно-речной fresh-water w. (C. l.
~ уссурийский = с. амурский.[ides).
~ чудской Chudskoe-Lake w. (C.l.maraeno-
сигилляриевые (сем.) bot:
Sigillariaceae (family, extinct).
сигмовидная кишка anat: sigmoid colon
~ пазуха anat: sigmoid sinus.
сигналёза ichth: small gizzard shad
(Signalosa atchafalayae). [label.
сигнальная система see первая
сигн. сист., вторая сигн. сист.
сигнатура pharm: signature, prescription
сигнифоры (сем.) entom: Signiphoridae.
сиговый ichth: coregonine, coregonoid.
сида bot: Sida, L.
сиделка = санитарка.
сидение прямо av med: sitting erect.
сидероз path: siderosis. [incubate.
сидеть на яйцах zool: hatch, brood,
сидонал = хиннокислый пиперазин.
сидячая ванна sitz bath, hip b.
~ инфузория zool: sessile ciliate.
~ профессия sedentary occupation.
сидячебрюхие (подотр.) entom:
Symphyta.
сидячеглазый zool: sessile-eyed.
сидячее положение sedentary position,
sitting position. [(sessifolius).
сидячелистный bot: sessile-leaved
сидячецветный bot: sessile-flowered
(sessifloris).
сидячие полихеты (подкл.) zool:
Sedentaria.
сидячий zool: sessile, sedentary,
stationary.

сидячий лист bot: sessile leaf.
~ образ жизни sedentary life.
сизаль-агава = сайсл.
сизая чайка orn: common gull (Larus c.
сизигий zool: syzygy. canus).
сизира entom: spongilla-fly.
сизоворонка = сивоворонка.
сизый glaucous, bloom-covered.
~ голубь orn: rock pigeon (Columba livia).
сизюринхий bot: blue-eyed grass,
satinflower (Sysyrinchium).
сикамор bot: sycamore maple (Acer
pseudoplatanus).
~ античный Ficus sycamorus,
Sycamorus antiquorum.
сикоз derm: sycosis, folliculitis barbae.
сиконоидный тип zool: syconoid type.
сикоп bot: false fruit, spurious fruit.
сила аккомодации ophth: accommodative
~ выдоха expiratory force. |power.
~ дивергенции ophth: power of
divergence. [convergence.
~ конвергенции ophth: power of
силена bot: catchfly, campion (Silene).
~ обыкновенная bladder campion,
maiden's tears (S. vulgaris).
силикоз path: silicosis.
сильвиев водопровод = мозговой в.
сильвиева борозда anat: Sylvian
fissure.
~ ямка anat: Sylvian valley.
сильная боль violent pain, throe.
~ рвота excessive vomiting,
hyperemesis.
сильноветвистый much-branched.
сильнодействующее лекарство pharm:
potent drug.
сильное месячное кровотечение
menorrhagia, hypermenorrhea.
~ облучение powerful irradiation.
~ разращение грануляций path:
hypersarcosis.
~ слабительное 1. pharm: strong
purgative; 2. vet: drench.
~ средство potent agent, strong a.
сильнооблиственная ботва agr bot:
leafiest haulm. [foliose.
сильнооблиственный bot: leafiest,
сильно худеть = исхудать.
сильно цианотичный path: hypercyanotic.
сильный strong, powerful, vigorous,
potent, violent, intense, sthenic.
~ запор obstipation.
сильт silt.
сильфон av med: sylphon.

сима ichth: salmon Oncorhynchus masu.
симарубовые (сем.) bot: quassia family (Simarubaceae).
симбиоз bio: symbiosis.
симбионт bio: symbiont.
симбиотический bio: symbiotic.
символизация symbolization.
симпатическая нервная система sympathetic nervous system.
симпатический нерв sympathetic nerve.
симпатическое воспаление path: sympathetic inflammation.
~ ~ глаза transferred ophthalmia.
симпатомиметический sympathomimetic.
симпатэктомия sympathectomy.
симпласт hist: symplast, symplasm.
симподиальное соцветие bot: sympodial inflorescence.
симподий bot: sympodium.
симптом symptom.
~ Аржиля-Робертсона ophth: Argyll Robertson symptom.
~ Ромберга Romberg sign.
симптоматика symptoms.
симптоматическая эпилепсия neur: symptomatic epilepsy.
симптоматический антракс vet: quarter ill.
симптоматичный symptomatic.
симптоматология symptomatology.
симптомокомплекс symptom complex.
симулировать simulate, feign.
симультанное возбуждение coexcitation
симулянт legl: simulator, malingerer.
симуляция simulation, malingering, malingery
симферобиус entom: Sympherobius amicus.
синапс anat: synapse, synapsis.
синапсида zool: Synapsida (extinct reptiles).
синапсис bio: synapsis.
синаптическая конъюгация genet: synaptic conjugation.
синаптозавры (подкл.) zool: Synaptosauria (extinct reptiles).
синартроз anat: synarthrosis.
сингенез bio: syngenesis.
сингиль ichth: mullet Mugil auratus.
синдактилия path: syndactyly, syndactilism, syndactilia, webbed fingers
синдактильный path: syndactylous.
синдесмоз anat: syndesmosis.
синдесмология anat: syndesmology.
синдром syndrome.
синева blueness.
~ древесины phytp: blue rot.
синеватый bluish.
синеголовник bot: rattlesnake master water eryngo (Eryngium aquaticum).
синедра стройная bot: Synedra gracilis (alga).
синее молоко vet: blue milk.
синезелёная водоросль bot: blue-green alga, cyanophyceen.
синезелёные водоросли (кл.) bot: blue-green a. (Cyanophyceae, Myxophyceae).
синергизм synergism.
синергист synergist.
синергический synergistic.
синергия synergy.
синестезия psych: synesthesia.
синехия ophth: synechia, iritic adhesion.
синец ichth: bream Abramis ballerus.
синие круги blue circles.
синий гной blue pus.
~ кит zool: blue whale, sulphur-bottom (Balaenoptera musculus).
~ полосатик = синий кит.
синица orn: titmouse, Brit: tomtil, tit (Parus).
~ болотная marsh titmouse, nun (Parus palustris longirostris).
~ лазоревка willow t. (P. atricapillus rhenanus).
~ усатая = бородатка.
синицевые (сем.) orn: titmouse family (Paridae).
синкарион zool: synkaryon.
синкарпический = синкарпный.
синкарпный bot: syncarpous.
~ плод bot: syncarp.
синовиальная жидкость synovial fluid, sinew f.
~ оболочка anat: synovial sheath.
~ сумка anat: synovial bursa.
синовит path: synovitis.
синовия = синовиальная жидкость.
синодонтиды ichth: lizard-fishes (Synodontidae).
синойкия bio: synoikia.
синокаротидный synocarotid.
синонимика synonymy.
синостоз anat: synostosis.
синтеризма bot: fingergrass, crabgrass (Digitaria).
синтэстрин syntestrin (diethylstilbestrol dipropionate).
синура bio: Synura (chrysomonadic flagellate organisms).
синусит path: sinusitis.
синусовая аритмия phasic sinus arrhythmia.
синусовое сокращение sinus beat (heart).
синусовый узел anat: pace maker, sinoatrical node (of the heart).
синусоида anat: sinus.
синхондроз anat: synchondrosis.
синцитиальный syncytial.
синцитий hist: syncytium.
синцитиотрофобласт embr: syncytiotrophoblast.
синэкология synecology.
синюха see 1. med: синюшность; 2. bot: полемониум.

синюха лазоревая bot: charity, see полемониум.
синюшное окрашивание = синюшность.
синюшность path: cyanosis, bluish tinge.
~ конечностей blueness of extremities, acrocyanosis.
синюшный path: cyanotic, bluish.
синявка = молиния голубая.
синяк bot: viper's bugloss (Echium).
~ обыкновенный blueweed, blue devil (E. vulgare).
синяя лихорадка blue fever, Rocky Mountain spotted f.
~ ртутная мазь pharm: blue ointment.
сип белоголовый orn: white-headed vulture (Gyps fulvus)
сиплый husky, hoarse.
сипункулида zool: sipunculid, sipunculoid (Sipunculoidea).
сипуха orn: tawny owl, barn owl (Strix).
~ обыкновенная white-barn owl (S. aluco)
сирена zool: siren (Siren).
сиреновые zool: sirenians, dugongs & manatees (Sirenia).
сирень bot: lilac (Syringa).
~ махровая double-flowering l.
~ обыкновенная common l. (S. vulgaris).
~ персидская Persian l. (S. persica).
сирин домовый orn: long-eared owl (Carine, Syrnium noctua).
сирингомиелия path: syringomyelia.
*сироп syrop.
сиропообразный syrupy.
сиси bot: seasea (Eugenia).
система system; bio: taxonomic system.
~ кровообращения circulatory system.
~ нестеснения no-restraint system.
~ обеспечения (кислородом) по потребности av med: demand (oxygen) system.
~ подачи кислорода по потребности с подсосом av med: deluter-demand system.
систематик bio: taxonomist, systematist.
систематика taxonomy.
~ растений plant taxonomy.
системный systemic.
систокс chem: systox.
систола systole.
систолический systolic.
~ шум systolic murmur.
систолическое давление systolic pressure.
ситник bot: rush, bogrush, heathrush (Juncus).
~ Жерарда blackgrass (J. Gerardi).
~ раскидистый soft r., common r., roundgrass, mat r. (J. effusus).
ситниковидные (сем.) bot: arrow-grass family (Juncaginaceae).
ситниковые (сем.) bot: rush family (Juncaceae).
ситовидная пластинка bot: sieve-plate.
~ трубка bot: sieve-tube.
ситовниковые = осоковые.
сифилис ven: syphilis.
~ мозга cerebral syphilis.
сифилитик syphilis afflicted person.
сифилитическая инфекция syphilitic infection.
сифилитический бубон syphilitic bubo.
~ психоз syphilitic psychosis.
сифоновые (пор.) bot: Siphonales order (algae).
сифоноглиф zool: siphonoglyph.
сифонофора физалия zool: Portuguese man-of-war (Physalia pelagica).
сифонофоры (подкл.) zool: Siphonophora.
сияние 1. gleam, see свечение; 2. hist: aster.
скабиоза bot: pincushion, Egyptian rose, morning bride (Scabiosa).
скакун entom: tiger beetle (Cicindela).
скампо zool: scampo (Nephrops norwegicus).
скандирующая речь neur: scanning speech.
скап ichth: scup (Lagodon rhomboides; Stenotomus chrysops).
скапус entom: scapus.
скарабей entom: scarab (Scarabaeus).
скарификация scarification.
скарифицировать scarify.
скарлатина infect: scarlet fever, scarlatina, canker rash.
скарлатинозная сыпь infect: scarlatinal eruption.
скармливание agr: feeding (cattle).
скаровая рыба parrot-fish (Scaridae).
скарус ichth: kakatua (Scarus).
скат anat: declive, dectivity, slope; 2. ichth: ray, skate, stingaree (Dasyatis, Molubidae, Pristidae, Torpenidae, Rajidae).
скаты (отр.) ichth: rays (Batoidei).
~ обыкновенные (сем.) Rajidae.
~ -хвостоколы (сем.) Trygonidae; see also хвостокол.
скатываться migrate down (of fish).
скафопода zool: scaphopod.
скафоподида zool: spadefoot toad, (Scaphopodidae).
скафоцерит zool: scaphocerite.
скачка идей psych: "race of ideas", rapid succession of unconnected ideas.

скачкообразное проведение saltatory conduction.
скачущая походка path: saltatory gait.
скашивание питательных сред bact: slanting of media.
сквамозная папиллома zool: squamous papillomata. [squarehead(wheat).
скверхедный bot: clavate, clubbed,
сквозное огнестрельное ранение surg: tunnel gunshot wound.
сквозной свищ surg: complete fistula.
скворец orn: starling, Brit: grackle (Sturnus vulgaris).
~ американский American house wren (Troglodytes aedon), oriole (Icterus).
~ обыкновенный orn: starling (Sturnus vulgaris)
скворцы (сем.) orn: starlings(Sturnidae)
скелет skeleton.
скелетизация skeletization.
скелетировать листья entom: skeletonize the leaves.
скелетная мышца anat: skeletal muscle.
скелетовытяжная аппаратура orthop: stretching gear.
скелетообразовательный embr: skeletogenous.
скерда bot: hawk's-beard (Crepis).
скиаскоп ophth: skiascope, retinoscope.
скиаскопия skiascopy, retinoscopy.
скидывать miscarry; zool:warp, slink.
скинуть p. a. of скидывать.
скипджэк ichth: skipjack (Elagatis bipinnulatus; Poronotus triacanthus; Labidestes siculus).
скипидар turpentine.
скипидарное дерево = фисташка дикая.
скирр path: scirrhus.
склад ума = умственный склад.
складка fold, plica, plication, duplicature.
~ мочевого пузыря anat: bladder bar.
складочка anat: small fold, plica(tion).
складчатый bot: plicate, conduplicate.
~ фильтр plaited filter.
склеивание conglutination, agglutination
склеивать conglutinate, agglutinate.
склеивающая способность agglutinative capacity.
склеивающее вещество conglutinant, agglutinant.
склеивающий conglutinant, agglutinant, agglutinating.
склеить p. a. of склеивать.
склера ophth: sclera.
склерит 1. ophth: scleritis; 2. entom: sclerite.
склеродерма scleroderma, dermatosclerosis
склероз path: sclerosis.
~ венечных сосудов = коронаросклероз.
~ почек nephrosclerosis.
склеротик path: sclerosed.
склеротиния phytp: sclerotiniosis; Sclerotinia (fungi).
склеротический sclerotic.
склеротом embr: sclerotome.
склероций bot: sclerotium.
склонность inclination, propensity, leaning.
~ к наркотикам drug addiction.
~ ~ поносу loose bowels.
~ ~ самоубийству suicidal tendency.
склянница = тыквенная с.
скобка для соединения краев раны surg: wound clip, skin c., Michel c.
сколекс zool: scolex.
сколии (сем.) entom: scoliids (Scoliidae).
сколиоз path: scoliosis.
сколит морщинистый peach black beetle (Scolytus regulosus).
сколопендреллы (отр.) zool: garden centipedes (Symphyla).
сколопидий entom: scolopidium.
скомбероидес ichth: leather-jack (Scomberoides).
скомбероморус ichth: cavalla, crevalle, seerfish, king mackerel (Scomberomorus).
скопа orn: fish hawk, osprey(Pandion).
скопаламин pharm: scopalamine.
скопление accumulation, gathering; cluster, blob, agglomerate; see also накопление.
~ в кучки clustering, agglomeration.
~ водяночной жидкости в области плевры hydrothorax.
~ воздуха в области плевры pneumothorax.
~ газов flatulence.
~ гноя empyema.
~ ~ в газовом пузыре pyopneumothorax.
~ крови congestion, hyperemia.
~ у края margination.
скорая помощь ambulance.
скорбный лист final note, death summary.
скорбут path: scurvy.
скорбутогенный scorbutigenic.
скорлупа shell, nutshell, hud, putamen; carapace. [(in worms).
скорлуповая железа zool: shell gland
скорняжный шов surg: glover's suture.
скоролёт = ежемуха.

скоропортящийся san: perishable (food, etc.)
скороспелка agr bot: 1. early-ripening variety, etc.,precosity; 2. see первоцвет.
скороспелый agr bot: early-ripening, early-harvest, early-naturing, hasting, precocious.
скорость восприятия perceptual speed.
~ всасывания absorption rate.
~ опознавания av med: speed of identification.
~ оседания hem: sedimentation rate.
~ подъема av med: rate of ascent.
~ реакции reaction velocity.
~ роста growth rate.
скоротечная чахотка collq:galloping consumption, florid phthisis.
скоротечный fulminant, fulminating, galloping.
скороувядающий bot: fugacious.
скорпена = морской ёрш черноморский.
скорпеновые (сем.) ichth: scorpion fishes (Scorpaenidae).
скорпион zool: scorpion (Scorpionida).
~ африканский African scorpion (Pandinus imperator).
~ итальянский Italian s.(Euscorpius italicus).
~ книжный Chelifer cancroides.
~ крымский E. tauricus.
скорпионовая муха entom:scorpion-fly (Panorpa, Boreus, Bittacus, etc.)
скорпионовые мухи (отр.) entom: scorpion-flies (Mecoptera).
скорпионы (отр.)zool: scorpions (Scorpionida).
скорцонер bot: scorzonera (Scorzonera crispatula, Boiss.)
скосарь золотистый entom: golden weevil (Otiorrhynchus aurosparsus).
~ крымский Crimea otiorrhynchid (O. asphaltinus).
~ люцерновый = долгоносик люцерновый большой.
~ малинный raspberry weevil (O. Tenebricosus).
~ плодовый = с. золотистый.
~ турецкий Turkish weevil (O. turca).
скотина cattle; beast.
скотоложство = содомия.
скотома ophth: scotoma.
скотство bestiality.
скребень helm: proboscis worm.
скребни (кл.)helm: proboscis worms (Acanthocephala).
скрежет = скрежетание.
скрежетание зубами teeth-grinding, stridor dentium.

скрещивание hybridization, cross-breeding, interbreeding.
скрипица пёстрая = гриб-зонтик пёстрый.
скрипун = капуста заячья.
скрофулёз path: scrofula.
скрупулёзность scrupulosity.
скрученные (пор.) bot: Contortae.
скрученный stranded, twisted, contorted, curled.
скручивание листьев phytp: leaf roll(ing), leaf curl(ing).
скрытая инфекция silent infection.
~ малярия dumb ague.
скрытноед entom: mold beetle (Cryptophagus).
скрытнохоботник = скрытохоботник
скрытое кровотечение path:concealed hemorrhage, occult bleeding.
~ поражение rad: latent injury.
скрытожаберник американский zool: hellbender (Cryptobranchus alleganiensis).
скрытожаберники (сем.) zool: Cryptobranchidae.
*скрытонос несходный entom:cabbage-seedpod weevil (Centhorrhynchus asimilis).
скрытохвосты orn: Tynami.
скрытохоботник entom: cryptorchid (Curculionidae);see also долгоносик, слоник.
~ галловый = с. капустный корневой.
~ капустный корневой cabbage root curculio (Ceutorrhynchus pleurostigma).
~ ~ стеблевой cabbage-seedstalk curcullio (C. quadridens).
~ крестоцветный листовой C. contractus.
~ луковый onion curculio(C.jakovlevi).
~ льняной S. sareptanus.
~ маковый корневой poppy-root curculio (Stenocarus fuliginosus).
~ ~ однопятнистый C.macula alba.
~ ольховый poplar borer (C.lapathi).
~ репный turnip curculio (C. rapae).
~ рыжиковый C. syrites.
~ семенной seed curculio (C.assimilis).
~ хреновый C. cochleariae.
~ четырёхточечный = с. маковый корневой.
скрытошейные черепахи (подотр.) zool: turtles Cryptodira.
скрытый concealed, latent; hidden.
скука boredom.
скула = скуловая кость.
скуловая дуга anat: zygomatic arch, suborbital a., subocular a.

скуловая кость anat: cheekbone, malar b., zygoma, os zygomaticum.
~ мышца anat: zygomatic muscle. [process.
скуловой отросток anat: zygomatic
скумбриевые (сем.) ichth: mackerel family (Scombridae).
скумбрия = макрель. See also японская скумбрия. [ный.
скумпия кожевенная = сумах дубиль-
скунс zool: skunk (Mephitis mephitis).
скутеллиста entom: Scutellista cyanea (Tridymidae).
скутум entom: scutum. [together.
скученный crowded, clumped, massed
скучивание crowding, clumping.
слабая инфекция subinfection.
слабительная каш(к)а pharm: laxative "mush", electuary of senna, etc.
~ соль pharm: laxative salt.
слабительное средство pharm: laxative, purgative, physic, aperient, cathartic, evacuant.
слабительные таблетки pharm: laxative tablets. [abulia.
слабоволие psych: lack of volition,
слабовоспалительный subinflammatory.
слабовыраженное помутнение ophth: faint opacity.
слабовыраженный бред subdelirium.
слабодикротический hypodicrotous.
слабодушие = чувственная неустойчивость.
слабое воспаление subinflammation.
~ увеличение mcscop: low power.
слабонаркотический subnarcotic.
слабоположительный slightly positive.
слаборастущая культура bact: dysgonic culture.
слабостебельчатый bot: slender-stemmed
слабость weakness, debility, lassitude, langour.
~ в коленях weakness in the knees.
~ воли = слабоволие.
~ желудка stomach weakness.
~ зрения ophthalmocopia, asthenopia.
~ родовых схваток obstet: weakness of
~ ступни path: weak foot. pains.
слабоумие psych: dementia, feeblemindedness, phrenasthenia, hypophrenia.
слабоумный psych: demented, feebleminded, phrenasthenic, hypophrenic.
слабощелочный chem: alkalescent.
слабый weak, feeble, debile, infirm; delicate, frail.
~ желтушный оттенок subicteric tint.

слабый объектив mcscop: low-power objective.
~ окуляр mcscop: searching eye-piece.
славка orn: (Old World) warbler (Sylvia).
~ -завирушка lesser whitethroat (S. curruca). [ская.
~ кентская = ржанка александрий-
~ -пересмешница = с.-завирушка.
~ полевая whitethroat (S. rufa).
~ садовая garden warbler (S. hortensis).
~ северная S. borin.
~ черноголовая pewit (S. atricaula).
славковые (сем.) orn: warblers (Sylviidae).
сладкие экскременты тлей и щитовок entom: honeydew.
сладкий картофель = батат.
~ корень = скорцонер.
~ папоротник = многоножка.
сладкокорень bot: see многоножка обыкновенная.
сланоягодниковые (сем.) bot: watermilfoil family (Haloragaceae).
слегка зазубренный subserrate, subdentate.
~ искривлённый semicontorted.
~ окрашенный кровью blood-tinged.
~ опушённый tomentulose.
~ теплый subtepid.
~ удлинённый subelongated.
~ ядовитый slightly toxic, noxious.
след trace, track, mark.
~ от укола иглой needle mark.
~ прикрепления листа bot: leaf scar (on the stem). [trace amount.
следы trackways, foil; chem: trace(s),
~ мух flyspeck.
слёзная борозда anat: lacrimal groove.
~ железа lacrimal gland.
~ жидкость lacrimal fluid, tears.
~ кость anat: lacrimal bone, os lacrimale.
слёзное мясцо lacrimal caruncle.
~ озеро lacrimal lake.
слёзно-носовой проток anat: nasolacrimal duct.
слёзный мешок anat: lacrimal sac.
~ проток lacrimal duct.
~ свищ ophth: dacryosyrinx.
слезообразный lachrymous.
слезоотделение tear secretion.
слезотечение 1. lacrimation; 2. ophth: epiphora.
слезоточивый газ tear gas, lacrimator.
слёзы = слёзная жидкость.

слепая кишка anat: blind gut, caecum.
~ рыба blindfish (Ambliopsis).
слепень entom: horsefly, tabanus.
~ бычий oxfly (Tabanus bovinus).
слепни (сем.) entom: horseflies (Tabanidae).
слепоглухонемой blind deafmute.
слепое отверстие языка anat: cecal foramen of the tongue.
~ пятно ophth: blind spot (of Mariotte).
слепо заканчивающийся blind-ended.
слепозмейка zool: blind little snake, worm-like s., blindworm (Typhlops vermicularis).
слепой 1. blind; 2. anat: cecal.
~ вырост кишки ichth: caecum.
~ мешок anat: culdesac.
слепок cast, mold, impression.
слепокишечный anat: cecal.
слепота ophth: blindness, amaurosis.
~ на зелёный цвет ophth: green blindness, red-sightedness. [protanopia
~ ~ красный цвет ophth: red blindness,
~ ~ красный и зелёный цвет ophth: red-green blindness, daltonism.
~ ~ ноты note-blindness.
~ ~ синий цвет blue blindness, acyanopsia, acy(an)oblepsia.
слепун = слепозмейка.
слепуны (сем.) zool: Typhlopidae (snakes)
слепыши (сем.) zool: Spalacidae (rodents).
слива bot: prune, plum (Prunus domestica)
~ абрикосовая apricot plum (P. simonii).
~ американская sand plum (P. angustifolia watsonii, Wangh.)
*~ вишнелистная mirabalan, cherry-plum (P. cerasifera).
~ дикая = алыча.
~ жёлтая крупная white plum (P. domestica alba).
~ испанская тропическая Spanish plum (Spondias purpurea).
~ китайская Chinese prune (Ziziphus jujuba, Lam.)
~ колючая spiny plum tree (P. spinosa).
~ мелкая чёрная damson, bullace (P. insititia).
~ настоящая = с. мелкая чёрная.
~ обыкновенная common plum (P. domestica).
~ песчаная = с. американская.
~ свиная hog plum (Ximenia americana, Spondias lutea).
~ Симона Simon plum (P. Simonii, Carr.)
~ узколистная Chickasaw plum (P. angustifolia, Marsh.)
слива яичная = с. жёлтая.
~ японская Japanese plum (P. salicina, Lindl.)
сливание с осадка lab: elutriation, decantation.
сливать с осадка chem lab: elutriate, decant.
сливающиеся очаги confluent foci.
сливки cream.
сливкообразный гной path: creamy pus.
сливная оспа path: coherent smallpox.
сливной confluent.
сливовые (подсем.) bot: plum subfamily (Pruneae or Prunoideae).
сливолистный bot: plum-leaved (prunifolius).
слившиеся нервные ганглии членистоногого syncerebrum.
слизевик bot: slime fungus, myxomycete.
слизевики bot: slime molds, myxophytes (Myxophyta).
слизевой slimy, myxomycetous (fungus, etc.)
~ гриб = слизевик.
слизень zool: slug (Limax).
~ голый пашенный = с. пашенный.
~ пашенный grey field slug (Agriolimax agrestis).
слизеобразный muciform.
слизеобразующий mucigenous.
слизеподобный mucoid, muciform.
слизистая anat: mucosa.
~ влагалища vaginal m.
~ гниль стеблей phytp: gummy stem blight (of watermelon).
~ гортани laryngeal m.
~ железа mucous gland.
~ желудка gastric m.
~ зева faucial mucosa.
~ кишок intestinal mucosa.
~ матки uterine mucosa, endometrium.
~ мочеточника ureteral mucosa.
~ носа nasal mucosa.
~ оболочка mucous membrane, mucosa.
~ пищевода esophageal mucosa.
~ почечной лоханки pelvic m.
~ пробка path: mucous plug.
~ прямой кишки rectal m.
~ пузыря vesical m.
~ рта oral m.
~ ткань hist: mucous tissue.
слизистогнойный path: mucopurulent.
слизистое перерождение path: mucoid softening.
~ тельце hist: mucous corpuscle.
слизистокровяной path: mucosanguineous.

слизистоперепончатый колит int: tubular diarrhea, colica mucosa.
слизистосерозный path: mucoserous.
слизистые споровики (отр.) zool: Myxosporidia.
слизистый mucous, muculent, mucilagenous slimy, glairy.
~ отёк = микседема.
~ покров anat: mucous lining.
~ цидиндр mcscop: mucous cast.
слизняк see 1. zool: слизень; 2. bot: слизевик.
слизь mucus, slime.
слинявший краб soft crab.
слипаемость пластинок hem: platelet adhesiveness.
слипчивое воспаление path: adhesive inflammation.
~ ~ плевры path: adhesive pleurisy.
слипчивый cohesive, tenacious.
~ тромб path: blood-plate thrombus.
слияние fusion, confluence.
~ гамет genet: gametic syngamy.
~ гиф fusion of (hyphae).
~ двух почек в одну path: solitary kidney.
~ пазух anat: confluens sinuum.
~ сегментов desegmentation.
словесная глухота = душевная глухота.
~ слепота neur: word blindness.
слоевище bot: thallus.
слоевцовое растение bot: thallophyte.
сложение habit, see телосложение.
сложенный вдвое biplicate, double-folded.
сложная киста path: compound cyst.
~ координация av med: complex coordination.
~ хинная настойка pharm: compound tincture of cinchona.
сложное деление (клеток) hist: indirect nuclear division, mitosis.
~ лекарственное средство pharm: compound medicine.
~ скрещивание genet: composite crossing
сложность complexity.
сложноцветные (сем.) bot: composite family, sunflower f. (Compositae).
сложный глаз entom: compound eye, complex eye.
~ зонтик bot: compound umbel, cyme.
~ лист bot: compound leaf.
~ настой александрийского листа pharm: compound infusion of senna.
~ панкреатиновый порошок pharm: peptonizing powder.
~ плод bot: aggregate fruit, bramble f., multiple f., syncarpous fruit, syncarp.
сложный порошок ипекакуаны = доверов порошок.
~ ~ солодкового корня pharm: compound liquorice powder.
~ ревенный порошок pharm: compound powder of rhubarb.
~ сустав anat: compound articulation.
~ цветок bot: composite flower.
~ эфир chem: ester.
слоистый laminar, laminated, lamellose, stratified.
слой многообразных (полиморфных) клеток anat: layer of fusiform cells.
~ нервных волокон nerve-fibre layer.
~ палочек и колбочек ophth: layer of rods and cones.
~ пирамид pyramidal layer.
~ пирамидальных клеток (мозга) anat: layer of pyramidal cells.
~ узловых клеток (мозга) anat: ganglionic layer, stratum gangliosum cerebri.
~ шиповидных клеток hist: prickle-cell layer.
сломанный broken.
слон zool: elephant (Proboscidea).
слоник 1. zool: small elephant; young e.; 2. entom: curculio, snout-beetle, see also долгоносик, скрытохоботник, смолёвка.
~ виноградный vine curculio, vine weevil.
~ гороховый pea beetle, bean weevil (Sitonia).
~ каштановый chestnut weevil (Balaninus elephas).
~ лещинный = долгоносик ореховый.
~ полосатый гороховый striped pea weevil (Sitona lineatus).
~ фасолевый = с. гороховый.
слоники (сем.) = долгоносики.
слоновая болезнь elephantiasis.
~ черепаха zool: elephantine turtle (Testudo elephantops).
слоновость = слоновая болезнь.
слоновый path: elephantiac, elephantiasic.
слух physl: hearing.
~ на шопотную речь hearing of the whispered voice.
слуховая амнезия = душевная глухота.
~ аура neur: auditory aura.
~ галлюцинация psych: hallucination of hearing.
~ косточка earbone, auditory ossicle.
~ труба anat: auditory tube.
слуховое ощущение auditory sense.
слуховой aural, auditory.
~ камешек ichth: otolith.

слуховой нерв anat: acoustic nerve, auditory n., eighth cranial n.
~ проход anat: auditory meatus.
~ пузырь embr: acoustic vesicle, otic v.
слуховые косточки anat: auditory ossicles, tympanic bones. [tympanic o-s.
~ органы anat: organs of hearing; entom:
~ пятна anat: acoustic spots.
случай контактного заболевания contact case.
~ неотложной помощи emergency case.
случайная находка chance finding.
случайное заражение mcbio: chance introduction.
~ опыление bot: random pollination.
случайный accidental, chance, fortuitous, adventitious.
~ шум path: adventitious sound.
случать zool agr: cover, have covered,
~ барана tup. mate.
случка covering, mating.
случной баран tupping ram.
~ бык bull kept for covering.
слушатель курсов усовершенствования postgraduate student.
слушательница курсов медсестёр student nurse. [epithelium.
слущенный эпителий path: cast-off
слущивание peeling, scaling, flaking off; exfoliation.
слюна saliva, spittle. [sialaden.
слюнная железа anat: salivary gland,
слюнное пищеварение physl: salivary digestion.
~ тельце hist: salivary corpuscle.
слюннокаменный path: sialolithic.
слюнный камень path: salivary calculus, sialolith.
~ проток anat: salivary duct.
~ свищ surg: salivary fistula, sialosyrinx
слюновидный sialoid.
слюногон = слюногонное средство.
слюногонное средство salivant, sialagog(ue), salivator.
слюногонный salivatory, sialogogic.
слюноотделение physl: salivary discharge.
слюнотечение path: salivation, sialorrhea, ptyalorrhea, driveling; vet: slobbering.
слюноточивый salivatory, etc. Cf. слюнотечение.
слюнявость vet: slobbering.
смазать p. a. of смазывать.
смазывание трудных согласных smudging (defective speech).
смазывать grease, oil, smear, paint, anoint; lubricate.
~ жиром grease, begrease.
~ кисточкой apply with a brush.
смарида ichth: sea bass (Spicava smaris).
смаридовые (сем.) ichth: Maenidae.
смегматический smegmatic.
смена поколений bio: alternation of generations.
сменить p. a. of сменять.
сменять повязку surg: rebandage.
смертельная доза pharm: lethal dose, fatal d.
~ травма fatal injury.
смертельное действие lethal effect.
~ поражение lethal injury.
смертельность lethality, deadlyness.
смертельный исход fatal termination.
~ яд deadly poison.
смертность mortality; death rate.
~ вследствие мечения zool: tagging mortality.
~ новорожденных neonatal mortality.
~ от облучения radiation mortality.
смерть death.
~ от сепсиса septic death.
~ (плода) в утробе матери obstet: intra-uterine death.
смесительная пипетка mixing pipet(te); blood-count p.
смесь mixture, mix; blend.
смех laughter.
смешанная инфекция concurrent
~ сыворотка pooled serum. |infection.
смешанноклеточная опухоль mixed-cell tumor.
смешанный с гноем path: mictopyous.
смешение mixing; blending.
смешивание = смешение.
смещение displacement, dislocation, shift(ing), heterotopy, ectopia.
~ зуба к губе odont: labioplacement.
~ ~ к языку odont: linguoplacement.
~ кзади retrodisplacement, retrodevia-
~ книзу infraplacement. tion.
~ кости path: ostectopy, bone displace-
~ кпереди antedisplacement. ment.
~ матки gyn: uterine displacement, metrectopy. [vertebra.
~ позвонка path: dislocation of a
~ слёзной точки ophth: displacement of the punctum.
смещённый displaced, dislocated, shifted, heterotopous, ectopic, atopic.

смещённый кзади retroposed.
смилакс bot: greenbrier, catbrier, smilax (Smilax).
ланцетовидный S. lanceolata.
~ шероховатый bamboo brier (S.pseudochina).
сминтурус entom: lucerne flea (Sminthurus viridis).
смирительная рубашка psych: strait-jacket.
смоковница bot: fig (tree)(Ficus carica).
~ бенгальская banyan (F. benghalensis).
*~ индийская Indian ficus (F.indica).
~ смирнская Smyrna fig.
~ стелящаяся creeping fig (F.pumila, F. repens).
смола tar; gum.
смолёвка 1.entom: curculio, snout-beetle (Pissodes); 2.bot: catchfly, campion (Silene).
~ волдырник bladder campion, cowbell, bladder catchfly, maiden's tears (S. cucubalus).
~ еловая P. harcyniae.
~ пятнистая = с. точечная.
~ сосновая жердняковая P.piniphilus.
~ ~ стволовая P. pini.
~сосновых шишек P. validirostris.
~ точечная small pine weevil (P.notatus).
смолёвщик = побеговьюн смолёвщик.
смолка = дрёма.
смородина bot: currant (Ribes).
~ белая white currant.
~ красная red currant (R. rubrum).
~ обыкновенная garden currant (R. vulgare).
~ чёрная black currant (R. nigrum).
смородинные (сем.) = крыжовниковые (сем.)
сморчковые (сем.)bot: Morchella fungi.
сморчок bot: morel (Morchella).
~ вонючий devil's egg (Phallus impudicus).
~ конический conical m.(M.conica).
~ съедобный morel, sponge mushroom (M. esculenta).
*сморщенная губка zool: urse sponge (Grantia compressa).
~ почка path: contracted kidney.
сморщенное зерно bot:wrinkled seed.
сморщенность wrinkling.
сморщенный = морщинистый.
сморщивание wrinkling, shrinkage, cirrhosis; cf. морщинистый.
~ (атрофия) глазного яблока shriveling (atrophy) of eyeball, ophthalmophthisis.
смыв washing.
смывание washing out, irrigation.
смягчающий emollient, soothing, softening.
смягчение softening, mollifying, abatement, subsiding. See also мягчение.
снабженный боковым шипом bio: lateral-spined.
~ клапаном valved.
~ крышкой operculate(d).
~ ножкой bio: pedunculated.
~ перегородкой septiferous.
~ сфинктером anat: sphincterate.
~ шипами bio:acanaceous, acanthaceous.
снегирь orn: European bullfinch (Pyrrhula vulgaris).
~ северный northern bullfinch.
снегозадержание agr: retention of snow.
снежная плесень = фузариум снежный.
~ слепота ophth: snow-blindness.
~ ягода bot: snowberry, waxberry (Symphoricarpos albus, Blake).
снежноягодник= снежная ягода.
снежный баран zool: sheep Ovis nivicola.
Снеллен Snellen.
снесение surg: removal, extirpation, ablation.
снести p. a. of сносить.
снеток ichth: whitebait (Osmerus eperlanus); see also корюшка.
снимание сливок skimming.
снимать мазок take a smear.
снимок picture, photo.
снова гнездиться renest.
~ заселять(ся) repopulate.
~ удобрять refertilize.
~ употреблять reuse.
сновидение dream.
сноподобное состояние psych: oneiroid state.
сносить surg: remove, extirpate, ablate.
снотворное (средство) pharm: somnifacient, soporific, hypnotic.
снотворный somniferous, somnifacient, soporific.
снохождение psych: sleepwalking, noctambulation, somnabulism.
сношение intercourse.
снытка пухлая = сныть обыкновенная.
сныть обыкновенная bot: goutweed (Aegopodium podagrarium).
снятие taking off (away), removal, ablation; subtraction. [vet: couching.
~ катаракты ophth: cataract removal;
~ (тампоном) материала с гортани laryngeal swabbing.
снятое молоко agr: skim milk.
снять p. a. of снимать.
соамин = пара-аминофенилмышьяковокислый натрий.
собака zool: dog (Canis). Cf.кобель, пёс, сука.

собака-рыба puffer (Spheroides
maculatus).
собаки (сем.)zool: dogs (Canidae).
*собакоголовая обезьяна zool:canine-
head monkey (Mandrill, baboon).
собачий глист dog tapeworm (Taenia
coenurus). [cus granulosus).
~ цепень helm: dog's tapeworm (Echinococ-
собачка морская blenny (Blenniidae).
собачковые (сем.)ichth: blenny fishes
(Blenniidae).
собачник = чернокорень аптечный.
собачье бешенство lyssa;canine rabies.
*собачья акула ichth: dogfish, sea dog
(Scyliorhinus canicula).
~ рожа = хатьма.
~ рыба = умбра. [canina.
~ ямка anat: suborbital fossa, fossa
собирание анамнеза history taking.
собирательная нога entom: pollen-
picking leg.
собирательные трубочки anat:
collecting tubules (renal).
собираться стаями swarm, school.
соблюдать диету keep diet.
*соболь zool: sable (Martes zibellina).
*~ русский sobol (Mustela zibellina).
собраться p. a. of собираться.
собственная мышца intrinsic muscle.
собственно зелёные водоросли =
зелёные водоросли, собственно.
~ круглые черви (кл.)zool: nematodes
(Nematoda).
~ мухи (подотр.) = короткоухие м.
~ чистики orn: auks (Cepphus).
собственное вещество (органа)
parenchyma.
собственный разгибатель 5-го
пальца anat: extensor digiti quinti
proprius. [indicis proprius.
~ ~ указательного пальца extensor
сова owl, strigid owl (Striges).
~ белая white owl,snowy o.(Nyctea scan-
~ -белянка = с. белая. diaca).
~ болотная orn: short-eared owl (Asio
flammeus). [wilsonianus).
~ длинноухая long-eared owl (Asio
~ домовая British tawny owl (Surnia
noctua). [flammeus.
~ короткоухая short-eared owl (Asio
совёнок orn: owlet. [majority.
совершеннолетие legl: age of consent,
совершенный лист bot: complete leaf.
~ цветок bot: perfect flower, complete f.
совиный попугай orn: New-Zealand
parrot Stringops.

совка entom: noctuid, owlet-moth.
~ восклицательная dart moth(Agrotis
exclamationis, Euxoa e.)
~ -гамма Phytometra gamma.
~ гороховая pea moth (Polia pisi).
~ горчаковая = с черноватая.
~ дикая wild moth (Euxoa conspicua).
~ зерновая grain moth (Hadena basilinea).
~ -ипсилон black cutworm (Agrostis
ypsilon). [islandica).
~ исландская Iceland moth (Euxoa
~ капустная cabbage moth (Barathra
brassicae). [(Hydroecia micacea).
~ картофельная potato-stem borer
~ клеверная clover moth (Scotogramma
trifolii). [configurata).
~ латуковая bertha armyworm (Mamestra
~ лиловатая = с. картофельная.
~ луговая meadow armyworm (Cirphis
unipuncta). [ononis).
~ льняная flax bollworm (Heliothis
~ люцерновая alfalfa worm (Chloridea
dipsacea). [(Laphygma exigua).
~ малая cutworm moth, beet army worm
~ маргаритковая земляная variegated
cutworm (Lycophotia margaritosa).
~ наземная = с. малая.
~ ночная owlet-moth.
~ огородная Polia oleracea.
~ озимая cutworm Euxoa segetum.
~ отличная Polia dissimilis.
~ подсолнечниковая sunflower beetle
(Zygogramma exclamationis);see also
с. восклицательная.
~ полынная Melicleptria scutosa.
~ пшеничная wheat moth (Euxoa tritici).
~ ржаная rye-stem moth (Trachea
secalis).
~ северная стеблевая = с. ржаная
~ синеголовка Diloba coeruleocephala.
~ сосновая pine moth (Panolis flammea).
~ стеблевая stem moth Oria musculosa.
~ табачная tobacco budworm (Heliothis,
Chloridea virescens, Euxoa obesa).
~ томатная tomato fruitworm(Chloridea
obsoleta, Heliothis armiger).
~ травяная grain worm (Cerapteryx
graminis.
~ хищная coccidophagous owlet-moth.
~ хлопковая cotton-ball worm
(Chloridea obsoleta).
~ цветочная fern caterpillar,southern
fern cutworm(Callopistria floridensis).
~ червецовая Oratocelis communimacula.
~ черноватая Polia persicariae.

совка шалфейная Chloridea peltigera.
~ щавелевая sorrel dagger moth (Acronycta rumicis).
~ яровая Apamea paludis.
совки (сем.)entom: noctuids, owlet-moths (Noctuidae).
совместимость compatibility.
совместное действие cooperative action, synergy.
совокупительная сумка zool: copulatory bursa (bursa copulatrix).
совокупительный орган zool: copulatory organ, penis.
совокупиться p. a. of совокупляться.
совокупление coition, coitus, copulation.
совокупляться copulate.
совокупность симптомов symptomatology, syndrome.
совы (отр.) orn: owls (Striges).
согласие legl: consent.
согнутая вперед поза av med: forward crouch position.
~ семяпочка bot: campylotropous ovule.
согнутое членорасположение (плода) obstet: flexed attitude.
согнутый внутрь inflexed.
согнуть p. a. of сгибать.
согревающий warming up, calefacient.
содержание content(s).
~ в организме body burden (of a radioactive substance).
~ гемоглобина hemoglobin content.
~ гумуса humus content.
~ железа iron content.
~ жира fat content.
~ иона хлора chlorinity.
содержащий вирус viruliferous.
~ гемоглобин hemoglobinated.
~ железо ferrated, siderous, martial.
~ куколку entom: pupigerous.
~ мало гумуса oligohumic.
~ много гумуса polyhumic.
содержимое глазного яблока eyeball interior.
~ желудка stomach content.
~ ~ натощак int: fasting contents.
~ кишечника intestinal content.
содоку path: sodoku, ratbite fever.
содомия psych: sodomy, bestiality, legl: buggery.
содружественное движение synkinesis.
~ косоглазие ophth: concomitant strabism.
содружественные параллельные движения ophth: associated parallel movements.

соевая клубеньковая бактерия bot: soybean nodulus bacterium (Rhisobacterium japonicum, Kirch.)
соединение connection, union, junction, joint(ing); chem: compound.
~ костей посредством связок anat: syndesmosis.
~ костных отломков surg: bony union.
~ ~ отломков или краев раны surg: coaptation.
~ ~ отломков проволокой surg: wiring.
~ между трубчатыми органами surg: anastamosis.
~ посредством связок anat: ligamentous union.
~ соустьем surg: anastomosis.
соединённые пальцы path: united fingers.
соединительная оболочка глаза anat: conjunctiva.
~ ткань hist: connective tissue.
соединительное звено двух больших полушарий мозга = большая спайка мозга.
соединительнотканная опорная структура anat: stroma.
соединительнотканный adj: connective-tissue.
соединяющиеся хромосомы pairing chromosomes.
сожительство cohabitation; zool: symbiosis.
сожительствовать cohabit.
сознание psych: consciousness.
сознательная деятельность conscious activities.
созоиодоловая ртуть pharm: mercury sozoiodolate.
созоиодоловый натрий pharm: sodium sozoiodolate.
созревание ripening, maturation.
созревать ripen, mature.
созревающий ripening.
соин soyin (a toxic protein from soybean).
сойка orn: jay (Cyanocitta, Ceanocephalus, Aphelocoma, Garrulus).
~ хохлатая blue jay (Cyanocitta cristata).
сок juice, succus, sap.
~ поджелудочной железы physl: pancreatic juice.
~ предстательной железы physl: prostatic fluid.
сокирки полевые = живокость посевная.
соклетие hist: syncytium.
сокодвижение bot: flow of sap.
сокол orn: falcon (Falco).
~ -сапсан = сапсан обыкновенный.
"соколий перелёт" = горечавка крестовидная.
сокопроизводящий succiferous.

сократимые нити zool: myoneme.
сократимый retractile.
сократительная вакуоль zool:
contractile vacuole.
сократительная волна contraction wave.
сокращающийся retractible, contractile.
~ пузырь = сократительная вакуоль.
сокращение желудка gastric
contraction. [contraction.
~ желудочков physl: ventricular
~ зрачков ophth: contraction of the
pupils.
~ икроножных мышц при ударе спереди physl: front-tap contraction.
~ матки obstet: uterine contraction.
~ (мышц) при замыкании анода physl:
anodal closure contraction, ACC.
~ ~ при размыкании анода physl:
anodal opening contraction, AOC.
~ привратника pyloric contraction.
солевая лихорадка path: salt fever.
~ нагрузка salt loading.
солевое полоскание saline gargle.
~ слабительное pharm: saline laxative.
солевой обмен salt metabolism.
~ раствор saline solution.
солевыносливый salt-tolerant.
соленая лягушка lab: salt frog.
солёноводный salt-water.
солёность salinity, saltness.
солёный saltly, saline.
солеобразующий saliferous.
солитарный solitary.
солитер helm: tapeworm, taenia, cestoda.
солнечная ванна phys-ther: sunbath.
~ морская звезда zool: sun star
~ радиация solar radiation. |(Solaster).
солнечник ichth: dory (Zeus faber); sun
animalcule (Heliozoa).
солнечники (отр.) zool: sun animalcules,
heliozoans (Heliozoa).
солнечное лечение solar therapy.
~ сплетение anat: solar plexus, celiac
plexus.
солнечные цапли orn: Eurypygae.
солнечный ожог sunburn, sun scald.
~ свет sun light.
~ удар path: sunstoke, insolation.
солнцелечение solar therapy,
solarization. [truncata).
солнце-рыба ocean sunfish (Ranzana
солнцецвет bot: rockrose, sunrose
(Helianthemum, Adans.)
соловей orn: nightingale.
~ восточный northern nightingale
(Luscinia philomela, Erithacus p.)

соловей западный nightingale
(Luscinia luscinia).
~ обыкновенный = с. восточный.
солодка гладкая = лакричник обыкновенный.
солодовая вытяжка wort.
солома bot: straw. [pipestaple.
соломина bot: stem, culm, ha(u)lm,
солоноватоводный brackish-water.
солоноватый brackish.
соль salt.
сольпуги (отр.) zool: vinegarones
(Solpugida, Solifugae).
соляная кислота hydrochloric acid,
muriatic a.
~ матка (ракообразное) zool: brine
worm (Artemia salina).
солянка bot: saltwort (Salsola);
common saltwort, barilla plant (S.kali).
~ американская spike grass, alkali
grass (Distichlis spicata, Greene).
соляной источник salt spring.
~ куст = мангро поблёскивающее.
солянокислый chem: chlorhydric.
~ бензилморфин pharm: benzylmorphine
hydrochloride.
~ кокаин pharm: cocaine chloride.
~ хинин pharm: quinine muriate.
солярий solarium, sunroom.
сом catfish, cat (Siluridae).
сома bio: soma.
соматическая клетка bio: body cell.
~ нервная система somatic nervous
system.
соматическое ощущение somatic
~ чувство somatic sense. |sensation.
соматобласт bio: somatoblastomere.
соматогения somatogeny.
соматогенный somatogenic.
~ психоз somatogenous psychosis.
соматологический somatologic.
соматология somatology.
соматоплевра embr: somatic mesoderm.
соматосенсорная аура neur:
somatosensory aura.
сомик ichth: horned pout, bullhead,
mud cat (Ameiurus); blue cat, channel c.
(Ictalurus); see also карликовый с.
сомит 1. embr entom: somite; 2. zool:
~ трункуса trunk somite. |arthromere.
сомкнутые носки toes touching.
~ пятки heels touching.
сомнамбул psych: somnambulist (male).
сомнамбула somnambulist (female).
сомнамбулизм psych: somnambulism.

сомовые (сем.) ichth: catfish family (Siluridae).
сомы-кошки (сем.) ichth: horned pouts, mudcats (Amiuridae).
сон sleep, somnus.
~ -трава = прострел раскрытый.
сонвелографический sonvelographic.
сонливость somnolence, somnolentia, drowsiness, sleepiness, doziness.
сонливый somnolent, somnolescent, drowsy, sleepy, dozy.
сонная артерия (внутренняя, наружная, общая) anat: (internal, external, common) carotid artery.
~ болезнь = летаргический энцефалит.
~ борозда (основной кости) anat: cavernous groove(of the sphenoid bone).
~ железа anat: carotid gland.
~ одурь = белладонна.
сонный бугорок anat: carotid tubercle.
~ нерв anat: carotid nerve.
соня садовая zool: garden dormouse (Eliomys quercinus).
сообщающиеся intercommunicating.
сообщество community, assemblage, association.
соответствие congruity, compatibility.
соотношение между весом и длиной zool: weight-length relationship.
~ полов sex ratio.
соплодие bot: fruit system, collective fruit, fructification.
сопор psych: sopor.
соприкасаться osculate.
сопровождающий 1. accompanying, concomitant; 2. av med: attendant.
сопротивление resistance.
~ легких дыханию pulmonary airflow resistance.
сопутствующий = сопровождающий 1.
~ сорняк bot: associated weed.
сорго bot: sorgo, sorghum, jowar.
~ алеппское многолетнее = гумай.
~ африканское = дурро.
~ веничное = с. метельчатое.
~ восточноазиатское = гаолян.
~ зерновое grain sorgo, broomcorn, Arabian millet (S. vulgare).
~ каффрское Kafir corn, milo maize, guinea corn (S. vulgare).
~ китайское = гаолян.
~ лимонное citronella grass(Andropogon nardus).
~ метельчатое broomcorn (S. vulgare).
~ обыкновенное sorghum (S. vulgare).
~ сахарное sweet s. (S. saccharatum).
сорго хлебное Johnson grass, Egyptian millet (S. halepense).
соредий лишайников bot: soredium, propagulum.
сорная трава agr bot: weed(s).
сорное растение weed plant.
сорные куры orn: megapods(Megapodiidae)
сорняк agr bot: weed(s).
сорока orn: magpie (Pica pica).
сороконожка zool: centipede Lithobius.
сорокопут orn: shrike (Lanius).
сортирующее скрещивание genet: assortative mating.
сортоводство bot: seed breeding.
сортоиспытание strain test.
сорус bot: sorus, fruit dot (of ferns).
сосальце entom: haustellum.
сосальщик zool: sucker, trematode.
сосальщики (кл.) zool: flukes, suckers, trematodes (Trematoda).
сосание suckling.
сосательная ямка helm: sucking groove.
сосательный желудок entom: sucking stomach.
~ хоботок zool: suctorial proboscis.
сосёнка водяная bot: mare's-tail (Hippuris vulgaris).
соскабливание surg: scraping (off), scratching (off), scaling (off), abrasion; graining.
соскабливать surg: scrape (off), scratch(off), abrade, scale(off); grain.
соскоб scraping, scale; biopsy specimen.
соскоблить p. a. of соскабливать.
сосковая линия anat: mammillary line.
сосковидный papillae-like.
сосна bot: pine (Pinus).
~ австрийская (чёрная) black p. (P. nigra, Arnold).
~ американская pitch p. (P. rigida).
~ банкова gray p., jack p., scrub p. (P. Banksiana, Lamb.)
~ белая white p. (P. strobus).
~ болотная = с. южная.
~ веймутова = с. белая.
~ дугласова Douglas fir, Oregon pine (P. douglassii).
~ горная mountain p. (P. montana, Mill.)
~ канадская spruce fir (Picea canadensis).
~ карликовая mountain p.
~ каури kauri p. (Agathis australis).
~ "кедровая" = с. сибирская.
~ норвежская Norway p., red p. (P. resinosa).
~ приморская maritime p., cluster p. (P. maritima).

сосна растопыренная = с. банкова.
~ сахарная sugar p. (P. lambertiana).
~ сибирская cedar pine, cembra p. (Pinus glabra, P. sibirica, P. cembra).
~ южная long-leaf p., yellow p. Georgia p. (P. australis, Michx.)
сосновая ванна phys-ther: pine bath.
сосновое масло pharm: pine oil.
сосновые (сем.) bot: pine family (Pinaceae).
сосновый bot: piney.
сосок anat: teat, nipple, papilla, pap.
~ груди anat: mammary papilla.
сосочек = сосок.
~ волоса anat: hair papilla.
~ зрительного нерва ophth: optic disk, o. papilla.
сосочковидный papillose.
сосочковое тело hist: papillary body.
состав крови blood composition.
~ преступления legl: corpus delicti.
составная часть constituent, component.
составные части крови blood constituents.
состояние аффекта psych: affective state, affective condition.
~ между бодрствованием и сном psych: subwaking.
сосуд vessel, vas; container, flask, receptacle, jar.
~ для жидкого кислорода av med: liquid oxygen storage flask.
сосудистая лакуна anat: lacuna vasorum.
~ мозговая оболочка = мягкая м.о.
~ оболочка anat: vascular tunic, v. membrane.
~ ~ глаза choroid.
~ опухоль oncol: angioma.
сосудистоволокнистый fibrovascular.
сосудистое растение vascular plant.
~ родимое пятно path: strawberry mark.
сосудистые тайнобрачные bot: vascular cryptogams (Pteridophyta).
сосудистый vascular, vasal, blood-vessel.
~ невроз angioneurosis.
~ тонус vascular tone.
сосудодвигательный anat: vasomotor.
сосудообразный bio: vasiform.
сосудорасширение vasodilatation.
сосудорасширяющее средство vasodilator.
сосудорасширяющий vasodilating, vasodilator.
сосудосуживающее средство vasoconstrictor.
сосудосуживающий vasoconstrictor.
сосудотрофический vasotrophic.
сосуды сосудов anat: vasa vasorum.
сосунок zool: suckling.
сосущая инфузория zool: suctorian.
сосущие инфузории (подкл.) zool: Suctoria, Acineta.
сосуществование coexistence.
сосущие ротовые части entom: sucking mouthparts.
сосущий entom: haustellate.
сосцевидная вырезка anat: mastoid notch, m. groove.
~ часть anat: mastoid part, pars mastoidea (of the temporal bone).
сосцевидный mammiform, mastoid.
~ отросток anat: mastoid process (of the temporal bone).
сосчитать p. a. of сосчитывать.
сосчитывать пульс take pulse.
сот entom: honeycomb.
сотовая губка zool: honeycomb sponge (Hippospongia equina elastica).
сотовый honeycombed.
сотообразный honeycomb-like.
сотрапезничество entom: inquilinism.
сотрясение commotio(n), concussion.
~ мозга commotio cerebri.
~ спинного мозга spinal concussion.
соустье Cf. соединение соустьем.
софол = муравьинонуклеиновокислое серебро.
софора bot: Sophora.
~ однобокоцветная mescal (S. secundiflora, Lag.)
~ японская waifa, pagoda tree, Chinese scholar tree (S. japonica).
сохатый zool: elk (Alces alces); see also лось.
сохранение preservation, conservation.
~ жизни preservation of one's life.
~ равновесия self-balancing, equilibration.
~ ~ в воздухе av med: aerial equilibration.
сохраняемость preservation ability.
соцветие bot: inflorescence.
~ в виде плюмажа или султана bot: plume-like inflorescence.
~ сложноцветных bot: anthodium, head of a composite flower.
социальная болезнь social disease.
сочевичник bot: bitter vetch (Orobus).
сочетание хромосом genet: apposition of chromosomes.
сочинительство = конфабуляция.
сочленение articulation, joint, junction.
сочленённая спора = артроспора.
сочленённый arthrous.
сочленовная поверхность anat: articular surface.
сочленовный выступ anat: condyle.

сочность juiciness, succulence.
сочный juicy, succulent.
со шлемом zool: cucullate.
сошник anat: vomer.
сошниковый anat: vomerine.
соя bot: soybean (Soja hispida, Munch.)
спавшийся collapsed (lung).
спадаться collapse.
спадение 1. collapse (sagging of an organ); 2. see затихание.
~ лёгких pulmonary collapse, lung c., atelectasis.
~ лихорадки defervescence.
спаечный anat: commissural.
спазм spasm.
~ аккомодации ophth: accommodation cramp.
~ артерии path: arteriospasm.
~ век ophth: blepharospasm.
~ входа в желудок cardiospasm.
~ гортани spasm of glottis, laringospasm
~ заднего прохода neur: anal cramp.
~ заднепроходной мышцы neur: anal sphincter spasm, sphincterismus.
~ ресничатых мышц ophth: ciliary spasm.
~ руки chirospasm.
~ сосудов angiospasm.
спазматическая кривошея path: spasmodic torticollis.
спазматический заворот век ophth: spastic entropion.
спазмофилический spasmophilic.
спазмофилия spasmophilia.
спаивающая субстанция hist: cement substance.
спайк spike.
~ -волна spike-wave, petit mal.
спайка anat: commissure (of nerve fibers); adhesion, accretion.
~ брюшины path: peritoneal adhesion.
~ мозга cf. большая спайка мозга.
~ плевры path: pleural adhesion.
спайнолепестные (подкл.) bot: Sympetalae, see вторичнопокровные.
спайнотычинковые (пор.) bot: Synandrae (ord.)
спальный самолет sleeper plane.
спаренный mated, paired.
спаржа bot: asparagus (Asparagus); a. spear, a. shoots.
спаржевая мушка = минёр спаржевый.
спаривание zool: pairing, mating.
спаривать zool: pair, mate.
спарить p. a. of спаривать.
спаровые (сем.) ichth: Sparidae.
спартина bot: cordgrass, marshgrass (Spartina).
спарто = альфа трава.

спасательная водная станция life boat station.
~ лодка life boat.
~ эскадрилья av med: rescue squadron.
спасательное мероприятие rescue measure.
спасательный плот life raft.
~ пояс life belt.
спасение по воздуху av med: air rescue.
~ экипажа av med: crew rescue.
спастическая параплегия neur: spastic paraplegia.
спастическое состояние spasticity.
спасться p. a. of спадаться.
спатангида zool: spatangid.
спатуля ornit: spoonbill (Spatula).
спаянный adherent, Cf. спайка.
спелость ripeness, maturity.
спелый ripe, mature.
спельтовидное растение bot: speltoid plant.
сперма sperm, seminal fluid.
сперматека zool: spermatheca.
сперматобласт = сперматозоид.
сперматогенез spermatogenesis.
сперматогоний spermatogonium.
сперматозоид spermatozoon, sperm(cell); bot: spermatozoid.
сперматозоидный spermatozoal.
сперматоррея path: spermatorrhea.
сперматофор spermatophore.
сперматоцидный spermatocidal.
сперматоцит spermatocyte.
~ второго порядка secondary s.
~ первого порядка primary s.
сперматурия path: spermaturia.
спермацет spermaceti.
спермаций bio: spermatium.
спермообразующий spermatopoietic.
спермофил entom: spermophil.
спёртый fusty, stale, stuffy (air).
специалист по глазным болезням ophthalmologist, oculist.
~ ~ двукрылым насекомым dipterist.
~ ~ млекопитающим mammalogist.
~ ~ мхам bryologist.
~ ~ нематодам nematologist.
~ ~ ушным болезням otologist.
специфический летальный фактор specific lethal factor.
специфичность specificity.
спигелия bot: pinkroot, wormgrass (Spigelia).
~ мериландская Indian pink (S. marilandica).
спикула spicule.
спина anat: back, dorsum.

спинальный ганглий = спинномозговой узел.
спинка dorsum.
~ седла anat: dorsum sellae. Cf. турецкое седло.
~ языка anat: tongue dorsum, d. linguae.
~ птицы вместе со сложенными крыльями orn: mantle.
спинная брыжейка anat: dorsal mesentery.
~ ость bot: dorsal awn.
~ сторона dorsum.
~ струн(к)а = хорда.
спиннобоковой zool: tergolateral.
спиннобрюшной dorsiventral, back-front.
спиннобульбарный anat: spinobulbar.
спинное щупальце (коловратки) zool: dorsal antenna.
спинной dorsal.
~ мозг anat: spinal cord, medulla spinalis.
~ панцырь dorsal shield.
~ плавник zool: dorsal fin.
~ хребет = позвоночный столб.
~ щит(ок) zool: dorsal shield.
спиннокортикальный anat: spinocortical.
спиннолобный dorsofrontal.
спинномозговая анестезия spinal anesthesia.
~ жидкость anat: cerebrospinal fluid, subarachnoid f.
~ оболочка anat: spinal membrane, meninx.
~ пункция surg: spinal tap.
спинномозговой cerebrospinal, see цереброспинальный.
~ канал anat: spinal canal.
~ нерв anat: spinal nerve.
~ узел anat: spinal ganglion, dorsal root g.
спинные позвонки anat: thoracic vertebrae.
спинорог trigger-fish (Balistidae).
спиноталамический путь anat: spinothalamic tract.
спиралересничные (отр.) zool: Spirotricha.
спиральнозавитой strombuliform.
спирамицин spiramycin.
спирейные (подсем.) bot: Spiraeae or Spiraeoideae subfamily.
спирея bot: spiraea (Spiraea).
~ белая meadowsweet (S. alba).
~ иволистная = с. белая.
~ плющелистная queen of the prairie (S. palmata).
спирилла mcbio: spirillum.
спирогира bot: pondscum (Spirogyra) algae
спирометр spirometer.
спирометрический spirometric.
спирометрия spirometry.
спирт 1. alcohol, ethyl alcohol; 2. methyl alcohol, wood alcohol.
спиртной alcoholic, alcohol-containing.
спиртно-эфирный раствор хлористого железа = бестужевы капли.
спиртные напитки alcoholic beverages.
спиртовая вытяжка chem: alcoholic extract.
спиртовое брожение chem: alcoholic fermentation.
спиртокислота chem: alcoholic acid.
спирторастворимый chem: alcohol-soluble.
спиртоустойчивый alcohol-fast.
спирулина bot: Spirulina, Arthrospira (alga).
список убитых и раненых casualty list.
спланхноптоз splanchnoptosis, splanchnoptosia.
спланхнотом embr: splanchnotome.
спленектомия surg: splenectomy.
сплетение anat: plexus; web.
~ корней bot: network of roots.
сплюснутый oblate, flattened.
сплющенный = сплюснутый.
сплющивание making oblate, flattening.
спокойное настроение quiet disposition, untroubled mind.
споласкивание rinsing.
споласкивать rinse, wash off.
сполоснуть p. a. off споласкивать.
спонгин zool: spongin.
спонгиозный spongy, see ноздреватый
спондилит path: spondylitis.
спонтанный spontaneous.
спора bot: spore.
спорангиевый bot: sporangial.
спорангиеспора bot: endogenous spore.
спорангий = спороносец.
спорангиофор bot: sporangiophore.
споровики (кл.) zool: sporozoans (Sporozoa).
споровый мешочек = спороносец.
спорогенез bot: sporogenesis, sporogeny.
спорозоит bio: sporozoite.
спорокарпий bot: sporocarpe.
споролистик bot: sporophyll, spore-bearing leaf.
спороносец bot: sporecase, sporangium.
спороноситель bot: sporophore.
спороносная ткань bot: sporogenous tissue.
спороносный слой bot: sporogenous layer, gills.
спорообразование bot: sporulation, spore formation.
спорообразующий spore-forming.
спорopочка bot: sporophydium.
споросак zool: sporosac.
спороубивающее средство bot: sporocide.
спороубивающий bot: sporocidal.

спорофил sporophyll.
спорофит bot: sporophyte.
спорофитовый bot: sporophytic.
спороцист zool: sporocyst, germinal sac.
спорт bot: sport.
споруляция = спорообразование.
споры головни phytp: smut balls.
спорынья phytp: ergot (Claviceps purpurea).
спорыш = горец птичий.
способ применения application method.
~ употребления = с. применения.
способность ability, capacity, faculty.
~ внутреннего понимания psych: insight.
~ глаз к отведению ophth: ability of the eyes to abduct.
~ к задержке дыхания ability to hold the breath.
~ ~ размножению bio: reproductive power.
~ менять окраску bio: metachrosis.
~ передвигаться bio: locomotivity.
~ разлагаться decomposability.
~ улетучиваться volatility, effumability.
способный бродить fermentable.
~ выделяться с мочей urinable.
~ дышать capable to breath.
~ колебаться vibratile.
~ к развитию productive (of an egg).
~ окрашиваться серебром hist: argyrophile.
способствующий всасыванию (ab)sorbefacient, resorbent.
~ отделению мокроты expectorative.
~ рубцеванию cicatrizant, ulotic.
~ фактор favoring factor, contributory cause.
спот ichth: spot (Leiostomus xanthurus; Roncador stearnsi, Sciaenops ocellatus).
спотыкание на слогах psych: stuttering.
спотыкающаяся походка path: stumbling gait.
справа налево dextrosinistral.
спринцевание syringing, irrigation; gyn: douching, lavage (of the vagina).
спринцевать irrigate; gyn: douch, lave.
спринцовка syringe, douch (device for douching).
спрут = осьминог.
спуск 1. pharm: cerate; 2. drain.
спутанность сознания psych: mental confusion, obfuscation, psychataxia.
спутанные стебли bot: tangled stems.
спячка zool: hibernation.
спящая клетка hist: resting cell.
~ почка bot: resting bud.
спящий глазок bot: resting bud.
~ побег (или черенок) bot: resting shoot.
сравнительная анатомия comparative anatomy.
срамная артерия anat: pudendal artery.
~ губа (большая, малая) anat: labium (majus, minus), labium pudendi.
~ щель anat: vulvar cleft, rima pudendi.
срамное сплетение anat: pudendal plexus.
срамный anat: pudic, pudendal.
~ фартук gyn: pudendal apron.
срастание growing together, adhesion, accretion.
срастаться посредством окостенения path: coossify.
сращение anat: synarthrosis, symphysis; path: concretion, adhesion, coalescence, concrescence.
~ краёв век ophth: ankyloblepharon.
~ между мягким нёбом и глоткой soft palate to pharynx adhesion.
~ пальцев path: palmature.
~ позвонков anat: fusion of the vertebrae.
~ 5-го поясничного позвонка с крестцом path: sacralization.
~ языка path: tongue-tie, ankyloglossia.
сращённый adnate, cf. сращение.
~ рубец adherent scar.
среда medium.
~ для пластинчатых разводок bact: plating medium.
~ ~ разведения lab: culture medium.
средиземноморская губка zool: Turkey solid sponge (Euspongia officinalis mollissima).
~ чайка orn: Mediterranean blackheaded gull (Larus melanocephalus).
срединная артерия anat: median artery.
~ жилка entom: media, medial vein, vena medialis.
~ локтевая вена anat: vena mediana cubiti.
срединный anat: medial, mesal, med-.
~ нерв anat: median nerve.
~ разрез surg: midline incision, midsection.
среднеазиатская черепаха zool: Central Asian turtle (Testudo horsfieldi).
средневлаголюбивый bot: mesophytic.
среднегрудинная линия anat: midsternal line.
среднегрудь entom: mesothorax.
среднее ухо anat: middle ear.
среднемозговой anat: mesencephalic.
среднепузырчатые хрипы medium bubbling rales.
средний anat: middle, media.

средний задний mednoposterior.
~ зародышевый листок bot: mesoblast.
~ мозг anat: midbrain, mesencephalon.
~ отдел живота anat: midabdomen.
~ отит otitis media.
~ палец (руки) anat: middle finger.
~ поморник orn: pomarine (Stercorarius
~ рост medium height. pomarinus).
средняя доля middle lobe.
~ жилка (листа) bot: midvein (of a
leaf); midrib, costa.
~ кишка zool: mid-gut.
~ лапка entom: middle leg.
~ носовая раковина anat: middle nasal
concha, middle turbinate bone. [life
~ продолжительность жизни average
~ температура average temperature.
~ фаланга anat: middle phalanx.
~ часть middle part, center, centrum.
~ ~ грудины anat: midsternum.
~ ямка черепа anat: middle cranial
fossa, mesocranial f.
средостение anat: mediastinum.
~ яичка anat: mediastinum testis, body
of Highmore. [pleura.
средостенная плевра anat: mediastinal
~ поверхность anat: mediastinal surface.
средство agent, means; medicine;
medicinal, drug, remedy.
~ для возбуждения аппетита appetizer
~ ~ втирания pharm: inunctum.
~ ~ закаливания организма hardening
agent, inuring agent.
~ ~ ингаляции pharm: inhalant.
~ ~ окуривания fumigant.
~ ~ усиления отделений secretion
prompting agent.
~ ~ фиксации hist: fixing agent.
~ ~ шелушения pharm: desquamative.
~ задерживающее рост бактерий
bacteriostat.
~ против бешенства antirabic.
~ ~ гноя pyostatic.
~ ~ головной боли cephalalgic.
~ ~ зубной боли antiodontalgic.
~ ~ зуда antipruritic.
~ ~ истерии anthysteric.
~ ~ крыс raticide.
~ ~ ленточного глиста pharm: taenia-
~ ~ лишая antherpetic. |fuge, teniacide.
~ ~ малокровия antanemic.
~ ~ мозолей anthelotic.
~ ~ ожирения antiobesic.
~ ~ ожогов antipyrotic.
~ ~ остриц oxyuricide.

средство против паразитов parasit-
~ ~ поноса antidiarrheal. |icide.
~ ~ потливости antihidrotic,
antisudorific, antisudoral.
~ ~ рвоты antemetic.
~ ~ свёртывания anticoagulant.
~ ~ сифилиса antisyphilitic.
~ ~ слюнотечения antisialic.
~ ~ сна anthypnotic. [emmenagogue.
~ стимулирующее менструацию
~ убивающее грызунов rodenticide.
~ ~ личинок larvicide.
~ ~ микробы microbicide, germicide.
~ ~ насекомых insecticide. [irritant.
~ уменьшающее раздражение counter-
~ усиливающее отделение молока
galactogogue.
~ ~ половое чувство aphrodisiac.
~ ~ родовую деятельность obstet:
срезание хвоста agr: docking. |oxytocic.
срезанная чешуйка bot: truncated glume.
сродство affinity.
~ к жировой ткани lipotropy.
сростись p. a. of срастаться.
сростнолепестные bot: sympetalous.
(Sympetalae). [gamopetalous.
сростнолепестный bot: sympetalous,
сростнолистный bot: gamophyllous.
сростночелюстные (отр.) ichth:
Plectognathi, Tetrodontiformes.
~ (сем.) ichth: Tetrodontidae.
сросток concretion, see also сращение
~ свекловичных семян bot: beet
seedball.
сросшиеся пальцы path: adherent
fingers; see also синдактилия.
сросшийся connate, adnate.
~ перелом united fracture.
срочные роды obstet: partus malurus,
срощение symphysis. |birth in time.
срыгивание regurgitation.
~ молока ped: milk r.
ссадина abrasion, excoriation.
ссаднение brush burn.
стабильность stability. [glasses, cup.
ставить банки med: apply cupping
~ клизму administer an enema.
~ пиявки apply leeches, leech.
~ прогноз prognosticate.
ставрида ichth: hardtail, cavalla,
skipjack, horse mackerel, blue runner
ставридка ichth: jack, jack- |(Caranx).
fish, ulua, omilu, crevally, trevally.
ставридовые (сем.) ichth: jackfishes
стагнация stagnation. |(Carangidae).

стагнация гиполимниона hypolimnetic stagnation.
стадия stage(definite period of a disease)
~ выздоровления convalescent stage.
~ высыпания path: eruptive stage.
~ деления (клетки) bio:division stage.
~ дочерних звезд hist: anaphase.
~ жара path: hot stage.
~ зрелости гонад gonad maturation stage.
~ клубка hist: prophase, coil stage.
~ куколки entom: pupal stage.
~ материнской звезды hist: metaphase.
~ между двумя высыпаниями path: intereruptive stage.
~ метацеркарии metacercarial stage.
~ нарастания path: anabatic stage.
~ озноба path: cold stage.
~ покоя bio: quiescent stage, resting s.
~ после зачатия postconception stage.
~ пота path: sweating stage.
~ предшествующая зачатию preconceptive stage.
~ ~ течке zool: prooestrum.
~ пупавки bot: pupal stage.
~ развития bio: developmental stage.
~ размножения bio: multiplicative stage
~ циприсовидной личинки (ракообразного) zool: cypris larva.
стадный gregarious.
~ инстинкт psych: herd instinct, group feeling.
стадо herd, flock(of geese, etc.), stock.
стажёр med: intern.
стажирование med: internship.
~ по разным специальностям rotating internship.
стажировка = стажирование.
стаз hem: stasis.
стазра = станция защиты растений.
стайный gregarious, of herd, of flock, of school.
стальник bot: restharrow (Ononis).
стально-головый лосось ichth: steelhead trout, salmon t.(Salmo gaidneri).
стаминодий bot: staminode, staminodium.
стандарт годности mil: standard of fitness.
станция защиты растений plant-protection station (entomological).
старение aging, growing old, senescence.
стареющее семя aged seed.
стареющий aging, growing old, senescent.
стародубка = адонис весенний.
старость old age, senility, gerontism.
старческая атрофия senile atrophy.
~ гангрена senile gangrene.
старческая дальнозоркость ophth: presbyopia.
~ дуга ophth: senile arc, arcus senilis.
~ катаракта ophth: senile cataract.
~ слабость path: decrepitude.
~ эмфизема senile emphysema.
старчески дальнозоркий ophth: presbyopic, presbyope, presbytic.
старческий senile, gerontal.
~ психоз senile psychosis.
старческое облысение derm: senile loss of hair. Cf. облысение.
~ перерождение senile degeneracy.
~ помутнение роговицы = старческая дуга.
~ слабоумие psych: senile dementia.
~ увядание involution, decline, decay.
старшая сестра head nurse.
старший ассистент senior assistant.
старый old, senile, gerontic, gerontal.
~ туберкулин pharm: old tuberculin, original tuberculin.
стати лошади conformation of a horse.
статица bot: statice(Statice sinuata).
статобласт zool: statoblast, statocyst, lithocyst, otocyst.
статолит zool: statolith.
статоцист zool: statocyst, otocyst.
статус status.
стать = стати лошади.
стаураструм bot: Staurastrum (algae).
стафилин(ид) entom: rove-beetle.
стафилиниды = коротконадкрылые жуки.
стафилококк mcbio: staphylococcus.
стафилококковый staphylococcal.
~ сепсис staphylococcus-sepsis.
стафилома ophth: staphyloma.
стафиломатический ophth: staphylomatic, staphylomatous.
стахис = хороги.
стационарное лечение hospital treatment.
~ микроядро zool: stationary (female) micronucleus.
стая flock, swarm, school, shoal.
ствол stem, stock, trunk, truncus.
~ аорты anat: aortic trunk.
~ блуждающего нерва anat: vagal trunk.
~ кишечника (у сосальщиков) zool: crus.
~ конечного мозга anat: corpus striatum.
~ нерва anat: nerve trunk.
~ слухового нерва anat: acoustic nerve trunk.
стволик entom: stipes.
*стволовая гниль bot: trunkrut.

ствольный truncal.
створаживаться (о молоке) clot.
створка valve.
створчатый leaved, valvate.
стебелёк bot: stemlet, caulicle, stalk, pedicel, peduncle.
~ глаза (раков) eyestalk.
стебель bot: stem, stalk; haulm; stipe
~ куста bot: cormus. (of a fern).
~ травы = соломина.
~ хмеля bot: hopbind, hopbine.
стебельковый bot: stipitate, stalked, pediculate, pedicellate, scapose.
стебельчатая гидра = длинностебельчатая гидра.
стебельчатобрюхое насекомое petiolate insect. [Pelmatozoa.
стебельчатые иглокожие zool:subphylum
стебельчатый pedunculate, see стебельковый.
~ глаз zool: stalked eye, projecting eye.
стеблевание bot: shooting, stooling stage. [stem-end rot.
стеблевая гниль phytp: stem blight,
~ головня phytp: stem smut, stipe s.
~ луковка bot: bulblet, bulbil.
~ ржавчина phytp: stem rust, black rust (Puccinia graminis).
стеблевой bot: stalked, cauline, see стебельчатый.
стеблеед капустный entom: curculio Lixus iridis.
~ свекловичный c. L. subtilis.
стеблеобъемлющий bot: stem-clasping, amplexicaulus.
стеблестой agr bot: haulm stand.
стегно orn: hock joint, haunch.
стегозавр zool: Stegosaurus (extinct).
стегоселяхии ichth: Stegoselachii (extinct).
стегоцефалы zool: Stegocephalia(extinct)
стекание draining, flowing off, escape.
стекать drain, flow off, run off, escape.
стекловатость = остеклённость.
стекловидное тело anat: viltreous body
стекловидный viltreous, glassy, flinty, hyaline.
стеклянная бусинка glass bead.
~ палочка glass rod. [spreading rod.
~ ~ для размазывания bact: glass-
стеклянница entom: clear-winged moth.
~ комаровидная Synanthedon culiciforme
~ малинная raspberry-root borer (Bembecia marginata, B. hylaeiformis).
~ муравейная Synanthedon formicaeforme.
стеклянница ольховая S. sphaeciforme.
~ смородинная currant borer (S. tipuliforme).
~ темнокрылая Sciapteron tabaniformis.
~ тополевая большая Sesia apiformis.
~ яблонная apple-tree borer (Synanthedon myopaeformis).
стеклянницы (сем.) entom: clear-winged moths (Aegeriidae).
стеклянные губки (отр.) zool: glass sponges (Hexactinellida, Triaxonida).
стеклянный наконечник glass nozzle.
стельная корова zool: pregnant cow,
стельность zool: pregnancy. | in-calf cow.
стелящееся растение bot: prostrate plant, trailing p., procumbent p. Cf. ползучее р. [decumbent plant.
~ ~ с поднимающейся вершиной bot:
стенка артерии anat: artery wall.
~ влагалища anat: vaginal wall.
~ грудной клетки anat: thoracic wall.
~ живота anat: abdominal wall.
~ желудка anat: stomach wall.
~ матки anat: uterine wall.
стенкоположный parietal.
стенница bot: wall lichen (Parmelia).
стеноз path: stenosis.
~ аорты int: aortic stenosis.
~ евстахиевых труб gyn: Eustachian
~ канальцев ophth: | tube stenosis. stenosis of the canaliculi.
стенокардия path: cardiac angina, angina cordis, a. pectoris. [parotid d.
стенонов проток anat: duct of Steno,
стенотафр bot: stenotaphrum (Stenotaphrum secundatum, Kuntze).
стенотермность stenothermy.
стенотермный stenothermic.
*стенотомус ichth: paugy, scuppaug, fair maid (Stenotomus chrysops).
стеночный mural, parietal.
степень использования (пищи) degree of utilization (of food).
~ питания nutriture.
~ разведения pharm: potency.
степная агама zool: Agama sanguinolenta. Cf. агамы.
степной удавчик zool: little prairie constrictor (Eryx jaculus).
стервятник orn: carrion crow, black vulture (Cathartidae); neophron (Neophron).
стерео-офталмоскоп stereo-ophthalmoscope.
стереоскопическое зрение stereoscopic vision, solid v.

стереоспецифический stereospecific.
стереоспондили zool: Stereospondyli (extinct amphibians).
стереотипная поза psych: stereotypic
~ речь s. speech. posture.
стереотипное действие psych: s. action
стереотипия psych: stereotypy.
стереотропизм bio: stereotropism.
стереть p. a. of стирать.
стержень волоса anat: hair-shaft.
~ пера orn: shaft of a feather.
плодоложа bot: medulla of receptacle.
~ початка bot: cob.
стержневой корень bot: taproot.
стерилизатор sterilizer.
стерилизация sterilization.
~ излучением radiation s.
~ катодными лучами cathode-ray s.
~ пищепродуктов food s.
стерилизовать sterilize. [dose.
стерилизующая доза rad: sterilizing
стерильная повязка sterile dressing.
стерильность sterility, acyesis.
стерильные припасы sterile supplies.
стерильный sterile, acyetic.
стериновый обмен bio: sterol metabolism
стеркулиевые (сем.) bot: cacao-tree family (Sterculiaceae). [rupestris).
стеркулия bot: bottle tree (Sterculia
стерлядь ichth: sterlet, small sturgeon (Acipenser ruthenus). [puncture.
стернальная пункция surg: sternal
стернальный пунктат surg: specimen obtained through the sternal puncture.
стернит (членистоногих) sternite.
стернитовый sternitic.
стероидный обмен bio: steroid metabolism
стерробластула embr: sterr(h)oblastula.
стерторозное дыхание path: stertor, sonorous breathing.
стеторус entom: beetle Stethorus
стетоскоп stethoscope. |punctillum.
стехиометрический stoichiometric.
стехиометрия stoichiometry.
стечение признаков syndrome.
стечь p. a. of стекать.
Стивенс Stevens.
стигеоклониум bot: Stigeoclonium
стигма entom: spiracle, stigma. |(algae).
стигмальные железы ent: stigmal glands
стизостедион ichth: jack salmon (Stizostedion vitreum), wall-eyed pike, yellow pike perch, dore; horsefish, sauger, blue pike (S. canadense).
стилбэстрол stilbestrol.

стилет zool: stylet.
стилопизация entom: stylopization.
стимул stimulus.
стимулирование stimulation.
стимулирующее рост вещество growth promoting substance.
стимулятор stimulant, stimulating agent.
~ кроветворения hematopoietic
стимуляция stimulation. |stimulant.
стипендия scholarship, fellowship.
стипес entom: stipes.
стиракс bot: alligator tree (Liquidambar styraciflua).
стирание detrition.
стирать (до крови) wear out, chafe.
стирол pharm: styrol, styrene, cinnamene.
стихать cf. затихание.
стихнуть p. a. of стихать.
стоваин pharm: stovaine.
стоимость суточного содержания больного patient day cost.
стойкий persistent, stable, permanent.
сток sink; drain(age), outflow, running
стокфиш stockfish. [off.
стол для вскрытий autopsy table.
~ ~ (вправления) переломов surg: fracture table.
столб column, pole.
столбик style; columella.
столбиковый columellar.
столбняк path: tetanus. [tetanus.
~ новорожденных path: umbilical
~ одной половины тела homitetany.
столбнячная судорога path: fixed
столбнячный path: tetanic. |spasm.
~ анатоксин tetanus toxoid.
столбочка bot: columella.
столбур phytp: big bud.
столбчатая паренхима hist: palisade parenchyma.
столетник bot: century plant, American aloe (Agava americana); pharm: aloe.
столик микроскопа microscope stage.
столон bio: stolon.
стоматит path: stomatitis, sore mouth.
стоматолог oral surgeon.
стоматологический stomatologic.
стоматология stomatology.
стонать moan. [peda).
стоножка centipede (Lithobius centi-
стоножник bot: fern Scolopendrium
стопа anat: foot. |officinarum, DC.
стопоходящий zool: plantigrade.
стотысячник обыкновенный bot: common yarrow, milfoil (Achillea millefolium).

сточная труб(к)а drainage pipe (or tubing).
сточные воды san: waste water, liquid waste, effluent; sewage.
стояние standing upright.
стоячее положение upright posture, standing, station.
страдание suffering, affliction, trouble
страдать suffer, be afflicted.
~ от ржавчины phytp: rust.
страдающий абазией abasic.
~ амнезией amnesiac.
~ анкилозом stiff-jointed.
~ безволием psych: abulic.
~ воздушной болезнью air-sick.
~ гастритом gastritic.
~ головокружением vertiginous.
~ грыжей herniated.
~ запором costive.
~ отрыжкой belcher.
~ эндокардитом endocarditic.
странгуляция strangulation.
странствование wandering, migration.
страстоцвет bot: passion flower (Passiflora).
~ лавролистный water lemon, Jamaica honeysucle (P. laurifolia).
~ настоящий barbadine (P.quadrangularis)
страстоцветные (сем.) bot: passion-flower family (Passifloraceae).
стратификация stratification.
стратосферная гондола av med: stratosphere gondola.
страус африканский = с. обыкновенный. [melus).
~ обыкновенный ostrich (Struthio ca-
страусник bot: fern Struthiopteris filicastrum, All.
страусово перо 1. orn: ostrich feather; 2. bot: see страусник.
страх psych: fear, terror, apprehension; see also боязнь.
~ быть обворованнымpsych:kleptophobia
~ перед полетом av med:fear of flying.
~ покраснеть psych: erythrophobia.
страхование insurance.
~ жизни life insurance. [insurance.
~ от несчастных случаев accident
стрекательная капсула zool: stinging capsule. [nematocyst.
~ клетка zool: stinging cell, nettling c.
стрекательный пузырёк zool:nematocyst
стрекающие (подтип) zool: stinging animals, cnidarians (Cnidaria).
стрекоза entom: damsel-fly, dragonfly (Odonata).

стрекоза-коромысло dragonfly Aeschna. [splendens).
~ -красотка blue damselfly(Calopterix
~ -лютка darning needle (damselfly Lestes).
~ обыкновенная skimmer, dragonfly
~ -стрелка = с.-лютка. |Libellula.
стрекозы (отр.) entom: dragonflies & damselflies (Odonata, Paraneuroptera).
~ равнокрылые (подотр.) damselflies (Zygoptera).
~ разнокрылые (подотр.) dragonflies (Anisoptera). [lineolatum.
стрела-змея zool: snake Taphrometoron
стрелка 1. arrow; 2.lab: pointer, indicator, hand, needle; 3. entom: see стрекоза-стрелка; 4. frog (in horse's hoof); 5.zool: arrow worm (Chaetognatha); 6.bot: spear, spire, flower
стрелкование bot: bolting. stalk.
стреловидный bot: gablet, sagittate, shaft-arrowform.
~ лист bot: sagittate leaf.
~ с расходящимися лопастями bot: hastate, halberd-shaped.
~ шов anat: sagittal suture.
стрелозубый палтус ichth: arrow-toothed halibut (Atheresthes stomias).
стрелолист bot: arrowhead, swamp potato (Sagittaria).
~ американский giant a. (S. montevidensis, Cham. & Schlect.)
~ китайский гигантский giant sagittaria (S. sinensis).[gittifolia).
~ обыкновенный old-world a. (S. sa-
стрельный яд arrow poison, curare.
стрельчатка щавелевая entom: Acronycta rumicis (Noctuidae).
стреляющая боль fulgurant pain, lancinating p., shooting p.
стремечко anat: stapes, stirrup.
стремечковый anat: stapedial.
стремительные роды obstet: precipitate labor.
стремление к нападению psych: aggressiveness. [tendency.
~ приспособиться accommodation
стремяобразный разрез surg: curved flap incision. [tactic.
стремящийся к дереву zool: ligno-
стрепашка американская или рисовая = рисовая птица.
стрепет orn: species Otis tetrax.
стрептокаин pharm: streptoquaine.
стрептококк bact: Streptococcus.

стрептококковый streptococcal.
стрептомицин pharm: streptomycin.
стрига жёлтая bot: pest Striga lutea.
стригущий лишай derm:ringworm;vet:born
стридор(озный звук) stridor. |itch.
стриж orn: swift (Micropodidae); martin
Cypselus apus.
~ силанган martin Collocalia.
стрижи (сем.) orn: swifts(Micropodidae, Cypselidae).
стрижка shearing.
стрик phytp: streak (of potatoes, etc.)
стриктура stricture.
стрихнин strychnine.
стрихнос ядоносный bot:strychnos plant.
стричь clip, shear, crop.
стробила helm: strobila.
стробиляция helm: strobilation.
строение structure, constitution, texture, fabric.
~ корня, листа и т.п. bot: root, leaf, etc. structure.
стройный лори zool:lemur Nycticebus
строма anat:stroma,framework. |coucang.
стромальный stromal, stromatic.
строматиния bot: Stromatinia, see склеротиния.
стронгилид palisade worm (Sclerostoma equinum, Strongylus armatus).
стронгилоидная личинка helm: strongyloid larva. [lura marina).
стронгилюра ichth: needle-gar (Strongi-
строчёк bot:Helvella fungus;H.crispa etc.
~ съедобный saddle fungus (H.esculenta).
~ ямчатый H. lacunosa.
строчки (сем.) bot: Helvellaceae family (fungi).
строящая сети гусеница webworm.
структура structure.
структурный structural.
струма struma, goiter.
струнец helm: thread worm (Nematoda).
~ мединский helm: Medina worm, see гвинейский червь.
струп scab, slough, eschar.
стручёчный = стручковый.
стручковые bot: pulses, siliquose.
~ крестоцветные bot: silique crucifers. Cf. стручочковые к.
стручковый bot: siliquose, siliquous.
стручок bot: pod, legume, cod, follicle.
~ со стяжениями между семенами bot: loment.
стручочковые крестоцветные bot: silicle crucifers. Cf. стручковые к.
струя мочи stream of urine.
студенистое животное jelly animal.
студент-медик medical student.
студень gel, jelly. [agr bot:rootball.
стул 1. stool(s),defecation;2.chair;3.
~ в виде овечьего кала path:sheep-dung stools.
~ грудных детей ped:breastmilk stool.
ступка lab: mortar.
ступор psych: stupor.
Стурмиус Sturmius.
стыдливый bot: humble (pudicus); bashful (verecundus).
стэнд lab: bench.
Стэпп Stapp.
стягивание adstriction.
~ под влиянием вяжущих astriction.
стяжение path: phimosis.
су-ауру vet: su-auru (camel disease due to Trypanosoma ninae kohljakimowi).
субарахноидальное пространство = подпаутинное пространство.
субарахноидальный subarachnoid.
субдорсальный subdorsal.
субдуральное пространство anat: subdural space.
субимаго entom: subimago.
~ подёнки dun.
субкортикальный subcortical.
субкоста(льная жилка) entom: subcosta(l vein).
субкрепитирующие хрипы subcrepitant rales.
субкультура lab: subculture.
субкутикула zool: subcuticula.
сублетальная доза sublethal dose.
сублимирование psych: sublimation.
сублиторальный sublittoral.
субментум entom: submentum.
субмикроскопическая структура submicroscopic structure.
субнормальный subnormal.
субординационный subordinational, subordinative.
субординация subordanation.
субстрат substratum.
субтотальный subtotal.
субтропический subtropical.
субфебрильный subfebrile.
субъективное зрительное ощущение entoptic sensation.
~ обследование subjective examination.
~ ощущение internal sensation.
~ слуховое ощущение entacoustic sensation.

субъективные данные subjective evidence.
~ симптомы subjective symptoms.
субэндокардиальное кровоизлияние av med: subendocardial hemorrhage.
сувойка zool: infusorium Vorticella.
сувойки (сем.) zool: Vorticellidae.
суггестия psych: suggestion.
судак ichth: pike perch (Lucioperca).
~ дальневосточный морской Lateolabrax.
судан chem: pigment brown.
~ chem: cerasin red.
суданка = суданская трава.
суданская трава bot: sudan grass (Sorghum vulgare sudanense, Stapf.)
судебная медицина legal medicine, forensic m., medical jurisprudence.
~ химия forensic chemistry.
судебномедицинский medicolegal.
судебномедицинское вкрытие medicolegal autopsy.
судебнопсихиатрическая экспертиза legal psychiatric test.
судебный врач legal physician.
судза = перилла.
судно san: bedpan.
судовой врач = корабельный врач.
судорога path: cramp, spasm, convulsion
~ век ophth: blepharospasm.
~ в икрах sural cramp.
~ глазного яблока nystagmus.
~ глазных мышц reader's cramp.
~ гортанных мышц phonic spasm.
~ затылочных мышц retrocollic spasm.
~ кузнецов hephestic cramp, smith's c.
~ музыкантов musicians' cramp.
~ привратника pylorospasm.
~ ручной кисти cheirospasm.
судорожная терапия psych: spasm therapy, cramp t.
судорожное сжатие голосовой щели spasmotic closure of the glottis, laryngospasm.
~ состояние path: convulsive state.
ж судорожный crampy, crampig, spasmous.
~ смех laughing spasm.
суеверие psych: superstition.
суеверный superstitious.
суждение psych: judgment.
сужение narrowing, stenosis arctation, constriction.
~ аорты int: aortic stenosis.
~ артерии path: arteriostenosis, arteriarctia.
~ бронхов bronchoconstriction.

сужение зрачка ophth: miosis, pupil contraction.
~ (канала, отверстия) arctation.
~ пищевода stricture of the oesophagus.
~ поля внимания narrowing of the field of attention.
~ привратника pylorostenosis.
~ прямой кишки stricture of the rectum.
~ сосудов vasoconstriction.
~ стенонова протока stenostenosis.
~ таза obstet: pelvic contraction.
~ устья лёгочной артерии pulmonary stenosis.
суженный зрачок ophth: miotic pupil.
~ таз path: reduced pelvis.
суживающая зрачок мышца anat: sphincter pupillae.
суживающее зрачок средство ophth: miotic.
сук bot: branch, bough, limb.
сука zool: female dog, bitch. Cf. кобель.
сукцессия bio: succession.
сукциндегидрогеназа succinic dehydrogenase.
сулема chem: mercury bichloride.
сулемовая почка = некронефроз.
сулла = эспарцет испанский.
султан bot: plume, spike-like panicle.
султанка = барабуля.
султанковые = барабулевые.
султанные злаки bot: spike-like panicle grasses, plume grasses.
сульфадиазин pharm: sulfadiazine.
сульфадиметин pharm: sulfadiametine.
скльфаниламид pharm: sulfonamide.
сульфапиразин pharm: sulfapyrazine.
сульфапиримидин pharm: sulfapyrimidine.
сульфат бензедрина pharm: benzedrine sulfate.
~ декстрана dextran sulfate.
~ эфедрина pharm: ephedrine sulfate.
сульфатиазоловая мазь pharm: sulfathiazole ointment.
сульфизоксазол pharm: sulfisoxazole.
сульфиргамид pharm: sulfirgamide.
сульфозин sulfosin (1% suspension of sulfur in a vegetable oil).
сульфозинотерапия psych: sulfosin therapy.
сульфонал pharm: sulfonmethane.
сульфонамид sulfonamide.
сульфорициновокислый натрий pharm: sodium sulforicinate.
сульфофеноловокислое серебро pharm: silver sulfophenate.

сульфоформ pharm: formylsulfide.
сульфофталеиновый краситель sulfophthalein dye.
сумасшедший psych: mad(man), insane, see психопат.
~ дом collq: lunatic asylum.
сумасшествие psych: madness, insanity; see психоз.
сумах bot: sumac (Rhus).
~ виргинский staghorn s., velvet s. (R. typhina).
~ дубильный tanner's s., wig-tree, smoke-tree, Venetian s. (R. cotinus).
~ конский Colpoon compressum.
~ миртолистный myrtle-leaved (Coriaria myrtifolia).
~ подсочный = с. резиноносный.
~ разнолепестный = с. ядоносный.
~ резиноносный wax-tree(R. succedanea).
~ сицилийский Sicilian s.(R. coriaria).
~ скунсовый skunk bush (R. trilobata).
~ уксусный = с. виргинский.
~ французский bot: French sumac (Coriaria myrtifolia).
~ ядовитый poison sumac, poison elder, poison dogwood (R. vernix); poison ivy (R. radicans).
~ ядоносный poison oak (R. toxicodendron)
сумаховые (сем.) bot: cashew family (Anacardiaceae).
сумаховый bot: anacardiaceous.
сумеречная бабочка = бражник.
сумеречное состояние psych: twilight state.
сумеречный crepuscular.
сумка pouch, sac, bag, capsula; zool: marsupium (of a kangaroo, etc.)
~ первой помощи med: first-aid kit, emergency bag.
~ цирруса zool: cirrus pouch.
сумочка capsule, utricle.
сумочная связка anat: capsular ligament.
сумчатая белка zool: marsupial squirrel (Petaurus).
~ крыса zool: bandicoot (marsupial ratlike animal of Australia).
~ стадия bot: ascigerous stage (of fungi, etc.)
сумчатые грибы bot: ascomycetes, ascomicetous fungi.
~ звери (подкл.) zool: Metatheria, see низшие звери.
~ лишайники (кл.) bot: ascolichens (Ascolichenes).
~ (отр.) zool: marsupials, pouched (Marsupialia).
сумчатый bot: ascomycetous.
~ волк zool: marsupial wolf (Thylacinus cynocephalus).
~ крот zool: marsupial mole (Notoryctes typhlops).
сумчатый медведь zool: Australian bear, coala (Phascolarctos cinereus).
суперпаразит bio: hyperparasite.
суперпозиция пальца ног path: superposition of a toe.
супинатор anat: supinator(radii brevis).
супинация anat: supination.
суповая черепаха zool: green turtle (Chelonia mydas).
супоросая свинья zool: pregnant swine.
супралитораль supralittoral.
супралиторальный supralittoral.
супранейстон supraneuston.
супраоптический supraoptical.
супротивный bot: accumbent, opposite.
сурдомутизм = глухонемота.
сурепица = сурепка.
сурепка bot: navew, wild turnip, (Brassica rapa campestris).
~ обыкновенная common wintercress, yellow rocket, upland cress (Barbarea vulgaris, R. Br.)
сурок zool: marmot(Mus marmota).
~ американский woodchuck, groundhog (Marmota monax).
суррогат surrogate.
сурьма antimony, Sb.
сурьмянистый chem: antimon(i)ous (trivalent).
сурьмяное масло chem: antimony butter, antimonic cloride.
сурьмяной chem: antimonic, stibial (pentavalent).
сусак bot: flowering rush(Butomus).
~ зонтичный f.r.(B. umbellatus).
сусаковые (сем.) bot: flowering rush family (Butomaceae).
суслик zool: suslik, spermophile, (pocket) gopher(Citellus).
суспекция suspicion.
сустав anat: joint, articulation; see also диартроз.
~ ключицы anat: clavicular articulation
суставная болезнь joint disease.
~ боль joint pain.
~ впадина лопатки anat: glenoid cavity.
~ головка anat: articular head.
~ площадка anat: articular surface.
~ поверхность joint surface.
~ полость anat: joint cavity, cavum articulare.
~ связка articular ligament.
~ сумка (или капсула) anat: joint capsule.
~ ямка anat: socket.
суставное чувство joint sense.
суставной диск anat: articular disk, intraarticular fibrocartilage.
~ ревматизм path: rheumatic fever.
суставный отросток anat: articular process, processus articularis.

суставный отросток (нижней челюсти) anat: condyloid process (of the mandible).
~ хрящ anat: arthroidal cartilage.
суставчатоногий zool: arthropod
суставчатый articulated. |(Arthropoda).
~ усик (или побег) bot: jointed tendril
сутяга psych: litigant.
сутяжническое помешательство psych: litigious paranoia, querulousness.
сухая банка dry cup.
~ гниль phytp: dry rot.
~ фосфорнонатриевая соль pharm: exsiccated sodium phosphate.
~ чешуя both: dry scale(s). [siccus.
сухие роды obstet: dry labor, partus
суховершинный bot: stag-headed (tree).
суховоздушный стерилизатор dry-air sterilizer.
сухожилие anat: tendon, sinew.
~ подколенной ямки anat: hamstring.
~ сгибателя anat: flexor tendon.
~ четырёхглавой мышцы бедра anat: thigh tendon.
сухожильная дуга anat: tendinous arch.
~ связка anat: tendinous connection.
~ струна anat: tendinous cord.
сухожильное влагалище anat: tendon
~ чувство tendon sense. sheath.
сухожильный рефлекс tendon reflex.
~ тяж anat: tendinous band.
~ центр anat: centrum tendineum.
~ шов surg: ten(din)osuture.
сухой кашель dry cough, nonproductive c.
~ лёд dry ice, carbonic acid snow.
~ плеврит path: dry pleurisy.
~ хрип dry rale.
~ шов surg: dry suture.
сухолюб = ксерофит.
сухонос orn: goose Cygnopsis cygnoides.
сухопарость sinewiness.
сухопутная черепаха zool: tortoise.
сухопутный краб land crab (Gecarcinus).
сухостойная корова agr: dry cow.
сухостойное дерево bot: dead standing tree, deadfall. [tion period.
сухостойный период zool: interlacta-
сухость dryness, siccity, xerosis.
~ в ноздрях path: xeromycteria.
сухотка phthisis, consumption.
~ спинного мозга path: tabes dorsalis.
сухоустойчивый siccostabile.
сухоцвет bot: immortelle, xeranthemum.
сухоядение xerophagia.
сушёная треска stockfish.

сушеница bot: cudweed, everlasting (Gnaphalium).
~ альпийская edelweiss (G. Leontopodium).
~ песчаная = цмин песчаный.
существенная причина essential cause.
существо 1. essence; 2. being, creature, animalcule.
суягная овца zool: pregnant sheep, in-
суягность pregnancy. lamb sheep.
сфагн bot: sphagnum, bog moss (Sphagnum).
сфагновые мхи = торфяные мхи.
сфагнум = сфагн.
сфексы (надсем.) entom: digger wasps, sphecoid wasps (Sphecoidea).
сфенотрипсия obstet: sphenotripsy.
сферический мешочек anat: sacculus.
сферотека phytp: Sphaerotheca mors uvea
~ роз = бель. (fungi).
~ хмеля S. humilis, DC. Burr.
сфигмограф sphygmograph.
сфигмографический sphygmographic.
сфигмография sphygmography.
сфигмоманометр sphygmomanometer.
сфинктер anat: sphincter; see also сжиматель.
~ заднего прохода anat: anal sphincter.
~ мочеиспускательного канала anat: sphincter urethrae.
схватка tormen (pl. tormina), pang, pain.
схватки в периоде раскрытия obstet: dilating pains.
схваткообразная боль = схватка.
схизогония zool: schizogony.
схизогрегарины (подотр.) zool: Schizogregarinaria.
схизонт bio: schizont.
схизоцель zool: schizocoel. [nus molle).
схинус bot: California pepper tree (Schi-
схистоцерка = саранча пустынная.
сходный с броненосцем zool: armadillolike. [aneurysmatic.
схожий с аневризмой aneurysmal,
сцедить p. a. of сцеживать.
сцеживание lab: elutriation.
сцеживать elutriate, see also отцеживать. [maceae (algae).
сценедесмовые (сем.) bot: Scenedes-
сценедесмус bot: Scenedesmus (algae).
сцепление cohesion, linkage, adhesion.
сцеплянки = конъюгаты. [(Sciaenidae).
сциеновые рыбы sciaenoid fishes
сциенопс ichth: reef bass, channel b., redhorse, red drum (Sciaenops ocellatus).
сцимнус entom: ladybug Scymnus.
сцинк zool: skink (Scincidae).

сцинковые skinks, scincoid lizards (Scincidae). [scincus scincus).
сцинковый геккон scincoid gecko(Terato-
сцитаминовые (пор.) bot:Scitaminales.
сцифистома zoo: scyphistoma.
сцифоидные zool:scyphozoans(Scyphozoa).
~ медузы = сцифомедузы.
сцифомедузы (кл.) zool: jellyfishes, true medusae.
сцэна ichth: black croaker, Chinese c. (Scoena saturna).
счет всех белых шариков total white count.
~ крови blood count.
~ красных шариков red count.
~ кровяных шариков blood count.
~ ~ пластинок platelet count.
~ лейкоцитов leucocyte count.
~ тромбоцитов platelet count.
~ эритроцитов red count.
счетная камера counting chamber.
~ пластинка bact: counting plate.
счетчик rad: counter.
~ -зонд counter probe.
~ -игла needle counter.
считать 1. count, compute, calculate; 2.p. a. of считывать.
считывать read (out, off).
сшивание surg: suturing.
~ вены surg: venesuture.
~ кишек surg: enterorrhaphy.
~ нерва surg: neurosuture.
съедаемая пища food intake.
съедать 1. eat; 2. corrode.
съедобная ракушка zool: edible mussel (Mytilus edulis).
~ сердцевидка zool: edible cockle(Car-
съедобность edibility. |dium edule).
съедобный edible (esculentus).
~ краб zool: edible crab (Cancer).
съёживаться shrivel.
съестьр. a. of сьедать.
сыворотка serum. See also молочная сыворотка.
~ жерёбой кобылы pregnant mare's serum.
сывороточная болезнь serum disease.
~ жидкость serous fluid.
~ среда bact: serum medium.
сывороточный serous, serumal.
~ альбумин serum albumin.
~ иммунитет seroimmunity.
~ (растительный) микроорганизм serophyte.
~ характер serosity.
сыга = водяника чёрная.

сыпной тиф infect: typhus, camp fever, Fleck typhus.
сыпнотифозный infect: typhous, typhic.
~ больной typhus fever patient.
сыпь path: rash, exanthem(a), efflorescence, eruption. [exanthem(a).
~ на коже eruption upon the skin.
~ при прорезывании зубов ped: tooth rash.
сырая вода raw water.
сырный cheesy.
~ яд cheese poison, tyrotoxin.
сыроежка bot: russule (Russula); pungent r. (R. emetica). [ноги.
сырой moist, damp; see also сырые
~ лекарственный материал gruff.
сырок = пелядь.
сырть ichth: Vimba v. vimba.
сырые ноги sodden feet.
сытость satiety. [(Cyperus).
сыть bot: galingale, umbrella sedge
~ длинная umbrella plant (C. longus).
~ круглая nutgrass, cocograss (C. rotundus).
~ съедобная = миндаль земляной.
*сыч owlet (Carine noctua); Tawny owl (Surnia noctua).
сычуг (четвёртый желудок) zool: abomasum, true stomach.
сычужная закваска rennet extract.
Сьюолл Sewall.
сэмотилюс ichth: horned dace, creek chub (Semotilus atromaculatus).
сяжковая железа zool: antennal gland.
сяжковый antennate, antennal.
сяжок entom: antenna, feeler.

Т

табак 1. tobacco; 2. bot: nicotiana (Nicotiana).
табачная мозаика phytp:tobacco mosaic.
табеллярия bot: Tabellaria (algae).
табельный дозиметрический комплект rad: dosimeter kit.
табес path: tabes.
табетик tabetic.
таблетка pharm: tablet, lozenge, troch(e), trochiscus, see пилюля.

таблетка яда pharm: toxitabella.
таблеткообразный scutulate, lozenge-like.
таблица table, chart.
~ доз pharm: posological table.
~ Егера ophth: Jaeger card.
~ Снеллена ophth: Snellen chart, test type.
табопаралич taboparalysis.
таволга = лабазник.
~ вязолистная = лабазник вязолистный.
~ -земляные орешки = лабазник шестилепестный.
~ иволистная = спирея белая.
тагуан = летяга-тагуан.
таз 1. anat: pelvis; 2. (large) dish.
~ карлиц anat: dwarf's pelvis.
~ с несросшимся лоном path: split pelvis
тазик 1. tray; 2. entom: coxa.
~ для гнойных перевязок surg: pus basin.
~ ~ инструментов instrument tray.
тазиковая впадина entom: cotyloid cavity.
тазобедренный сустав anat: coxofemoral joint, hip j.
тазовая кость anat: hipbone, coxae, innominate bone
~ полость anat: pelvic cavity.
тазовое дно anat: pelvic floor.
~ предлежание obstet: pelvic presentation.
тазовый вход anat: pelvic inlet, brim of the pelvis.
~ ~ или выход anat: pelvic strait.
~ выход anat: pelvic outlet.
~ гамак surg: pelvic hammock.
~ нерв anat: nervus pelvicus.
~ пояс anat: pelvic girdle.
тазоизмерение obstet: pelvimetry.
тазокрестцовый anat: pelvisacral.
тазомер obstet: pelvimeter.
тазометрия = тазоизмерение.
тай ichth: tai, porgy (Taius tumifrons).
тайлфиш tilefish (Caulolatilus).
таймень ichth: salmon trout (Hucho taimen).
тайник овальнолистный bot: twayblade (Listera ovata R. Br.)
тайнобрачный bot: cryptogamic, cryptogamous.
тайное лекарство arcanum, secret medicine.
такадиастаза pharm: taka-diastase.
такса 1. German badgerdog (Canis familiaris vertagus), dachshound, basset; 2. rate, price; see also аптекарская такса.
таксодиевые (сем.) bot: taxodium family (Taxodiaceae).
таксодиум bot: bald cypress (Taxodium, Rich.)
таксономическая ботаника
таксономия bio: taxonomy.

таксус = тисс.
тактильная оценка размеров (предмета) tactile size judgment.
~ чувствительность sense of touch.
тактильное восприятие tactile perception.
~ ощущение tactile sensation.
тактический tactic.
такусса = просо африканское.
талассография thalassography.
талассотерапия thalassotherapy.
талеихтис ichth: candlefish (Thaleichthys pacificus), eulachon, oolican.
талипот = веерная пальма талипот
таллом bot: thallus.
таллофит bot: thallophyte.
таллус bot: thallus.
таляссия bot: seaweed, turtle grass (Thalassia testudinum, Konig.)
тамарин zool: tamarin (Hapale argentata).
тамаринд bot: tamarind, Indian date (Tamarindus).
тамариск bot: tamarisk (Tamarix).
тамарисковые (сем.) bot: tamarisk family (Tamaricaceae).
тампон surg: pledget, pad, dossil; gyn: tent.
~ на палочке swab.
тампонада = тампонирование.
тампонирование packing (a wound etc.)
~ влагалища gyn: columnization.
~ прямой кишки surg: rectal packing.
тампонировать pack, plug (a wound, etc.)
танатоз entom: thanatos.
танатология thanatology.
тангенциальная занавеска ophth: tangent curtain.
тангерин bot: tangerine (Citrus tangerina, Hort.)
танджерин = тангерин.
таннал pharm: aliminum tannate.
танниген pharm: diacetyl tannin.
таннисмут pharm: bismuth bitannate.
таннокол pharm: tannogelatin.
танноформ pharm: tannin formaldehyde.
тапиока = маниок.
тапир zool: tapir (Tapirus).
тапиры (сем.) zool: tapirs (Tapiridae).
таракан entom: cockroach.
~ американский American c. (Periplaneta americana).
~ -пруссак German c., croton bug (Blatta germanica).
~ чёрный oriental cockroach (Blatta orientalis).
тараканы (отр.) entom: cockroaches (Blattoidea, Blattoptera).
таранная кость anat: talus, astragalus, ankle bone.
таранопяточный anat: talocalcanean.

тарантул zool: tarantula (Trochosa singoriensis, Aviculariidae).
тарань ichth: roach Rutilus rutilus heckeli.
тарашка = густера.
тардиф bot: behindhand.
тарзальный entom: tarsal.
*тарпон silver-fish (Tarpon atlanticus), savanilla, grandy-key, grand ecaille.
тархун = эстрагон.
татарник bot: Scotch thistle, cotton t. (Onopordum).
~ колючий cotton t. (O. acanthium).
~ обыкновенный = т. колючий.
таутога ichth: salt-water chub (Tautoga onitis), Will George.
таутоголябрус ichth: sea perch, nipper, chogset, bergall, cunner, bait-stealer (Tautogolabrus adspersus).
тафрина phytp: Taphrina (fungus).
~ косточковых T. pruni, Tul.
тахикардия tachycardia, rapid heart.
*тахинное масло benne oil, teel oil.
тахины = ежемухи.
тахифилаксия imm: tachyphylaxis.
твёрдая мозговая оболочка anat: dura mater.
~ среда solid medium.
твёрдое нёбо anat: hard palate, palatum durum.
твёрдокорый bot: hard-shelled.
твердошанкерный ven: chancrous.
твёрдые каловые массы scybalum, scybalous masses.
твёрдый рак path: scirrhus.
~ режим fixed regime.
~ шанкр ven: hard chancre, Hunterian c., true c.
~ щиток entom: nasus.
творог pot cheese, cottage cheese.
творожистое перерождение path: caseation, cheeselike necrosis.
творожисто перерождаться caseate.
творожистый caseous, cheesy.
*~ гной gurdy pus.
театральная мания psych: histrionic mania.
тевяк = длинномордый тюлень.
тегула entom: tegula.
тека zool: theca (of hydroids).
текодонты zool: Thecodontia (extinct reptiles).
текома = трубная лоза.
текучепаровой стерилизатор bact: steam sterilizer.
текущая дезинфекция concurrent disinfection.
телейтоспора teleutospore.
теленомус entom: egg-eater Telenomus.
телепатия psych: telepathy.
телескопоглазая рыба telescope-eyed fish (Opisthoproctus).

телесный bodily, somatic.
телиться zool: calve, fawn.
тёлка heifer, cow calf.
тело body.
~ грудины anat: body of the sternum, midsternum.
~ длинной кости anat: diaphysis.
~ клитора anat: corpus clitoridis.
~ кости anat: shaft.
~ ленточного червя zool: strobila.
~ матки anat: uterine body, corpus uteri.
~ ногтя anat: nail body.
~ подостемового bot: thallus.
~ позвонка anat: vertebral centrum, v. body.
~ рясок bot: frond.
телодонты zool: Telodontia, Coelolepida (extinct).
телолецитальный telolecithal.
телопея = варатах.
телорез bot: frog's bit, frogbit (Limnobium).
телосложение body structure, body build, physique, conformation, stature; constitution, genotype.
телоспоридии (подкл.) zool: Telosporidia.
телофаза hist: telophase.
тельматодитес orn: long-billed marsh wren (Telmatodytes palustris).
тельсон zool: telson (of crustaceans).
тельце corpuscle, body.
~ Гейнца Heinz body.
~ Гольджи Golgi body.
~ Краузе hist: Krause's corpuscle.
~ Мелиса helm: Mehlis gland, shell g.
~ Негри hist: Negri body.
телячья оспа cowpox.
тембр голоса timbre.
теменная доля anat: parietal lobe.
~ извилина anat: parietal gyrus.
~ кость anat: parietal bone, os parietale.
теменное отведение sincipital (electric) take-off, sincipital contact point.
~ предлежание obstet: vertex presentation.
теменно-затылочная борозда мозга anat: fissura parietooccipitalis.
теменной anat: sincipital, bregmatic.
~ бугор anat: parietal eminence.
тёмная комната dark room.
темновая адаптация ophth: dark adaptation.
тёмное вещество (ножки мозга) anat: substantia nigra.
темп роста rate of growth.
темперамент temperament.
температура temperature.
температурная кривая temperature curve.
~ чувствительность temperature sense.
температурное чувство = т. чувствительность.

температурный листок temperature
~ скачок thermocline. chart.
темя 1.anat:sinciput,bregma; 2. entom:
тенар anat: thenar. vertex.
теневое напыление shadow casting.
теневыносливый bot: shade-enduring,
shade-bearing, shade-tolerant.
тенезм tenesmus.
тенелюбивый bot:shade-loving, shade-
тенёта zool: spider web. |requiring.
тенётный паук zool: web spider.
тениаз helm: Taeniasis.
теннисная нога surg: tennis leg.
теннисный локоть path: tennis elbow.
тенонит ophth: inflammation of Tenon's
capsule.
тенонова капсула ophth:Tenon's capsule.
тень камня x-ray: stone shadow.
~ лёгких x-ray: lung shadow.
~ эритроцита mcscop: shadow corpuscle.
теозинт bot: teosinte (Euchlaena,Schrad.)
теофиллин theophylline.
тёплая кровь warm blood.
теплица bot agr: greenhouse.
тепличное растение bot agr:greenhouse
plant, warmhouse plant.
тепличный бассейн bio: conservatory
тепловатый lukewarm,tepid. pool.
тепловая смерть heat death.
~ точка heat spot.
тепловодный warm-water.
тепловое чувство heat sense.
тепловой удар path: heat stroke.
тепловые судороги path:heat cramps.
теплокровный zool: warm-blooded,
homoiothermal, hematothermal.
теплолюбивый thermophylic.
теплообразовательный thermogenic,
calorifacient. [тельный.
теплообразующий = теплообразова-
теплоотдача испарением evaporative
cooling. [regulating centre.
теплорегулирующий центр anat: heat
тёплый источник hot spring.
терапевт therapeutist, internist.
терапевтика therapeutics.
терапевтический therapeutic.
терапия therapy, therapeutics;see also
лечение.
~ лучами = лучевая т.
~ сном psych: sleep therapy.
терапсида zool:Therapsida (extinct
тергит zool:tergit,tergum. |reptiles).
тёрен = терновник.
тёрка zool:lingual ribbon(of a mollusk).

термен = терминальный край крыла.
терминальный terminal.
~ край крыла entom:outer margin of
the wing, termen.
~ период terminal period (of life,etc.)
терминология terminology.[bellicosus).
термит entom:termite,white ant(Termes
термитная постройка = термитник.
термитник entom: termitary.
термитный entom: termitine.
термиты (отр.) entom:termites,white
термический ожог thermal burn.|ants
термокаустика thermocautery.|(Isoptera).
термолабильный heat-labile.
термометр thermometer.[lanceolata,R.Br)
термопсис bot:thermopsis(Thermopsis
терморегуляция thermoregulation.
термостабильный heatproof, thermo-
термотерапия thermotherapy. |stable.
термощуп lab:thermosound. [колючая.
тёрн = 1. терновник; 2. слива
терновник bot:blackthorn, sloe
(Prunus spinosa).
тернослива = слива колючая.
терпентинные (пор.) bot:Terebinthales.
терпингидрат pharm: elixir of terpin
hydrate. [gramidae).
*терпуг ichth:starling,rock trout(Hexa-
~ многолинейный Hexagrammos.
~ однопёрый Pleurogrammus.
терпуговые (сем.)ichth:Hexagrammidae.
террамицин terramycin.
террапина zool: terrapin (turtle).
терригенный terrigenous.
терфа bot: kames fungus (Terfezia).
теснородственное опыление genet:
close pollination,close fertilization.
тест test.
~ -бактерии test bacteria.
~ на внимание av med:test of attention.
~ ~ выносливость endurance test.
~ ~ координацию движений обеих
рук av med:two-hand coordination test.
~ Ринне otolar: Rinne test. [test.
~ с задержкой дыхания breath-holding
~ ~ карандашом и бумагой av med:
pencil-and-paper test. [chair test.
~ ~ креслом Барани av med: Barany
~ ~ мотками шерсти ophth:wool yarn
~ ~ походкой gait test. test.
~ ~ ручкой и рулём av med:
stick-and-rudder test. [reading test.
~ ~ чтением таблицы av med: table
~ ~ чтением шкалы av med: dial
reading test.
~ умственных способностей psych:
intelligence test.

тест Швабаха otolar: Schwabach test.
тестикула anat: testicle.
тестостерон testosterone.
тетанические судороги гортани neur: gutturotetany.
тетания path: tetany, tetania.
тетанус path: tetanus.
тетерев orn: black grouse(cock)(Lyrurus tetrix).
~ -глухарь = глухарь.
~ -косач = косач.
~ луговой heath cock(Tetrao cupido).
~ полевой = косач.
~ шалфейный capercaillie (Centrocercus urophasianus).
тетеревиные orn: grouses, ptarmigans (Tetraonidae).
тетеревятник orn: goshawk (Astur palumbarius).
тетёрка orn: gray hen, heath hen(Lyrurus tetrix). Cf. тетерев.
тетракаин солянокислый pharm: tetracaine hydrochloride.
тетраптурус ichth: spearfish, spikefish, billfish (Tetrapturus).
тетраспора bot: tetraspore.
тетраспорангий bot: tetrasporangium.
тетрастихиды (сем.) entom: tetrastichidae.
тетрахлорметан chem: carbon tetrachloride
тетрациклин pharm: tetracycline.
тетраэтилсвинец chem: tetraethyl lead.
тефф = просо африканское.
техника пилотирования av med: pilotage technique.
течение (процесса) course, process.
"течёт нос" path: running nose.
течка zool: estrus, (sexual) heat, rut, ruttishness, lasciviousness, lewdness.
тиамин thiamin.
тибетский бык = як.
тигмотаксис thigmotaxis.
тигмотактическая реакция thigmotactic response.
тигр zool: tiger (Felis tigris).
тигрица tigress.
тигровая кошка = кошка тигровая.
~ саламандра zool: tiger salamander (Amblystoma tigrinum).
тигровый хорёк zool: mottled polecat (Vormela peregusna, Putorius sarmatius).
тигроидный hist: tigroid.
тик 1. path: tic; 2. bot: see тиковое дерево.
тиковое дерево teak (Tectoma grandis)
тиланин pharm: sulphurated lanolin.
тилландзия = лишайник тилландзия.
тимиан bot: thyme (Thymus).
~ душистый garden t. (T. vulgaris).
тимиан широколистный citron t. (T. citroclarus).
тимин thymine.
тимофеевка bot: timothy grass, herd's grass (Phleum pratense).
тимпальные органы = слуховые о.
тимпанит tympanites, see вздутие.
тимпанический звук int: tympanic resonance.
тимпания жвачных vet: ruminant bloat.
тимьян = тимиан.
тина bot: pond scum, blanket algae.
тинкториальный tinctorial.
тинктура tincture.
тиннитус tinnitus.
тиокарбамилпиперазин pharm: thiocarbamylpiperazine.
тиокол = гваяколсульфонокислый калий.
тиомалат thiomalate.
тиомерсалат thiomersalate.
тиомочевина thiourea.
тиоурацил pharm: thiouracil.
тиоформ pharm: bismuth dithiosalicylate.
тиоцианат thiocyanate.
тип 1. bio: phylum; 2. type.
типец = овсяница овечья.
типирование identification, observation of species.
типируемый штамм mcbio: typable strain.
типично хордовые zool: Euchordata.
типология typology.
типоспецифический mcbio: type-specific.
типун vet: pip. [bird.
тиранн orn: tyrant flycatcher, kingbird.
тиреоидэктомированный thyroidectomized.
тиреотропный thyrotropic.
тиротоксин tyrotoxin, cheese poison.
тирситес ichth: barracouta(Thyrsites atum).
тисс bot: yew (Taxus).
~ ягодный yew (T. baccata).
тиссовое дерево = тисс.
тиссовые (сем.) bot: yew family (Taxaceae).
титр chem: titer.
титрование chem: titration.
титровать chem: titrate.
тифии (сем.) entom: tiphiids(Tiphiidae).
тихий бред psych: quiet delirium, d. mite.
тихиус entom: curculio Tychius.
~ жёлтый T. flavus.
~ люцерновый галловый T. medicaginis.
~ рыжий T. femoralis.
~ пятиточечный T. quinquepunctatus.
тихое бешенство sullen rabies.
~ помешательство psych: melancholic insanity, paranoid melancholia.
тихоокеанская сардина ichth: Pacific sardine (Sardinops).

тихоокеанская сельдь ichth: Pacific herring, California h. (Clupea pallasii).
~ треска ichth: Pacific cod, Alaska c. (Gadus macrocephalus).
тихоокеанский лосось ichth: Pacific salmon, Oriental s. (Oncorhynchus).
тихопланктер bio: tychoplankter.
тихоходки zool: tardigrades, water bears (Tardigrada). [tinct).
тихоходы (сем.) zool: Gravigrada (ex-
тканевая гипоксия path: tissue hypoxia.
~ доза rad: tissue dose.
~ жидкость hist: interstitial fluid.
~ клетка hist: tissue cell.
~ культура lab: tissue culture.
~ стадия bio: tissue stage.
тканевое дыхание physl: tissue respira-
тканевой сок physl: tissue juice. |tion.
~ футляр av med: fabric container.
тканеэквивалентная газовая смесь rad: tissue equivalent gas mixture.
~ ионизационная камера rad: t. e. ionization chamber.
тканеэквивалентный пропорциональный счётчик rad: t.e. proportional
ткань anat: tissue, web, tela. |counter.
ткач orn: wattlebird (Ploccus).
ткачик orn: weavebird (Quelea).
ткачиковые (сем.) orn: weaverbirds (Proceidae). [(Aphidodea).
тли (подотр.) entom: plant-lice, aphids
тля entom: aphid, plant louse (Aphidodea).
~ акациевая a. (Aphis laburni).
~ бахчевая melon aphid, cotton a. (Doralis aphis gossypii, A. frangulae).
~ берёзовая birch aphis (Callipterus betulaecoleus).
~ бобовая bean aphis (Aphis fabae).
~ виноградная = филлоксера.
~ вишнёвая black-cherry aphid (Myzus cerasi).
~ вязовая красногалловая red-gall elm (Byrsocrypta caerulescens).
~ вязово-кукурузная elm-and-corn a. (Byrsocrypta gallarum). [pisi).
~ гороховая pea aphis (Acyrthosiphon
~ грушевая pear-leaf a. (Dentatus pyri).
~ злаковая листовая spring grain a., green bug (Toxoptera graminum).
~ зонтичная umbel-plant a. (Cavariella aegopodii).
~ камышовая = тля сливовая.
~ капустная cabbage aphis (Brevicoryne brassicae).
~ картофельная potato a. (Macrosiphum solanifolii).

тля кизиловая Anoecia corni.
~ конопляная hemp a. (Phorodon cannabis).
~ крапивная nettle a. (Aphis urticaria).
~ кровяная = тля мохнатая.
~ крыжовниковая gooseberry-leaf a. (Aphis grossulariae).
~ кувшинковая Rhopalosiphum nympheae.
~ кукурузная листовая corn-leaf a. (Aphis maydis). [diradicis).
~ ~ корневая corn-root a. (Aphis may-
~ лиственничная larch a. (Chermes
~ листовая leaf-feeding a. |laricis).
~ люпинная lupine a. (Macrosiphum albi-
~ люцерновая = т. акациевая. |frons).
~ мохнатая woolly apple a., European red mite (Eriosoma lanigera, Schizoneura lanigera).
~ мятная mint-leaf a. (Aphis menthae).
~ овсяная oat a. (Amphorophora avenae, Sitobion avenae).
~ ольховая alder blight (Prociphilus tessellata, Pemphigus t.) [persicae).
~ оранжерейная greenhouse a. (Myzodes
~ персиковая green peach louse (Lachnus persicae).
~ растительная 1. see тля; 2. psylla, jumping plant-louse (Chermidae).
~ розанная rose aphis (Macrosiphium rosae, Myzus rosarum).
~ розовая rose scale (Aulacaspis rosae).
~ салатная green fly (Macrosiphum lactucae).
~ свекловичная sugar-beet root a. (Pemphigus betae); beet a. (Aphis fabae).
~ сливовая мучнистая mealy plum a. (Hyalopterus pruni).
~ смородинная большая greater currant a. (Rhopalosiphum lactucae).
~ ~ волосистая currant woolly a. (Capitophorus ribis).
~ табачная = тля оранжерейная.
~ тепличная = тля оранжерейная.
~ хлопковая = тля бахчевая.
~ ~ большая greater cotton-plant a. (Acyrthosiphon gossypii).
~ ~ корневая cotton-root a. (Trifidaphis phaseoli).
~ хмелевая hop aphid (Phorodon humuli).
~ черёмуховая Siphonaphis padi.
~ чёрная black a. (Aphis rumicis).
~ щитковая = кошениль.
~ щитовковая = щитовка.
~ яблонная бурая = т. я. серая.
~ ~ зелёная apple-tree green a. (Aphis pomi).

тля яблонная серая apple-tree gray a. (Dentatus communis).
~ ячменная barley a.(Brachycolus noxius)
тмин bot: caraway (Carum carvi).
~ волошский cumin(Cuminum cyminum).
~ римский = т. волошский.
~ чёрный nutmeg flower(Nigella sativa).
тминное масло pharm: caraway oil.
Т-образная повязка surg:T-bandage.
тождественного типа isotypical.
ток current, stream, flow.
~ действия physl: action current.
~ крови, лимфы blood, lymph stream.
~ Удена phys-ther: Oudin current.
токовать orn: bell.
токоферилгидрохинон tocopherylhydroquinone.
токоферол tocopherol.
токсемический toxemic.
токсемия toxemia.
токсикогенный toxicogenic.
токсикоз toxicosis.
токсиколог toxicologist.
токсикологический toxicologic(al).
токсикология toxicology.
токсикопатический toxicopathic.
токсин toxin.
~ -антитоксин toxin-antitoxin.
токсинообразование toxin production.
токсинообразующий toxigenic.
токсическая амблиопия path: toxic amblyopia.
~ анемия path: toxic anemia.
~ инфекция path: toxinfection.
токсическое действие toxic effect.
токсичность toxicity.
~ мочи path: urotoxy.
токсичный toxic, toxinic, toxiferous, toxicant.
токсоплазмоз toxoplasmosis.
толай zool:(Central Asian hare)Lepus tolai
толерантная доза rad:tolerance dose.
толерантность tolerance, toleration.
толкачик = муха-танцовщица.
толкунчик = муха-танцовщица.
толокнянка bot: bearberry(Arctostaphylos, Adans.);common b., kinnikinick, mealberry, hog-cranberry(A.uva-ursi, Spreng.)
~ дубильная manzanita.
~ красильная = т. дубильная.
толстая кишка anat: large intestine, intestinum crassum.
~ мозговая оболочка anat:pachymeninx, dura mater.
толстоголовка мальвовая entom: skipper Carcharodus alceae.
толстоголовки (сем.) entom:common skippers (Hesperiidae).
толстокишечный anat:colonic, colic.
толстолоб ichth: Hypophthalmichthys.
толстоножка entom: eurytoma.
~ акациевая acacia e.(Eurytoma caragana).
~ клеверная = т.люцерновая.
~ люцерновая clover-seed chalcid (Bruchophagus gibbus).
~ пшеничная = изозома галловая.
~ ~ узловая Harmolita noxialis.
~ ржаная галловая Harmolita rossica.
~ туркестанская Harmolita turkestanica.
~ урюковая Erytoma samsonovi.
*толстоножки (сем.) entom:erytomas (Erytomidae).
толстопалый pachydactylous.
толстостенный thick-walled.
толстый кишечник = толстая кишка
~ лори zool: lemur Loris tardigradus.
~ мазок mcscop: thick film.
толстянковые (сем.)bot:orpine family, stonecrop family (Crassulaceae).
толуиленовый синий toluylene blue.
томат = помидор.
томатик bot:tomatillo(Physalis ixocarpa, Brot.)
томатилло = томатик.
томатное дерево bot: tree tomato (Cyphomandra betacea, Sendt.)
томатный 5- и 6-точечный червь tomato worm (Phlegethontius quinquemaculata, Ph. sextamaculata).
томка = душистый колосок.
томкод ichth:tomcod (Menticirrhus saxatilis; Microgadus).
тонзиллит path: tonsillitis.
тоническая судорога tonic cramp, t. spasm.
тонический рефлекс tonic reflex.
тоническое средство tonic.
тонкая ветка bot: wand.
~ кишка anat:small intestine, intestinum tenue.
~ мозговая оболочка anat: piarachnoid, leptomeninx.
тонкие кишки anat: small intestines.
тонкий перепончатый scarious.
~ кишечник = тонкая кишка.
тонковолокнистый = мелковолокнистый.
тонкоисчерченный striolate.
тонкокожий thin-skinned, thin-shelled.
тонкокорый bot:thin-barked, see тонкокожий.
тонкоморщинистый rugulose.
тонконог bot: koeleria(Koeleria cristata).
тонкопалый leptodactylous.
~ суслик zool: suslik Spermophilopsis leptodactylus.
тонкопанцырные раки (отр.) zool: Leptostraca.

тонкопозвонковые = лепоспондили.
тонкопряд хмелёвый entom: swift Hepialus humuli.
тонкопряды (сем.) entom: swifts, macrojugatae (Hepialidae).
тонкостенный thin-walled.
тонометрия tonometry.
тонофибриллы hist: tonofibrils.
тонсиллотом surg: tonsillotome.
тонус tonus.
~ сосудов vascular tone.
тоны сердца physl: heart sounds.
топинамбур =груша земляная.
тополь bot: poplar,aspen(Populus).
~ бальзамический balsam p., taccamahac (P. balsamifera).
~ душистый = т. бальзамический.
~ жёлтый tulip p. (Liriodendron tulipifera). [Lombardy p.(P.nigra).
~ итальянский пирамидальный black p.
~ канадский cottonwood,necklace p., Canadian p. (P. deltoides,Marsh.)
~ пирамидальный Bolle's p. (P. pyramidalis, Bunge). [abele,P.alba.
~ серебристый white p.,silver-leaved p.,
~ трёхгранный = т. канадский.
топорики 1. orn: puffins(Fratercula);2. bot:see живокость посевная.
топоровидный bot: axe-shaped, hatchet-shaped, dolabriform, securiform.
топорок orn: puffin.
топорообразный = топоровидный.
топтать orn: tread, copulate.
Тор Thor.
тор torus.
торакальный anat: thoracic.
торакокаустика surg:thoracocautery.
торакопластика surg: thoracoplasty.
торакоскопия thoracoscopy,pleuroscopy.
торакоцентез surg: thoracocentesis.
торица bot: spurrey (Spergula).
~ полевая corn s. (S. arvensis).
~ посевная corn s. (S. sativa).
торичник bot: sand spurrey(Spergularia).
Торичелли Torricelli.
торможение inhibition, restraint, checking;retarding,slowing down; drag.
тормоз inhibitor, restraint, check.
тормозить inhibit, restraint, check.
тормозная педаль braking pedal,stop.
тормозящий агент inhibitor.
~ слюноотделение antisialic.
Торн Thorne. [angle of the wing.
торнальный угол крыла entom: anal
торотраст thorotrast.

торпидный torpid. [forceps.
торсионный пинцет surg: torsion
торула bot: torula (Cryptococcus, Torulopsis). [mosses(Sphagnales).
торфяные мхи (пор.) bot:peat-bog
тоска по родине homesickness,nostalgia.
тотальный total.
тофус path: tophus.
точечка puncticulum.
точечное кровоизлияние path: petechial hemorrhage.
~ отверстие minute opening, stigma.
точечный punctate(d).
точильщик домовый entom: house borer (Coleostethus pertinax).
~ зерновой corn borer,lesser grain b. (Rhizopertha dominica).
~ мебельный furniture borer(Anobium domesticum).
~ полосатый deadwatch(Anobium striatum).
~ сельдерейный листовой celery leaf miner(Acidia,Philophylla heraclei).
~ хлебный bread beetle, drug b. (Stegobium paniceum).
~ -шишкоед сосновый pine-cone beetle (Ernobius abietinus).
точка point, punctum.
~ приложения point of application.
~ роста bot: growing point,apical p.
~ смерти bact: death point.
точная установка mcscop: fine
тошнота nausea. adjustment.
тошнотворный nauseant, nauseating.
тощая кишка anat: jejunum.
тощий lean.
трабекула anat: trabecula.
трабекулярная структура hist:trabe-
трабекулярный trabecular. |cularism.
трава bot: grass, herb, herbage.
~ Наталя = натальская трава.
травка-муравка = горец птичий.
травление etching, pickling.
травма trauma.
~ во время родов obstet:birth-injury.
~ с размозжением surg: crushing
травматизация traumatism. |injury.
травматизировать traumatize.
травматическая лихорадка surg: traumatic fever. [neurosis.
травматический невроз traumatic
~ психоз traumatic psychosis.
~ разрыв surg: traumatic rupture.
травматическое слабоумие psych: traumatic dementia.
травматолог traumatic surgeon.

травматология traumatology.
травник zool: redshank.
травостой grasses.
травоядное (животное) herbivore, grass-eater, grazing animal.
травоядный herbivorous, graminivorous.
травяная губка zool: grass sponge (Hippospongia graminea, H. cerebriformis).
травянистый grassy, herbaceous, graminеous.
травяное дерево bot: grass tree (Xanthorrhoea australis, X. hastilis R. Br.)
травяной bot: grassy.
трагаканта pharm: tragacanth, goat-thorn.
традесканция bot: spidewort (Tradescantia)
тракт tract.
трамвайная болезнь trolley sickness.
траметес сосновый = трутовик с.
транзиторное слабоумие psych: transitional dementia.
транзиторный синдром transient syndrome.
трансаминаза transaminase.
трансгрессивное расщепление genet: transgressive segregation.
транспирационный ток bot: transpiration stream.
транспирация bot: transpiration.
трансплантат surg: graft.
трансплантация surg: transplantation.
транспортабельный transportable.
транспортная болезнь travel disease, motion sickness.
~ лихорадка vet: shipping fever.
трансфузия transfusion.
траншейная лихорадка = волынская л.
~ нога path: trench foot.
трепецевидная мышца anat: trapezius.
траурный голубок = голубь каролинский траурный.
траут-пэрч ichth: trout perch (Percopsis omiscomaycus; Columbia transmontana).
трахеальная канюля anat: tracheal cannula.
трахеида tracheid.
трахейная жабра zool: tracheal gill.
трахейные (подтип) zool: tracheates (Tracheata).
трахейный anat: tracheal.
трахеломонас bio: Trachelomonas (Green flagellated organisms).
трахеоля tracheole.
трахеостомия surg: tracheostomy.
трахеотомическая трубка surg: tracheal tube.
трахеотомия surg: tracheotomy.
трахеоцеле path: tracheocele.
трахея anat: trachea, windpipe.
трахикарпус bot: palm Trachycarpus excelsa.
трахимедузы (отр.) zool: trachiline medusae (Trachylida).

трахинотус ichth: permit, pompano (Trachinotus).
*трахихтодес ichth: nannygai (Trachichthodes affinis).
трахома ophth: trachoma.
трахоматозный trachomatous.
трахомные включения ophth: trachoma inclusions.
трахуропс akule (Trachurops brachychira).
трезвенник abstinent (from alcohol).
трематодоз path: trematodiasis.
тремблер av med: trembler.
тремор path: tremor.
тренажёр Линка av med: Link trainer.
трение friction, rub(bing).
тренировочный центр av med: training center.
треножник tripod.
трентеполиевые (сем.) bot: Trentepohliaceae (algae).
трентеполия Trentepohlia (algae).
треонин threonine.
трепан surg: trepan, trephine.
трепанация surg: trepanning, trephining.
трепанг zool: trepang, balatan, see голотурия.
трепанировать surg: trepanize, traphine.
трепел = диатомит.
трепетание throbbing, fluttering, palpitation, fibrillation, quivering.
~ предсердий path: atrial flutter.
~ сердца heart flutter.
трепетать palpitate, throb, etc., cf. трепетание.
треска ichth: cod (Gadus morrhua).
трескание ногтей path: schizonychia.
трескаться chap, crack.
тресковые (сем.) ichth: gadoids, cod fishes (Gadidae).
тресковый жир cod liver oil.
трескообразные (отр.) ichth: Gadiformes.
треснуть p. a. of трескаться.
третий желудок zool: omasum, see книжка.
~ желудочек anat: third ventricle, ventriculus tertius.
~ от конца antepenultimate.
третичный tertiary.
третья колосковая чешуя злаков bot: sterile lemma.
треугольник пузыря anat: vesical triangle.
треугольный triangular, triquetral, triquetrous, trigonal, trigonous, delta-shaped, deltoid; see also трехгранный.
~ краб = паук-краб.
~ лист bot: deltoid leaf.

трефин surg: trephine.
трёхбугорчатые млекопитающие zool: Trituberculata (extinct).
трёхбугорчатый zool: tritubercular(tooth)
трёхветвистые турбеллярии (отр.) zool: triclads (Triclada, Tricladida).
трёхветвистый triramose.
трёхглавая мышца anat: tricipital muscle, triceps.
~ ~ голени anat: triceps surae.
~ ~ плеча anat: triceps brachii.
трёхгнёздный trilocular.
трёхгранная кость запястья anat: cuneiform of carpus, triquetrum, pyramidal bone.
трёхгранный trihedral, triquetrous.
трёхдневная лихорадка path: tertian malaria.
трёхдольный trilobate, trilobed.
трёхдольчатый = трёхдольный.
*трёхзубчатый trudentate.
трёхиглая колюшка ichth: brook stickleback, three-spined s. (Gasterosteus
трёхкольчатый triannulate. |aculeatus).
трёхконечный лист bot: tricuspidate
трёхлепестный bot: trifoliolate. |leaf.
трёхлопастный лист bot: trilobed leaf.
трёхокись мышьяка chem: arsenic trioxide
трёхосные кремниевые губки = стеклянные г.
трёхосный сустав = многоосный с.
трёхпёрстки orn: Turnices.
трёхраздельный trifid.
трёхрёберный tricostate.
трёхстворчатый tricuspid, trivalve.
~ клапан anat: tricuspid valve.
трёхцветковый triflorous.
трёхчленистый triarticulate, 3-segmented
трёхшипный three-thorned, triacanthos.
трещалка лилейная = коровка л.
трещина fissure, cleft, chap, scissura.
~ заднего прохода path: anal cleft, anal
~ на пыльнике bot: anther slit. |fissure
~ прямой кишки rectal fissure.
триацетилхризаробин pharm: chrysarobin
триба bio: tribe. triacetate.
трибромсалол pharm: tribromphenyl sali-
трибулька = лук резанец. |cylate.
триглепсис ichth: deep-water sculpin (Triglopsis thompsoni).
тригловые (сем.) ichth: triglids, gurnards (Triglidae).
тригонелла bot: trigonella (Trigonella).
тридакна гигантская zool: bivalve mollusk Tridacna gigas.

тридентигера ichth: Tridentiger.
трижды перистый bot: tripinnate.
~ рассечённый bot: trisected.
Триже Triger.
тризм path: trismus.
~ челюсти path: lockjaw.
тризмический trismic.
трииодистый метан pharm: triiodomethane, iodoform.
трииодтиронин triiodothyronine.
триклада zool: triclad (Triclada).
трикуспидальный tricuspid.
трилистник = клевер.
~ водяной = вахта трёхлистная.
~ луговой shamrock, see кислица обыкновенная.
трилистный bot: trifoliate.
триллиум bot: wood lily (Trillium).
трилобиты zool: trilobites (Trilobita).
триметилксантин trimethyl xanthine.
тринатрийфосфат chem: trisodium phosphate. [chin).
триостренник bot: arrow grass (Triglo-
триостренниковые (сем.) bot: arrow-grass family (Juncaginaceae).
трипанозомоз vet: trypanosomosis.
трипаносомы (сем.) zool: trypanosomes (Trypanosomatidae, Herpetomonadidae).
~ сонной болезни sleeping-sickness t. (Trypanosoma gambiense).
триперстовые entom: Tridactyloidea.
триплоидный triploid.
триппер ven: gonorrhea. [thread.
трипперная нить bact: gonorrheal
трипс entom: thrips.
~ апельсинный orange t. (Scirtothrips citri); see also эутрипс цитрусовый.
~ бобовый bean t. (Heliothrips fasciatus). [thrips gladioli).
~ гладиолусовый gladiolus t. (Taenio-
~ гороховый pea t. (Kakothrips robustus)
~ грушевый pear t. (Taeniothrips inconsequens). [niella tritici).
~ земляничный strawberry t. (Frankli-
~ камфорный camphor t. (Cryptothrips floridensis).
~ овсяный oat t. (Ctenothrips graminum).
~ огуречный = т. тепл.
~ оранжерейный = т. тепличный.
~ пшеничный wheat t. (Haplothrips tritici).
~ пустоцветный Haplothrips aculeatus.
~ ржаной rye t. (Limothrips denticornis).
~ рисовый rice t. (Haplothrips oryzae).
~ солнечный = т. тепличный.
~ табачный onion t. (Thrips tabaci).

трипс тепличный greenhouse t. (Heliothrips hemorrhoidalis).
~ тимофеечный timothy t. (Limothrips angulicornis).
~ цитрусовый = эутрипс ц.
трипсин trypsin.
трипсинный tryptic.
трипсы (отр.)entom: thrips (Thysanoptera).
триптон tripton, abioseston.
триптофан tryptophan.
трисомик genet: trisomic.
тритома = книфофия.
тритон 1. zool: newt, eft, triton (Triturus); 2.chem:triton (detergent).
триунгулин entom: triungulin (larva of blister beetles).
трифенилтетразолий chem: triphenyltetrazolium.
трифоль = вахта трёхлистная.
триформол pharm: triformol.
трихиаз ophth: trichiasis.
трихина helm:trichina (Trichinellidae).
~ спиральная helm: nematode Trichinella spiralis.
трихиноз path: trichinosis.
трихия bot: Trichia (algae).
трихлоризобутиловый спирт trichloroisobutyl alcohol.
трихогина bot: trichogyne.
трихограммы (сем.) entom:Trichogrammatidae.
трихом trichome.
трихостронгилоидный trichostrongyloid
трихотомический trichotomous.
трихофитон mcbio: thread fungus, Trichophyton.
трихоциста zool: trichocyst.
трицератопс zool:triceratops(extinct).
трищетинник луговой = овёс желтеющий.
триэтиленмеламин triethylenemelamine.
троакар surg: trocar.
трогоны orn: trogons (Trogones).
тройничный нерв anat: trigeminal nerve, fifth cranial n.
тройной triple, threefold.
тройственный = тройчатый.
тройчатый trimerous, ternate.
тромб path: thrombus.
тромбангиит path: thrombangiitis.
тромбин hem: Thrombin.
тромбоген hem: thrombogen.
тромбоз thrombosis.
тромбокиназа hem: thrombokinase, thromboplastin, thrombozyme.
тромбообразующий path:thrombogenic.
тромбопластин hem: thromboplastin.
тромбопластический tromboplastic.
тромбофлебит path: thrombophlebitis.
тромбоцит hem: thrombocyte,(blood) platelet.
тромооцитопения hem: thrombocytopenia.
тронутый гнилью putrescent.
тропизм tropism.
тропическая болезнь tropical disease.
тропическая лихорадка path:tropical malaria.
тропический миндаль = миробалан.
тростник bot: cane, reed (Phragmites, Trin.);sandreed, psamma, marram (Ammophila, Host.)
~ обыкновенный common r.(P.communis).
~ пёстрый spire-r.(P.communis variegata) variegata).
~ песчаный European beachgrass,marram, sandreed (A. arenaria, Link.)
~ сахарный = сахарный тростник.
тростниковый bot: reedy, cany.
~ сахар cane sugar.
трофамнион entom: trophamnion.
трофика trophical system.
трофический trophic.
~ ряд bio: trophic(al) series.
трофическое влияние trophism.
трофобласт embr: trophoblast.
трофобластический trophoblastic.
трофогенный слой trophogenous layer
трофодинамический trophic-dynamic.
трофозоит zool: trophozoite.
трофозой trophozoit.
трофолитический tropholitic.
трофоневроз trophoneurosis,trophesy.
трофоневрозный trophesial,trophesic.
трохельминт trochal worm (Trochelminthes).
трохофора zool: trochophore,Loven's larva.
трояжий trimorphous.
труба tube, salpinx.
трубач zool: trumpet-shaped ciliate [Stentor.
~ агами orn:agami (Psophia crepitans).
трубка tube, tubing.
~ для выслушивания stethoscope.
трубковёрт берёзовый entom: Deporaus betulae.
~ грушевый Byctiscus betulae.
~ осиновый B. populi.
трубковёрты (сем.)entom: Attelabidae.
трубкозуб zool: oryx, gemsbok (Orycteropus).
трубкозубые zool: Tubulidentata.
трубконосые (отр.)orn: tube-nosed swimmers(Tubinares,Procellariiformes).
трубкохвостые (подотр.) entom: Tubulifera.

*трубкоцветные bot: Tubiflorae; Tubiliflorae (subfam.) [pregnancy.
трубная беременность obstet: tubal
~ воронка (яйцевода) anat: infundibulum of uterine tube.
~ лоза bot: trumpet creeper, t. vine, cowitch (Campsis radicans, Seem.)
~ миндалина anat: tubal tonsil.
трубнобрюшная беременность obstet: tuboabdominal pregnancy.
трубноматочная беременность obstet: tubouterine pregnancy, utero-tubal p.
трубнояичниковая беременность obstet: tuboovarian pregnancy.
~ связка anat: ligamentum tubo-ovarialis.
трубный аборт gyn: tubal abortion
~ занос ostet: tubal mole.
труборог zool: edible whelk Buccinum.
труб(оч)ка tubule. [tubes.
трубочки Беллини hist: Bellini's
трубочник zool: sewage worm (Tubifex).
трубчатая железа anat: tubular gland.
~ кость anat: tubular bone.
трубчатый tubular, fistulosus.
~ венчик bot: tubular corolla.
~ цветок bot: tubular flower.
трудно поддающийся лечению difficult to cure, rebellious
трудные роды obstet: dystocia, partus difficilis. [occupational therapy.
трудовая терапия ergotherapy,
труп corpse, cadaver.
трупное окоченение cadaveric rigidity rigiditas cadaverica, rigor mortis.
трупные пятна cadaveric lividity.
трупный cadaveric, cadaverous.
~ бугорок cadaver tubercle, dissectiont.
~ жировик adipocere.
трусость psych: cowardliness, see боязливость.
трут bot: touchwood, tinder, spunk, agaric
~ белый = губка лиственичная.
трутень entom: drone, male bee.
трутовик 1. entom: ciid beetle; 2. bot: fungi Polyporus, Fomes, Trametes, Boletus, etc.; beefsteak fungus (Polyporus fomentarius, Fries.); see also полипорус.
~ ложный tinder (Fomes igniarius).
~ настоящий yellowish sapwood rot (F. fomentarius). [(P. destructor).
~ разрушающий destroying polyporus
~ сосновый redheart fungus (Trametes pini).
трутовиковые (сем.) bot: polyporus family (Polyporaceae), fungi.

трутовый гриб pharm: white agaric.
трюфелевые (сем.) bot: truffle family (Tuberacei).
трюфель bot: truffle (Tuber). [cocos).
~ американский tuckahoe (Pachyma
~ белый white t. (Choiromyces meandriformis, Vitt.) [Horn.)
~ ложный false t. (Scleroderma vulgare,
~ настоящий winter t. (Tuber melanosporum)
~ Перигора = т. настоящий.
~ съедобный T. estivum, Vitt.
~ чёрный black t., see т. настоящий.
тряпичник ichth: Australian sea horse (Phyllopteryx eques).
трясогузка orn: wagtail (Motacilla).
~ белая white w., pied w. (M. alba).
~ жёлтая yellow w., blue-headed w. (M. flava).
трясогузковые (сем.) orn: wagtails and pipits (Moticillidae). [g. (Briza).
трясунка bot: quaking grass, trembling
~ средняя bird's eye (B. media).
тсуга = гемлок.
туалетная губка zool: bath sponge (Euspongia).
~ комната = уборная.
туберкул tubercle.
туберкулёз path: tuberculosis.
~ кожи lupus.
~ лёгких pulmonary tuberculosis.
~ (рогатого скота) = жемчужница 2.
туберкулёзная бактерия tubercle bacillus.
туберкулёзный tuberculous, tubercular.
~ бугорок path: tubercle.
~ узелок path: tubercle.
туберкулин tuberculin.
~ Коха pharm: Koch's tuberculin, see старый туберкулин. [test.
туберкулиновая проба tuberculin
тубероза bot: tuberose (Poliantes tuberosa). [sclerosis.
туберозный склероз path: tuberose
тубифицида zool: tubificid worm.
тубус mcscop: (draw) tube.
тугоухость hardness of hearing.
тужиться на рвоту retch.
туземный aboriginal, indigenous.
тузлук brine.
туканы orn: South-American woodpeckers Rhamphastidae.
туловище anat: trunk, torso.
туловищная мускулатура body musculature.
~ ножка zool: trunk limb.
~ складка embr: trunk fold.

туловищный anat: truncal.
тулузский гусь orn: Toulose goose.
туляремийный микроб tularemia microbe.
туляремия vet: tularemia.
туман перед глазами dimness of vision.
тумор path: tumor.
тунг bot: Japan wood-oil tree, China w.-o.t., tung t.(Aleurites cordata,R.Br.)
тунговое дерево = тунг.
тунговое масло wood oil.
тунец ichth: tuna.
~ длиннопёрый long-finned tuna, albacore (Germo alalunga).
~ обыкновенный bluefin tuna (Thunnus thynnus).
туника tunic(a).
туннельная болезнь helm: tunnel disease.
тунцовые (сем.) ichth: tuna family (Thunnidae).
тунцы ichth: tuna group (Thunnoidea).
тупайя zool: insectivorous South-Asian animal Tupajida.
тупая боль dull ache.
~ головная боль dull headache.
тупело = нисса.
тупик orn: puffin, (Fratercula arctica): pal, bottlenose, sea parrot (F.a.grabae).
тупой obstuse, blunt, dull.
~ инструмент blunt instrument.
тупоконечный blunt-ended, obtuse.
тупость селезенки path: splenic dulness.
тупоумие psych: hebetude, stupidity.
тур zool: goat Capra cylindricornis; see also кавказский тур.
~ европейсикий European extinct buffalo (Bos primigenius).
тура bot: fucus (Fucus) algae.
~ пузырчатая bot: bladder, wrack, lady (Fucus vesiculosus).
~ широколистная bot: flat wrack (Fucus platicarpus).
турако фиолетовый orn: turakoo (Musophaga violacea).
~ шлемоносный turakoo (Corythaix).
турацин turacin.
турбеллярии (кл.) zool: free-living flatworms (Turbellaria), see ресничные черви.
турбоспираль zool: spiral shell; cf. прудовик.
тургесцентное состояние bot: turgescence.
тургесцентные клетки turgid cells.
тургор turgor, turgescence.

турецкая губка zool: Turkey-cup sponge (Euspongia officinalis mollissima).
турецкое седло anat: Turkish saddle, sella turcica.
турион bot: turion.
турнепс = репа (кормовая).
турникет surg: tourniquet.
турпан orn: scoter (Oidemia).
~ чёрный black scoter (O. nigra).
турунда surg: wick drain.
турухтан orn: ruff (cock), reeve (hen), (Philomachus pugnax, Totanus pugnax).
турча bot: featherfoil (Hottornia).
~ болотная water violet (H.palustris).
тускарора bot: tuscarora, see рис болотный.
тусклокрасный dull red.
туссол pharm: antipyrine mandelate.
тута bot: mulberry (Morus).
~ американская red m. (M. rubra).
~ белая white m. (M. alba).
~ индийская Indian m. (Morinda citrifolia).
~ чёрная black m. (Marus nigra).
тутовик пергаментный bot: polystictus (Polystictus pergamenus).
~ разноцветный P. versicolor.
тутовое дерево = тута.
тутовые (сем.) bot: mulberry family (Moraceae).
туфелька zool: slipper limpet (Paramaecium caudatum).
тучная клетка hist: mast cell.
тучность obesity, corpulence, adiposis, adiposity, ventrosity.
тучный obese, corpulent.
тушканчик zool: jerboa.
тушканчики (сем.) zool: jerboas (Dipodidae).
туя bot: arbor vitae, tree-of-life (Thuja).
~ восточная biota (T. orientalis).
~ западная a. v., white cedar (T. occidentalis).
тщательное исследование indagation, careful investigation.
тыква bot: gourd, squash, pumpkin (Cucurbita).
~ большая столовая squash(C.maxima, Duch.)
~ бутылочная g., tendril vine (C. lagenaria).
~ вонючая calabazilla (Cucumis foetidissima, James).
~ восковая wax g., zit-kwa (Benincasa hispida, Cogn.)
~ горлянка crookneck s.(C. pepo condensa).
~ диковинная = момордика харантская.
~ кустовая = кабачок.

тыква летняя cymling (Cucurbita pepo).
~ мозговая = кабачок.
~ мочальная rag g., see люфа.
~ мускатная summer s. (C. moschata).
~ мускусная China s., cushaw.
~ обыкновенная pumpkin.
~ тарелочная = патиссон.
~ тюрбанная = т. фигурная.
~ фестончатая = патиссон.
~ фигурная ornamental g., see тыква бутылочная, т. горлянка.
~ чалмовая = т. фигурная.
тыквенная склянница entom: squash-vine borer (Sesia).
тыквенное семя pharm: pumpkin seed.
тыквенные (сем.) bot: gourd family (Cucurbitaceae).
тыквоцветные (пор.) bot: Cucurbitales order.
тыл back, dorsum.
~ ручной кисти anat: back of the hand.
~ стопы anat: back of the foot.
тыльная предплюсне-плюсневая связка anat: dorsal tarsometatarsal joint.
тыльный tergal, dorsal, rear.
~ нерв лопатки anat: dorsal scapular nerve, posterior scapular n.
тысячеголовка bot: cowherb, cow cockle, red soapwort (Saponaria vaccaria).
тысячелистник bot: milfoil, yarrow (Achillea millefolium).
тысяченожка entom: myriapod (Myriapoda).
тычинка bot: stamen.
~ без пыльников bot: staminodium, staminode.
тычинковый of a stamen; see also тычиночный.
тычинконосное растение bot: staminiferous plant, staminate p., stamen-bearing p.
тычиночная колонка bot: staminal column.
~ нить bot: filament, anther stalk, connective.
тычиночный bot: staminal.
~ цветок bot: staminate flower.
тэк zool: wild goat Capra sibirica.
тэнгуса bot: tengusa (Gelidium) algae.
тюленевый phocine, of seal.
тюлень zool: seal (Phoca).
~ -крабоед crab-eating seal (Lobodon carcinophaga).
~ -монах West Indian seal (Monachus tropicalis).
~ обыкновенный common seal, harbor seal (Phoca vitulina).
~ пятнистый = т. обыкновенный.
~ Росса Ross's seal (Ommatophoca rossi).
~ Уэдделя Weddell's seal (Leptomychotes weddelli).
тюлька ichth: Clupeonella.
тюльпан bot: tulip (Tulipa).
тюльпанное дерево bot: tulip tree (Liriodendron).
тюрбо ichth: halibut, ling (Rhombus).
тюремная больница prison hospital.
тюремный тиф = сыпной тиф.
тяга к полётам av med: taste for flying.
тяж cord, strand, tract, band, bar; bot: strand; see also клеточный тяж.
~ протоксилемы bot: protoxylem strand.
тяжёлая травма major injury
тяжело дышать breathe hard, pant.
тяжёлое состояние poor condition.
тянущая пластинка zool: unguitractor plate.

У

уайтинг ichth: whiting (Menticirrhus saxatilis; Peprilus alepidotus).
Уайтмор Whitemore.
убежище asylum, shelter.
~ для прокажённых leprosarium.
убивать kill, slay, destroy.
убивающий бактерии bactericidal. germicidal.
~ микробы microbicidal.
~ трипанозомы trypanolytic.
убийство murder.
убирать со стола clear the table.
убитый жаром heat-killed.
убить p. a. of убивать.
ублюдок mongrel.
убой slaughter.
уборная san: privy, toilet, lavatory.
уборщик = питающийся падалью.
убрать p. a. of убирать.
увеличение 1. mcscop: magnification; 2. enlargement.
~ желез path: glandular enlargement.
~ зобной железы path: thymic enlargement.
~ печени path: enlargement of the liver.
~ плотности кости path: eburnation.
~ ручной кисти path: chiromegaly, pseudoacromegaly.
~ сердца path: cardiac enlargement.
~ щитовидной железы path: thyroid enlargement, goiter.
уверенный в себе self-reliant.

увирандра bot: lace-leaf (Aponogeton
fenestralis, Hook., or Ouvirandra f.,
увлажнитель lab: dampener. |Poir.)
увядание bot: wilting, withering.
увядать fade, wither.
угай = краснопёрка дальневосточ-
угасание extinction. ная.
угасать extinguish.
угаснуть p. a. of угасать.
углевод chem: carbohydrate. [metabolism.
углеводный обмен carbohydrate
углежелезистая соль с сахаром pharm
saccharated ferrous carbonate.
углекислая ванна phys-ther: carbon
dioxide bath. [gas.
углекислый газ chem: carbon dioxide
~ гваякол pharm: guajacol carbonate.
~ литий pharm: lithium carbonate.
углерод carbon, C. [dental arch.
угловатая дуга зубов path: angular
угловая извилина anat: angular
convolution.
~ ость anat: spine of the sphenoid.
угловое движение anat: angular
угловой горох = нут. |movement.
углозубы (сем.) zool: Hynobiidae.
углокрыльницы (сем.) entom:
anglewings (Nymphalidae).
углубление recess, pit.
~ соска ophth: cupped disc.
углублённое место recess, pit, hilus.
угнетать depress.
угнетающий inhibitory.
~ развитие growth-inhibiting.
угнетение depression, oppression.
угнетённая детка bot: oppressed
multiplier. [mood.
угнетённое настроение psych: depressed
~ психическое состояние depression,
dejection.
угнетённость depression, dejection.
угнетённый psych: depressed, somber,
dejected.
угол век ophth: canthus, palpebral
~ глаза = угол век. angle.
~ глазной щели = угол век.
~ зрения visual angle. [blade.
~ лопатки anat: angle of the shoulder
угольная кислота chem: carbonic acid.
~ рыба skilfish, sablefish, black cod,
black candlefish, beshow (Anoplopoma
fimbria); cobia, crabeater (Rachycentron
canadum).
угольный ангидрид chem: carbon dioxode.
угорка = слива обыкновенная.

угорь 1. derm: blackhead, comedo; acne;
2. ichth: eel (Anguilla).
~ обыкновенный ichth: common eel
(Anguilla rostrata).
~ -удав ichth: gulper eel (Gastrostomus).
угревые (сем.) ichth: eels (Anguillidae).
угрица entom: eelworm.
~ пшеничная eelworm of wheat
(Tylenchus scandens); vibrio
(Anguillula tritici).
угрястость coccidiosis (turkey disease).
удав zool: constrictor (Boa constrictor).
~ дерево = деревогубец вьющийся.
удавы (сем.) zool: constrictors
удаление removal, ablation. |(Boidae).
~ алкоголя dealcoholization.
~ альвеолярного отростка surg:
alveolectomy.
~ веснушек derm: emaculation.
~ внутренностей evisceration.
~ волос derm: depilation.
~ геморроидальных шишек surg:
hemorrhoidectomy.
~ глаза surg: eye removal.
~ грудной железы surg: mastectomy,
mammectomy.
~ дермоидной кисты surg: dermo-
~ десны surg: gingivectomy. |idectomy.
~ железы surg: adenectomy.
~ жировой ткани surg: lipectomy.
~ зуба extraction of a tooth.
~ зубного камня odont: removal of
tartar, scaling.
~ канюли surg: detubation, decannulation.
~ клитора surg: clitoridectomy.
~ корки decrustation.
~ костных осколков surg: ebonation.
~ крайней плоти surg: prepucectomy.
~ лопатки surg: scapulectomy.
~ малых губ gyn: nymphectomy.
~ матки gyn: hysterectomy, metrectomy.
~ ~ через влагалище gyn: colpohys-
~ миомы surg: myomectomy. |terectomy.
~ ~ матки через влагалище surg:
colpomyomectomy.
~ мозолей surg: helotomy.
~ морщин erugation.
~ надпочечной железы surg:
adrenalectomy.
~ носовой раковины surg: turbinectomy.
~ околоушной железы surg:
parotidectomy.
~ (опухоли) посредством лигатуры
surg: removal (of a tumor) by ligature.
~ отбросов san: waste disposal.

удаление отрезка кишок surg: enterectomy.
~ питуитарной железы surg: hypophysectomy.
~ пластинки дуги позвонка surg: laminectomy.
~ половины зобной опухоли surg: hemistrumectomy.
~ ~ щитовидной железы surg: hemithyroidectomy.
~ половых желез surg: orchiectomy, castration.
~ поперечного отростка позвонка surg: transversectomy.
~ по частям surg: morselation.
~ почки surg: nephrectomy.
~ ручным способом obstet: manual removal.
~ селезенки surg: excision of the spleen, splenectomy.
~ сточных вод san: sewage disposal.
~ сустава surg: arthrectomy.
~ суставного конца кости surg: osteoarthrectomy.
~ трубки surg: extubation.
~ трубы gyn: tubectomy, salpingectomy.
~ фибромиомы surg: fibromyectomy.
~ хирургическим путем surgical removal.
~ части перегородки surg: septectomy.
~ ~ крестца surg: sacrectomy.
~ ~ ребра surg: costectomy.
~ ~ ребра и поперечного отростка позвонка surg: costotransversectomy
~ ~ сальника surg: omentectomy.
~ ~ язычка surg: staphylotomy
~ шейки матки gyn: cervicectomy.
~ щитовидной железы surg: thyroidectomy.
~ эмбола surg: embolectomy.
~ языка surg: elinguation.
~ яичек emasculation, castration.
удалить p. a. of удалять.
удалять remove, ablate.
~ волосы remove hair, (d)epilate.
~ головной мозг decerebrize, disbrain.
~ зобную железу surg: thymectomize.
~ зубной камень odont: scale.
~ надпочечник surg: adrenalectomize.
~ посредством лигатуры surg: remove by ligature.
~ почку surg: nephrectomize.
~ селезёнку surg: splenectomize.
удар blow; stroke; beat, impulse, throb (heart).
~ паралича path: paralytic stroke.
удвоение doubling, reduplication.
~ органов organ reduplication.
удержание retention.
удержание в памяти psych: retentiveness.
~ равновесия equilibration.
удерживаемая клизма retention enema.
удильщик 1. ichth: angler (Lophiomus setigerus); 2. angler, fisherman.
~ трёхзвёздный three-starred anglerfish (Bathyceratias trilynchnus)
удлинение elongation.
удлинённо-веретеновидный bot: linear-fusiform.
~ -овальный ovate-oblong.
~ -скверхедный bot: linear-clavate.
удлинённое основание (лепестка или чашелистика) bot: claw.
удлинённый выдох prolonged expiration.
~ стручок bot: silique.
уд/мин. [удар в минуту] beat per minute.
удобоваримость digestibility.
удобоусвояемость = усвояемость.
удобрение agr: 1. fertilizer; manure; 2. manuring.
удобрить p. a. of удобрять.
удобрять agr: fertilize, manure.
удод обыкновенный orn: hoopoe (Upupa epops).
удоды orn: hoopoes (Upupae).
"удочка с наживкой" ichth: illicium.
удушающее вещество asphyxiant.
удушающий зоб path: suffocative goiter.
удушение choking, strangulation.
удушье dispnea, suffucation, chokes, smothering.
удушливый suffocative.
Удэн Oudin.
уж zool: grass snake, ring snake (Tropidonotus natrix).
~ обыкновенный zool: common grass snake, water s., ringelnatter (Natrix natrix).
ужалить p. a. of жалить.
ужевые (сем.) zool: colubrine snakes (Colubridae).
ужин supper.
ужовка (улитка) = фарфорка.
ужовник bot: adder's tongue (Ophioglossum vulgatum).
ужовниковые (сем.) bot: adder's-tongue family (Ophioglossaceae).
уз ooze.
уза propolis (of bees).
узамбара = фиалка узамбара.
уздечка bridle, frenulum.
~ клитора anat: frenulum of the clitoris.
~ крайней плоти anat: frenulum of the prepuce.

уздечка языка anat: frenulum of the tongue.
уздечковый anat: frenal.
узел node, ganglion; knot.
~ Тавара anat: atrioventricular node.
узелковый nodular.
узелок nodule.
~ на связках path: singer's node.
узик = лапчатка-узик.
узкая грудь narrow chest, stenothorax.
узкий таз obstet: contracted pelvis.
узкобрюх = златка узкотелая.
узкоголовость anat: stenocephaly, stenocephalia.
узкоголовый anat: stenocephalous.
узкозаострённый apiculate.
узколепестный bot: stenopetallous.
узколистный bot: angustifoliate, angustifolious, stenophyllous, narrow-leaved.
узконогость sickle-hochadness(in horses).
узконосые обезьяны (подотр.) zool: narrow-nosed monkeys, catarrhinians (Catarrhini).
узкородственное размножение inbreeding.
узкоротость stenostomia.
узкоротый zool: narrow-mouthed, stenostomatous.
узловато-расширенный varicose.
узловатость nodosity.
узловатый nodular, nodose, nodulose, nodulous.
~ корень bot: nodose root.
~ усик entom: nodose antenna.
~ ~ или побег bot: jointed tendril.
~ шов surg: loop suture, button s.
узловая лихорадка derm: nodal fever erythema nodosum
~ почка bot: nodal bud.
узловой шов = прерывистый шов.
узловые корни bot: nodal roots.
узнавание psych: recognition.
Уилмер Wilmer.
указательный палец anat: index finger, forefinger.
"уканье" path: stridor (congenital).
укачивание 1. av med: motion sickness; 2. ped: rocking.
уклейка = уклея.
уклея ichth: alburnum, bleak (Alburnus).
уклонение от нормы deviation from normal, abnormality; aberration.
укол 1. prick, puncture; 2. shot, injection.
~ иглой surg: acupuncture.
~ Клод Бернара Bernard's puncture.
уколочная разводка bact: stab culture, thrust c.
~ ~ на желатине gelatin stab.
укоренение bot: rooting, taking root, ecesis.
укорениться p. a. of укореняться.
укореняться bot: take root.
укореняющееся растение rooted plant.
укореняющийся побег bot: stolon.
~ у уреза воды bot: water-line-rooted.
укорочение shortening.
~ уздечки языка path: ankyloglossia, tongue-tie.
укороченность пальцев рук path: shortness of the fingers.
укрепление strengthening, reinforcing.
~ органа surg: organopexy.
укреплять strengthen, reinforce.
укрепляющее средство alterative (agent), analeptic, restorative agent.
укрепляющий память anamnestic.
укроп bot: dill (Anethum graveolens); pharm: fennel (Foeniculum vulgare).
~ конский water dropwort (Oenanthe phellandrium, Lam.)
~ сладкий = фенхель душистый.
укропная вода pharm: fennel water.
укропное масло pharm: oil of fennel.
уксус vinegar.
~ морского лука pharm: squill vinegar.
уксусная кислота acetic acid.
уксусник = сумах виргинский.
уксусно- aceto-.
уксусновиннокаменнокислый алюминий aluminium acetotartrate.
уксусное дерево = сумах виргинский.
уксуснокислая бактерия Bacterium xylinum.
~ тимоловая ртуть pharm: mercury thymolacetate.
уксуснокислый хинин pharm: quinine acetate.
уксусомёд морского лука pharm: squill honey
укус bite, morsus.
~ в лицо surg: face bite.
~ змеи snake bite.
~ пчелы beesting.
~ собаки dog bite.
улей beehive.
~ -колода stabile hive.
улекс = утёсник.
улетучивание volatilization.
улетучиваться volatilize.
улита orn: sage cock, s. grouse(Totanus).
улитка snail, limpet, helmet shell (Gastropoda).
~ виноградная edible snail (Helix pomatia).
~ пресноводная periwinkle (Viviparidae, Pleuroceridae).
улитковая впадина anat: cochlear recess.
~ пиявка zool: snail leech (Glossosiphonia complanata).
улитковый ход anat: cochlear duct, ductus cochlearis.
улиткообразный conchiform, helical.

уличное бешенство infect: street rabies.
"уличные роды" obstet: precipitate labor, partus precipitatus.
уличный мусор san: street sweepings.
уловистость catching rate.
улотрикс bot: Ulothrix (filamentary alga).
~ опоясанный U. zonata, Kutz.
улотриксовые (пор.) bot: Ulotrichales order (algae).
улучшение improvement, betterment, amelioration; remission, abatement of symptoms, subsidence of symptoms.
ульва = морской салат.
ульвовые (сем.) bot: Ulvaceae (algae).
ультравирус ultravirus.
ультразвуковое поле phys-ther: ultrasonic field.
ультрамикроопределение ultra-microdetermination.
ультрамикроскопический ultramicroscopic.
ультрафиолетовые лучи ultraviolet rays.
ульцерозный ulcerous, ulcerative.
ум psych: intelligence; mind.
умбра ichth: mud minnow (Umbra krameri).
умбрина = горбыль светлый.
умбровые (сем.) ichth: Umbridae.
умение планировать ability to plan.
уменьшающий застой decongestive.
~ потоотделение antisudorific, antihidrotic.
~ раздражение abirritant.
~ секрецию молока anti(ga)lactic.
~ слюноотделение antisialic.
уменьшение застоя disgorgement.
~ потоотделения anaphoresis.
~ раздражения abirritation.
~ хлоридов в моче dechloruration.
умеренно выраженная депрессия mild depression.
умеренно вяжущий subastringent.
~ желтушный subicteric.
~ кислый subacid.
~ наркотический subnarcotic.
~ тёплая ванна phys-ther: tepid bath.
умеренный moderate, temperate.
умертвить p. a. of умерщвлять.
умерщвление mortification, killing.
~ плода legl: feticide, aborticide.
умерщвлять mortify, kill.
умирающий dying, moribund.
умозаключение conclusion, inference.
умозрительный speculative; psychovisual.
умопомешательство madness, insanity.
умственная гигиена mental hygiene.
умственная отсталость psych: mental debility, moronity, mental retardation.
умственно дефективный psych: mentally deficient.
умственное недоразвитие psych: mental deficiency.
~ переутомление mental overwork, psychentonia.
~ состояние psych: mental condition.
умственные способности psych: mental faculties, intelligence.
умственный возраст mental age.
~ склад mental make-up, cast of mind.
унаследование inheritance.
унаследованное заболевание inherited disease.
унаследовать inherit.
ундулирующая мембрана zool: undulating membrane.
ундулирующий undulatory.
универсальное лечебное средство cure-all, panacea; quack remedy.
уничтожать комплемент decomplementize.
уничтожающий закупорку deobstruent.
уничтожение destruction, extermination.
~ блох depulization.
~ вшей delousing.
~ запаха deodorization.
уничтожить застой decongest.
унцинула phytp: fungi Uncinula.
унция ounce.
уоллеровская дегенерация Wallerian degeneration.
Уомек Womack.
упадок вида или расы bio: paracme.
~ сердечной деятельности cardiac failure.
~ сил path: loss of strength.
упитанность zool: beefiness, fat(ness).
уплотнение в формалине hist: formol fixation.
~ лёгкого path: pulmonary consolidation.
уплотнённый гиф грибов bot: sclerotium.
уплощение flattening.
уплощённый flattened, deplanate.
упорная головная боль intractable headache.
~ невралгия obstinate neuralgia, persistent n.
упорный приступ кашля prolonged fit of coughing.
упорядочение coordination.
управление рулями av med: rudder control.
управляющий аптекой pharmacy manager.
упражнение exercise.
упряжная собака sled dog (Canis familiaris domesticus borealis); spitz, pomeranian.
урат chem: urate.
уратный chem: uratic.
~ камень calculus of urates.

урацил uracil.
уреаза ureasa.
урежение slowing down (of pulse), decrease in frequency.
уремическая кома = уремия.
уремический uremic.
уремия uremia.
уретан urethane (ethyl carbamate).
уретра anat: urethra.
уретральная лихорадка urethral fever
~ нить urethral thread.
уретрит path: urethritis.
уретровезикальный urethrovesical.
урина urine.
уринозный urinose, urinous.
уровень кальция в крови blood calcium level.
~ сахара в крови blood sugar level.
урогенитальный anat: urogenital.
~ сосочек urogenital papilla (in fish).
урод path: monster.
~ без конечностей amelus.
~ ~ нижней челюсти agnathus.
~ ~ пальцев adactyl(us).
~ ~ спинного мозга amyelus.
~ с двумя головами разной величины heterocephalus.
~ ~ двумя туловищами disomus.
~ ~ карликовой головой nanocephalus.
~ ~ малой головой leptocephalus.
~ ~ неразвитыми конечностями micromelus.
~ ~ одной рукой monobrachius.
~ ~ четырьмя руками tetrabrachius.
уродливость = уродство.
уродливый teratic, abnormal, monstrous; cf уродство.
уродство path: monstrosity, teratism, malformation, deformity.
~ стопы foot deformity.
~ черепа cranial deformity.
урожай agr: harvest, crop, yield.
урожайность agr: yield.
уролог urologist.
урологический urologic.
урология urology.
урометр urinometer.
уропода uropod.
уросепсис urosepsis.
уросептический uroseptic.
урофицис ichth: white hake, king h., squirrel h., codling (Urophycis).
уртикария derm: urticaria.
урутевые (сем.) bot: water-milfoil family (Halorhagidaceae).
уруть bot: water-milfoil (Myriophyllum
урчание rumbling, borborygmus.
~ в животе borborygmus.
ус barb.
усатый bearded.
усач 1. entom: long-horned beetle, capricorn b., cerambycid. 2. ichth: barbel (Barbus barbus).
~ валериановый valerian beetle (Agapanthia violacea).
~ днепровский Dnieper barbel (B. borysthenicus).
~ домовый domestic capricorn beetle (Hylotrupes bajulus).
~ ~ рыжий red d.c.b. (Stromatium fulvum).
~ дубовый большой great capricorn beetle (Cerambyx cerdo).
~ ~ малый lesser capricorn beetle (Cerambyx scopoli).
~ ивовый корневой willow-root lamiid (Lamia textor).
~ ~ красношеий Oberea oculata.
~ конопляный hemp beetle Thyestilla gebleri.
~ круглоголовый roundheaded borer (Saperda candida).
~ люцерновый alfalfa beetle Plagionotus floralis.
~ осиновый большой greater aspen beetle (Saperda carcharias).
~ ~ малый lesser aspen b. (Saperda populnea).
~ пастернаковый parship-stem worm (Phytoecia icterica).
~ подсолнечниковый sunflower cerambycid (Agapanthia).
~ серый тополевый poplar borer (Saperda calcarata).
~ сосновый southern pine sawyer, goat chafer.
~ среднеазиатский Central Asian cerambycid (Aelosthes sarta).
~ хлебный grain cerambycid (Dorcadion).
~ чанари ichth: barbel Barbus capito.
усачи (сем.) entom: long-horned beetles, cerambycids (Cerambycidae).
усваивать assimilate.
усваиваться be assimilated.
усваивающий assimilating, assimilative, assimilatory.
усвоение assimilation, intussusception.
усвоить p. a. of усваивать.
усвояемость assimilability, digestibility, utilization.
усвояемый assimilable, digestible, utilizable.
усечённая чешуйка bot: emarginate glume.
усечённый truncate.
усеянный шипами = шиповатый.

усик clasper, cirrus, tendril, barbel; entom: antenna, tendril.

усиковая ямка entom: antennary socket.

усиковый entom: antennal, antennary.

усиление amplification.

~ аппетита increase in appetite.

~ действия лекарства acuition.

усиленная перистальтика path: hyperperistalsis.

~ секреция молока superlactation.

усиленное дыхание hyperpnea.

~ потение path: hyperhidrosis.

усиленный перкуторный звук hyperresonance.

усиливать слюноотделение ptyalize.

~ тонус tonicize.

усиливающий родовую деятельность obstet: parturifacient, ecbolic.

~ слюноотделение salivatory.

~ тонус сосудов vasostimulant, vasotonic.

~ экран x-ray: intensifying screen.

усилитель amplifier.

ускорение дыхания acceleration of breathing.

ускоренная деятельность сердца accelerated heart rate.

ускоряющий рост growth-promoting.

~ фактор precipitating cause.

условия жизни life conditions.

~ оттока outflow conditions, drainage c.

условное торможение psych: conditioned inhibition.

условнорефлекторный conditioned-reflex.

условный раздражитель neur: conditioned stimulus.

~ рефлекс conditioned reflex.

уснея bot: usnea lichens (Usnea).

~ бородатая old-man's beard (U. barbata).

~ волосовидная hair-like usnea (U. longissima).

усоногие (отр.) zool: barnacles, cirripedes (Cirripedia).

усоногий рак zool: barnacle (Cirripedia).

усообразный придаток tendril.

успокаивать calm, assuage, allay, relieve, comfort.

~ боль allay, relieve.

успокаиваться abate.

успокаивающее средство pharm: sedative, calmative, calmant.

успокаивающий боль pain-allaying.

~ зубную боль antiodontalgic.

~ зуд antipruritic.

~ кашель cough-allaying, antitussive.

~ раздражение soothing irritation, abirritant.

~ рвоту antiemetic.

успокоительное средство = успокаивающее с.

успокоить p. a. of успокаивать.

успокоиться p. a. of успокаиваться.

уссурийский когтистый тритон zool: Ussuri long-claw newt (Onychodactylus fischeri).

усталость fatigue, tiredness.

~ мышц muscle fatigue.

~ от боёв mil: battle fatigue, shellshock.

~ ~ жизни psych: weariness of life, taedium vitae.

усталый tire(d), weary.

установка для переливания surg: transfusion outfit.

установочно-слуховой аппарат anat: auditory adjusting apparatus.

устареваемость obsolescence.

устаревание obsolescence.

устой top milk, cream.

устойчивость stability; fastness.

~ к мышьяку arsenic resistance.

~ ~ парше и т.п. bot: scab, etc. resistance.

устойчивый stable; fast.

~ к сыворотке serum fast.

устранение инвагинации surg: disinvagination.

устрица zool: oyster (Ostrea).

~ съедобная edible oyster (Ostrea edulis).

устрицевод oysterman.

устрицеводство oyster rearing.

устрицы (сем.) zool: oysters (Ostreidae).

устричник oyster ground.

устричный парк oyster park.

~ промысел oyster fishery.

устройство для энтомологических коллекций pinning unit.

уступающий характер recessive character.

устье mouth, entry, ostium, terminal opening.

~ евстахиевой трубы anat: ostium of the Eustachian tube.

устьевой anat: ostial, ostiary.

устьице mouth-like opening, stoma, ostiole.

устьичная транспирация bot: stomatal transpiration.

устьичные клетки bot: stomatal cells.

усыпление inducing sopor; hypnotization, applying general anesthesia.

усыпляющий soporific; narcotizing.

утёнок zool: duckling.

утёсник bot: furze, gorse (Ulex).

~ европейский f., g., (U. europaeus).

~ обыкновенный = у. европейский.

утиная походка = гусиная п.

~ трава = манник.

утиные (сем.) orn: duck family (Anatinae).

утихание subsidence

"утка" san: urinal.

утка orn: duck (Anas).

утка обыкновенная common duck (Anas boscas).
~ -пеганка sheldrake (Tadorna cornuta).
~ -свиязь обыкновенная widgeon (Anas, Mareca penelope).
~ -широконоска shoveler (Spatula clypeata); spoonbill (Anas clypeata).
утконос zool: duckbill, platypus (Ornithorhynchus anatinus).
утолщение thickening, bulge. enlargement; bot: struma.
~ барабанной перепонки thickening of the drum membrane.
~ брюшины peritoneal thickening.
~ заднего конца мозолистого тела anat: pad of corpus callosum.
~ мягкой мозговой оболочки pial thickening.
~ плевры pleural thickening.
~ стенки артерий arteriosclerosis.
~ ~ мелких артерий arteriolosclerosis.
утоляющее жажду (средство) adipsa.
утомление = усталость.
утомляемость fatigability.
утомляемый fatigable.
утопление drowning, submersion.
утрата голоса aphonia.
~ женственности defemination.
~ реактивности absence of reaction, anergy.
утренняя тошнота obstet: matutinal nausea, morning sickness.
утроба maw.
утробная артерия anat: celiac artery.
утробный плод fetus.
утята p. a. of утёнок.
ухаживать (за больным) care, tend, nurse.
ухаживающий персонал nursing personnel.
ухо anat: ear, auris.
уховёртка entom: European earwig (Forficula auricularia).
~ огородная F. tomis.
~ Федченко Oreasiobia fedtschenkoi.
уховёртки = кожистокрылые.
уход (за больными) care, attendance, nursing.
~ за постельными больными bedside nursing.
~ ~ терапевтическими больными medical nursing.
~ ~ хирургическими больными surgical nursing.
~ роя (из улья) bee escape.
уходящий от засухи bot: drought-escaping.
*уxоносовой Aurinasal.
ухудшение worsening, aggravation, deterioration, decline (of health).
ухудшение интеллекта intellectual deterioration.
~ памяти memory impairment.
~ состояния aggravation of symptoms.
~ ~ после улучшения recrudescence.
уцелеть survive.
учащение rate increase, increase in frequency.
~ дыхания increase in respiratory rate.
~ пульса increase in pulse rate.
~ сердечной деятельности waxing of the heart (rate).
учащённое дыхание hurried breathing.
учащённый пульс increased pulse rate.
учебное задание av med: practice mission.
учение science.
~ о болезнях мочевых органов urology.
~ об опухолях oncology.
~ ~ органах чувств esthesiology.
~ о веслоногих рачках copepodology.
~ ~ грибах mycology.
~ ~ гормонах hormonology.
~ ~ грыжах surg: celology.
~ ~ детских заболеваниях pediatrics.
~ ~ железах adenology.
~ ~ жизни biology.
~ ~ млекопитающих zool: mammalogy.
~ ~ нервах neurology.
~ ~ нервных болезнях neuropathology.
~ ~ питании alimentology, trophology.
~ ~ пищевых веществах bromatology.
~ ~ признаках болезней semiology, symptomatology.
~ ~ размножении bio: genesiology.
~ ~ растениях phytology.
~ ~ связках syndesmology.
~ ~ смерти thanatology.
~ ~ сосудах angiology.
~ ~ старости gerontology, geratology.
учрежденческий врач health officer, medical officer.
ушан zool: bat Plecotus auritus.
ушастая круглоголовка zool: Phrynocephalus mystaceus. Cf. круглоголовки.
~ лисица = ушастая собака.
*~ собака ear's-dog (Otocyon megalotis).
ушастые тюлени (сем.) zool: eared seals (Otariidae).
ушастый окунь ichth: rock bass (Ambloplites rupestris); sunfish (Centrarchidae); long-eared sunfish (Lepomis megalotis).
~ тюлень eared seal.
ушиб bruise, contusion.
ушибать bruise, contuse.
ушибить p. a. of ушибать.
ушко auricle.

ушко сердца anat: auricle, auricular appendix, auricula cordis.
ушковидная поверхность anat: auricular surface (sacrum).
ушная артерия (глубокая, задняя) anat:(deep,posterior) auricular artery.
~ болезнь aural disease.
~ втулка av med: ear plug.
~ крсточка ichth: earbone.
~ мочка anat: ear flap; zool: earlobe.
~ наковальня anat: anvil, incus.
~ петля ear snare.
~ раковина anat: auricle, pinna (of the ear).
~ сера physl: earwax, cerumen.
~ улитка anat: cochlea.
ушного происхождения otogenous.
ушное зеркало otolar: ear mirror, ear speculum.
ушной зонд aural probe, ear spud.
~ катетер otolar: ear catheter.
~ кашель ear cough.
~ нерв (большой, задний) anat:(great, posterior) auricular nerve.
~ пинцет otolar: ear forceps.
~ тампон ear plug.
~ шприц ear syringe.
ушнораковинный anat: pinnal.
ушные капли pharm: ear-drops.
ущемление strangulation, impaction, incarceration; protrusion(of hemmorrhoids).
~ камня path: calculus impaction.
ущемлённая грыжа path: strangulated hernia
ущемлённый strangulated, impacted, incarcerated.
уязвимый vulnerable.

Ф

фагеденическая язва path:phagedenic ulcer.
фаголизат phage lysate.
фаготипирование phage typing.
фаготрофия phagotrophy.
фагоцит hist: phagocyte.
фагоцит(ар)ный hist: phagocytal, phagocytic.
фагоцитоз phagocytosis.
фаза phase.
фазан orn: pheasant.
~ обыкновенный pheasant (Phasianus colchicus).
фазаньи (сем.) orn: pheasants (Phasianidae).
фазеолин phaseolin.
фазеолюнатин phaseolunatine.
фазии (сем.) entom: Phasiidae.
фазоконтрастная микроскопия phase contrast microscopy.
фактический factual, actual.
фактор X av med: "X" factor.
факторы внешней среды environmental factors.
факультативный facultative, optional.
~ анаэроб bact: amphimicrobian.
факус bio: Phacus (green flagellated organisms).
фаланга 1. phalanx; 2. zool: "tarantula" (Galeodes arancoides).
фаланговый phalangeal.
фалангоходящий zool: phalangigrade.
фалла = гельминтоспориоз.
фаллозома entom: phallosoma.
фаллопиева труба anat: Fallopian tube, uterine t.
фальцет falsetto.
фанерогамное растение phanerogam.
фантазирование = конфабуляция.
фантазм psych: phantasm.
фантом model, cast.
фарадизация phys-ther: faradism.
*фараонов муравей pharaon's ant.
фарингит path: pharyngitis.
фарингоскоп pharyngoscope.
фарингоскопия pharyngoscopy.
фармакогнозия pharmacognostics.
фармакография pharmacography.
фармаколог pharmacologist.
фармакологический pharmacologic.
фармакология pharmacology.
фармакопея pharmacopeia.
фармакотерапия pharmacotherapy.
фармапия pharmapia.
фармацевт pharmacist.
фармацевтика pharmacy.
фармацевтическая химия pharmaceutical chemistry.
фармация pharmacy.
фарфорка zool:cowrie(Cypraea moneta).
фасетка роговицы entom:corneal facet.
фасеточный глаз entom:faceted eye.
фасоль bot:kidney bean (Phaseolus).
~ адзуки adzuki b. (P. angularis).
~ азиатская mungo b., Oregon pea (P. aureus, Roxbg.)
~ аконитолистная moth b.(P. aconitifolius,Jacq.)
~ ароматная caracol (P. caracolla).
~ безволокновая snap b., brittle b., stringless b.
~ волокнистая string b.
~ вьющаяся climbing b., running b., pole b.
~ зерновая common b., haricot (P. vulgaris).
~ карликовая dwarf b.
~ коловая pole b., running b., climbing b.,case-knife runner b.

фасоль кустовая bush b.
~ лимская Lima b. (P.limensis, Macfad.)
~ ~ мелкая civet b., sieva b.
~ ломкая = ф. безволокнистая.
~ лучистая = ф. адзуки.
~ мексиканская frijol.
~ мелкосемянная pea b.
~ многоцветковая scarlet runner, multiflora b. (P. coccineus).
~ низкорослая dwarf b.
~ обыкновенная kidney b. (P. vulgaris)
~ огненная = ф. многоцветковая.
~ полулунная = ф. лимская мелкая.
~ почечная = ф. обыкновенная.
~ почечновидная = ф. обыкновенная
~ с жёлтыми лопатками wax pod.
~ сахарная French b.
~ со съедобным бобом = ф. сахарн.
фасциолёз = глистопечёночная болезнь.
фасция anat: fascia.
~ глазного яблока eyeball fascia.
фатер-пачиниево тельце hist:Pacinian corpuscle.
фауна fauna.
фаунистика faunistics.
фаунистический faunistic, faunal.
фахак ichth:swellfish (Tetraodontidae).
фебрильный febrile.
фекалии feces.
фекалия zool: fecal pellet.
фекальный fecal.
фелландр = укроп конский.
фельдшер doctor's assistant, surgeon's assistant; Brit: dresser.
фельдшерица female assistant, see фельдшер.
фенакобиус bot: suckermouth minnow (Phenacobius mirabilis, Girard).
фенёк = большеухая лисица.
фенестрация fenestration.
феникс bot: phoenix (Phoeniceae).
фенилаланин phenylalanine.
фенилпирувиновый phenylpyruvic.
фенилсерин phenylserine.
фенол chem: phenol.
фенологический phenological.
фенология phenology.
фенолят ртути = карболовая ртуть.
феномен phenomenon.
~ Санарелли-Шварцмана Sanarelli-Scwartzmann phenomenon.
фенотип bio: phenotype.
фенотипический phenotypic.
фенхель bot: fennel (Foeniculum, Mill.)
~ душистый finocchio (F. vulgare).
~ итальянский = ф. душистый.
фенхель обыкновенный = ф. душистый.
~ флорентийский = ф. душистый.
феоделлы bot: phaeodellae.
феомеланин phaeomelanin.
фермент ferment.
ферменты разлагающие клетчатку cellulocytic enzymes.
фермицидин pharm: fermicidin.
Ферне Fernet.
ферноксон chem: fernoxone.
фертильный fertile.
фетиш psych: fetish.
фетишизм psych: fetishism.
фетишист psych: fetishist.
фиалка bot: violet (Viola).
~ душистая sweet v., English v. (V. odorata).
~ ночная 1. night-smelling rocket (Hesperis matronalis); 2. see любка двулистная.
~ рогатая tufted pansy (V. cornuta).
~ трёхцветная = анютины глазки.
~ узамбара African violet (Saintpaulia ionantha, Wendl.)
~ швейцарская = ф. рогатая.
фиалковые (сем.) bot: violet family (Violaceae).
фиалковый violaceous.
~ корень pharm: orris root (Iris germanica florentina, I. pallida).
фибриллярное подёргивание path: fibrillary twitching.
фибриллярный тремор path:fibrillary tremor.
фибрилляция fibrillation.
фибрильный fibrillar, fibrillary.
фибрин hem: fibrin.
фибриноген hem: fibrinogen.
фибринозный слепок path: fibrinous cast.
фибринолиз hem: fibrinolysis.
фибринолитический hem: fibrinolytic.
фибринообразующий fibrinogenous.
фибробласт hist: fibroblast, fibrocyte, connective-tissue cell.
фибробластический fibroblastic.
фиброзная оболочка anat: fibrous membrane.
~ ~ почки anat: capsule of the kidney, capsula fibrosa.
~ ткань hist: fibrous tissue.
фиброзное растяжение anat: lacertus fibrosus.
~ сращение fibrous adhesion.
фиброзный слой fibrinous layer.
~ тяж hist: fibrous band.
фиброин fibroin.
фиброма path: fibroma.
~ матки gyn: uterine fibroma.
фибросаркома oncol: fibrosarcoma.

фибросерозная оболочка anat: fibroserous membrane.
фига bot: fig.
фиговое дерево = смоковница.
физалис bot: ground cherry, bladder c. (Physalis).
~ ананасный = ф. перувианский.
~ перуанский cape gooseberry, apple of Peru (P. peruviana).
~ перувианский = ф. перуанский.
физикулюс ichth: red cod (Physiculus bacchus).
физиографический physiographic.
физиолог physiologist.
физиологическая диплопия ophth: physiologic diplopia, introspective d.
~ психология physiologic psychology.
~ химия physiologic chemistry.
~ экскавация ophth: physiologic cup(ping); excavation of the optic disk.
физиологический возраст physiologic age.
~ раствор поваренной соли physiologic saline solution.
физиология physiology.
~ животных zoophysiology.
~ растений plant physiology.
физиотерапевт physical therapeutist.
физиотерапевтическое отделение physical therapy department.
физиотерапия physical therapy, physical medicine.
физическая активность physical activity.
~ инертность physical sluggishness.
~ ловкость physical dexterity.
~ пригодность летчиков av med: physical fitness of pilots.
~ структура physique.
~ химия physical chemistry.
~ недостаток physical handicap.
~ труд manual labor.
физкультурник athlete.
фикомицетный bot: phycomycetous.
фикомицеты bot: phycomycetous fungi (Phycomycetes).
фикофеин phycophaein.
фикохризин phycochrysin.
фикоциан phycocyanin.
фикоэритрин phycoerythrin.
фиксатор lab: fixative, fixing fluid.
фиксаторный орган organ of attachment.
фиксационная точка периметра ophth: fixation point of the perimeter.
фиксационный пинцет ophth: fixation forceps.
фиксация fixation.
~ отвислой груди surg: mazopexy.
фиксация пузыря cystopexy.
~ слепой кишки surg: cecopexy, fixation of the cecum.
фиксирование белков в организме metab: proteopexy.
~ матки gyn: metropexy, hysteropexy.
~ (органа) к брюшной стенке surg: ventrosuspension.
~ печени surg: hepatopexy.
~ прямой кишки surg: rectopexy, proctopexy.
~ фаллопиевой трубы gyn: salpingopexy.
фиксированная идея psych: fixed idea.
фиксировать fix.
фиксирующее средство fixative.
фиксирующий пигмент chromopexic.
фикус bot: ficus (Ficus).
~ каучуконосный India-rubber plant (Ficus elastica, Roxbg.)
филадельфийская чайка orn: Bonaparte's gull (Larus philadelphia).
филариаз path: filariasis.
филин orn: great horn owl, Brit: eagle-owl, tawny owl (Bubo bubo, B. maximus).
филлодий bot: phyllode, phyllodium.
филлоксера entom: phylloxera, vine louse, root-louse (Phylloxera vastatrix, Ph. vitifolii).
филлопода zool: phyllopod (Phyllopoda).
филлофора bot: red algae: phyllophora (Phyllophora).
~ пленчатолистная P. membranifolia.
филогенез phylogenesis.
филогенетика phylogeny.
филогенетический phylogenetic.
филогения phylogeny.
~ органов organophyly.
филодендрон bot: philodendron (Philodendron), ceriman (P. pertusum, Kunth).
филоподия zool: filopod, filose pseudopod.
филотаксия bot: phyllotaxy.
фильтр filter.
фильтрат filtrate, colature.
фильтрация filtration, colation, straining; seepage.
фильтровальщики zool: filtration type.
фильтрующее планктонное животное filter-feeding plankton animal.
фильтрующийся вирус filtrable virus.
филярий zool: filander.
филяриидоз filariasis.
фимбрия = бахрома.
финвал = сельдяной полосатик.
финик bot: date.
~ индийский = тамаринд.
~ китайский Chinese date (Zizyphus jujuba).

финик морской zool: mollusk Lithophaga.
финиковая пальма bot: date palm (Phoenix dactylifera, L., Ph. cycadifolia, Hort.)
финка = цистицерк.
финна = цистицерк.
финноз vet helm: measles.
~ свиней helm: pork measles.
*финнозное мясо helm: cysticerc-infested meat.
финнозный helm: measled.
финта ichth: herring Alosa f. fallax.
фисташка bot: pistachio (Pistacia vera).
~ дикая wild nard (P. mutica).
фисташковое дерево = фисташка.
*фисташковые (сем.) bot: cashew family (Anacadiaceae).
фистула fistula.
фистульное исследование fistula test.
фисция bot: physcia lichens (Physcia).
фитобентос bot: phytobentos.
фитогенез phytogeny.
фитогеографический bot: phytogeographical.
фитолакка = лаконоска, кермес.
фитономус = долгоносик люцерновый листовой.
фитопалеонтология = палеоботаника.
фитопатолог phytopathologist.
фитопатология phytopathology.
фитопланктон phytoplankton.
фитопланктонный phytoplanktonic.
фитосоциология phytosociology.
фитофармакология phytopharmacology.
фитофил bio: phytophil.
фитофтора bot: late blight, potato b., Phytophtora (fungus).
фитоценология phytocenology.
флавон bot: flavonoid.
флаг bot: flag, vane, banner, dorsal standard.
Флак Flach.
флакон vial, small bottle.
фламбировать mcscop: flame.
фламинго orn: flamingo (Phoenicopterus ruber roseus).
Фланаган Flanagan.
фланелевый бинт surg: flannel bandage
флатчидетца = фляшерия.
флебит phlebitis, inflammation of a vein.
флебография phlebography.
флеболит path: phlebolith.
флеболитный phlebolithic.
флеботомная лихорадка phlebotomus fever.
флегмона path: phlegmon.
флегмональный phlegmonous.
флегмонозный phlegmonous.
флексура flexure.
*флемингия собранная bot: waras (Flemingia congesta Roxbg.)
флерницы = златоглазки.
флеш bot: tea shoot.
флокс bot: phlox (Phlox).
флора диатомей diatom flora.
~ ила silt flora.
~ литоральных луж tidepool flora.
~ папоротников fern flora.
флоридзин floridzin.
флоридская губка wire sponge.
флористика floristics.
флористический floristic.
флороглюцин floroglucine.
флотация chem: flotation.
флотский врач naval medical officer, n. surgeon.
флоэма phloem, conducting tissue.
флоэмная прядь bot: phloem strand.
Флэк Flack.
флюктуация fluctuation.
флюоресцеин fluorescein.
флюорохром(ирование) fluorochrom(ing).
флюс odont: alveolar abscess, gumboil.
фляшерия entom: flasheria.
фобия psych: phobia, see боязнь.
фовальное зрение foveal vision.
фокальный focal.
фокус focus.
Фолей Foley.
фолиевая кислота folic acid.
фолиниевая кислота folinic acid.
фолиурус bot: hardgrass, thin tail (Pholiurus, Trin.); sickle-grass (P. incurvus Schinz. et Thell)
фолликул follicle.
фолликулярная ангина follicular angina.
~ железа anat: follicular gland.
~ жидкость anat: follicular fluid, liquor folliculi.
фомес bot: wood rot (Fomes) fungi; see корневая губка, трутовик.
фомоз phytp: phomosis; foot rot of flax.
фомопсис phytp: phomopsis, fruit rot, stem-end rot.
фонендоскоп phonendoscope.
фонокардиография phonocardiography.
фонтан кита spouting of a whale.
форамнифера foramnifera.
форамниферы (отр.) zool: Foraminifera.
форезия entom: phoresia.
форель ichth: trout (Salmo).
~ озерная lake t. (S. trutta lacustris).
~ радужная S. irideus.
~ ручьевая brook t. (S. trutta fario).

форель севанская Sevan Lake t. (S. ischchan).
форменный элемент formed element.
формидиум bot: Phormidium (algae).
формиланилинуксусная кислота formyl-aniline-acetic acid.
формолвакцина formalin vaccine, formolvaccine.
формообразование shaping, form development.
формула рецепта pharm: inscription.
формы раздражения Тюрка hem: Türk's irritation forms.
форникс (ветвистоусых рачков) fornix.
форометр ophth: phorometer.
фороскоп ophth: phoroscope.
форотон ophth: phorotone.
форципатный жевательный аппарат zool: forcipate jaws.
фосген phosgene, carbonyl chloride.
фосфат chem: phosphate.
фосфатемия phosphatemia.
фосфатный phosphatic.
фосфен phosphene.
фосфолипид phospholipid.
фосфопептон phosphopeptone.
фосфор phosphorus, P.
фосфоресцирующий phosphorescent.
фосфорилирование phosphorylation.
фосфорилирсвать phosphorylate.
фосфорный обмен phosphorus metabolism.
фотодинамический photodynamic.
фотопериод photoperiod.
фотопериодический photoperiodic.
фотопигмент photopigment.
фотопсия ophth: photopsia.
фоторедукция bot: photoreduction.
фотосинтез photosynthesis.
фотосинтетический photosynthetic.
фототаксис bio: phototaxis.
фототактический phototactic.
фототропизм phototropism.
фототропический phototropic.
фотофобия = светобоязнь.
фотохимия photochemistry.
фотохроматическая терапия photochromatic treatment.
фрагилярия bot: Fragilaria (algae).
фрагментация bio: fragmentation.
фрагмобазидиальные грибы (подкл.) bot: Phragmobasidiomycetes (fungi).
фрагмобазидиомицеты = фрагмобазидиальные грибы.
фрактура fracture.
фрамбезия infect: frambesia, yaws, pian.
французский скипидар pharm: French oil of turpentine.
фрегат orn: frigate bird (Fregata).
фремитус fremitus.
френикотомия surg: phrenicotomy.
френикоэкзерез surg: phrenicoexeresis, phrenic avulsion.
фреон chem: freon.
фринозома zool: Phrynosoma cornutum (lizard).
фронтальный орган frontal organ.
фруктовый сад agr bot: orchard.
~ сахар fruit sugar.
фтиза path: phthisis.
фтор fluorine, F.
фторгидрокортизон fluorohydrocortisone.
фтористый натрий pharm: sodium fluoride.
фузариоз phytp: fusariosis; field withering; seedling blight (of cereals); fusarium wilt (of potatoes); stem-end rot (of potatoes); flax wilt.
фузариозное увядание bot: fusarium wilt.
фузариум phytp: Fusarium (fungi).
~ розовый F. roseum, Link.
~ снежный F. nivale, Ces.
фузионный центр fusion center (of the brain).
фузоспирохетоз mcbio: fusospirochetal group.
фукоидин fucoidin.
фукоксантин fucoxanthin.
фукофеин fucofein.
фуксия bot: fuchsia.
фукус bot: fucus (Fucus) algae.
~ пильчатый black wrack, serrated seaweed, sea oak, prickly tang (F. serratus).
~ пузырчатый bladder wrack, seaware, kelpware (F. vesicolosus).
~ узловатый sea whistle (F. nodosus).
фукусовые bot: fucuses (Fucales).
фукусовый bot: fucoid.
×фумигант agr: fimigant.
фумигация agr: fumigation.
фунгин fungin.
фунгистатический agr: fungistatic.
фунгицид fungicide.
фунгицидный порошок fungicidal dust.
фунгозная язва path: fungous ulcer.
фунгозный fungous, fungal.
фундук = лещина.
фуникулюс (мшанки) zool: funiculus, funicle.
функия bot: plantain lily, funkia (Hosta Spreng.)
функциональная проба functional test.

функциональная проба печени liver
function test.
~ способность functional capacity.
функциональное заболевание
functional disease.
~ расстройство functional
derangement. [coliformis,G.intricata)
фунори bot: funori algae (Gloiopeltis
фурациллин furacillin.
фурка zool: furca (of crustaceans).
фуркрея bot: furcraea (Furcraea, Vent.)
~ гигантская giant lily (F.gigantea).
~ клубневая = агава колючая.
фурункул furuncle, boil.
фурункулёз path: furunculosis.
фурункульный path: furuncular.
фуцин fucin.

Х

хадроптерус ichth: crawl-a-bottom
darter (Hadropterus nigrofasciatus).
халаза bio: chalaza.
халазион = халацион.
халат gown. [cyst.
халацион ophth: chalazion, Meibomian
халикоз path: chalicosis, flint disease.
Халлей Halley.
хальциды (надсем.) entom:
chalcid-flies (Chalcidoidea).
хамелеон zool: chameleon.
~ обыкновенный chameleon (Chameleon
vulgaris). [(Chameleontes).
хамелеоны (подотр.) zool: chameleons
хамеропс bot: chamaerops (Chamaerops
humilis).
хамеципарис bot: white cedar
(Chamaecyparis thyoides). [cholus).
хамса ichth: anchovy (Engraulis encrasi-
ханка = тыква бутылочная, тыква
горлянка.
ханос ichth: milkfish, bangos, awa (Cha-
хара bot: chara, stonewort (Chara). |nos).
~ хрупкая muskgrass (C. fragilis).
характерный вид bio: representative
species.
~ представитель рода bio: generitype.
харвистфиш harvest fish (Peprilus
alepidotus; Poronotus triacantus).
хариус ichth: grayling (Thymallus).
хариусовые (сем.) ichth: graylings
(Thymallidae).

харкать кровью to spit blood.
харовые (кл.) bot: Chareal (algae).
хат bot: khat (Catha edulis, Fors.)
хатка бобра zool: beaver room.
хатыс = сибирский осётр.
хатьма bot: lavatera, levatera
(Lavatera Thuringiaca).
хашам = жерех южнокаспийский.
хватательная нога entom: prehensile
leg, forcipate leg, seizing limb.
хватательный тип zool: prehensile
type, forcipate type.
хвойник двухколосковый = эфедра.
хвойниковые (сем.) bot: gnetaceous
plant family (Gnetaceae).
хвойные bot: coniferous (Coniferales).
хворост bot: brushwood, slash, debris
(branches, trimmings, etc.)
хворый = больной, болезненный.
хвост tail, cauda, terminus.
~ лошади horsetail.
хвостатая доля (печени) anat:
caudate lobe, lobus caudatus.
~ церкария zool: furcocercous cercaria.
хвостатое земноводное zool:
caudate, urodete.
~ ядро neur: caudate nucleus, n. cau-
хвостатость caudation. datus.
хвостатые (отр.) zool: (Urodela,
Caudata).
хвостатый caudate, caudiferous, tailed.
хвостец zool: urostyle.
хвостик little tail, scut.
хвостник = водяная сосенка.
хвостовая кишка entom: tail gut.
~ нить entom: cercus. Cf. веснянка.
~ почка bot embr: tail bud.
~ складка embr: tail fold.
~ часть tail, rump.
хвостовой caudal, caudate.
~ плавник zool: caudal fin, tail fin.
~ придаток tail appendage.
хвостовые позвонки tail vertebrae.
хвостокол ichth: white sting ray
(Trygon microps).
хвостоножки = ногохвостки.
хвощ bot: horsetail, mare's-tail
(Equisetum).
~ большой E. majus, Gars.
~ полевой common h., field h., bottle
brush, cat's tail (E. arvense).
хвощовые (сем.) bot: horsetail family
(Equisetaceae).
хвоя bot: needles, acerose leaves.
Хейм Heim.

хелат chem: chelated compound.
хелицера zool: chelicera.
хелицеровые (подтип) zool: spiders, etc. (Chelicerata).
хелицероносные = хелицеровые.
хелонея bot: turtlehead, snakehead, shell flower (Chelone).
хемиптеронотус razor-fish (Hemipteronotus).
хемихромис jewel fish (Hemichromis bimaculatus).
хемоз ophth: chemosis, swelling of the conjunctiva.
хемолиз chemolysis.
хеморецептор zool: chemoreceptor.
хеморецепция chemoreception.
хемосинтетический chemosynthetic.
хемотаксис chemotaxis, chemotaxy.
хемотактический chemotactic.
хемотический ophth: chemotic.
хенна bot: mignonette (Lawsonia inermis)
хеноа = лебеда киноа.
хеноподиевое масло pharm: chenopodium oil, wormseed oil.
хеноподий bot: wormseed.
хепатус doctor-fish, tang (Hepatus hepatus).
херес sherry.
хермес еловый entom: spruce gall aphid (Chermes abietis).
хермесы (сем.) entom: jumping plant-lice (Chermesidae, Chermidae).
хета entom: seta, chaeta.
хетерандрия least mosquito-fish (Heterandria formosa).
хетерантера bot: mud plantain (Heteranthera).
хетерофиес helm: Heterophyes.
хетогната zool: chaetognath.
хетодиптерус spadefish (Chaetodipterus faber).
хетотаксия entom: chetotaxy.
хетофоровые (сем.) bot: Chaetophoraceae (algae).
хиазма anat: chiasma.
хиборинхус ichth: blunt-nosed minnow (Hyborhynchus notatus).
хилёзный chylous.
хило entom: rice-stem borer (Chilo auricilia).
хилое растение depauperate plant.
хилокорус entom: ladybug Chilocorus.
хилурия path: chyluria.
хилус physl: chyle.
химера 1. ratfish, rabbit fish (Chimaera); 2. bot: chimera.
~ мериклинальная bot: mericlinal chimera.
химеровые = цельноголовые.

*химизм chemicity.
~ тканей tissue chemistry.
химик chemist.
химикат chemical (substance).
химиотаксический chemotactic.
химиотерапия chemotherapy.
химификация physl: chymification.
химическая война chemical warfare.
~ обработка chemical treatment.
~ стойкость chemoresistance.
химически чистый chemically pure.
химические войска Chemical Corps.
химический ожог chemical burn.
~ раздражитель chemical stimulus.
~ состав chemical composition.
химическое превращение chemical transformation.
~ средство chemical affinity.
~ уравнение chemical equation.
химия chemistry.
~ живых клеток cytochemistry.
~ обмена metabolic chemistry.
~ растений phytochemistry.
~ тканей histochemistry.
химус physl: chyme.
химусный chymous.
хина pharm: cinchona.
хинафенин pharm: quinaphenin.
хинафтол pharm: quinaphthol.
хинидин pharm: quinidine.
хинин pharm: quinine.
хинная кислота pharm: quinic acid.
~ корка pharm: cinchona bark.
~ настойка pharm: tincture of cinchona.
хиннодубильная кислота quinotannic acid, cinchotannin.
хинное дерево bot: cinchona-tree, fever-tree (Cinchona ledgeriana, C. calisaya, etc.)
хиннокислый пиперазин pharm: piperazin quinate.
хинный отвар pharm: decoction of cinchona.
хиновин pharm: quinovin, kinovin.
хинозол pharm: quinosol.
хинопирин pharm: quinopyrine.
хинотропин pharm: urotropin quinate.
хиноформ pharm: quinoform.
хиодон ichth: mooneye (Hiodon).
хипераспис entom: ladybug Hyperaspis.
хипсипопс ichth: damsel-fish (Hypsypops rubicundus).
хирономида entom: chironomid.
хирот zool: Chirotes canaliculatus. Cf. амфисбены.
хирургическая болезнь surgical disease.

хирургическая игла surgical needle, suture n.
~ палата surgical ward.
~ помощь surgical service.
~ шейка anat: surgical neck, collum chirurgicum (of the humerus).
хирургически surgically.
хирургический нож operating knife.
~ пинцет dressing forceps.
~ узел surgeon's knot.
хирургическое вмешательство surgical intervention.
~ лечение surgical treatment.
~ отделение surgical department.
хирургия surgery.
~ брюшной полости abdominal surgery.
~ нервной системы neurosurgery.
~ почек renal surgery.
~ суставов joint surgery.
хиспанискус ichth: Spanish flag (Hispaniscus rubrivinctus).
хистрио mousefish (Histrio).
хитин chitin.
хитинизация entom: chitinization.
хитинизированный chitinized.
хитиновый chitinous.
хитон zool: chiton, coat-of-mail shell (Loricata).
хитоны zool: chitons (Polyplacophora), see панцырные.
хитридия zool: chytrid.
Хичкок Hitchcock.
хищная птица bird of prey.
хищник zool: carnivore, beast of prey, preyer, predator; cf. дневные хищники.
хищники = плотоядные.
хищничество carnivorism, predatism.
хищное животное beast of prey, see хищник.
хищное питание zool: carnivorous food habits.
хищность predatoriness.
хищные zool: flesh-eating mammals, carnivores (Carnivora).
хищный predatory, predacious, rapacious, raptorial, carnivorous, flesh-eating.
хламидомонада bot: chlamydomona (Chlamidomonas).
*хламидомонадовые (сем.) bot: Chlamidomonadinaceae family (algae).
хлебное дерево bot: breadfruit tree (Artocarpus incisa).
хлебные дрожжи bot: yeast fungus (Saccharomyces cerevisiae).
хлебный злак bot: cereal.
хлебоядный panivorous.
*хлёрофтальмус ichth: cucumber fish (Chlorophtalmus nigripinnis).

хлоазма derm: chloasma, melanoderma.
хлопающий шум flag sound, flapping s.
хлопок bot: cotton.
хлопушка = смолёвка.
хлопчатник bot: cotton plant (Gossypium herbaceum).
~ древесный tree c. (G. arboreum).
~ египетский Egyptian c. (G. barbadense).
~ перуанский kidney c. (G. peruvianum, Cav.)
~ приморский sea-island c. (G. barbadense maritimum).
хлопчатое дерево = капок.
хлопьевидный flocculent.
хлопья flocs, flakes.
хлоралгидрат pharm: chloral hydrate.
хлорамфеникол pharm: chloramphenicol.
хлорат chem: chlorate.
хлорборнокислый натрий pharm: sodium chloroborate.
хлорелла bot: Chlorella (algae).
хлореллин chlorellin.
хлоренхима chlorenchyma.
хлорид chem: chloride.
хлорирование san: chlorination.
~ воды san: water chlorination.
хлорированный chlorinated.
хлористая ртуть pharm: mild mercurous chloride.
хлористоводородная кислота = соляная кислота.
хлористоводородный хинин pharm: quinine hydrochloride.
хлористый барий chem: barium chloride, barium chloratum.
~ водород chem: hydrogen chloride.
~ калий potassium chloride.
~ кальций calcium chloride.
~ магний pharm: magnesium chloride.
~ натрий sodium chloride.
хлорная вода pharm: chlorine water.
~ известь chem: lime chloride, chlorinated lime.
~ кислота perchloric acid.
хлорноватая кислота chloric acid.
хлорноватистый hypochlorous.
хлорное голодание chlorine hunger.
хлорогеновый chem: chlorogenic.
хлороз path: chlorosis.
хлорокись висмута pharm: bismuth oxychloride.
хлорококк bot: Chlorococcum (algae).
хлорококковые (сем.) bot: Chlorococcaceae (algae).
хлорома path: chloroma; Brit: Balfour's disease.
хлоромицетин pharm: chloromycetin.
хлоропласт bot: chloroplast.

хлоротический path: chlorotic.
хлорофилл bot: chlorophyll.
хлорофиллоносный chlorophyllous, chlorophyll-bearing.
~ организм bot: chlorophyll bearer.
хлорофильный bot: chlorophyllous.
хлороформ pharm: chloroform.
хлороформирование chloroformization, anesthesia by chloroform.
хлорохитриум bot: Chlorochytrium (algae).
хлорпромазин chloropromazine.
хлортетрациклин chlortetracycline.
хлорэтил pharm: chlorethyl.
хлорэтон pharm: chloretone, chlorobutanol.
хлуп orn: fluff (of a cock).
хлыстовик = человеческий власоглав.
хмелевидный bot: hop-like (lupulinus).
хмелевое дерево = птелея.
хмелеграб bot: hophornbeam, ironwood.
хмелёк шуршащий = люцерна хмелевидная.
хмель bot: hop (Humulus lupulus).
хоановые (надкл.) ichth: Choanichthyes.
хоанодышащие = хоановые.
хоаноцит zool: collared flagellate cell.
хобот zool: proboscis, manubrium (in hydromedusae).
хоботковый rostellar.
хоботная пиявка zool: leech Rhynchobdellida.
хоботноголовые zool: rhynchocephalians (Rhynchocephalia, almost exinct reptiles
хоботное zool: proboscidian.
хоботные (отр.) zool: proboscidians (Proboscidea).
хоботок zool: proboscis, stylet (of an aphid), sucking beak, sucker (of bugs), rostel(lum).
х-образные ноги 1. path: knock-knees, genu valgum; 2.in-knees (horse defect).
хогфиш hogfish (Lachnolaimus maximus; Orthopristis chrysopterus; Selene vomer).
ход anat: duct(us).
~ бинта surg: turn of bandage.
~ лошади tread.
~ насекомаго в листе leaf mine.
~ обследования procedure of examination.
~ развития course of development.
~ рыб run of fish.
~ чесоточного клеща derm: cuniculus.
Ходжкин Hodgkin.
ходильная нога zool: walking leg, ambulatory leg, podite (of a crustacean).
ходильный zool: walking, ambulatory, gressorial, gradatory.

ходулочник orn: black-necked stilt (Himantopus mexicanus); see also зуёк долгоногий.
ходулочные корни stilt roots.
ходульник = ходулочник.
хозяин bio: host.
холангиография cholangiography.
Холден Haldane.
холёлепис ichth: Florida swamp darter (Hololepis barratti).
холелитиаз path: cholelithiasis.
холера infect: cholera.
холерина = летний понос.
холерный микроб cholera germ.
холероподобный cholera-like.
холестеатома path: cholestealoma, pearly tumor.
холестерин cholesterol.
холёцентрус squirrel-fish(Holocentrus).
холецистит path: cholecystitis.
холецистография cholecystography.
холзан = беркут.
холинергический neur: cholinergic.
холинестераза cholinesterase.
"холмик" = "горка".
холодильник refrigerator.
холодильный вагон refrigerator car.
холодная ванна cold bath.
холодное обёртывание phys-ther: cool pack, cold p.
~ обливание phys-ther: cold affusion.
холоднокровное животное cold-blooded animal, poikilotherm.
холоднокровный zool: cold-blooded, hematocryal.
холодный cold, algid.
~ пот (от страха) psych: cold sweat (due to fear).
холодовое расширение сосудов cold vasodilatation.
холостить geld, castrate, spay, emasculate, extesticulate.
холостой unmarried(man); zool: nonbreeding.
холостяк bachelor.
холощение gelding, etc. Cf. холостить.
~ самок spaying.
холстомер = мерин.
хомяк zool: hamster (Cricetus cricetus).
хондриом bio: chondriome.
хондриосома hist: chondriosome.
хондрома path: chondroma.
хондрус bot: red algae: tobera, etc. (Chondrus); kotoji-tsunomata (C. etatus); see also ирландский мох.
Хоппе Hoppe.
хорда see next page.

хорда zool: chorda, notochord, chorda dorsalis; embr: cord, see also клеточный тяж.
~ филум bot: devil's shoelace, sea lace, catgut, dead-men's-ropes (Chorda filum) brown alga. [sheath.
хордальная оболочка notochordal
хордовые (тип) zool: chordates (Chordata)
хордовый zool embr: chordal, chordate, notochordal.
хореатическая речевая спутанность psych: choreatic speech confusion.
хореический path: choreic, choreatic.
хорейный path: choreal.
хорёк zool: fitchew, fitch(et), polecat, foumart (Pitorius). [choromania.
хорея path: chorea, St. Vitus' dance,
хорион embr: chorion, serosa.
хорионический chorionic.
хорионный chorial, chorionic.
хороги = чистец клубненосный.
хорография bio: chorography.
хороидальное сплетение anat: choroid
хороидальный ophth: choroid(al) | plexus.
хорошее самочувствие sense of well-being.
хорошо упитанный well-nourished.
хорь = хорёк.
хохлатая крачка orn: Sandwich tern (Sterna s. sandvicensis).
хохлатка bot: birthwort, fumitory (Corydalis, sp. Medic.)
хохлатки (сем.) entom: prominents (Notodontidae).
хохлатый tufted, crested, copped; comose.
хохлач crested seal, hooded s. (Cystophora cristata).
хохолок 1. orn: crest, hood, cirrus, topknot; 2. coma, tuft of hairs, pappus
храмуля ichth: Varicorhinus.
храп(ение) snoring, stertor, rhonchus.
храпеть snore.
хребет = позвоночный столб.
хрен bot: horseradish (Cochlearia armoracia, L., Radicula armoracea, Rob.)
~ дикий wild h. (Rorippa armoracia, Rob.)
~ татарский = катран.
~ японский Japanese h., wasabi (Eutrema wasabi, max.) [kell.
хризалида entom: chrysalis, nymph(a),
хризантема bot: chrysanthemum (Chrysanthemum); see also златоцвет.
~ индийская = хризантема.
*хризомонадовые жгутиковые bio: chrysomonadic fagillate organisms.

хризомонады (отр.) zool: Chrysomonadina.
хризофановая кислота rheic acid.
хриопеопс ichth: red-finned topminnow (Chriopeops goodei).
хрип rale, rhonchus.
хриплый hoarse.
хрипота hoarseness.
хрипящий raling, rhonch(i)al.
хробуст = осот полевой.
~ салатный bot: cultivated sow thistle (Picridium vulgare Desf.)
хрозомус ichth: red-bellied dace (Chrosomus erythrogaster).
хроматида hist: chromatid.
хроматин hist: chromatin. [chromatin.
~ с половыми признаками sexuated
хроматиновая нить hist: chromatin fibre, spireme.
хроматиновый аппарат ядра hist: chromonemata. [aberration.
хроматическая аберрация chromatic
~ адаптация chromatic adaptation.
хроматография на бумаге paper chromatography.
хроматолиз path: chromatolysis.
хроматофор bot: chromatophore.
хроматофоротропный hist: chromato-
хромать limp. phorotropic.
хромоген chromogen.
хромогенный chromogenic.
хромой path: lame, limping.
*хромомицин pharm: chromomicin.
хромосома hist: chromosome. [chromosome.
хромосомная нить bio: thread of
~ перестройка genet: chromosomal rearrangement.
хромосомный обмен genet: chromosome
~ разрыв chromosome breakage | exchange.
хромота path: lameness, limping, claudication.
хронаксиметрия chronaxymetry.
хронаксиметрический chronaxymetric.
хронаксия chronaxie, chronaxy.
хронический алкоголизм chronic alcoholism. [exposure.
хроническое облучение rad: chronic
~ отравление металлами chronic metallic poisoning.
~ ~ морфином = морфинизм.
~ утомление av med: chronic fatigue.
хрупкий fragil, frail, brittle.
хрупкое телосложение slight build.
хрупкость fragility, fragilitas, frailness, brittleness.

хруст новой кожи path: new leather murmur.
* хрусталик anat: chrystalline lens.
хрусталиковая звезда ophth: lens star.
хрусталиковый ophth: lenticular
хрущ entom: scarabaeid, lamellicorn beetle
~ апрельский April beetle (Rhizotrogus aequinoctialis).
~ белый white beetle Polyphylla alba.
~ волосатый Anoxia pilosa.
~ дальневосточный июньский Far-East June beetle (Holotrichia sichotana).
~ ~ чёрный Far-East black beetle (Holotrichia diomphalia).
~ июньский June beetle, June bug, small cock chafer (Amphimallon solstitialis).
~ майский May-beetle, May-bug, cockchafer (Melolontha vulgaris).
~ ~ восточный M. hippocastani.
~ ~ западный M. melolontha.
~ мраморный закавказский Polyphylla olivieri.
~ ~ июльский Polyphylla fullo.
~ опаловый Aserica japonica.
~ хлебный Cyrioptera glabra.
хрущак entom: darkling beetle (Tenebrionidae).
~ мучной flour beetle, meal-worm (Tenebrio molitor).
~ ~ малый confused flour beetle (Tribolium confusum).
хрущи (сем.) entom: scarabaeids, Lamellicorn beetles (Scarabaeidae).
хрущик полевой entom: Anomala dubia.
~ садовый Phyllopertha horticola.
хрюканье grunt.
хрюкать grunt.
хряк = кнур.
хрящ anat: cartilage, gristle.
~ века anat: palpebral cartilage.
~ перегородки anat: septal cartilage.
хрящевая клетка hist: cartilaginous cell.
~ кость anat: cartilage bone.
~ опухоль path: chondroma.
~ ткань hist: cartilaginous tissue.
хрящевидный cartiliginiform, cartilaginoid.
хрящевой cartilaginous, chondral, gristly.
хрящевые ганоиды = костнохрящевые.
~ рыбы ichth: cartilaginous fishes (Chondrichthyes).
хрящеобразующий chondrigenous.
худение = похудание.
худеть become thin, grow lean.
хурма кавказская мелкоплодная dateplum (Diospyros lotus).
~ японская Japanase persimmon, kaki (D. kaki).
хэк ichth: hake, whiting, merluccio.
хэмулён ichth: grunt (Haemulon); margate-fish (H. album); etc.
хэмулида = хэмулён.
хэтчинсоновские зубы odont: notched teeth, pegged t.

Ц

цапля orn: 1. heron (Ardeidae). 2. Cf. солнечные цапли.
~ большая белая egret (Ardea alba).
~ колпица spoonbill (Platalea leucerodia).
~ малая orn: bittern (Ardea garzetta).
~ серая common heron (Ardea cinerea).
царапина scratch.
царица ночи bot: queen of the night (Cereus grandiflorus, Mill.)
царские кудри = сарана большая.
царский гриб = кесарев г.
~ корень = горичник.
~ скипетр = коровяк.
царь-зелье = 1. горичник; 2. живокость высокая.
цвёлый = заплесневелый.
Цвемер Zwemer.
цвести bot: bloom, blossom.
цвет 1. bot: bloom, blossom, see цветение; 2. color.
~ глаз eye color.
~ лица complexion.
цветение bot: flowering, bloom(ing), blossoming, florescence, anthesis.
~ водорослей bot: algal bloom.
~ воды bot: water-bloom, phytoplankton bloom, green scum.
~ планктона plankton bloom.
цветень bot: pollen, beebread.
цветковая чешуя bot: floral glume, lemma, see внутреняя, наружная ц. ч.
цветковые органы bot: floral organs.
~ растения flowering plants (Spermatophyta), see покрытосеменные.
цветная реакция chem: color reaction.
~ таблица colored plate
цветневой катар = сенная лихорадка.
цветной показатель hem: color index.
цветные коренья agr: yellow vegetables.
~ очки tinted spectacles.
цветовая слепота ophth: color blindness, achromatopsia.
цветовод floriculturist.

цветовое зрение color vision.
~ чувство color sense.
цветоед entom: "blossom-eater" (a beetle of the Curculionidae or Nitidulidae family feeding on flower buds, etc.)
~ гвоздичный pepper weevil (Anthonomus eugenii).
~ грушевый pear weevil (Anthonomus pedicularis).
~ земляничный strawberry weevil (Anthonomus signatus).
~ малинный raspberry weevil (A. rubi).
~ рапсовый blossom beetle, pollen b. (Meligethes aeneus).
~ хлопковый cotton-boll weevil (Anthonomus grandis).
~ яблонный apple-blossom weevil (Anthonomus pomorum), apple fly weevil.
~ ~ четырёхбугорчатый A. pomorum quadrigibbus.
цветок bot: flower, blossom, floret.
~ без прицветников ebracteate flower.
~ ~ шпоры ecalcarate flower.
цветоложе bot: floral receptacle, floral disk, torus, hypoblast.
цветоножка bot: flower stalk, pedicel, peduncle, scape.
цветонос(ный побег) bot: floral shoot, floriferous s.
цветоощущение ophth: color sensation.
цветорасположение bot: arrangement of flower(s), inflorescence.
цветочек bot: floret, floweret, floscule.
цветочная головка bot: flower head, anthodium, head of a composite flower.
~ мутовка bot: flower whorl.
~ почка bot: flower bud.
~ пыльца bot: pollen.
цветочный лист bot: floral leaf.
~ побег bot: floral shoot.
цветуха свёклы bot: beet-seed stalk.
цветущий bot: blossoming, blooming, florid, flowering (floridus).
~ ночью bot: noctiflorous.
цедра zest (peel of orange or lemon).
цезальпиниевые (сем.) bot: senna family (Caesalpiniaceae).
цезальпиниевый bot: caesalpiniaceous.
цезальпиния бразильская bot: bahia wood (Caesalpinia brasiliensis).
~ коротколистная algarobilla (C. brevifolia).
~ красивейшая Barbados pride (C. pulcherrima, Swartz).
цейлонская болезнь Ceylon sickness, beriberi.
~ корица pharm: Ceylon cinnamon.
цейлонский мох bot: Ceylon moss (Gracilaria confervoides) red alga.

целандин(а) = 1. боккония; 2.мак целандинный.
целебный источник healing spring.
целёринхус ichth: whiptail (Coelorhynchus).
целеустремлённость tenacity of purpose.
целительный salubrious, see also лечебный.
целлоидин celloidin, soluble guncotton, pyroxylin.
целлоидиновый срез hist: celloidin section.
целлулоза cellulose.
целлюлит path: cellulitis.
целлюлярный cellular.
целозия = петуший гребешок.
целом embr: coelom, celom.
целомический coelomic.
целоплана zool: crawling ctenophore Coeloplana metschnikowi.
цельная кровь whole blood.
цельноголовые ichth: Holocephali.
цельное молоко whole milk.
цельнокрайний лист bot: entire leaf, smooth-margin l.
цельнолистый bot: integrifolious, smooth-margin leaved, entire-leaved.
цельночерепные = котилозавры.
цемент cement.
*цененхима zool: coenenchim(a).
ценобий coenobium.
ценогенетический cenogenetic.
ценокрепис entom: chalcid (Caenocrepis bothynoderi).
ценолестовые zool: Caenolestoidea.
центаурин centaurine.
центез surg: centesis, puncture; perforation.
центр вращения глаз ophth: center of rotation of the eyes.
~ потоотделения anat: sweat center.
~ речи anat: speech center.
центральная борозда мозга anat: central sulcus, Rolandic s.
~ долька anat: central lobe.
~ жилка (листа) bot: mildrib.
~ капсула zool: central capsule.
~ нервная система central nervous system.
~ ось central axis.
~ ямка ophth: fovea centralis.
центральное тело клетки centroplasm.
~ углубление = центральная ямка.
~ цветовое зрение ophth: central color vision.
центральный канал спинного мозга anat: central canal of the spinal cord.
~ стержень central column.

центрарховые (сем.) ichth: Centrarchidae.
центриоля hist: centriole.
центрипетальный centripetal.
центрифуга centrifuga.
центрифугальный centrifugal.
центрифугат centrifugalized deposit.
центрифугирование centrifugation.
центрифугировать centrifuge.
центрические диатомеи bot:Centricae
центробежный centrifugal. (algae).
~ нерв efferent nerve.
центродесмоз hist: centrodesmos.
центропомус ichth: robalo (Centropomus undecimalis).
центропристес ichth: hannahills, black Harry (Centropristes striatus).
центросеменные (пор.) bot: Centrospermae order.
центросома hist: centrosome, central body, aster.
центростремительный centripetal, abterminal, afferent.
~ нерв anat: afferent nerve.
~ путь neur: centripetal tract.
центросфера hist: centrosphere.
ценура helm: coenurus bladder (larva).
ценуроз = вертячка 2.
цепень крысиный helm: rat tapeworm (Hymenolepis diminuta).
~ невооружённый = бычий ц.
~ свиной вооружённый pork tapeworm (Taenia solium).
цепеобразный cateniform, catenulate.
цепка entom: chela.
цепкое растение trailing plant,see стелящееся р. [Cebidae.
цепкохвостые (сем.) zool: monkeys
цепочечная пила surg: chain saw.
цепочечный catenulate.
~ кокк bact: chain coccus, Streptococcus.
цепь пищевых организмов bio: chain of food organisms.
церазин cerasin.
церамий красный bot: red ceramium (Ceramium rubrum, Ag.) red alga.
церарий entom: cerarium.
церастиум = ясколка полевая.
церат сосновой смолы = жёлтый пластырь.
цератихтис ichth: bullhead minnow (Ceratichthys perspicuus).
цератод = австралийский рогозуб.
цератоптерис bot: horn fern,floating f. (Ceratopteris).

церва = резеда жёлтая.
цервикальная беременность obstet: cervical pregnancy.
цервикальный anat: cervical.
церебральный артериосклероз psych: cerebral arteriosclerosis.
~ паралич cerebral palsy.
церебрин chem: cerebrin. [acid.
церебриновая кислота cerebri(ni)c
цереброспинальная нервная система cerebrospinal nervous system.
цереброспинальное средство cerebrospinant.
цереброспинальный cerebrospinal,see спинномозговой. [meningitis.
~ менингит path: cerebrospinal
~ сифилис path: cerebrospinal syphilis.
церея = летучая мышь.
церка entom: cercus.
церкария helm: cercaria.
церкопода zool: cercopod.
церкоспороз phytp: cercosporiasis, leaf scorch of beet.
цертация genet: certation.
церцис = иудино дерево.
цесарка orn: guinea fowl, pearl hen, pintado (Numida meleargris).
цесарь = цесарка.
цестода helm: cestode, cestoid.
цестодообразные (подкл.) helm: monozoic tapeworms (Cestodaria).
цестоды helm: cestodes (Cestoda), see ленточный червь.
цетрария исландская bot: lichen Cetraria islandica, Ach.
цефалодиск zool: Cephalodiscus.
цефалопода zool: cephalopod.
цефалоспорий bot: fungus Cephalosporium lecanii.
цефалякантус 1. ichth: flying gurnard (Cephalacantus). 2. buttonbush (Cephalacanthus occidentalis).
цеце entom: tsetse.
цецидия bot: earcockle (of wheat).
цианистая ртуть mercury cyanide.
~ ~ с цианистым цинком pharm: mercury and zinc cyanide. [cyanide.
цианистый калий chem: potassium
цианоз cyanosis. cyanide.
~ симметричных конечностей neur:
цианотичная окраска cyanotic discoloration. |acrocyanosis.
цианофициновое зерно bot: cyanophycin granule (in algae).
циатий bot: cyathium.

цибета = виверра.
циветта = виверра. [ponica, Pers.)
цидония bot: Japan quince (Cydonia ja-
цикада zool: leafhopper, cicada
(fam. Cicadidae). [ca).
~ азиатская Asian c. (Zyginidia asiati-
~ большая белокрылая Paharia zevara.
~ полосатая Psammotettix striatus.
~ розанная rose c.(Edwardsiana rosae).
~ тёмная dark c.(Delphacodes striatella).
~ хлопковая cotton-boll c. (Cicadatra ochreata, C. querula).
~ шеститочечная six-pointed c. (Macrosteles sexnotata).
цикадка entom: leafhopper, spittlebug, Cicadellida.
~ белая Egerna sinuata noxia.
цикадные растения bot: cycads.
цикадовые (подотр.) entom: cicads (Cicadoidea, Auchenorhincha).
цикл Cycle.
~ развития bio: developmental cycle.
~ течки estrous cycle, estrual cycle.
цикламен bot: cyclamen (Cyclamen).
~ европейский sow bread (C.europaeum).
циклантовые (сем.) bot:Cyclanthaceae.
циклётоне ichth: round-mouth
(Cyclothone). [schoephi).
циклихтис piny boxfish (Cyclichthys
циклическая альбуминурия path: cyclic albuminuria.
циклогександиол cyclohexanediol.
циклоид psych: cycloid.
циклоидный cycloid.
цикломорфоз cyclomorphosis.
циклоп zool: crustacean Cyclops.
циклосерин cycloserine.
циклотелла bot: cyclotella (alga).
циклотимик psych: cyclothymiac.
циклотимический cyclothymic.
циклотимия psych: cyclothymia.
циклотропия ophth: cyclotropia.
циклофораза cyclophorase.
циклофория ophth: cyclophoria.[rium).
цикорий bot: chicory, succory (Cicho-
~ корневой rooted c., coffee c.
~ листовой leaved c. |(C. intybus).
(C. intybus foliosum).
~ обыкновенный common c.,blue sailors
~ полевой = ц. корневой.|(C.intybus).
~ салатный = ц. листовой.
цикута = вех.
~ ядовитая = вех пятнистый.
цикутолистный bot: resembling Cicuta (cicutarium).

цилиарная инъекция ophth: ciliary injection.
цилиндр cylinder, cast.
цилиндрическая мерцательная клетка ciliated columnar cell.
цилиндрический сустав anat: pivot joint,trochoid j.
~ эпителий hist: columnar epithelium.
цилиндроид mcscop: cylindroid.
цилиндроклеточный hist: columnar-celled. [cea manatorum, Aschers.)
цимодоцея bot: manatee grass (Cymodo-
цимозиметр zymo(si)meter.
цинерария = зольник.
цинкдиметилдитиокарбамат chem: ziram, zinc dimethyldithiocarbamate.
цинковая мазь pharm: zinc ointment.
цинния bot: zinnia (Zinnia); youth-and-old-age (Z. elegans, Jacq.) [Zinn.
циннова связка anat: ligament of
циногнат zool: Cynognathus (extinct).
циносцион ichth: salt-water trout, (Cynoscion regalis); sea t., gray t., shad t., sun t., squit, drummer, yellowfin, chickwit, weakfish; etc.
цинхонидин cinchonidine.
цинхонин cinchonin.
циперус bot: galingale (Cyperus).
циприсовидная личинка (усоногих раков) zool: cyprid.
циркулирующий в крови blood-circulating. [amputation.
циркулярная ампутация surg:circular
циркулярное слабоумие psych: circular dementia. [psychosis.
циркулярный психоз circular
~ ход (бинта) surg: circular turn.
циркуляторный circulatory.
~ шок path: circulatory shock.
циркуляция крови blood circulation.
циррипедия zool: cirriped(Cirrepedia).
циррия (инфузории) zool: cirrus,
цирроз path: cirrhosis. style.
цирротический cirrhotic.
циррус = циррия.
цист(а) cyst.
цистерна anat: cistern.
~ между мозжечком и продолговатым мозгом anat: cerebellomedullary cistern.
цистин cystine.
цистит path: cystitis.
цистицерк helm: cysticercus, bladder worm, measle.
цистицеркоз path: cysticercosis; vet: measles.

цистицеркоид helm: cysticercoid.
цистоаденома path: cystoadenoma.
цистокарп bot: cystocarp.
цистолист cystolith.
цистообразующая железа entom: cystogenous gland.
цистоскоп cystoscope.
цистоскопировать cystoscope.
*цистотомия surg: cyctotomy.
цитаза cytase.
цитарин pharm: sodium anhydromethylenecitrate.
цитварное семя pharm: santonica seed, aniseed.
цитобиология cytobiology.
цитобластема cytoblastema.
цитогенез cytogeny.
цитогенетика cytogenetics.
цитогенетический cytogenetic(al).
цитодиагностика cytodiagnosis.
цитозин cytosine.
цитолиз cytolysis.
цитолизироваться cytolyze.
цитолитический cytolytic.
цитолог cytologist.
цитологический cytological.
цитология cytology.
цитоплазма cytoplasm.
цитоплазматический cytoplasmic.
цитоплазменный cytoplasmic.
цитосома cytosoma.
цитостом = ротовое впячение.
цитотаксономический cytotaxonomical.
цитотаксономия cytotaxonomy.
цитотрофобласт embr: cytotrophoblast, Langhans' layer.
цитофизиологический cytophysiological
цитохимический cytochemical.
цитохром cytochrome.
цитратная кровь citrated blood.
цитратное время свертывания hem: citrate clotting time.
цитрин citrin, see витамин P.
цитрон bot: citron (Citrus medica).
~ -мелисса = мелисса.
цитронелла bot: citronella, see сорго лимонное.
цитрофен = лимоннокислый парафенетидин.
цитрусовая улитка citrus tree snail.
цицаниопсис bot: water millet (Zizaniopsis).
цицания = зизания.
цмин bot: cudweed, everlasting, helichrysum (Gnaphalium).
~ песчаный sandy e., yellow e., immortelle (G. arenarium).
цмин прицветниковый straw flower, helichrysum (Helichrysum bracteatum, Willd.)
цуно-мата bot: tsunomata (Chondrus).
цуцугамуси = японская речная лихорадка.
цынга path: scurvy.
~ у взрослых adult scurvy.
цынготная трава = ложечная трава.
цынготный scorbutic.
цыплёнок young chicken.
цыплята pl: of цыплёнок.

Ч

чаб ichth: chub (Leiostomus, xanthurus; Kyphosus sectatrix; Ptychocheilis lucius; Tautoga onitis).
чабёр bot: savory, calamint (Satureja).
~ горный winter s. (S. montanata).
~ душистый = ч. летний.
~ летний summer s., annual s. (S. hortensis).
~ многолетний = ч.горный.
чабрец = богородская трава.
чавыча ichth: king salmon, chinook, spring, quinnat salmon, tyee (Oncorhynchus tschawytscha).
чагас path: chagas disease (due to Trypanosoma cruzi).
чагерак = верблюжья колючка.
чай bot: tea (Thea sinensis).
~ канадский = гаультерия.
~ капорский great willow herb, fireweed, wickup, blooming sally, rosebay (Epilobium angustifolium).
~ китайский China tea (T. sinensis).
~ луговой = вербейник.
~ парагвайский = мате
~ почечный orthosiphon (Orthosiphon stamineus, Benth.)
чайка orn: gull (Larus); seagull, cob (L. marinus).
~ белая white gull (Gavia).
~ обыкновенная blackheaded gull (Larus r. ridibundus).
~ серебристая атлантическая herring gull (Larus argentatus).
~ -хохотунья pewit.
чайки (пор.) orn: larines, gulls, seagulls (Lari).

чайконосая крачка orn: gull-billed tern (Gelochelidon n. nilotica).
чайная ложка teaspoon.
чайные (сем.) bot: tea family, camellia f. (Theaceae).
чайный куст bot: tea shrub, tea plant, see чай.
чайот = огурец мексиканский.
чалтык = рис болотный.
чальжа = альфа трава.
чанари = усач чанари.
чаполочь = дубровка душистая.
часовое стеклышко watch glass.
частица particle.
частицы примешанные к планктону pseudoplankton.
частичная закупорка path: partial obstruction.
~ потеря зрения meropia.
~ сердечная блокада path: partial heart block.
~ слепота path: partial blindness; amaurosis partialis fugax.
частично переваренный partially-digested.
~ разделённый subseptate.
частичное уродство demimonstrosity.
частичный partial, in part; embr: meroblastis.
~ антиген = неполный антиген.
~ перекрёст semidecassation.
частная лечебница private hospital.
~ обвёртка соцветия bot: partial involucre.
~ обёртка = частная обвёртка соцветия.
частный летчик av med: private pilot.
частое мочеиспускание frequent urination.
~ сердцебиение tachycardia.
частота дыхания respiration rate.
~ пульса pulse rate.
~ сердечных сокращений cardiac rate.
~ слияния flicker critical frequency.
~ сокращения желудочков ventricular rate.
частуха bot: water-plantain, mud-plantain (Alisma).
~ обыкновенная w.-p. (A. triviale, Pursh).
~ узколистная narrow-leaved w.-p. (A. gramineum, Gmel.)
частуховые (сем.) bot: water-plantain family (Alismataceae).
часть пробы subsample.
часы приема office hours.

чахлость scragginess, scrawniness, see мачиленца.
чахлый stunted, scraggy, scrawny, scrubby.
чахнуть emaciate; cf. чахлый.
чахотка path: phthisis, consumption.
чахоточный phthisic.
чашелистик bot: sepal, calix lobe.
чашеобразный bot: cup-shaped, cyathiform.
чашечка calyx, (small) cup; theca (of hydroids).
~ для красок lab: staining dish.
чашечкообразный calyciform.
чашечный calycine, calycinal.
чашка dish.
~ Петри lab: Petri dish, double d.
~ со средою эндо bact: endo-plate.
чебак = 1. плотва сибирская; 2. язь амурский.
чебрец = богородская трава.
*чеграва orn: Caspian tern (Hydropogne caspia).
чейн-стоксово дыхание Cheyne-Stokes' type of respiration.
чеканка pinching.
чеканчик луговой orn: whinchat (Saxicola, Pratincola rubetra).
челат chem: chelate.
*челночница ивовая entom: butterfly Earias chlorana.
челночницы (сем.) entom: Cymbidae.
человек zool: man (Homo sapiens).
человекообразная обезьяна anthropoid ape.
человекообразные (подотр.) zool: Anthropoidea.
~ обезьяны (сем.) zool: anthropoid apes (Antropomorphidae).
человекообразный anthropomorphic.
человекоубийство legl: manslaughter, homicide.
человеческая анатомия human anatomy.
~ аскарида helm: man's ascarid (Ascaris lumbricoides).
~ сыворотка human serum.
человеческий власоглав helm: whipworm (Trichuris trichiura).
человечность humanism, humanity.
челюстегрудь = головогрудь.
челюстная артерия anat: maxillary artery.
~ конечность feeding limb (of a crustacean).
~ нога zool: maxilliped.
~ пиявка zool: jaw leech (Gnathobdellida).
челюстножаберные ichth: Aphetohyoidea (extinct).

челюстно-подъязычная линия anat: mylohyoid line.
~ ~ мышца anat: mylohyoid muscle.
~ -скуловой anat: maxillojugal.
челюстной anat: maxillary, mandibular.
~ жир (китообразных) zool: jaw-oil (of Cetacea).
~ придаток zool: paragnath.
~ рефлекс jaw-jerk reflex.
~ щупалец entom: maxillary palpus.
челюстноротые zool: Gnathostomata.
челюстный сустав anat: temporo-maxillary articulation.
челюсть anat: jaw.
чемерица bot: false hellebore (Veratrum)
~ американская white hellebore, itchweed, Indian poke (V. viride, Ait.)
~ белая = ч. американская.
чепура белая = цапля большая.
чепуранужда = цапля малая.
черва entom: grub, brood (bees).
червеобразное движение physl: vermicular motion, peristalsis.
~ животное worm(like animal).
червеобразные мышцы anat: lumbricals.
червеобразный wormlike, worm-shaped, vermiform, vermicular, vermiculate.
~ отросток anat: vermiform appendix.
червеуловитель caterpillar-picking machine or device.
червец entom: coccid, scale, mealybug (Coccidae, Pseudococcidae); see also кокцида, тля щитковая, щитовка.
~ австралийский желобчатый = ицерия.
~ акациевый = щитовка европейская.
~ вишнёвый calico scale (Lecanium cerasorum).
~ Комстока Comstock mealybug (Pseudococeus comstocki).
~ кошенильный = кошениль.
~ левканида одноточечная armyworm (Leucania unipuncta). [nupera).
~ ложный false armyworm (Calocampa
~ можжевеловый juniper scale (Diaspis carveli). [adonidum).
~ мучнистый mealy bug (Pseudococcus
~ ~ виноградный grape mealybug (P.citri)
~ ~ цитрусовый citrus mealybug (P. gahani).
~ оранжерейный = ч. щетинистый.
~ ортезия orthesia (Orthezia insignis).
~ устрицеобразный = щитовка устрицевидная.
~ церопластес barnacle scale (Ceroplastes cirropediformis).
червец щетинистый long-tailed mealybug (Pseudococcus longispinus).
~ яблонный mussel scale (Lepidosaphes).
червивость (in)vermination.
червивый wormy, vermiculose, vermiculous,(in)verminated.
червоточина worm dust; wormhole, canker, pith fleck.
червь zool: worm.
~ дождевой zool: rainworm, dewworm, earworm, brandling (Lumbricus terrestris, Dendrobaena, Alldobophora).
~ земляной = ч. дождевой.
~ клюквенный жёлтоголовый yellow-headed cranberry worm, yellow-headed fireworm (Acleris minuta). [molitor).
~ мучной entom: meal worm (Tenebrio
~ плодовый cankerworm (fruit-damaging caterpillar.
~ проволочный = проволочник.
~ рисовый rice worm (Tilenchus angastus).
~ розовый кукурузный Pyroderces rileyi (Tineidae).
~ хлопковый (коробочный) cotton-worm (Aletia argillacea).
~ шелковичный silkworm (Bombyx, Sericaria mori).
~ шиповатый коробочный entom: moth Earias inculana (Cymbidae).
червяги (сем.) zool: Coeciliidae.
червяк = червь. [small worm.
червячок 1. anat: vermis; 2. zool:
~ мозжечка anat: brainworm.[(Bidens).
череда bot: bur-marigold, cuckold
~ ветвистая beggar ticks, sticktight, bootjack bur (B. frondosa).
~ облиствённая = ч. ветвистая.
~ сорная = ч. ветвистая.
чередование поколений bio:digenesis.
чередующийся alternate.
через влагалище transvaginal, per
~ задний проход per rectum.|vaginam.
черёмуха bot: European bird cherry (Prunus padus).
~ американская rum cherry, (wild) black c. (P. serotina, Ehrh.)
черемша = лук медвежий.
черенок 1. agr bot: scion, graft; 2. zool: razor shell, spout fish (Solen siliqua); 3. handle, haft.
череп anat: skull, brain case, cranium
~ внутренностный anat: cranium viscerale.
~ лицевой = ч. внутренностный.

череп мозговой anat: cranium cerebrale.
черепаха zool: tortoise, turtle.
~ (материал) tortoise-shell.
~ снедная = ч. съедобная.
~ съедобная tortoise (Chelonia mydas).
~ сухопутная land tortoise (Testudo).
черепахи zool: turtles, tortoises (Chelonia).
черепашка zool: 1. young turtle; 2. entom: stink-bug (Eurygaster); 3. entom: tortoise-beetle (Coleoptera).
~ австрийская Austrian bug(Eurygaster austriacus).
~ баклажанная = листоед баклажанный
~ вредная Eurygaster integriceps.
~ маврская E. maura, E. meridionalis.
~ пшеничная американская chinch bug (Blissus leucopterus).
черепашки entom: sting-bugs Eurygaster.
черепитчатый bot: tegular.
черепица bot: tegula.
черепная крышка anat: calvaria, skullcap, skullroof.
черепная полость anat: cranial cavity.
~ ямка anat: cranial fossa.
черепной свод anat: arch of the cranium.
черепномозговой нерв cranial nerve.
черепные zool: craniates (Craniata, Vertebrata), see позвоночные.
черепoдержатель anat: calvaria clamp.
черешковый bot: petiolate, petioled, petiolar.
~ лист petiolate leaf.
черешня bot: sweet cherry, mazzard (Prunus avium).
черешок bot: petiole, stalk, stipe (of a leaf blade).
~ лепестка bot: petiolule.
~ -лист bot: phyllodium.
~ листа bot: petiole, foot-stalk of a leaf.
~ ~ папоротника bot: stipe, leaf-stalk of a fern-frond.
~ листочка bot: petiolule, stipel.
черешочек bot: petiolule.
чёрная ворона orn: carrion crow (Corvus corone).
~ гагара orn: coot (Fulica atra).
~ гниль = раковый нарост на дереве.
~ короста = ч. парша.
~ казарка orn: black brant, brent goose (Bernicla brenta).
~ корь black measles.
~ крачка orn: black tern (Chlidonias n. niger).
~ личинка entom: nigger.
~ ножка phytp: blackleg, black stem rot, wire stem, damping out.

чёрная оспа black smallpox, hemorrhagic smallpox.
~ парша phytp: black scab, black scurf, rhizoctonia (disease of potatoes).
~ пелена av med: blackout, amaurosis fugax.
~ примочка pharm: black wash.
~ пыльная плесень phytp: black dusty mold.
~ пятнистость phytp: black spot; see also пятнистость.
*~ ~ томата phytp: black spot of
~ ржавчина phytp: black rust.
~ рыба Alaska blackfish (Dallia pectoralis).
~ стеблевая ржавчина phytp: black stem rust.
чёрнеть ошейниковая orn: ringneck (Fuligula collaris).
черника bot: bilberry, whortleberry (Vaccinium myrtillus).
чернильный гриб = навозник.
~ мешок zool: ink sac.
~ орешек pharm: gall nut.
чернобровый альбатрос orn: black-browed albatross (Diomedea melanophris).
чернобурая лисица zool: fawn-colored fox (Vulpes vulpes, V. fulvus).
чернобыльник bot: mugwort (Artemisia vulgaris); see also полынь.
черноголовая чайка orn: black-headed gull.
черноголовка 1. orn: blackcap(Sylvia atricapilla); 2. bot: see кровохлёбка лекарственная; лойник.
черноголовник кровохлёбковый = кровохлёбка лекарственная.
черноголовый хохотун orn: great black-headed gull (Larus ichthyaetus).
черногорка = адонис весенний.
чёрное вещество substantia nigra.
~ дерево bot: persimmon, blackwood, ebony (Diospyros).
чернозобая гагара orn: loon Colymbus arcticus.
черноклювый гусь = китайский г.
чернокорень bot: hound's tongue, beggar's lice (Cynoglossum).
~ аптечный common h.t., tailhead, sticktight (C. officinale).
чернолесье = лиственный лес.
чернослив = слива.
черноспинка ichth: Caspialosa kessleri (of herring family).
чернота чешуек phytp: black chaff of wheat).
чернотал bot: bay-leaf willow (Salix pentandra).

чернотелки (сем.) entom: darkling beetles (Tenebrionidae).
чернохвостый олень mule deer.
черношляпка = черноголовка.
чернушка bot: love-in-a-mist, fennel-flower (Nigella); black cumin (N.sativa); see also тмин чёрный.
~ дамасская N. damascena.
~ полевая N. arvensis.
чёрный дрозд orn: blackbird, ouzel (Turdus m. merula).
~ коралл black coral (Antipathes).
~ корень = скорцонер. [tibetanus).
~ медведь black bear, Baribal b. (Ursus americanus); Himalayan b. (Ursus
~ морской окунь ichth: black sea-bass (Stereolepis gigas; Centropristes striatus).
~ окунь ichth: black bass (Micropterus).
~ пожиратель ichth: black swallower (Chiasmodon niger).
~ рак = раковый нарост на дереве.
~ удильщик ichth: black angler (Crypto-
~ хлеб "black" bread, rye b. |sparas).
~ язык black tongue.
черпаловидно-надгортанная складка anat: aryepiglottic fold.
черпаловидный хрящ anat: arythenoid cartilage.
чертополох bot: thistle (Carduus).
~ ланцетолистный bull thistle (Carduus lanceolatus or Cirsium lanceolatum).
чеснок bot: garlic (Allium sativum).
чесночник bot: garlic mustard(Alliaria).
~ аптечный g.m.(A.officinalis,Andrz.)
чесночницы (сем.) zool: spadefoot toads (Pelobatidae).
чесночный гриб bot: fairy-ring fungus (Marasmius oreades).
чесотка path: scabies, itch, seven-year
чесоткобоязнь scabiophobia. |itch.
чесоточный mangy, scabbed, scabious.
четвероногий four-footed, quadrupedal.
четвероногое животное four-footed animal, quadruped, tetrapod.
*четверохолмие anat: qudrigeminal bodies, corpora quadrigemina.
четвёртый желудочек anat: fourth ventricle, ventriculus quartus.
~ желудок (сычуг) zool: abomasum, true
чётковидный moniliform. stomach.
~ скребень helm: rodents' parasitic worm Moniliformis moniliformis.
~ усик entom: moniliform antenna, necklace-form a.

чёткообразный = чётковидный.
четырёхглавая мышца бедра anat: quadriceps femoris muscle.
*четырёхглазка ichth: Anableps tetraphtalamus. [tetrathecal.
четырёхгнёздный quadrilocular,
четырёхдневная лихорадка quartan malaria.
четырёхжаберные головоногие моллюски (подкл.) zool: Tetrabranchia.
четырёхзубчатый bot: quadridentate.
четырёхкопытное zool: quadrisulcate.
четырёхкратная повторность quadruplication.
четырёхкруговые bot: Tetracycliceae.
четырёхкрылый entom: tetrapterous.
четырёхкрыльник пурпуровый = лядвенец четырёхлопастный.
четырёхлёгочные пауки (подотр.) zool: spiders Tetrapneumones.
четырёхлепестковый bot: tetrapetalous.
четырёхлетний bot: quadrennial.
четырёхлистный bot: tetraphyllous, quadrifoil (quadrifolius).
четырёхлопастный bot: quadrilobate, quadrilobed.
четырёхлучевой bot: tetrarch (roots).
четырёхосные кремневые губки zool: tetractinellids (Tetraxonida, Tetractinellida).
четырёхпалый four-digited.
~ тритон = сибирский ч. т.
четырёхпарный bot: quadrijugous.
четырёхраздельный bot: quadrifid, quadripartite.
четырёхрукое животное quadrumane.
четырёхстворчатый quadrivalve.
четырёхтычинковый bot: tetrandrous.
четырёххлористое олово chem: tin butter, stannic chloride.
четырёххлористый углерод chem: carbon tetrachloride.
чехлик cap. See also корневой чехлик.
~ хризалиды pupal chamber, case.
чехловидная болезнь phytp: disease of dewgrass, etc; cf. епихлоа.
чехонь ichth: Pelecus.
чечевица bot: lentil (Lens, Mill.)
чечевицеобразный lenticular, lens-shaped.
~ отросток anat: lenticular process.
чечевичка bot: lenticel.
чечётка orn: aberdevine (Acanthis
чешуевидный лист scale leaf.|linaria).

чешуекрылые (отр.) lepidopterons: moths, skippers, butterflies(Lepidoptera).

чешуекрылый lepidopterous.

чешуистый = чешуйчатый.

чешуйка scale, squama; bot: tegula.

чешуйница entom: fish-moth, silver fish (Lepisma saccharina).

чешуйчатая часть anat: squamous portion.

чешуйчатые zool: squamates (Squamata).

чешуйчатый scaly, squamous, squamate; bot: tegular.

~ шов anat: scaly suture, sutura squamosa.

чешуя scale, squama.

~ (височной кости) anat: squamous part (of the temporal bone), squama, squamosa.

~ в соцветии bot: palea.

чибис orn: green plover (Vanellus cristatus), pewit, lapwing.

чиж orn: siskin, pine siskin (Spinus pinus).

чий перистый = ковыль.

чикл bot: chicle.

чилибуха bot: poison nut, dog button (Strychnos nux vomica).

чилига = акация жёлтая.

чилижник = акация жёлтая

чилим bot: water caltrop, ling,(Trapa natans).

чина bot: vetchling, wild pea, lathyrus (Lathyrus).

~ клубненосная tuberous v., tuberous rooted pea, earthnut (L. tuberosus).

~ красящая Tangier pea, scarlet pea (L. tingitanus).

~ лесная everlasting pea, perennial p., flat p. (L. sylvestris).

~ многолетняя everlasting pea, perennial p. (L. latifolius).

~ посевная chickling vetch, khesari (L. sativus).

~ танджерская = ч. красящая.

чинар = платан.

~ кавказский = платан восточный.

чир ichth: whitefish Coregonus nasus.

чирей path: abscess; vet: anbury,ancome.

чирикать chirp, chirrup, twitter, pip.

чирок orn: teal (Anas circia, A. crecca); garganey (Querquedula).

*~ -свистунок seal (Anas crecca).

чирьеватость furunculosis.

число бактерий bacterial count.

~ белых кровяных шариков hem: white count.

~ венерических заболеваний venereal disease rate.

~ верхушечных толчков сердца (в минуту) apical rate.

~ дыханий (в минуту) respiratory rate.

число коек bed capacity(of a hospital).

~ лейкоцитов hem: white count.

~ ударов сердца (в минуту) heart rate.

~ эритроцитов hem:red count.

чистая разводка lab mcbio: pure growth.

~ ~ плесени lab: neat mold.

чистец bot: hedge nettle (Stachys).

~ болотный woundwort (S. palustris).

~ клубненосный knotroot, Chinese artichoke, Japanese a. (S. tubifera).

~ лесовой = звездчатка лесная.

чистик orn: auk (Alea, Cepphus, Plautus impennis).

чистики (отр.) orn: auks (Alcae).

чистиковые (сем.) orn: auks (Alcidae).

чистить клювом перья orn: preen.

чиститься orn: plume.

чистка рук перед операцией surg: scrub-up.

чисто-колбочковая сетчатка pure-cone retina.

чистокровный agr zool: true-bred.

чистопородный agr: purebred.

чистосортный agr bot: true-bred.

чистота голоса clarity of voice.

чистотел bot: celandine, swallowwort, yellow dock (Chelidonium majus).

чистяк лютичный bot: Ficaria ranunculoides, Moench.

чихание sneezing.

чихательный газ mil: sternuator (gas).

чихать sneeze.

чих-ли bot: Chih-li (Chinese cabbage).

чихнуть p. a. of чихать.

чихотник обыкновенный bot: sneezeweed (Achillea ptarmica).

член anat: 1. limb; 2. penis.

членик segment, somite.

~ антенны entom: antennary segment, antennal s.

~ колосового стержня bot: rachis

~ ленточного глиста helm: proglottis, segment of a tapeworm.

членистогрудые раки (отр.) zool: Arthrostraca.

членистоногие (тип) zool: arthropods (Arthropoda).

членистоногий zool: arthropod, arthropodous.

членистоногое zool: arthropod.

членистость segmentation, jointing.

членистые = клинолистные.

членистый articulated, jointed.

членораздельное произношение articulation.

членорасположение (плода) obstet: attitude (of fetus).
чобрик = богородская трава.
чоглок = кобец.
чолка forelock (of a horse).
чомга orn: grebe (Colymbus).
чоп ichth: Aspro.
чортов кал bot: asafetida.
чортово дерево = аралия.
чревная артерия anat: celiac artery.
чревный нерв (большой, малый) anat: (greater, lesser) splanchnic nerve.
чревосечение surg: laparotomy, celiotomy, abdominal section.
чрезбрюшинный anat: transperitoneal.
чрезвычайная слабость adynamia.
чрезвычайно вирулентный supervirulent.
чрезкожный percutaneous.
чрезмерная возбудимость hyperexcitability.
~ доза pharm: overdose.
~ жажда excessive thirst, polydipsia, anadipsia.
~ кислотность peracidity.
~ подвижность supermotility, hypermotility.
~ чувствительность hypersensitiveness.
~ ~ осязания oxyaphia.
чрезмерно чувствительный hypersensitive.
чрезмерное возбуждение superexcitation.
~ вытяжение hyperextension.
~ напряжение overstrain.
~ облучение overirradiation.
~ образование костной ткани path: hyperosteogeny.
~ ороговение path: hyperkeratinization.
~ отведение superabduction.
~ отделение слюны excessive secretion of saliva, salivation.
~ ~ сока excessive secretion, hypersecretion.
~ раздражение overstimulation.
~ разрастание overgrowth.
~ растяжение hyperdistension, overextension.
~ сгибание superflexion.
чрезмерный объем ткани или органа hypertrophic size (volume).
~ рост отдельных частей тела endocr: acromegaly.
чтение шкалы av med: dial reading.
чубушник = жасмин.
чувственная амбивалентность psych: emotional ambivalence.
~ неустойчивость psych: emotional instability.
чувственная тупость psych: emotional hypesthesia, lack of affect.
чувственное восприятие sensory perception.
чувствительность sensitivity, sensitiveness, sensibility, response; tenderness, soreness.
чувствительный neur: sensitive, sensory.
~ к излучению radiosensitive.
~ ~ свету photosensitive.
~ нерв anat: sensory nerve.
чувство 1. sense, feeling, sensation; 2. emotion, sentiment.
~ боязни sensation of anxiety, see боязнь.
~ вкуса sense of taste.
~ времени time sense.
~ давления pressure sense, baresthesia.
~ ~ в голове head pressure.
~ ~ под ложечкой path: epigastric pressure.
~ обоняния sense of smell.
~ онемения behumbed sensation.
~ опоясывания path: cincture feeling.
~ осязания tactile sense, s. of touch.
~ ответственности sense of responsibility.
~ оттягивания книзу path: bearing-down feeling.
~ подкатывающегося шара neur: lump sensation.
~ покалывания neur: pin sensation.
~ ползание мурашек neur: formication, paresthesia.
~ полноты sense of fullness.
~ положения posture sense.
~ пространства sense of space.
~ равновесия vestibular sense, equilibrium sense.
~ сжатия в груди thoracic constriction sense.
~ стеснения oppression sense.
~ страха sensation of fear.
~ тепла thermic sense.
~ тяжести feeling of weight, sense of heaviness.
~ усталости sense of fatigue.
~ царапанья scraping sensation.
чувствовать sense, feel.
чувствующий тошноту qualmish, feeling nausea.
чудесная палочка bact: prodigious bacterium (Bacterium prodigiosum).
~ сеть (капилляров) anat: rete mirabile.

чуждый foreign, adventitious.
чужеродная пыльца bot: foreign pollen.
чужеродность heterology.
чужеродный heterologous.
чукучан ichth: common sucker (Catostomus commersonii).
чукучановая рыба white mullet, sucking m. (Moxostoma); silver carp, carp sucker (Carpioides); etc.
*чукучановые (сем.) ichth: Calostomidae
чума infect: plague, pest(is).
~ водяная = болотница 2.
~ рогатого скота vet: rinderpest, Russian cattle plague.
~ свиней vet: swine fever, s. pest.
чумиза bot: chumiza, Turkestan millet, see просо итальянское.
чумной plague-infected.
чумный = чумной.
чумоподобный plaguelike.
чуфа chufa, see миндаль земляной.
чушь нести psych: talk drivel.

Ш

шабдар bot: shaftal, see клевер перевернутый.
шагающие движения пиявки zool: looping movements of a leech.
~ птицы = голенастые.
шайнер ichth: shiner (Lagodon rhomboides; Notropis cornutus).
шалфей bot: sage (Salvia).
~ голый scarlet s. (S. splendens, Selle).
~ декоративный = ш. голый.
~ мускатный muscat s., clary (S. sclarea)
шалфейный тетерев orn: sage cock grouse (Centrocercus urophasianus).
шампиньон champignon, meadow mushroom (Agaricus campestris).
~ ложный = поганка бледная.
~ луговой field mushroom, horse m.
шанкр ven: chancre.
шапка Гиппократа surg: hippocratic [cap.
шапочка сморчковая bot: fungus Verpa bohemica, Schr.
шар дробления embr: cleavage cell, segmentation cell, blastomere.
шарик globule, small sphere.
шариковый дефлегматор bead column.
Шарко Charcot.
шарлахрот chem: scarlet red.
шаровидная головка цветка bot: glomerule.
шаровидный = шарообразный.
~ плод или ягода bot: seedball (of potato, etc.)
~ сустав anat: ball-and-socket joint, spheroid articulation.
шаровка zool: bivalve mollusk [Sphaerium.
шарообразные цветы globular flowers.
шарообразный spherical, globular, globose, ball-shaped; bot: aegagropilous (alga, etc.)
шаровница = вольвокс.
Шарпей Sharpey.
Шассеньяк Chassaingnac.
шатание staggering.
~ зубов looseness of the teeth.
шатающаяся походка staggering gait, tottering g., wobbly g., reeling g.
шафран bot: saffron (Crocus sativus).
шашень = корабельный червь, сверлило корабельный.
Швабах Schwabach.
шванновская оболочка anat: sheath of Schwann, neurilemma.
шванновские клетки neur: Schwann [cells.
шварцвассерфибер = острая гемоглобинурийная лихорадка.
шейка neck, collum, cervix.
~ бедра anat: femoral neck.
~ жёлчного пузыря anat: neck of the gallbladder.
~ зуба anat: collum dentis.
~ корня bot: root collar.
~ матки anat: cervix of the uterus.
~ пузыря anat: cervix vesicae, neck of the bladder.
~ ребра anat: rib neck, collum costae.
~ розетки bot: top neck.
шейковая гниль phytp: foot rot.
шейная артерия (восходящая, глубокая, поверхностная, поперечная) anat: (ascending, deep, superficial, transverse) cervical artery.
~ борозда = затылочная б.
~ железа anat: cervical gland.
~ перемычка entom: jugular channel-[furrow.
шейное ребро anat: cervical rib.
~ сплетение anat: cerviciplex, plexus cervicalis.
~ утолщение anat: cervical enlargement.
~ ядро cervical nucleus.
шейные мускулы anat: neck muscles.
~ позвонки anat: cervical vertebrae, v. cervicales.
шейный аденит path: cervical adeni-[tis.

шейный сосочек helm:cervical papilla.
шёлк silk.
~ -сырец floretta.
шелковистый silky, sericeous, flossy.
шелковица = тута.
~ бумажная = бруссонеция.
~ русская Russian mulberry = тута белая.
шелковичное дерево = тута.
шелковичные = тутовые.
шёлковое дерево bot: West Indian silk tree (Zanthoxylum, Xanthoxylum, Fagara flava).
шёлковый каучук bot: silk rubber (Funtumia elastica, Stapf.)
шелкоотделительные железы entom: silk-excreting glands.
шелкопряд entom: silkworm moth (Bombycidae, Attacidae, Lasiocampidae, etc).
~ айлантовый tree-of-heaven silkworm (Attacus cynthia).
~ американский tent caterpillar (Malacosoma americana, M. disstria).
~ дубовый китайский China oak silkworm (Antheraea parnyi).
~ ~ походный oak processionary moth (Thaumatopoea processionea).
~ ~ японский oak silkworm (Antheraea jama mai).
~ дуболистный oak-leaf silkworm (Gastropacha quercifolia).
~ ивовый satin moth (Leucoma salicis).
~ индийский Indian silkworm (Antheraea militta).
~ клещевинный castor-bean silkworm (Attacus arrindia).
~ кольчатый lackey moth (Malacosoma neustria).
~ малинный raspberry moth (Macrothylacia rubi).
~ -монах black arches moth, nun moth (Lymantria monacha).
~ непарный gypsy moth (Lymantria dispar, Ocneria dispar).
~ походный = ш. дубовый походный.
~ сосновый pine moth (Dendrolimus pini).
~ тутовый bombyx (Bombyx, Sericaria mori)
~ хмелевой tussock moth (Hydraecia immanis).
шелудивость vet: rot.
шёлудь vet: rot.
шелуха bot: peelings, hull, husk, cortex.
шелуха креветок shrimp bran.
шелушащийся desquamative, scurfy, cf. шелушение.
шелушение derm: desquamation, scaling off, flaking off, peeling; shelling, husking, hulling.
шелушить dehusk.
шемая ichth: Chalcalburnus.
шенобиус = сверлильщик рисовый стеблевой.
шепелявить lisp.
шереспер = жерех.
шероховатая линия anat: rough line, linea aspera.
~ ~ бедра femoral crest.
шероховатый rough, rugged, asperous, scabrous, scabby.
~ лист bot: scabrous leaf.
шерстистый woolly.
шёрстный woollen.
~ скот wool cattle.
шерстокрыл zool: Galeopithecus.
шерстокрылы (отр.) zool: Dermaptera.
шерсть 1. wool; fleece; 2. zool: hair, fur.
шерстяк раскидистый water grass, dallis g.(Paspalum dilatatum).
шерстяное дерево = капок.
шершавоволосистый bot: aristate, barbelate, hirsutus, hirtus.
шершавость chap, roughness.
шершавый chapped, rough(ened), hirtus; cf. шероховатый.
шершень European hornet, giant hornet (Vespa crabro).
~ туркестанский Turkestan giant hornet (Vespa orientalis).
шестикрючная личинка helm: hexacanth larva, oncosphere.
шестилепестный bot: hexapetalous.
шестилинейная ящерица zool: six-lined lizard, race runner (Cnemidophorus sexlineatus).
шестилучевые кораллы (подкл.) zool: zoantharian polyps (Zoantharia, Hexacorallia).
шестиногий zool: hexapod.
шестипалый sexdigitate.
шестипестичный bot: hexagynous.
шеститычинковый bot: hexandrous, hexastamenous.
шестицветный спектр hexachromic spectrum.
шефердия bot: buffalo berry (Shepherdia argentea, Nutt.)
шея anat: neck, collum.
шизоид psych: schizoid.
шизомания psych: schizomania.
шизофазия psych: schizophasia.
шизофит bot: fission plant.
шизофреник psych: schizophrenic.
шизофрения psych: schizophrenia, dementia praecox.
шиловидный awl-shaped, subulate, styloid.

шиловидный отросток anat: styloid process, processus styloideus.
шилоклюв(ка) orn: avocet, avoset (Recurvirostra avosetta).
шило-нижнечелюстная связка anat: stylomandibular ligament.
шилоноска = шилоклювка.
шилоподъязычная мышца anat: styloglossus muscle.
шилососцевидное отверстие anat: stylomastoid foramen. [(Anas acuta).
шилохвость orn: American pintail duck
шильбеоидес ichth: tadpole catfish (Schilbeoides gyrinus).
шильная трава = дрок.
шильник bot: awlwort (Subularia).
"шильце" bot: mucro (shoot), spire, pip.
Шимановский Szymanowski.
шимпанзе zool: chimpanzee (Antropopithecus troglodytes).
шина surg: splint; cradle.
~ для ноги leg spint.
~ ~ руки arm splint.
~ ~ стопы foot splint.
шинная повязка surg: splint bandage.
шиншилла zool: chinchilla (Eriomys).
~ большая big chinchilla (Eriomys chinchilla). [lanigera).
~ малая little chinchilla (Eriomys
шип 1. thorn, prickle, barb, acantha, awn; spine; 2. ichth: sturgeon Acipenser
шипо- acanth(o)-. nudiventris.
шиповатый bot: thorny, prickly, echinate.
~ скат ichth: Raja clavata.
шиповидная клетка hist: prickle cell.
шиповидные разрастания path: tinea.
шиповник bot: wild rose, hedge r., dog r., brier (Rosa canina).
~ эглантерия eglantine, sweetbriar (R. eglanteria).
шипоноска конопляная entom: Mordellis-
~ люцерновая M. punila. |tena micans.
~ подсолнечниковая M. parvula.
шипоноски (сем.) entom: Mordellidae.
* шипсхед ichth: sheepshead (Aplodinotus grunniens; Archosargus probatocephalus; Pimelometopon pulcher; Poronotus tria-
шипучее вино sparkling wine. |canthus).
шипучий порошок pharm: effervescent
шипящий звук hissing |powder. sound; sibilant; av med: "whoosing" noise
ширина аккомодации глаза ophth: range of accomodation.
ширма screen.
широкая мышца спины anat: latissimus dorsi muscle, l. thoracis m.
широкая связка anat: broad ligament.
~ ~ матки broad ligament of uterus.
~ фасция бедра anat: fascia lata.
широкие бёдра broad hips.
широкий лентец helm: broad tapeworm, fish t., Swiss t. (Diphyllobothrium
широко ветвящийся diffuse. |latum).
~ расходящийся divaricate. [flask.
широкогорлая колба wide-mouthed
широколиственный лес angiospermous forest. [latifolius.
широколистный bot: broad-leaved,
широколобка ichth: 1. Cottocomephorus; 2. see подкаменщик сибирский.
~ длиннокрылая C. comephoroides.
~ красная Procottus jeittelesi.
широконосые обезьяны (подотр.) zool: wide-nosed monkeys, platyrrhinian suborder (Platyrrhini).
широкослойный bot: broad-ringed (wood).
широта аккомодации = ширина а.
шистосом(ат)оз helm: schistosomiasis.
шистоцерка = саранча пустынная.
шишечник = каштан земляной.
шишка 1. boss, knob, lump; 2. bot: cone.
~ геморроидальная pile, hemorrhoid.
шишковатость bosselation, tuberosity.
шишковатый bosselated, tuberculate, tubercular.
шишковидная железа anat: pineal gland, glandula pinealis. [pineal.
шишковидный strobiloid, strobilous,
шишконосные (кл.) bot: coniferous plants (Coniferophyta).
шкала scale, dial. [cabinet.
шкаф для инструментов instrument
школа медсестёр med: nurse training school. [high) school nurse.
школьная медсестра (elementary or
школьносанитарная работа school health work.
школьный врач (elementary or high)
шкура hide, pelt. |school physician.
~ ластоногого sealskin.
шлем helmet. [crash helmet.
~ с мягкой обивкой av med: padded
шлеммов канал anat: canal of Schlemm.
шлемовидная часть bot: galea (of a perianth).
шлемовидный bot: galeate, helmet-shaped
шлемофон av med: headset.
шляпка (гриба) bot: pileus, cap.
шляпочный bot: pileate.
~ гриб bot: hymenomycete (Hymenomycetes
шмель entom: bumblebee (Bombus).

Шнейдер Schneider.
шнит-лук = лук-резанец.
~ -салат = срывной салат.
шнуровая печень = корсетная п.
шов seam, stitch, raphe; suture.
~ кости surg: osteosuture.
~ ослабляющий напряжение surg: tension suture, relaxing s.
шовные косточки (черепа) anat: Wormian bones, sutural bones.
шовный sutural.
шок shock.
шоковая терапия psych: shock therapy.
шоколад chocolate.
шоколадное дерево bot: cocoa tree
шопот whisper. (Theobroma cacao).
шопотная речь whispered voice.
шорстка bio embr: lanugo.
шотландская борзая deerhound (Canis familiaris sagax acceptorius).
~ куропатка orn: ruffed grouse
шотландский душ = переменный д.
шпадель tongue blade, t. depressor.
шпажник bot: field flag, corn f. (Gladiolus imbricatus).
шпанка = 1. королёк; 2. шпанка ясеневая; 3. черешня.
~ красноголовая = ш. ясеневая.
~ ясеневая entom: Spanish fly, blister beetle (Lytta vesicatoria, Cantharis vesicatoria).
шпанская мушка = шпанка ясеневая.
шпат vet: ironspat; cf. болотный костный шпат.
шпатель = шпадель.
шпергель = торица.
шпилант bot: Para cress (Spilanthes oleracea).
шпинат bot: spinach (Spinacia oleracea).
~ английский = щавель а.
~ индийский Malabar nightshade (Basella rubra cordifolia).
шпора spur, armature; calcar.
шпорец bot: calcar, spur (of a flower).
шпорная борозда (мозга) anat: calcar-
шпорник = живокость. |ine fissure.
шпоровидный bot: calcariform.
шпорцевая лягушка zool: Xenopus.
шпорцевый bot: spurred (flower).
шприц syringe; gun.
~ для подкожного впрыскивания hypodermic syringe.
шпрот ichth: sprat, brisling (Sprattus).
~ черноморский S. sprattus phalericus.
шрадан chem: shradan.

Шретер Schrötter. [in the Black Sea).
шримс zool: shrimp (Crandon vulgaris,
штамм mcbio: strain, stock.
штатив lab: stand, rack support.
~ для бюреток burette support.
~ ~ воронок filtering stand.
~ ~ пипеток pipette support, p. rack.
~ ~ пробирок test-tube rack.
~ ~ реторт retort stand.
~ ~ флакончиков bottle stand.
штифтовая колодка odont: pivot crown.
штокроза = алтей розовый.
штопфер odont: plugger.
штриховатость phytp: stripe (of barley), streak (of potatoes, etc.)
штриховая пластинчатая разводка bact: streak plate. [streaking.
~ разводка bact: streak culture,
штыковая рана surg: bayonet wound.
шум murmur, sound, souffle.
~ водяной дудки water-whistle sound.
~ волчка humming-top murmur.
~ в ушах tinnitus aurium.
~ знамени flag sound.
~ над аортой aortic murmur.
~ ~ митральным клапаном mitral murmur.
~ плеска splashing sound, succussion s.
~ при недостаточности regurgitant murmur. [funic m.
~ пуповины obstet: umbilical sound,
~ раздувальных мехов bellows sound.
~ точки пилы path: stridor serraticus.
~ трения friction murmur, rubbing sound. [to-and-fro m.
~ ~ перикарда pericardial murmur,
~ треснувшего горшка cracked pot sound.
шумящий карбункул vet: black quarter.
шэд ichth: shad (Alosa sapidissima).
шютте phytp: pine-leaf cast, pine-twig blight, needle-shedding disease.
шюттль-аппарат bact: shaking machine.
шюфнеровская зернистость hem: Schüffner's dots.

Щ

щавелевая кислота oxalic acid.
щавель bot: sorrel, dock (Rumex, L.)
~ английский English s., patience d. (R. patientia).
~ кислый garden s., sour d. (R.acetosa).
~ клубненосный canaigre (R. hymenose-palus).
~ культурный = щ. курчавый, щ. английский. [(R. crispus).
~ курчавый yellow d., curly d.
~ мексиканский = щ. клубненосный.
~ обыкновенный = щ. кислый.
~ прерийный wild quinine, American feverfew (Parthenium integrifolium).
~ садовый крупнолистный large s., French s. (R. sculatus).
~ столовый garden s.
~ шпинатный spinach d., see щавель английский.
щадить spare.
щадящая терапия sparing therapy.
щеглёнок orn: young goldfinch.
щегол orn: goldfinch (Carduelis, Spinus).
щека anat: cheek, bucca, gena.
щеки ent: genae.
щекотка tickling.
щелевая лампа ophth: slit lamp.
щелевидная трубка anat: slitlike tube.
щелевой fissural, rimose.
~ перелом surg: fissured fracture.
щелкающий звук clicking sound, clicks.
щелкун ent: click beetle, snap.
щелкуны (сем.) ent: click beetles, elaters (Elateridae).
щелочный alkaline.
~ раствор lye.
~ резерв alkali reserve.
щелочность alkalinity.
~ мочи alkalinity of urine, alkalinuria.
щелочь alkali.
щелчок click.
щель slit, slot, chink, cleft, rima;
~ в органе fissure. [fissure, crack.
~ для роговицы в склере anat: corneal cleft.
~ между десной и поверхностью зуба anat: gingival crevice.
щемящая боль gripping pain, constricting p., pinching.
щениться zool: litter, pup, whelp, cub.
щенок zool: puppy.
щенята pl: of щенок.
щетина bristle, seta, chaeta.
щетинистый bristly, setose.
щетинка bristle, seta, chaeta, cirrus.
~ усика ent: arista.
щетинковая пиявка zool: leech Acanthobdella peledina. [cirrous.
щетинковидный setiform, setose,
~ усик ent: setaceous antenna, bristle-like a.
щетинконогие черви zool: bristle(-bearing) worms, chaetopods (Chaetopoda).
щетинконосные пиявки (отр.) zool: Acanthobdellae.
щетинконосный aristate, setiparous, barbellate.
~ усик ent: arista-bearing antenna.
щетинник bot: bristly foxtail (Setaria, Beauv.) [ское.
~ итальянский = просо итальян-
~ сибирский Kursk millet (S. rubrofructa, Hubb.)
~ сизый foxtail, pigeon grass (S. glauca, Beauv.)
щетинозубая рыба kikakapu (Chaetodon); angel fish (Holacanthus).
щетинохвостки (отр.) entom: bristle-tails (Thysanura).
щётка 1. brush; 2. zool: fetlock (of a
~ для пробирок test-tube b. | horse).
~ ~ рук hand brush.
щёчная железа anat: genal gland.
~ мышца anat: buccinator.
щёчный anat: genal, buccal.
щиколотка = лодыжка.
щиповка ichth: mudfish (Cobitis).
*щипцы forceps.
~ для камней urol: lithotomy forceps.
~ ~ корней odont: root-forceps.
~ ~ осевой тракции obstet: axis-traction forceps, Tarnier's forceps.
~ ~ раздавливания шпоры surg: spur crusher.
~ ~ стерилизатора sterilizer forceps.
~ ~ удаления осколков surg: splinter forceps.
~ мозолистого тела anat: forceps of the corpus callosum.
щипчики surg: tweezers.
щирица = амарант. [систый.
~ запрокинутая = амарант коло-

щирицевые (сем.) bot: amaranth family (Amaranthaceae). [crustacean).
щит shield, shell, carapace (of a
щитень исполинский zool: extinct crustacean Gigantostraca.
~ ракообразный crustacean Triops (Apus) canciformis.
~ хвостатый Lepidurus productus.
✱щитковые zool: Ostacodermi (extinct).
щитковый bot: cymose.
щитник 1. bot: aspidium (Aspidium felix mas, Swartz); 2. entom: stinkbug
~ большой = щитовник. |(Pentatomida).
щитники (сем.) entom: stink-bugs
щитовидки (сем.) ent: Ostomatidae.
щитовидная железа anat: thyroid gland.
щитовидный лист bot: peltate leaf.
~ хрящ anat: thyroid cartilage, cartilago Thyroidea.
щитовка entom: (armored) scale, mealybug, shield louse (Coccidae); see кокцида, тля щитковая, червец.
~ -алейрод citrus white fly (Aleurodes citri).
~ апельсиновая запятовидная purple scale (Lepidosaphes becki).
~ европейская European fruit lecanium (Lecanium corni).
~ запятовидная oyster-shell bark louse (Lepidosaphes ulmi).
~ калифорнийская San Jose scale (Diaspidiotus perniciosus).
~ лимонная red scale (Chrysomphalus aurantii, C. aonidum).
~ туманная small green tortoise-beetle (Cassida nebulosa). [pis pentagona).
~ тутовая mulberry scale (Pseudaulacas-
~ устрицевидная oyster-shell scale (Diaspidiotus ostreaeformis).
~ фиолетовая violet scale (Parlatoria oleae).
~ яблонная = щ. запятовидная.
~ японская палочковидная Leucaspis japonica. [(Diaspididae).
щитовки (сем.) ent: scale-insects
щитовник bot: shield fern, wood f. (Dryopteris); see also папоротник.
~ болотный marsh f., meadow f., snuffbox f. (D. Thelypteris, Gray).
щитогрудые раки (отр.) zool: Thoracostraca.
щиток escutcheon; entom: scutellum; bot: corymb, cyme, fascicle see also твёрдый щиток.
~ переднеспинки pronotal disk.

щитолистник bot: water pennywort, navelwort (Hydrocotyle).
щитомордник zool: poisonous snake Ancistrodon halys.
щитоноска зелёная entom: Cassida
~ маревая C. nobilis. viridis.
~ свекловичная C. nebulosa.
щитоноски (подсем.) entom: tortoise beetles (Cassidini).
щито-черпаловидная мышца anat: thyroarytenoid muscle.
~ шейный ствол anat: thyrocervical
щокур = чир. trunk.
щук = щурка.
щука ichth: pike, jackfish (Esox lucius); chain pickerel (E. niger); etc. see also мелкая щука, панцырная щука.
щуковые ichth: pikes (Esocidae).
щукообразные (отр.) ichth: Esociformes.
щупальце zool: tentacle, feeler, palpus; arm (of cephalopods).
~ рыбы illicium.
щупальцевая битиния zool: tentacled bithynia (Bithynia tentaculata).
щупальцевидный хоботок helm: rostellum. [(Tentaculata).
щупальцевые zool: tentacled animals,
щупальцежвало zool: chelicera.
щупальщики zool: grasping type.
щупик palp, palpus.
щуплое зерно bot: imperfect grain,
щурёнок = мелкая щука. | starveling.
щурка orn: coraciform Merops. Cf. ракши.
~ золотистая bee bird, bee-eater (Merops apiaster).
щурок = щурка.
щучка 1. ichth: small pike; bot: see аира дернистая.

Э

эбеновое дерево = чёрное дерево.
эбеновые (сем.) bot: ebony family (Ebenaceae).
эвакуационный госпиталь mil: evacuation hospital.
~ пункт mil: evacuation point.
эвакуация evacuation.
~ больных и раненых mil: evacuation of sick and wounded.
~ по воздуху mil: air evacuation.
~ раненых по воздуху av med: air evacuation of the wounded.
эвгенол pharm: eugenol.
эвглена bio: Euglena (green flagellated organisms).
эвгленовые (отр.) zool: Euglenoidea, Euglenoidina.
эверния bot: Evernia furfuracea, Mann. (lichen).
эвисцерированный eviscerated.
эвкалипт bot: eucalyptus (Eucalyptus).
~ бугорчатый blue gum-tree (E. globulus, Labill).
~ двуцветный black box (E. bicolor).
~ дивес broad-leaved peppermint (E. dives).
~ клювовидный red gum (E. rostrata, Schlecht.)
~ крупноклювый stringybark (E. macrorhyncha).
~ лавролистный Murray redgum (E. laurifolia).
~ пунктированный leather jacket (E. punctata).
~ разноцветный karri (E. diversicolor).
~ резиноносный kino eucalypt, red mahogany (E. resinifera, Smith.)
~ царственный peppermint gum (E. amygdalina regnans).
эвкомия bot: eucommia (Eucommia).
эвмезофитный bot: eumesophyte type.
эволюционный evolutionary.
эволюция evolution.
эвриале устрашающая bot: Euryale ferox, Salish. (of Nymphaeaceae).
эвригалинный euryhaline.
эвритермный eurythermal.
эвритома = толстоножка.
эвритомуха = толстоножка.
эвтермический euthermic.
эвтрофикация eutrophication.
эвтрофия eutrophy.
эвтрофный eutrophic.
эвфагус orn: grackle (Euphagus).
эвфорбий euphorbium.
эвфотическая зона euphotic zone.
эгагропильный bot: aegagropilous (alga, etc.)
эгле мармеладное bot: bael (Crateva marmelos).
эго bot: ego alga (Campylaefora hypno-ides).
эгофония egophony, goat voice.
эдатамилдинатрий tox: edathamil disodium.
~ -монокальций tox: edathamil calcium-disodium, versenate.
эдафический edaphic.
эдафическое растение edaphophyte.
эдеагус zool: aedeagus.
эдельвейс = сушеница альпийская.
Эдельман Adelman.
эдогоний bot: Oedogonium (brown algae).
эзериновая мазь pharm: eserine (sulphate) ointment.
эзотропия ophth: esotropia.
эзофагоскопия esophagoscopy.
эзофория ophth: esophoria.
эйгаллол = моноуксусный пирогаллол.
эйгенол pharm: eugenol.
эйнатрол pharm: sodium oleate.
эйрезол = резорцинмоноацетат.
эйробин = триацетилхризаробин.
эйфорическое настроение psych: euphoric mood.
эйфория psych: euphoria.
эйхинин pharm: euquinine.
эйхорния = водяной гиацинт.
экваториальная борозда embr: equatorial furrow.
~ стафилома ophth: equatorial staphyloma.
эквационное деление genet: equation dividing.
ЭКГ = электрокардиограмма.
экдемичный ecdemic.
экзагерация genet: exageration.
экзальтация psych: exaltation.
экзантема derm: exanthem(a)
экзема derm: eczema, teller, salt rheum.
~ пекарей baker's itch.
~ прачек washerwomen's itch.
экзематозный eczematous.
экзит zool: exite (of crustacea).
экзоаск берёзовый bot: Exoascus betulinus, Sab. (fungus).
экзоасковые грибы bot: Exoascales.
экзобазидиевые грибы (пор.) bot: Exobasidiales (fungi).

экзобазидиум phytp: Exobasidium vaccinin, Wor. (fungus).
экзогаструляция bio: exogastrulation.
экзогенный exogenous, exogenic.
экзокарп exocarp.
экзокарпий bot: exocarp.
экзоплазма genet: exoplasm.
экзоподит zool: exopodite.
экзостоз surg: exostosis.
экзостозный path: exostosed, exostotic.
экзот bot: exotic.
экзотический bot: exotic.
экзотропия ophth: exotropia.
экзофория ophth: exophoria.
экзофталм path: exophthalmos, exophthalmus.
экзувий zool: exuvia (molt).
экиофиты bot: eciophytes.
эклампсия path: eclampsia.
эколог ecologist.
экологическая валентность ecological valence.
экология ecology.
~ животных animal ecology, zooecology.
экономка matron (in a hospital).
экотип ecotype.
экотоп bot: ecotope.
эксгибиционизм psych: exhibitionism.
эксгибиционист exhibitionist.
эксикатор desiccator.
экскавация excavation; cup(ping). Cf. физиологическая экскавация.
экскориация derm: excoriation, skinning; see also шелушение.
экскременты excrement(s).
экскретирующие пигмент клетки chromatoblast.
экскреторное отверстие zool: excretory pore.
экскреты excreta.
экскреция excretion.
экспансивность psych: expansiveness.
экспансивный psych: expansive.
экспекторация expectoration.
эксперимент experiment.
экспериментальная психология experimental psychology.
экспериментальные данные experimental evidence, e. findings.
экспериментирование experimentation.
экспирация expiration.
эксплозивное действие explosive (manic) action, psychokinesia, psychokinesis.
экстерорецепция bio: exteroreception.
экстероцептор psych: exteroceptor.
экстерьер conformation (of a horse, etc.)

экстирпация extirpation.
экстирпировать surg: extirpate.
экстορзия extorsion.
экстравазат extravasation (substance).
экстраверзия psych: extroversion.
экстрагировать extract.
экстракт extract.
экстрактивное вещество extractive.
экстракция extraction.
экстраперитонеальный anat: extraperitoneal.
экстрариус ichth: speckled dace (Extrarius aestivalis).
экстрасистола path: extrasystole.
экстрацеллюлярный extracellular.
экстренный вызов emergency call.
эксудат exudate.
эксудативный exudative.
~ плеврит = выпотной п.
эксудация exudation.
эксфолиативный exfoliative.
эксцесс excess.
эксцизия surg: excision.
эктодерма embr: ectoderm.
эктодермальный ectodermal, ectodermic.
~ бластомер embr: ecto(blasto)mere.
эктодермический = эктодермальный
эктокарповые (пор.) bot: Ectocarpales (algae).
эктокарпус bot: Ectocarpus (algae).
эктопаразит ectoparasite, epizoon.
эктопаразитический ectoparasitic.
эктопический ectopic.
эктопия ectopy.
эктоплазма hist: ectoplasm.
эктоплазменный ectoplasmic.
*эктоцеллюлярный extocellular.
эктропион ophth: ectropion, eversion of eyelid.
эластическая связка zool: elastic ligament.
эластический коллодий pharm: flexible collodion.
эластическое волокно hist: elastic fiber.
элеваторий surg: elevator.
элексир pharm: elixir.
электрическая ванна electrical bath.
~ грелка electric pad.
электрический раздражитель electrical stimulus.
~ скат ichth: electric ray, crampfish (Torpedo).
электрическое сокращение electrocontractility (of a muscle).
электроартериограф plethysmograph.
электрокардиограмма electrocardiogram.
электрокардиограф electrocardiograph.

электрокардиографический electrocardiographic. [graphy.
электрокардиография electrocardio-
электрокаутеризация electrocautery.
электрокоагуляция electrocoagulation.
электрология electrology.
электромиограф electromyograph.
электромиография electromyography.
электронаркоз electronarcosis.
электрорассекатель electrodissector.
электрорассечение electrodissection.
электроретинограмма electroretinogram.
электроретинографический electroretinographic.
электросудорожная терапия psych: electrospasm therapy.
электротерапия electrotherapeutics.
электротомия = электрорассечение.
электротонический electrotonic.
электротонус electrotonus.
электроуретограмма electrouretogram.
электрофорез на бумаге paper electrophoretic study.
электрохирургия electrosurgery.
электрохромограмма electrochromogram.
электрошок electroshock.
электрошоковая терапия electroshock therapy.
электроэнцефалограмма electroencephalogram, EEG. [graph.
электроэнцефалограф electroencephalo-
электроэнцефалографический electroencephalographic.
элёпс ichth: bony fish, piojo (Elops
элеттария = кардамон. saurus).
элефантиаз path: elephantiasis.
элита genet: elite, mother seeds.
элитра = надкрылье.
элитрообразный elytroid.
эллипсовидный сустав anat: condyloid articulation.
эллиптический elliptical.
~ лист bot: elliptical leaf.
элодея bot: waterweed, waterthyme, ditchmoss (Elodea, Michx.)
элягатис ichth: shoemaker, runner (Elagatis bipinnulatus).
эмалевая кожица hist: enamel cuticle.
~ призма hist: enamel rod.
эмалевый орган embr: enamel organ.
эмаль enamel.
эмбии (отр.) entom: embiids (Embiodea, Embiidina).
эмбиотоцида ichth: sparada (Embiotocidae).
эмблика = миробалан.
эмбола path: embolus.
эмболия path: embolism. [artery e.
~ венечной артерии coronary
~ концевой артерии end artery e.
~ лёгочной артерии pulmonary a.e.
эмболомери zool: Embolomeri (extinct
эмбриогенез embryogeny. | amphibians).
эмбриологический embryologic(al).
эмбриология embryology.
эмбрион embryo.
эмбриональный embryonic, embryonal.
~ остаток embryonal rest.
эмбриофиты land plants (Embriophyta).
эмбриэктомия surg: embryectomy.
эммер bot: bearded wheat, larger spelt (Triticum dicoccum).
эмметроп ophth: emmetrope.
эмметропический глаз emmetropic eye.
эмметропичный emmetropic.
эмметропия ophth: emmetropia.
эмоциональная вспышка psych: emotional outburst.
~ неустойчивость emotional instability.
~ реакция emotional response.
эмоциональное напряжение psych: emotional stress.
~ состояние emotional state.
эмоция emotion.
эмпиема path: empyema.
эмпиемный empyemic, empyematous.
эмпирик empiric (person).
эмпирический empiric(al).
эмподий entom: empodium.
эмпуза bot: Empusa (fungus).
Эмсден Amsden.
эму orn: emu (Dromaius).
эмульгатор emulsifier (substance).
эмульгация emulsification.
эмфизема path: emphysema.
~ лёгких path: pulmonary emphysema.
эмфизем(атоз)ный path: emphysematous.
~ карбункул vet: black quarter.
энантема path: enanthem(a).
энантемный enanthematous.
эндартерит path: endarteritis.
эндемическая болезнь endemic disease, local disease.
эндемический характер endemicity.
эндемия endemism.
эндивий bot: endive (Cichorium endivia)
~ курчавый curly e. (C. e. crispa).
эндит zool: endit (of crustacea).
эндогенное развитие endogeny.
~ отравление endointoxication.

эндогенный bio: endogenous.
эндодерм endoderm, entoderm.
эндодермический endodermal.
эндокард anat: endocardium.
эндокардиальный шум int: endocardial murmur.
эндокардит int: endocarditis.
эндокарп bot: endocarp.
эндокринная железа endocrine gland.
эндокринное расстройство endocrine disturbance.
эндокринология endocrinology, incretology.
эндокринопатия path: endocrinopathy.
эндолимфа endolymph.
эндометрий anat: endometrium.
эндометрит endometritis.
эндомиксис bio: endomixis.
эндопаразит zool: endoparasite.
эндопаразитический endoparasitic.
эндоплазма hist: endoplasm.
эндоподит zool: endopodite.
эндоскоп endoscope.
эндосперм bio: endosperm.
эндоспора bio: endospore.
эндост hist: endosteum.
эндостиль endostyle.
эндотелиальный endothelial.
эндотелий hist: endothelium.
эндотелиома oncol: endothelioma.
эндотоксин endotoxin.
эндофит endophyte.
эндофитизм endophytism.
эндофитический bio: endophytic.
эндофитный bio: endophytic.
эндохондральный endochondral.
энергетика energetics.
энергетическая единица дозы rad: energy unit.
~ ценность (пищи) energy value (of a diet).
энергетический обмен bio: energy metabolism.
энергия прорастания bot: viability (of seeds).
энзим enzyme.
энзиматический enzymatic, enzymic.
энзимология enzymology.
энотера bot: European evening primrose (Oenothera biennis); see also ослинник.
~ яйцевидная golden eggs (O. ovata, Nutt.)
эноцит entom: enocyte.
энтеробиоз path: enterobiasis.
энтеролит = кишечный камень.
энтероморфа bot: sea grass, limu eleele (Enteromorpha algae).
энтероптоз enteroptosis.
энтодерма hist: entoderm, gastrodermis.
~ желточного мешка embr: yolk-sac entoderm.
энтодермический entodermal.
энтодиноморфные (подотр.) zool: Entodinomorpha.
энтомолог entomologist.
энтомологический entomological.
энтомология entomology.
энтомофаг bio: entomophage.
энтоплазма bio: entoplasm.
энтропион ophth: entropion, inversion of eyelid.
энуклеация enucleation.
энцефалит path: encephalitis.
энцефалитический encephalitic.
энцефалограмма encephalogram.
энцефалограф encephalograph.
энцефалография encephalography.
энцефаломиэлит encephalomyelitis.
энцирты (сем.) entom: Encyrtidae.
эоанура zool: Eoanura (extinct amphibians).
эогиппус zool: Eohippus (extinct).
эозин lab: eosin.
эозинопеническая реакция eosinopenic response.
эозинофил eosinophil.
эозинофильный eosinophilic, eosinophilous.
эозухии (отр.) zool: Eosuchia (extinct reptiles).
эпендима anat: ependyma.
эпендимальный ependymal.
эпигенез bot: epigenesis.
эпидемиолог epidemiologist.
эпидемиологический epidemiologic.
эпидемиология epidemiology.
эпидемический epidemical.
эпидемичность epidemicity.
эпидемия epidemic.
эпидерма epidermis.
эпидермальный epidermal.
эпидермис epidermis.
эпидидимит path: epididymitis.
эпидуральное пространство anat: epidural space.
эпизоотический epizootic.
эпизоотия epizootic, epizooty.
эпизоотолог epizootologist.
*эпизоотологический epizootiological
эпизоотология epizootology.
эпикард anat: epicardium.
эпикриз path: epicrisis.
эпилепсия path: epilepsy, epilepsia.
эпилептик epileptic (person).
эпилептиформный epileptoid.

эпилептическая болезнь = эпилепсия. [seizure.
эпилептический припадок epileptic
эпилептическое слабоумие psych: epileptic dementia.
эпилептогенный epileptogenic.
эпилимнион epilimnion. [dose.
эпиляционная доза rad: epilating
эпиляционный пинцет epilating forceps.
эпиляция epilation.
эпимер zool: epimeron.
эпимерит zool: epimerite; entom: epimerum.
эпинастия bot: epinasty.
эпинефелюс ichth: red grouper, banded g., red-bellied snapper (Epinephelus morio).
эпинефрин epinephrine.
~ солянокислый pharm: epinephrine hydrochloride.
эпиниктичный bot: epinictic.
эпиплевра entom: epipleuron.
эписклерит ophth: episcleritis.
эписпадиальный path: epispadial, epispadiac.
эписпадия path: epispadias.
эписперм episperm.
эпистаз genet: epistasis.
эпистернит entom: episternum.
эпистом (мшанки) zool: epistome.
эпистофей anat: epistopheus, axis.
эпителиальная жемчужина path: epithelial pearl.
эпителиально-железистый hist: epithelioglandular.
эпителий epithelium.
эпителиома path: epithelioma.
эпифаринкс entom: epipharynx.
эпифиз anat: epiphysis.
эпифиз(ар)ный anat: epiphyseal.
эпифит bot: air plant, epiphyte.
эпифитизм epiphytism.
эпифитный epiphytic.
эпифитотическая болезнь bot: epiphytotic disease.
эпихлоа phytp: fungi Epichloe.
эргазиапофиты bot: ergaziapophytes.
эргазил щучий zool: crustacean Ergasilus sieboldii.
эрготизм path: ergotism.
эрготин ergotin.
эрготионеин ergothioneine.
эректор anat: erector (muscle).
эрекция physl: erection.
эризифе злаковая phytp: fungus Erysyphe graminis, D.C.
эрика bot: heath (Erica).
эримизон ichth: chub sucker (Erymison sucetta).
эриокаулён bot: pipewort, button rods (Eriocaulon).
эриокаулёновые (сем.) bot: pipewort family (Eriocaulaceae).
эритема derm: erythema.
эритемальность erythemal factor.
эритемальный erythemal, erythematous.
эритематозная волчанка derm: lupus erythematosus.
эритеметр rad: erythemeter.
эритрина bot: aloalo (Erythrina indica); coral tree (E. crista-galli, E. corallo-dendron).
эритробласт hist: erythroblast.
эритробластома oncol: erythroblastoma.
эритродермия derm: erythroderm(i)a.
эритромицин pharm: erythromycin.
эритропоэз erythropoiesis.
эритроцит hem: erythrocyte.
эритроцитный erythrocytic.
эрленмейеровская колба lab: Erlenmeyer flask.
Эрлих Ehrlich.
эрогаля ichth: southern spot-tail shiner (Erogala cercostigma).
эрозия erosion.
эротомания psych: erotomania.
эрука = рокет-салат.
эруковидная личинка entom: eruciform larva.
эскариоль = салат эскариоль.
эскимосская собака = упряжная собака. [bandage.
эсмарховский бинт surg: Esmarch's
~ жгут surg: Esmarch's elastic constrictor.
эспарто = альфа трава.
эспарцет bot: sainfoin, esparcet (Onobrychis).
~ испанский French honeysuckle (Hedysarum coronarium).
~ колючий O. echidna.
эссенциальный essential.
эстезиология esthesiology.
эстезиометр esthesiometer.
эстивация entom: aestivation.
эстрагон bot: estragon, tarragon (Artemisia dracunculus).
эстроген bio: estrogen.
эсшольция bot: California poppy (Eschscholtzia californica, Cham.)
этеостома ichth: rainbow darter (Etheostoma caeruleum).
этеостомовая рыба darter (Etheostomidae).

этикетирование labelling.
этикетка label.
~ "яд" pharm: poison label.
этил chem: ethyl.
этилен chem: ethylene.
этилендиамин pharm: ethylenediamine.
этилендиаминотетраацетат chem: ethylene diaminetetraacetate.
этилениминпикрат ethylenimine picrate.
этилкарбамат ethyl carbamate (urethane).
этиловый спирт chem: ethyl alcohol.
~ эфир chem: ethyl ether.
~ ~ парамидобензойной кислоты pharm: ethyl aminobenzoate, benzocaine.
этилтиоаденозин ethylthioadenosine.
этиолирование etiolation; see also беление.
этиолированный etiolated.
этиолировать etiolate.
этиология etiology.
*этрумеус ichth: round herring (Etrumeus sadina).
эугрегарины (подотр.) zool: Eugregarinaria.
эукалипт = эвкалипт.
эупланктер euplankter.
эупомотис ichth: ruff (Eupomotis bosus).
эупротогония zool: Euprotogonia (extinct).
эутрипс цитрусовый citrus thrips (Euthrips citri).
эуфаусиида zool: euphausiid (Euphasiidae).
эфедра bot: ephedra (Ephedra vulgaris).
эфедрин pharm: ephedrine.
эфедровые (сем.) bot: ephedra family (Ephedraceae).
эфемер bot: ephemera.
эфемер(ида) entom: ephemerid, ephemeron, see подёнка.
эфемерный ephemeral.
эфиппиум ephippium.
эфир chem: 1. ether, see простой эфир; 2. ester, see сложный эфир.
эфирная кислота chem: ether acid.
эфирное горчичное масло mustard oil.
~ масло pharm: ethereal oil.
~ ~ дягиля pharm: angelica oil.
эфирный наркоз ether narcosis, etherization.
~ экстракт мужского папоротника pharm: oleoresin of aspidium.
эфирокислота chem: ether acid.
эффект Бора av med: Bohr effect.
эффективный effective, efficient.
эффективный период полувыведения rad: effective half-life.
эффектор neur: effector.
эффекторный рефлекс effector reflex.
эфферентный efferent.
эхинодорус bot: burhead (Echinodorus).
эхинококк helm: hydatid tapeworm (Echinococcus); see also собачий цепень.
эхинококковая киста path: echinococcus cyst, hydatid.
эхинококковый пузырь = эхинококковая киста.
эхинококкоз helm: echinococcosis.
эхиноплутеус zool: echinopluteus.
эхирида = эхиуровые.
эхиуриды (кл.) zool: echiurids (Echiurida).
эхиуровые zool: Echiuroidea (class of Annelides).
эхолалический psych: echolalic.
эхолалия psych: echolalia, echophrasia.
эхопраксия psych: echopraxia, echomatism.
эцидий bot: aecidium.
эякуляция physl: ejaculation.

Ю

ювенальный наряд zool: juvenile plumage.
ювенильный гормон entom: juvenile hormon.
~ паралич juvenile paralysis.
югальная жилка entom: jugal vein.
~ складка entom: jugal fold, plica jugalis.
югальный bio: jugal.
югулярный anat: jugular.
южная лихорадка vet: southern fever.
южноамериканские копытные zool: Notungulata (extinct).
*южноафриканская антилопа springer, springbook (Antidorcas euchore).
южный кит southern right whale (Balaena australis).
~ морской лев zool: Southern sea lion (Otaria byronia).
~ ~ слон zool: Southern sea elephant (Mirounga leonina).
юкка большая yucca palm (Yucca arborescens).
~ волокнистая Adam's needle (Y. filamentosa).
~ мечевидная Spanish bayonet (Yucca).
~ нитчатая = ю. волокнистая.
~ уиплея yucca-like plant (Hesperoyucca whipplei).

юла = жаворонок лесной.
юлка = жаворонок лесной.
юморка = люцерна серповидная.
юнгерманиевые (пор.) bot: leafy
liverworts (Jungermanniales).
юнко orn: junco.
Юно Junod.
юра Jurassic period.
юссиэя bot: primrose willow, water
primrose (Jussiaea).
ююба = финик китайский.

Я

яблоко 1. ophth: globe; 2. bot: apple.
~ розовое bot: jambo, jambos(a)
(Eugenia jambos).
~ сахарное = аннона чешуйчатая.
яблоневые (подсем.) bot: apple
subfamily (Pomoideae).
~ растения malaceous plants.
яблонь = чёрный рак. [lus communis).
яблоня bot: apple tree (Pyrus malus, Ma-
~ дикая wild a.t., wilding, crab apple.
~ домашняя Malus domestica, Borkh.
~ лесная = яблоня дикая.
~ райская = дусен.
~ сибирская Siberian crab, dwarf a. (P.
~ ягодная = я. сибирская. |baccata).
яблочная кислота chem: malic acid.
яблочнокислое железо pharm: iron
яблочный pomaceous. malate.
яборанди bot: jaborandi (Pilocarpus, Lam.)
явление phenomenon, manifestation,
effect, event.
явнобрачное растение phanerogam.
явнокристаллический phanerocrystal-
явный explicit, manifest. line.
явор восточный = платан восточный.
явственно выраженный well-marked.
ягель = олений лишайник.
ягнёнок zool: lamb.
ягниться lamb, ean, see котиться.
ягнятник бородатый = бородач 2.
ягода bot: berry, small fruit.
ягодица anat: buttock.
ягодичная артерия anat: gluteal artery.
~ линия anat: gluteal line.
~ мышца (большая, средняя, малая)
anat: gluteus (maximus, medius, minimus).
~ складка anat: gluteal fold.

ягодичное предлежание obstet:
breech presentation.
ягодичный нерв anat: gluteal nerve.
ягóдки = волчеягодник.
ягодковое растение thymelaeaceous
plant.
ягóдковые (сем.) bot: mezereum
family (Thymelaeaceae). [(shrub).
ягодник bot: vacciniaceous plant
ягодообразный berry-shaped, bacciform.
ягоды кустовые bot: bush-fruits.
*ягуар zool: jaguar
(Felis hernandesii).
яд poison; venom.
~ для грызунов rodenticide.
~ животного происхождения venom.
ядерная краска hist: nuclear stain.
~ оболочка hist: nuclear membrane.
~ пересадка hist: nuclear
transplantation.
~ полость hist: nuclear cavity.
~ сетка hist: linin network.
~ химия nuclear chemistry.
*ядерное веретено hist: kakyokinetic
spindle, nuclear s.
ядерный листок hist: nuclear plate,
~ сдвиг nuclear shift. | equatorial p.
~ сок hist: nuclear sap.
~ эндосперм bot: nuclear endosperm.
ядовитая железа zool: venom gland.
~ змея poison snake.
ядовитое вещество toxicant.
~ действие poisonous action,
venom poisoning.
~ соединение chem: poisonous
ядовитость toxicity. compound.
~ пчелиного укуса apisination.
~ укуса паука arachnidism.
ядовитый poisonous; venomous.
~ для крови haemotoxic.
~ зуб zool: fang.
~ сок helenon.
ядозуб zool: Gila monster (Heloderma
suspectum).
ядозубы zool: Helodermatidae.
ядоносный toxiferous, veneniferous,
venom-carrying.
ядообразующий toxicogenic.
ядро nucleus, kernel.
~ дробления genet: cleavage nucleus.
~ окостенения hist: bony nucleus,
ossific n.
~ оливы anat: olivary nucleus.
~ тройничного нерва anat:
trigeminal nucleus.

ядровая древесина bot: heartwood.
ядрышко nucleole, nucleolus, plasmosome.
язва path: ulcer.
~ двенадцатиперстной кишки duodenal ulcer.
~ желудка gastric ulcer.
~ кожи cutaneous ulcer.
~ от пролежня decubitus ulcer.
язвенник обыкновенный bot: woundwort, kidney vetch (Anthyllis vulneraria).
~ рогатый = я. обыкновенный.
язвенное поражение ulcerative lesion.
язвенный ulcerous, ulcerative.
~ блефарий ophth: blear eye.
язвочка ulcuscule.
~ на слизистой рта aphtha.
язык 1. anat: tongue; see морской язык.
языкоглоточный нерв anat: glossopharyngeal nerve, ninth cranial n.
языкодержатель surg: tongue forceps.
языкообразный linguiform.
языкоцветные (подсем.) bot: Liguliflorae subfamily.
язычки entom: glossae, paraglossae.
язычковые 1. zool: Linguatulida, Pentastomida (class of subphylum Chelicerata); 2. bot: see языкоцветные.
язычковый anat: uvular.
~ цветок bot: ray flower, ligulate flower.
язычная артерия anat: lingual artery.
~ извилина anat: glossiform gyrus.
~ миндалина anat: lingual tonsil.
язычно-нёбная дужка anat: glossopalatine arch.
язычок 1. anat: uvula; 2. bot: ligule.
язь ichth: id, ide (Leuciscus idus).
~ амурский Amur id (L. waleckii).
яичко anat: testicle, testis.
яичная скорлупа eggshell.
~ слива bot: egg plum.
~ среда bact: egg medium.
яичник anat: ovary.
~ (коловраток) zool: germarium (of rotiferae).
яичниковая беременность obstet: ovarian pregnancy.
~ киста gyn: ovarian cyst.
яичниковый ovarian.
яичный белок egg-white.
~ бульон bact: egg-infusion broth.
~ желток egg-yolk.
яйца акул и скатов ichth: shark and ray eggs, mermaids' purses.
яйцевая капсула entom: ootheca.
яйцевая клетка = яйцеклетка.
~ трубка ovarian tube, egg t.
яйцевидная впадина ovoid cavity.
яйцевидно-копьевидный bot: ovate-lanceolate.
яйцевидный ovate, ovatus.
~ лист bot: ovate leaf.
~ сустав = эллипсовидный сустав.
яйцевод anat: oviduct.
*яйцеводный anat: ovidu(t)al.
яйцевой зуб zool: egg-tooth.
~ мешок zool: ovisac, egg sac, brood pouch (of a copepod).
~ фолликул ovarian follicle.
яйцееды (сем.) entom: egg-eaters (Scelionidae).
~ -наездники entom: oöphagous trichograminae (Microphanus Vassiliewi et Telenomus Sokolowi).
яйцеживородящий ovoviviparous.
яйцеклад entom: ovipositor.
яйцекладка oviposition, egg laying.
яйцекладные трипсы (подотр.) entom: egg-laying thrips (Terebrantia).
яйцекладущие млекопитающие prototheria.
яйцекладущий oviparous, oötocous.
яйцеклетка embr: ovum, egg cell, ovicell.
яйцемёт helm: ovijector.
яйценосная самка zool: ovipara.
яйцеобразная ампутация surg: oval amputation, elliptic a.
яйцеобразный колос bot: ovate head.
яйцеродная самка zool: ovipara.
яйцеродность zool: oviparity.
яйцеродный zool: oviparous.
яйцерождение zool: oviparity.
яйцо egg, ovum.
~ в яичнике ovarian egg.
~ оболочника zool: tunicate egg.
як zool: yak (Poëphagus).
~ дикий wild yak (P. grunniens).
~ домашний domestic yak.
ялапа bot: four-o'clock, marvel-of-Peru (Mirabilis jalapa).
яловая корова zool: nonpregnant cow, barren cow, farrow.
ям bot: yam (Dioscorea).
~ белый yampi (D. alata).
~ клубненосный air polato (D. bulbifera).
ямка pit, cavity, alveolus, depression, recess.
~ для придатка мозга anat: hypophyseal fossa, fossa hypophyseos.
~ стекловидного тела ophth: patellar fossa, hyaloid f.

ямка турецкого седла (для мозгового придатка) anat: pituitary fossa.
ямовые (сем.) bot: yam family (Dioscoreaceae).
ямочка fossette, dimple, foveola, small depression.
ямс = ям.
ямчатый pitted, alveolate, lacunar, lacunosus.
Янский Jansky.
янтарножёлтый amber-colored.
япономорской of the Japan Sea.
японская речная лихорадка Japanese river fever, Kedani disease.
~ скумбрия ichth: little mackerel (Pneumatophorus, Scomber japonicus), bull m., chub m., big-eyed m., Easter m., California m., tinker m.
японское лаковое дерево = лаковое дерево.
яремная вена (внутренняя, наружная, передняя) anat: jugular vein (internal, external, anterior).
~ вырезка anat: jugular notch, incisura jugularis.
~ пульсация jugular undulation.
~ ямка anat: jugular fossa.
яремное отверстие anat: jugular foramen.
ярка agr: female lamb.
~ до отлучения от матери zool: teg.
ярко выраженный pronounced, well marked, distinct.
яровая культура agr bot: spring crop.
яровизация agr bot: vernalization.
*ярутка полевая bot: pennycress, (Thlapsi arvense).
ясенец "неопалимая купина" bot: dittany, fraxinella, burning bush (Dictamnus).
ясень bot: ash (Fraxinus, L.)
~ американский white a. (F.americana).
~ белый = я. американский.
~ высокий taller a. (F. excelsior).
~ китайский = айлант.
~ колючий prickly a. (Xanthoxylum, Gmel.)
~ ~ американский northern prickly a., toothache-tree (X. americanum).
~ пушистый red-leaved a. (F.pubescens).
~ тыквенный pumpkin a., red a. (F. tomentosa, Michx.)
~ цветочный = я. американский.
ясколка mouse-ear chickweed (Cerastium).
~ полевая field chickweed, starry grassword (C. arvense).
*ясли nursery.
ясменник душистый sweet woodruff (Asperula odorata).
ясменник красильный dyer's woodruff (A. tinctoria).
яснотка dead nettle (Lamium); see крапива глухая.
~ пурпурная purple d.n.(L.purpureum).
~ пятнистая splashed d.n. (L.maculatum).
~ стеблеобъемлющая henbit (L. amplexicaule).
ясный звук clear sound.
ястреб orn: hawk (Accipiter).
~ -перепелятник sparrow hawk (Accipiter nisus).
~ тетеревятник goshawk (Accipiter gentilis).
ястребинка bot: hawkweed, autumnal hawkbit (Hieracium).
~ жилистая rattlesnake weed, poor robin's plantain (H. venosum).
~ золотистая orange h., devil's paint-brush, devil's bit(H.aurantiacum).
~ оранжевокрасная = я. золотистая.
ястребиные (сем.) orn: hawks [(Accipitridae).
ятропа bot: coral plant (Jatropha multifida). Cf. маниок.
*ятрышник bot: orchis, cillions(Orchis).
~ мужской early purple o.(O.mascula).
~ пятнистый O. maculata.
ятрышниковые = орхидные.
яцица = подёнка.
ячеечный = ячеистый.
ячеистая структура hist: honeycomb [structure.
ячеистый honeycombed, alveolate, alveolar, faveolate, cellular.
ячейка 1. cell, alveolus, alveole; zooecium; 2. mesh.
~ крыла entom: wing cell, cellula.
~ пестика bot: locule.
ячейный = ячеистый.
ячменевые (подсем.) bot: barley sub-family (Hordeae, Lindl.)
ячменная вода = ячменный отвар.
ячменные = ячменевые.
ячменный отвар pharm: barley water, decoction of barley.
ячмень 1. ophth: hordeolum, stye; 2. bot: barley (Hordeum).
~ голый naked b., hull-less b.
~ двухрядный two-rowed b.
~ дикий wild b., squirrel-tail grass (H. jubatum).
~ заячий mouse b.(H.leporinum,Link.)
~ обыкновенный common b., four-rowed b.
~ пивоваренный brewer's b.

ячмень четырёхрядный four-rowed
~ шестирядный six-rowed b. barley.
ящерица zool: lizard (Lacertilia).
ящерообразные zool: Sauropsida.
ящеротазовые zool: Saurischia (extinct reptiles).
ящерохвостые orn: Saururae, Archaeornithes (extinct).
ящеры zool: Pholidota.
ящик с инструментами instrument chest, instrument kit.
ящур vet: foot-and-mouth disease (Aphtha epizootica).

CORRIGENDA

акатка orn: stilt (Himantopus).
амии (отр.) ichth: Amiidae.
аравийская камедь pharm: gum arabic.
балобан orn: shrike (Lanius).
бекас болотный обыкновенный orn: common snipe (Capella gallinago).
белогрудый дрозд orn: ring ouzel (Turdus torquatus).
белоносая гагара orn: white-billed diver (Colymbus adamsii).
береговая ласточка orn: sand martin (Riparia riparia).
бескрыл orn: apteryx.
бесхвостый угорь ichth: bob-tailed snipe eel (Cyema atrum).
болезненный тик neur: tic douloureux.
болотная курочка orn: Brit: moorhen, see камышница.
большие рулевые перья orn: rectrices.
бургомистр orn: glaucous gull (Larus hyperboreus).
бычок 1. ichth: etc...; 2. zool: etc...
венерин бугорок anat: mons veneris.
верблюдки (отр.) entom: snakeflies (Raphidioidea).
водяная курочка orn: Brit: moorhen, see камышница.
волосный capillary; anat: minute (blood vessel, etc.)
восковой waxy, ceraceous.
воспаление венчика копыта vet: inflammation of coronary band.
вошь свиней swine louse (Haematopinus suis).
высота (тела) при сидячем положении sitting height.
~ ~ при стоячем положении standing height.
галка orn: daw, jackdaw, a kind of European crow (Corvus monedula).
галстучник orn: ringed plover (Charadrius hiaticula).
гаршнеп orn Brit: jack snipe (Lymnocryptes minimus).
глазок 1. bot: bud, oculus, burgeon; stigma; 2. zool: eyespot, ocellus.
глупыш orn: 1. fulmar (Fulmarus glacialis); 2. gannet (Sula bassana, etc.
голавль ichth: bullhead, chub, roach (Leuciscus).
голуби (отр.) orn: doves and pigeons (Columbiformes).
голубь-трубач trumpeter.
грифовые (сем.) orn: vulture family (Aegypiidae).
грудная нога zool: pereiopod, trunk leg (of a crustacean).
губка "слоновое ухо" elephant's ear sponge.
гусь белый white-fronted goose, etc.
дикий голубь orn: rock dove (Columba livia).
дитиосалициловый висмут pharm: bismuth dithiosalicylate.
дно пузыря anat: vesical base, fundus vesicae.
древолаз orn: brown creeper; Brit: tree creeper (Certhia familiaris).
дрозд чёрный blackbird (Turdus merula)
дрофа orn: great bustard (Otis tarda).
дупель orn: double snipe, great s. (Capella media).
жадно проглатывать gobble up.
завязывать плоды (семена) bot: set the fruits (seeds).
законы патологии laws of pathology, pathonomy.
запылённость лёгких кремнистой пылью silicosis.
звездочёт ichth: stargazer (Uranoscopus).
зимородок-великан kookaburra (Dacelo gigas).
златок bot: king's spear, asphodel (Asphodelus, Asphodelina lutea, Recsh.)
избегающий света light-avoiding, lucifugal.
имбирь bot: ginger, zingiber (Zingiber officinale, Roscoe).
индийская конопля pharm: bang, bhang.

кабанчик zool: young wild boar.
канюк orn: buzzard (Buteo).
кардамон bot: cardamom (Elettaria cardamomum).
клещ сахарный sugar mite (Glycophagus).
клык 1. anat: canine tooth, cuspid t.; 2. zool: tusk, fang (dog, wolf, boar).
клюворылый кит zool: xiphioid whale.
коклюш infect: whooping cough, pertussis.
коклюшный pertussal.
копытный лемминг .... (Dicrostonyx).
костёр униольный fescue grass (B. unioloides, HBK).
краб-разбойник robber crab (Birgus latro).
крупнолистый bot: large-leaved (grandifolius, macrophyllus).
кунджа ichth: trout Salvelinus leucomaenis.
кусочки льда cracked ice.
лабиринтовые (отр.) ichth: Anabantidae.
лекарственное лечение medication, drug treatment.
лесная куница zool: forest marten (Martes martes).
лось zool: moose (Alces).
лунь ... (Circus pygargus).
майоран садовый bot: annual marjoram (Origanum marjorana, M. hortensis, Much)
мальма ichth: trout Salvelinus malma.
микроб microbe, germ.
мирофис ichth: worm eel (Myrophis).
молоки ichth: milt, soft roe, testicular fluid.
моль пестрянка сиреневая motley lilac moth (Caloptila syringella).
морская корова ... (Uranoscopus).
~ черепаха hawksbill turtle (Eretmochelys imbricata).
морской налим ... (Motella).
~ язык .... (Solea vulgaris); slippery
мохообразный bot: bryophytic.
муха шведская frit-fly (Oscinosoma ...
мышечная сократимость myocontractility.
мышь лесная wood mouse (Apodemus silvaticus).
мягкая ракушка zool: soft clam (Mya arenaria).
накипной лишайник bot: crustaceous lichen.
нарыв abscess, pus blister.
настоящие саранчовые (сем.) entom: true locusts (Acrididae).
нёбо anat: palate, roof of the mouth.
нереоцистис bot: nereocyst (Nereocystis); ribbon kelp (N.lutkeana), brown algae.

ночница .... owlet-moth ....
оболочка семени bot: husk, seed-pod.
односторонняя невралгия hemialgia.
озёрная палия ichth: lake trout (Cristivomer namaycush).
олуша orn: gannet (Sula).
~ красноногая red-legged gannet (Sula piscator).
орех индейский .... moluccana, Willd)
орлица orn: female eagle.
осот розовый Canada thistle (Cirsium arvense).
ответвление .... stem shoot.
палоло (червь) palolo (worm) (Palolo viridis).
палочкоядерный stabnuclear, with rod-shaped nucleus.
пальцы мертвеца zool: dead-man's-...
перистые диатомеи bot: Pennales (diatoms).
перья plumage, feathers.
пищуха-сверчок orn: brown creeper (Certhia familiaris).
планктон солоноватых вод hyphamyroplankton.
племенная кобыла brood mare.
плотоядный carnivorous, flesh-eating.
плаутус orn: garefowl (Plautus impennis).
подгрудок zool: dewlap.
полевица каменистая fiorin-grass (A. stolonifera). [Huds.
полипорус шероховатый P. squamosus,
поморники (сем.) orn: Stercorariidae.
поражённое гнилью дерево decayed tree.
пороговый liminal, threshold.
потрошение disemboweling, evisceration.
потрошить agr zool: disembowel, gib, paunch, gut, eviscerate.
почесуха path: pruritus.
пощипывание tingling, prickling.
промывание желудка через свищ gastro(sto)lavage.
птицеводство agr: poultry raising.
пузырчатка 1. path: cystitis; 2. bot: bladderwort (Utricularia).
пустельга orn: kestrel, windhover ...
пяденица-обдирало orange moth (Erannis defoliaria); mottled umber moth (Hybernia defoliaria).
райские зёрна bot: cardamom.
резистентный к мышьяку arsenic-fast.
репа семиголовая Italian rape ....
речная крачка .... (Sterna hirundo).
ромб ichth: turbot (Psetta); ....
сайсл bot: yaxche (Agave ....).
сбрасывать кожу zool: slough, cast, shed (the skin, shell, etc.)
сеанс seance, sitting, single treatment.

себастомус ichth: corsair (Sebastodes rosaceus).
северный олень американский caribou (Rangifer caribou).
селитра saltpeter, niter.
семеед клеверный clover-seed eater weevil (Apion apricans).
сироп syrup.
скрытонос несходный entom: cabbage-seedpod weevil (Cryptorhynchus assimilis
слива вишнелистная myrobalan, cherry-plum (Prunus cerasifera).
смоковница индийская Indian fig (Ficus indica).
сморщенная губка zool: purse sponge
собакоголовая обезьяна zool: dog-headed monkey (Mandrill, baboon).
собачья акула ichth: dogfish, sea dog (Scyllium canicula).
соболь zool: sable (Mustela zibellina).
~ русский sobol, see соболь.
солёный salty, saline.
солнечный удар sunstroke.
средний поморник orn: pomarine jaeger (Stercorarius pomarinus).
стволовая гниль bot: trunkrot.
стенотомус ichth: scup, scuppaug, fair maid (Stenotomus chrysops).
стреловидный bot: gabled, ...
судорожный crampy, cramping, ...
сыч orn: little owl (Athene noctua).
тарпон silver-fish, tarpon (Tarpon atlanticus), savanilla, grand ecaille.
тахинное масло benne oil, til oil.
творожистый гной curdy pus.
терпуг ichth: greenling, rock trout (Hexagrammidae).
тля вязовая красногалловая red-gall elm aphid (Byrsocrypta caerulescens).
толстоножки (сем.) entom: eurytomas (Eurytomidae).
трахихтодес ichth: nannygai (Beryx affinis).
трёхзубчатый tridentate.
трубкоцветные (подсем.) bot: Tubiflorae, Tubuliflorae (subfam.)
усач пастернаковый parsnip-stem worm (Phytoecia icterica).
ухоносовой anat: aurinasal.
ушастая собака zool: long-eared fox (Otocyon megalotis).
фараонов муравей Pharaoh's ant.
финнозное мясо helm: cysticercus-infested meat.
фисташковые (сем.) bot: cashew family (Anacardiaceae).
флемингия собранная bot: warras
фумигант agr: fumigant.
харовые (кл.) bot: Characeae ....
хатка бобра zool: beaver lodge.
хвостатое земноводное zool: caudate, urodele.
химизм chemicity, chemism.
хиодон ichth: mooneye (Hyodon).
хламидомонадовые (сем.) bot: Chlamydomonadinaceae family (algae).
хлёрофтальмус ichth: cucumber fish (Chlorophthalmus nigripinnis).
хризомонадовые жгутиковые bio: chrysomonadic flagellate organisms.
хромомицин pharm: chromomycin.
хрусталик anat: crystalline lens.
цененхима zool: coenenchyma.
цистотомия surg: cystotomy.
чеграва orn: Caspian tern (Hydroprogne caspia).
челночница ивовая entom: moth Earias chlorana.
червь дождевой zool: rainworm, dew-worm, earthworm, brandling (Lumbricus terrestris, Dendrobaena, Allolobophora).
~ рисовый rice worm (Tylenchus angustus).
чёрная пятнистость томата phytp: black spot of tomato.
четверохолмие anat: quadrigeminal
четырёхглазка ichth: Anableps tetrophthalmus.
чирок-свистунок teal (Anas crecca).
чувство онемения benumbed ...
чукучановые (сем.) ichth: Catostomidae.
шипсхед ichth: sheepshead (Haplonotus
щипцы forceps, claspers.
щитковые zool: Ostracodermi (extinct).
эктоцеллюлярный ectocellular.
эпизоотологический epizootological.
этрумеус .... sardina).
южноафриканская антилопа springer, springbok (Antidorcas euchore).
ягуар zool: jaguar (Felis onca).
ядерное веретено hist: karyokinetic spindle, nuclear spindle.
яйцеводный anat: oviduc(t)al.
ярутка полевая bot: pennycress (Thlaspi arvense).
ясли crèche, day nursery.
ятрышник bot: orchis, cullions (Orchis).